CHEMICAL ZOOLOGY

Edited by **MARCEL FLORKIN**
DEPARTMENT OF BIOCHEMISTRY
UNIVERSITY OF LIÈGE
LIÈGE, BELGIUM

and

BRADLEY T. SCHEER
DEPARTMENT OF BIOLOGY
UNIVERSITY OF OREGON
EUGENE, OREGON

Volume V

ARTHROPODA Part A

ACADEMIC PRESS New York and London 1970

ACADEMIC PRESS, INC.
111 Fifth Avenue, New York, New York 10003

United Kingdom Edition published by
ACADEMIC PRESS, INC. (LONDON) LTD.
Berkeley Square House, London W1X 6BA

LIBRARY OF CONGRESS CATALOG CARD NUMBER: 67-23158

PRINTED IN THE UNITED STATES OF AMERICA

Contents

Chapter 1. Arthropods: Introduction

S. M. Manton

Chapter 2. Arthropod Nutrition

R. H. Dadd

Chapter 3. Digestion in Crustacea

P. B. van Weel

Chapter 4. Digestion in Insects

R. H. DADD

Chapter 5. Carbohydrate Metabolism in Crustaceans

LYLE HOHNKE AND BRADLEY T. SCHEER

Chapter 6. Metabolism of Carbohydrates in Insects

STANLEY FRIEDMAN

Chapter 7. Nitrogenous Constituents and Nitrogen Metabolism in Arthropods

E. SCHOFFENIELS AND R. GILLES

Chapter 8. Lipid Metabolism and Transport in Arthropods

LAWRENCE I. GILBERT AND JOHN D. O'CONNOR

Chapter 9. Osmoregulation in Aquatic Arthropods

E. SCHOFFENIELS AND R. GILLES

Chapter 10. Osmoregulation in Terrestrial Arthropods

MICHAEL J. BERRIDGE

Chapter 11. Chemistry of Growth and Development in Crustaceans

LARRY H. YAMAOKA AND BRADLEY T. SCHEER

Chapter 12. Chemical Aspects of Growth and Development in Insects

COLETTE L'HÉLIAS

List of Contributors

Numbers in parentheses indicate the pages on which the authors' contributions begin.

MICHAEL J. BERRIDGE (287), A.R.C. Unit of Invertebrate Chemistry and Physiology, Department of Zoology, Cambridge, England

R. H. DADD (35, 117), Department of Entomology and Parasitology, University of California, Berkeley, California

STANLEY FRIEDMAN (167), Department of Entomology, University of Illinois, Urbana, Illinois

LAWRENCE I. GILBERT (229), Department of Biological Sciences, Northwestern University, Evanston, Illinois

R. GILLES (199, 255), Department of Biochemistry, University of Liège, Liège, Belgium

LYLE HOHNKE (147), Department of Biology, University of Oregon, Eugene, Oregon

COLETTE L'HÉLIAS (343), Centre National de la Recherche Scientifique, Laboratoire de Génétique Évolutive et de Biométrie, Gif-Sur-Yvette, France

S. M. MANTON (1), Queen Mary College, and Department of Zoology, British Museum (Natural History), London, England

JOHN D. O'CONNOR (229), Department of Biological Sciences, Northwestern University, Evanston, Illinois

BRADLEY T. SCHEER (147, 321), Department of Biology, University of Oregon, Eugene, Oregon

E. SCHOFFENIELS (199, 255), Department of Biochemistry, University of Liège, Liège, Belgium

P. B. VAN WEEL (97), Department of Zoology, University of Hawaii, Honolulu, Hawaii

LARRY H. YAMAOKA (321), Department of Biology, University of Oregon, Eugene, Oregon

Preface

Zoology is currently undergoing a period of transition in which chemical knowledge is progressively integrated with the more classic knowledge of morphology and systematics. Biochemical studies of species, as well as of higher taxa, open new disciplines to the zoologist and offer new viewpoints in considering problems of structure, function, development, evolution, and ecology. The biochemist has considerable opportunities for broadening his sphere of investigation because of the enormous selection of animal species available for study from which a great variety of compounds can be obtained and reactions observed. There are abundant prospects for fruitful collaboration between the biochemist and zoologist in studies in which the characteristics of the animal and the biochemical constituents and processes interact in significant ways.

Very often the initial obstacle in undertaking investigations in new fields is the complexity and scattered character of the literature. This treatise is aimed primarily at making it possible for zoologists and chemists, who have a limited knowledge of the literature in fields other than their own, to gain a valid impression of the present state of knowledge in chemistry and zoology and an introduction to the existing literature. Thus, we have invited research workers who have contributed significantly to problems involving combined chemical and zoological approaches to summarize the knowledge in their specific disciplines of interest and competence. The authors have been encouraged to be critical and synthetic and to include mention of gaps in knowledge as well as the established information.

The treatise is arranged by phyla, an arrangement which seemed most suitable for presenting chemical information of zoological significance and for bringing to the attention of chemists those aspects of biochemical diversity of greatest potential interest. Each section, dealing with a major phylum, is introduced by a discussion of the biology and systematics of the group. This is followed by chapters dealing with various aspects of the biochemistry of the group. In general, the authors of individual chapters have been given full freedom, within the limitations of space, to develop their assigned topic. We thought that in this way the reader would have the advantage of the author's personal experience in and attitude toward his field, and that this would more than compensate for any unevenness in coverage that might result.

We are grateful to Professor K. M. Wilbur for his help in the early planning of this treatise, to the authors for their cooperation and patience, and to the staff of Academic Press for their careful work.

July, 1970

MARCEL FLORKIN
Liège, Belgium

BRADLEY T. SCHEER
Eugene, Oregon

Contents of Other Volumes

Volume I: PROTOZOA

Volume VI: ARTHROPODA Part B

CHAPTER 1

Arthropods: Introduction

S. M. Manton

I. General Characteristics of Arthropoda

The Arthropoda form the largest phylum of the animal kingdom, comprising three quarters of the 1,120,300 species of animals described by 1958. In size the arthropods range from the parasitic mite *Demodex,* less than 0.1 mm. in length, to the giant Japanese crab *Macrocheira,* which has a leg span of 11 feet. Fossil Eurypterida (Merostomata) reached a body length of nearly 6 feet. Arthropods occur in every conceivable habitat from the deepest seas (Crustacea and Pycnogonida) to an elevation of 22,000 feet on Mount Everest (spiders), from north polar waters to far in the antarctic continent (Collembola and Entomostraca), and as external and internal parasites on other animals. The Arthropoda include the insects, with some 850,000 described species, which dominate the land and are of economic importance both as pests and as beneficial pollinators of crop plants. Alone among invertebrates, the winged insects (Pterygota) fly, by one or two pair of wings. The wingless insects comprise four separate classes: the Collembola, Diplura, Thysanura, and Protura. All are small in size; they differ from one another fundamentally, although they all show convergently acquired hexapodous states. They have special accomplishments, often conferring speedy running or jumping, which compensate for the lack of flying ability. The Myriapoda, with many pairs of legs, comprise a group of related classes, centipedes (Chilopoda), millipedes (Diplopoda), Symphyla, and Pauropoda; they are all terrestrial and restricted almost entirely to damp habitats and are of little economic importance. The Onychophora at the present day are mainly confined to the southern hemisphere. They are terrestrial and remain under cover during the day. Their evolution and relationships are of considerable interest, and they stand closest to the Myriapoda (see below). The Merostomata, aquatic, are extinct except for the marine king crab, *Limulus*. The related Chelicerata, with 35,000 known species of spiders, mites, scorpions, etc., live on land and exist in many millions per acre of arable country. They provide the majority of invertebrate carnivores and are therefore of great importance in the balance of life on land. The 25,000 known species of Crustacea are abundant in salt and fresh waters; they are of great economic importance in marine food supplies, serving to nourish other invertebrates, fishes, and whales.

The trilobites were the dominant arthropods of the early Paleozoic seas; their earliest fossil remains are found near the bottom of the Lower Cambrian rocks some 600 million years old. Trilobites declined in the Silurian epoch and became extinct by the Permian, a reign of some 250 million years.

In association with all these environments, arthropods show a great range in both structure and habits which fit them to the types of life they lead. But also to be found are the most striking examples of ability to withstand unusual, infrequent, or extremely disadvantageous conditions. Winter perils are often met by resting stages, such as eggs and pupae. Dormant, heavily protected eggs can actually withstand desiccation and live for many years to hatch out and grow rapidly when rain falls and temporary ponds form. Resting eggs of the brine shrimp *Artemia* withstand drying of their tissues and in the desiccated state all metabolic processes cease and time makes no impact. Hydration starts up the metabolism and development of such eggs. Even more remarkable is the similar ability of the larvae of the midge *Polypedilum vanderplanki* to withstand desiccation. This they regularly do when the shallow rock pools in which they live dry up. In the desiccated state this highly organized animal undergoes no metabolism. Dry larvae, which are whole or cut into pieces, can withstand extreme ranges of temperatures, $-270°$ to $+104°$C, as well as years of suspended activity in the absence of metabolism (Hinton, 1960a,b, 1968).

The Arthropoda have in common a metamerically segmented body with a differentiated anterior end which forms either a localized head or the anterior part of a cephalothorax or prosoma, according to the class. They possess serially repeated limbs along a trunk, an ostiate heart, a hemocoelic body cavity, and a cuticle, which even when thin and flexible, is constructed in a definite arthropodan manner. Growth is intermittent, owing to periodic ecdysis of the cuticle. The features which link the arthropods together are thus few in number.

The Arthropoda share with the annelids a metamerically segmented and bilaterally symmetrical body, a ventral nerve cord, the position of the main blood vessels, and the direction of flow of the blood. The articulate form of the exoskeleton, which gave the early name Articulata to the group, is not always present, and the cuticle, when thin, is flexible, and the muscular body wall below is well developed, as in annelids.

One pair of limbs is typically present on each segment of an arthropod, either uniramous or biramous (Fig. 1), and each has a mechanism of

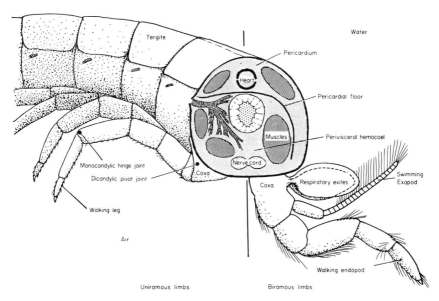

FIG. 1. Diagrammatic representation of some of the essential features of the body organization of an aquatic crustacean (*Anaspides*) on the right and a terrestrial myriapod (*Scolopendra*) on the left. Genital and excretory organs are omitted.

movement which is quite unlike those of annelid parapodia and which could not have been derived therefrom. The anterior end of the body is structurally modified to form a head on which feeding and sensory organs are elaborated and within which are lodged the cerebral ganglia, which are larger and more elaborate than those on the trunk. This head differs from those of annelids. The form of the head is sufficient to distinguish each of the major groups of arthropods.

A reduction of the coelom and enlargement of the hemocoel characterize all arthropods. The "segmentation cavity" of the developing eggs becomes synonymous with the adult hemocoel, while the embryonic coelom, sometimes large, but usually small or even absent, becomes reduced during ontogeny to the end sacs of segmental organs, gonoducts, and other small spaces. The perivisceral and the pericardial spaces are hemocoelic. Paired mesodermal coelomoducts communicate with the exterior on many or few segments. Ectodermal nephridia are absent, as are ciliated epithelia, with rare exceptions.

It is probable that the Arthropoda represent a grade of advancement that has been reached more than once during their evolution, and that they are not a monophyletic group. The differences between the several classes and the convergencies they show, in which the same general need has been met in manners differing fundamentally in detail, are incompatible with a concept of monophyletic arthropodan evolution.

The basic characteristics of the Arthropoda will now be reviewed before considering the classification and the relationships of the component classes. Author references will not be given for well known facts which can be found in textbooks and monographs. References will be resticted to comparatively new work and to data which indicate that earlier views or common statements are no longer tenable.

II. The Skeleton and Associated Features

The most characteristic feature of the arthropods is a covering which, when thickened, forms an articulated exoskeleton over body and limbs (Fig. 1). But the conspicuous sclerites on the body and limbs of most arthropods are not necessarily basic arthropodan features. Many arthropods have a cuticle which is little sclerotized and bends easily. Many sclerites support the insertions of trunk and limb muscles, but others are not associated in any way with muscles and perform protective and other functions. Muscles actually insert upon subcutaneous sheets of connective tissue, on basement membranes, and on internal tendon systems which are often far removed from the body surface. Muscles frequently pull on arthrodial membranes as well as on sclerites. Muscles are attached only indirectly to the sclerites, tonofibrils from the subectodermal connective tissues, which carry the muscles, traversing the ectodermal cells to reach the cuticle. Extreme sclerotizations, coupled with the formation of elaborate joints, leverlike apodemes, etc., of paramount functional significance represent arthropodan advances which are far less basic than the possession of a hemocoel, although heavy sclerotization is found among the earliest recognizable arthropodan remains.

The cuticle is secreted by the surface layer of ectodermal cells and lies external to them. When thin or little sclerotized (tanned), this cuticle bends freely, as on maggots, caterpillars, *Peripatus*, and the soft parts of a barnacle. But when local areas are sclerotized, thickened, or heavily impregnated with lime salts, stiff sclerites are formed which are separated by joints. Cuticles which are stiffened mainly by lime salts are rigid and may crack rather than bend (e.g., Diplopoda), but cuticles in which there is much sclerotization become fairly rigid, but are still capable of bending, when calcification is low. The elastic properties of such sclerotized cuticles are sometimes of functional importance. The inner layers of the cuticle are usually less sclerotized than the outer layers. A breaking up of the outer sclerotized zones into small units, or cones, sunk into more flexible endocuticle, as in geophilomorph centipedes and in certain insect larvae, provides a strong armor which can at the same time bend in any direction (Manton, 1965). The more superficial layers of the cuticle are usually the most sclerotized and the least stretchable regions. The extreme surface layer is usually the most sclerotized part, but owing to its thinness this layer can bend easily, and it covers arthrodial membranes as well as the sclerites. Often a thin surface layer is made particularly waterproof or hydrofuge by wax and a variety of other means. The cuticle is usually perforated by ducts of many kinds; some from gland cells, either in or below the ectoderm, and others connect with hollow spines, sensory setae, etc. Some glands secrete a surface layer after each ecdysis, their products flowing out, sometimes a long way, before setting over the entire new cuticle.

Arthropodan joints may be simple loose folds of unsclerotized cuticle which permit movement in many directions, or flexures may be restricted to certain planes by the arthrodial membrane between adjacent sclerites being locally short, and by imbricating thickenings being present at the marginal overlap of the sclerites themselves. A close union at one place between two cylindrical sclerites, with ample arthrodial membrane elsewhere, forms a hinge joint, and two close articulations situated on opposite sides of overlapping cylindrical segments form pivots allowing flexures to take place in two directions about the long axis of the body or limb (Fig. 1). Rarely, ball-and-socketlike joints occur, as seen between the trunk segments of millipedes (Diplopoda), which allow a twisting movement besides flexures in any direction (Manton, 1954, 1965).

Arthropoda have perfected the use of skeleton to control the movements of their parts in such a manner as to make the maximum use of their available musculature for propulsive and other purposes. Herein lies one of the bases of the great success of this group of animals. A few examples may be given. Many arthropods gain protection of their more vulnerable parts by rolling up into a sphere, an accomplishment shown by trilobites, many diplopods, by woodlice and *Sphaeroma* among the crustaceans, and by many others. This feat is often facilitated mechanically by a half cylindrical shape to the body, in which the axis of the nodding movement of one segment upon the next is located near the flat ventral surface. Least compression on rolling up therefore takes place at the ventral side, which becomes the middle of the sphere, and considerable intersegmental expansion occurs dorsally. The fixing of the axis of movement to the ventral part of a half cylindrical body is essential and is achieved by many devices, all including the lengths of arthrodial membranes and the nature of the imbrications of the sclerites.

Another example is the nature of the joint between the base of the leg and the body. This joint is very varied in structure. If the cuticle permits a great variety of movements of the leg at the coxa-body joint, then the extrinsic muscles of the leg are correspondingly elaborate. Besides causing movement in any one direction, these muscles must also maintain the stability of the coxa against movements in other directions. The total extrinsic musculature which is possible for an arthropod to carry is limited, and therefore the strength or rapidity of the momentarily wanted movement is limited when this joint is very free, because only some of the muscles can be used to cause it. When the converse obtains, and close articulations between sclerites of trunk and leg restrict the coxal movements to those about a single plane or axis, then promotor-remotor movements are achieved by simpler large antagonist pairs of muscles which can cause a much stronger swing of the leg. Such dicondylic pivot joints between coxa and body exist in the larger cructaceans, the diplopods, some insects, etc., and the majority of arthropods employ sclerite detail to allow the maximum amount of musculature to operate the promotor-remotor swing of the leg.

In centipedes, Symphyla, and Pauropoda, the coxal movement on the body is more complex. There is one point of close articulation of the coxa with the sternite, and about this articulation, or region of close union, of the sclerites, the proximal dorsal side of the coxa swings toward and away from the head end of the body during each cycle of stepping movements. This rocking of the coxa about its ventral articulation is superimposed up a normal promotor-remotor swing, and the rocking serves particular needs concerning extension of distal leg joints which lack extensor muscles (Manton, 1965, 1966). The musculature controlling these two superimposed movements is much more complex than that of diplopods exhibiting only a promotor-remotor swing of the coxa on the body. There are 34 extrinsic muscles to each leg of the centipede *Scutigera* in contrast to two extrinsic muscles to each leg of most diplopods.

An extreme condition exists in the jumping Collembola where there is no articulation or close union of any kind between coxa and body. This state is correlated with a hydrostatic jumping mechanism utilized by these animals (Manton, 1971). A hydrostatic blast, caused by contraction of trunk muscles, drives the terminal springing organ downward and backward against the ground, so effecting the jump. The whole of the body architecture is correlated with resisting this hydrostatic pressure at a jump. The cuticle lacks typical arthrodial membranes; normal leg joints and coxa-body joints would have no power to resist such internal pressures without expansion and dislocation at the imbricating points. The difficulty is circumvented by the presence of an elaborate system of internal suspensory muscles and tendons which sling the coxa from the endoskeleton and tergites, linking also the trochanter and femur, so preventing the joints at either end of these leg segments from being blown out and dislocated at a jump. Suitable leg movements can thereby be maintained, both for the take off and the landing after a jump. The absence of any cuticular stability at the coxa-body joint and the absence of articulations is not here a primitive arthropodan feature, but a collembolan necessity correlated with the jumping organ at the posterior end of the abdomen, and with extreme specializations of endoskeleton and of motor and suspensory extrinsic leg muscles.

The skeleton of an arthropod is seldom restricted to the external position. Intucked folds of sclerotized cuticle form apodemes which are either solid or hollow. They give insertion sites for muscles deep in the body or additional areas to those always provided by the body wall. Such intuckings form the stiff, and often elaborate, endophragmal skeleton of the larger arthropods; the smaller species have few or no apodemes. These structures are sometimes rigid and rodlike, acting as levers to mobile hard parts (e.g., the mandibles of a crab), and they are sometimes hinged to the moving parts by flexible cuticle (e.g., the mandible of diplopods). At ecdysis all apodemes are pulled out of the body with the surface cuticle.

The internal face of the ectoderm also secretes skeletal structures, the thick or thin layer of subcutaneous connective tissue fibers or simple basement membrane, to which the muscle fibers are attached. On this connective tissue layer local thickenings occur which sometimes become prolonged as internal struts performing mechanical functions or bearing muscles. This connective tissue skeleton may be elaborate but is not shed at ecdysis, it grows with the body. Some elaborate tendon systems become detached from the surface ectoderm, but they carry with them formative ectodermal cells which maintain their growth. Substantial endosternites (e.g., *Limulus* and some crustaceans), transverse tendons bearing mandibular muscles (e.g., many crustaceans and myriapods), and segmental paired tendons uniting segmental musculature all along the body (e.g., centipedes and some hexapods) are thereby formed. The subcutaneous endoskeletal layer of connective tissue, so conspicuous in the Onychophora, is merely an exaggeration of what is typical for the Arthropoda. It is substantial in the Onychophora in association with the enormous powers of body deformation and the flexibility of the body wall of these animals.

The movements of arthropod bodies, limbs, and wings, mediated by muscles and cuticular sclerites, are much more rapid, precise, strong, and varied than are the movements of other invertebrates. The plan of the musculature is more elaborate than is that of the segmented worms in which circular, oblique, and longitudinal cylinders of muscle lie below the ectoderm, the individual fibers being supported by nonstretching connective tissue fibers. In the Arthropoda much of the longitudinal musculature is in segmental units, united longitudinally by paired tendinous junctions, such as seen in the abdomen of the malacostracan Crustacea or in the trunk of centipedes, but often separate segmental muscles are inserted either on to the flat inner face or on to the anterior and posterior margins of the main segmental sclerites. Circular muscles are sparsely developed in arthropods unless the integument is flexible; and oblique and dorsoventral muscles, superficial and deep, are present in abundant complexity, exceeding those of annelids in bulk and in variety. Limb musculature is partly intrinsic, strands passing through one or more limb segments; and the abundance of extrinsic muscles linking the basal segments of a leg with surface sclerites and endoskeleton, often several segments removed, provides both leverage and stability.

As in vertebrates, the skeletal muscles of arthropods are "striped." The fine structure and the properties of the striped muscles vary, some contract slowly, but the flight muscles of a fly can twitch 330 times per second. If the movements caused by a muscle are rapid and large, they cannot also be strong. Much of the complex anatomy of arthropods meets one or other of these two incompatibles, which suit different ways of living. The strongest movements, such as those employed by millipedes using the motive force of very many legs simultaneously, as they force their way through soil by head on pushing, are always executed slowly. Where movements are very rapid, as in some running movements of centipedes and flight in insects, the force exerted by each extrinsic muscle is small, and the muscles are often very numerous and long (Manton, 1958a, p. 501; 1965, p. 309 and Table 2, p. 364). Elastic properties of the cuticle, and of other special structures, are also sometimes utilized for the conservation of energy (Manton, 1958a, p. 522; Weis-

Fogh, 1959). Slow rhythmic movements of the alimentary canal are mediated, as in vertebrates, by "unstriped" muscle, and the immense body deformations of which the Onychophora are capable necessitate the trunk musculature being unstriped. The movements here must also be slow in order to avoid great changes in internal hydrostatic pressure.

Dead sclerites and apodemes cannot grow in the same way as vertebrate bones. Growth is intermittent in arthropods. The mineral salts of the external cuticle and internal apodemes are periodically absorbed and the internal parts dissolved. A new cuticle is secreted below the old one, followed by a splitting of the old cuticle, so allowing the animal to climb out of it. The apodemes are pulled out from the body, and the tonofibrillar junctions from the subcutaneous membranes and connective tissue, which carry the tension of the muscles, are temporarily severed from the cuticle. During the enforced period of quiescence following a molt, a swelling of the body takes place with a stretching of the new cuticle. This is then hardened by sclerotization and by impregnation with lime salts in appropriate places, tonofibrillar connections to the new cuticle being formed. These periodic ecdyses of the cuticle continue throughout life, or until adult size is achieved.

Changes in body form at each ecdysis are usually not confined to increase in size alone. When all segments are not present at birth or at hatching, there is often a steady development, from in front posteriorly, with increase in the number of segments and of limbs at each molt, as in anostracan crustaceans, centipedes, Symphyla, etc. New segments are formed within the functional cuticle, usually from a subterminal growth zone, and they expand with the new cuticle after a molt. In specialized life cycles the growth and development along the body is uneven, and there may be other growth zones than a subterminal one, as in decapod larvae where thoracic as well as abdominal segments and limbs are added during the larval stages. There are many examples in which segments and functional limbs are entirely changed in form at one molt. Hooked endopods, used for holding food and situated on the antennae in nauplius larvae of certain harpacticid copepods, disappear and are replaced by identically shaped and similarly functioning maxillipedes at the change from the last naupliar to the first copepodite larva. Some limbs, present in early stomatopod larvae, disappear in later stages and are reformed again later still.

When the change in body form at one ecdysis is spectacular, as it is at the molt between the nauplius and cypris larvae of a barnacle and between the larva and pupa or pupa and adult of a butterfly, the changes are aptly described as a metamorphosis in the life cycle. But such transformations are only extremes of a great range of growth phenomena of arthropods. Pupal stages during which no feeding takes place, and often no movement, undergo entire reorganization of the body and represent a complete dissociation of organ development from growth.

The sclerites or sclerotizations on one segment may be evenly distributed, forming a single skeletal unit (e.g., some Diplopoda), or a number of separate sclerites may be present (e·g., Chilopoda and Arachnida). The edges of sclerites are usually rigid and fixed, but sometimes they are capable of furling inward and outward from an intucked groove of arthrodial membrane, thus altering the shape of the sclerite, as the trunk musculature shortens or thickens the body. The surface armor thus remains intact although the shape changes. Such movements are made possible by the structure of the cuticle (Geophilomorpha) (Manton, 1965, p. 261, Figs. 6, 8).

Fusion of the exoskeletal units of several successive segments provides sections of the body with great rigidity and strength against which legs can push (e.g., thorax of some insects), and a solid basis for the movement of the mouth parts and sensory limbs is given by the head capsule. These fused zones differ from class to class, for example the cephalothorax of a lobster, the prosoma of a spider or scorpion, the central larger tergite on the trunk of the centipede *Scutigera* which covers four segments and supports the bases of legs 6–9.

The head end is formed ontogenetically in a manner unlike that in other phyla. Ventrolaterally the anterior segmental mesodermal somites (which form most of the internal tissues of the adult) and the corresponding ectodermal areas, many of which bear limb rudiments, grow forward relative to the mouth. The oral aperture with the unsegmented rudiment forming the upper lip (labrum) at the same time shifts backward. Some of the anterior limb rudiments are thereby carried to a preoral level while the mouth becomes subterminal and ventrally directed, unless other specializations ensue.

A preoral cavity is frequently formed by these shifts, and into it the mouth parts crush, grind or bite the food. The mouth does not shift out of one segment and into another (Tiegs, 1940; Tiegs and Manton, 1958, p. 269; Manton, 1960). It is the lateral parts of the segments which bend forward round the mouth. The anterior segments are not even roughly cylindrical in shape, as are those of the trunk. The dorsal tissue of much of the head end is formed by unsegmented acron, tissue which has persisted from the embryonic or developmental stage previous to that in which segmentation is initiated.

The diagrams published in many textbooks showing a theoretical arthropodan head consisting of a series of cylindrical segments behind an unsegmented acron are not substantiated by the actual modes of head development in arthropods. There are no dorsal segmental tissues appertaining to the most anterior segments of known arthropods. Comparative embryology of the more primitive members of the larger arthropodan groups does not substantiate Weber's theoretical concept, accepted by Størmer and others.

The limbs which become preoral in position tend to become sensory or trophic, in whole or in part, and perform other functions according to the group. Limbs just behind the mouth are usually specialized for feeding to some extent, and the unsegmented acron provides eyes of various kinds.

The major classes of arthropods each have a characteristic head structure which alone is sufficient to separate one class from another. The differentiating characters comprise: (1) the number of segments which have shifted to a preoral position—one in the Onychophora, two in the Chelicerata, and three in Crustacea, Myriapoda, and Hexapoda; (2) the number and nature of the preoral limbs—prehensile chelicerae characterize the Chelicerata (Merostomata, Arachnida); two pairs of antennae occur in Crustacea, and one pair in the Onychophora, Myriapoda, and Hexapoda; (3) the presence or absence of mandibular appendages just behind the mouth, and the nature of these limbs; the mandibles in Crustacea are formed by the leg base, and those of the Onychophora, Myriapoda, and Hexapoda by a whole limb which bites with the tip and not with the base (Manton, 1964); (4) the number of paired postoral limbs used in feeding; the Chelicerata usually employ one or more pairs of gnathobases for chewing or cutting and use a movement (and associated morphology) quite unlike that operating the crustacean gnathobases (see below). The Crustacea and some Myriapoda and Hexapoda show two pairs of limbs largely or entirely devoted to feeding (maxillules and maxillae), and additional limbs may be used in part, or entirely, for such purposes in Crustacea and certain Myriapoda. Cephalic segmentation and limb equipment in fossil arthropods is seldom known with certainty. We do not know whether trilobite antennules correspond with the antennules or antennae of Crustacea and whether the four following biramous limbs of some trilobites are common to the class and may correspond with the postantennulary head appendages of Crustacea. The many middle Cambrian merostome-like arthropods cannot be assigned with certainty to Crustacea, Trilobita, or Merostomata on their imperfectly known cephalic features (Raymond, 1935; Størmer, 1944; Simonetta, 1962, 1963, 1964). There is every probability that many extinct Arthropoda such as *Sidneya* (Simonetta, 1963) do not belong to any of the well-known classes.

The arthropodan trunk region may or may not be divisible into definite tagmata, but these regions, when clearly defined, are characteristic of certain classes and orders. The tagmata shown by the Arthropoda are well known and need not be enumerated here.

A characteristic of great evolutionary and classificatory significance concerns the limbs. Simple uniramous limbs occur in the Onychophora-Myriapoda-Hexapoda assemblage (Fig. 1, left). Biramous limbs of two contrasting types exist in the primarily aquatic groups (Fig. 1, right); a limb with the exopod arising distally on the protopod occurs in Crustacea, but in the Trilobita the outer ramus arises proximally on the protopod, so corresponding with the exites on the protopod of Crustacea which are situated proximal to the exopod. Reconstructions from sections of the trilobite *Olenoides* (Størmer, 1939) show flattened respiratory filaments on the outer ramus, quite unlike the exopod setae of Crustacea so often used in swimming (Tiegs and Manton, 1958, p. 282). A uniramous trunk limb in many Crustacea results from the progressive reduction of the exopod and is used for walking and not swimming. A corresponding reduction of the outer ramus is presumed to have occurred also in the Chelicerata, only a few biramous limbs remaining, such as the branchial and sixth prosomal limbs of *Limulus*. There is no indication of a biramous limb in the Onychophora, Myriapoda, or Hexapoda. The fossil record does not in any way bridge the gap between these three limb types; they may all have evolved independently from the limbs of soft-bodied ancestors. Regretably little information of a precise nature is available concerning limb structure in fossil arthropods, and great care is needed before a limb can be assigned either to the crustacean or to the trilobite type or to something different.

Small arthropods, both aquatic and terrestrial, often lack particular respiratory organs, their cuticular permeability sufficing for gaseous exchange. But the sclerotization of the surface of many arthropods restricts the access of air to the tissues by direct diffusion. Aquatic arthropods, except the smallest, usually respire by means of gills, thin walled projections from the body containing a copious blood circulation. Woodlice and scorpions breathe air by means of air-filled chambers, the walls or processes of which are vascular, but the majority of land species utilize tracheae, fine air-filled tubes opening on the body surface and ending within tissue cells. Air is carried directly to the tissues from external openings or spiracles, which are few or many per segment. Blood no longer transports the respiratory gases as it does in the majority of animals. In the Onychophora, Myriapoda, Hexapoda, and Arachnida the tracheal tubes are varied in form, differing from class to class, and have doubtless been evolved independently several times in adaptation toward land life.

III. The Vascular System and Associated Features

The second outstanding characteristic of Arthropoda, and which is not primarily associated with the cuticle and features of the metameric segmentation just described, is the form of the blood system. No fine vessels, such as the capillary nets of worms and vertebrates, are present.

On the left of Fig. 1 the basic organization existing in the terrestrial myriapod and hexapod classes is shown diagrammatically, and on the right, that of aquatic crustaceans. The Onychophora resemble the left-hand side but lack all jointing in their flexible cuticle. Excretory and genital organs are not shown. A dorsally situated long or short heart discharges its blood forward, outward, and downward into main arteries, and most of these lead ultimately into large vascular spaces which bathe the organs and replace the coelomic body cavity of vertebrates and worms.

A pericardial floor divides the hemocoel into a dorsal pericardium and a ventral perivisceral space. Usually the floor dips down to the base of each leg, as shown on the right of Fig. 1 and intersegmentally the floor is usually attached to the body wall high up, as shown on the left. Blood travels into the legs and out again, and then passes superficially up the flanks in channels just internal to the ectoderm, to enter the pericardium once more. The simplest respiratory organs are the thin-wall exites of crustaceans arising from the basal part of a biramous limb. More elaborate gills arise from the leg base and flanks of the body of larger species of crustaceans and elsewhere in other classes. In either case these organs carry a good blood circulation and a permeable cuticle, and thus the blood returning to the pericardium is aerated. The blood may even be filtered by nephrocytes en route, and there is usually good water circulation round the gills. Blood enters the heart by paired ostia which permit a flow in one direction only. They open to receive blood and then close while the heart is contracting, so forcing blood into the arteries.

Arthropodan blood may be red, green, blue, or colorless, according to the presence and nature of "respiratory pigments," comparable with the red hemoglobin of human blood, which increase the carrying or the storage capacity of the blood for oxygen and carbon dioxide. An exchange of respiratory gases usually takes place at each circulation round the body. The output of CO_2 and intake of O_2 occurs at the general body surface and particularly at the gills when present, so that oxygenated blood enters and leaves the heart. But sometimes the respiratory pigments are largely in the oxygenated state and function in external conditions of oxygen lack or reduced tension. Extra hemoglobin appears in the blood of *Daphnia* as a result of oxygen deficiency, and performs several functions. The hemoglobin in pink *Daphnia* increases the time of survival in semianaerobic conditions; it enables the animals to gather more food in oxygen-deficient water; ˙nd more parthenogenetic eggs are produced than would otherwise be the case (Fox *et al.*, 1951). In *Chironomus plumosus* the hemoglobin enables the larva to maintain active filter feeding when relatively little oxygen is present; at very low oxygen concentrations the hemoglobin acts in oxygen transport, and the pigment greatly increases the rate of recovery from periods of oxygen lack (Walshe, 1951). The centipede *Lithobius* possesses a purple pigment which is normally fully oxidized. This also may provide an emergency mechanism under conditions of low oxygen tension in narrow crevices in the ground, etc. (Needham, 1958, 1960).

It is not equally easy to acquire oxygen and to eliminate carbon dioxide. The large sinuslike tracheae of the centipede *Plutonium,* with narrow connections, elliptical section, and changeable volume, are likely to serve the needs of storage of gases under conditions of respiratory difficulty deep in rock fissures and to be of particular importance in the elimination of CO_2 from the tissues (Manton, 1965, p. 288). Large terrestrial arthropods show increase in the relative size of their main tracheal trunks, linkage between the segmental systems, and sometimes a one-way route exists with inhalant and exhalant spiracles, which facilitates rapid exchange of respiratory gases. In terrestrial arthropods employing considerable shape changes of the body during their normal ways of life (Onychophora), or considerable changes in internal hydrostatic pressure due to mode of feeding (*Craterostigmus,* a centipede), there is little or no branching of the tracheal tubes, which are consequently very numerous. Such minute tubes, 2 to 8 μ in diameter, are the most suited to resist deformation from changes in the hydrostatic pressures of the body fluids (Manton, 1965, p. 345).

Arthropodan blood also carries out the normal vascular functions of food distribution, transport of excretory material to the sites of its elimination, and, with the osmoregulatory organs, maintains suitable osmotic pressures in the tissues and general body turgor.

IV. Other Systems of Body Organization

The alimentary and nervous systems of arthropods are not unlike those of other metamerically segmented invertebrates, but both may be more elaborate and specialized for various purposes. The mouth leads into an ectodermal pharynx which may be armored and very elaborate. The midgut follows and is usually the seat of digestion and absorption of food. The hindgut is ectodermal, it may be long or short, and usually absorbs water, so consolidating feces. In terrestrial Arthropoda, Malpighian tubes are often present at the junction of hind- and midgut, they absorb waste material from the blood spaces which bathe them and discharge crystalline uric acid (pterygote insects) to the hindgut, so conserving water loss, an advantage to a terrestrial animal, but in myriapods the products may be fluid and largely ammoniacal. There may be special devices for drawing in fluid food, for internal triturition, for the production of digestive juice and for food storage.

The nervous system, as in annelid worms, consists of paired ventral nerve cords with paired ganglionic swellings in each segmented from which segmental nerve pass out to the limbs and organs. Anteriorly a dorsal supraesophageal "brain," which innervates the eyes, is united by circumesophageal commissures with a subesophageal ganglionic mass often representing the fused ganglia of the immediately postoral segments. The antennal ganglia are primarily postoral, but more often become preoral and associated with the supraesophageal brain during embryonic development. Great internal complexity of nervous systems exists.

The range of arthropodan sense organs exceeds those of all other invertebrates and makes possible the varied and precise responses and the appreciation of geographical detail shown by the most advanced members. The considerable powers of transmission of information by some arthropods resides in the acuity of their sense organs and in their nervous equipment; for example, bees can transmit information to other bees in a hive as to the direction, distance, and quality of food which they have found up to 6 miles distant from the hive.

Sense organs, both simple and complex, provide arthropods with: the ability to perceive light intensity (simple ocelli); acute vision (simple and compound eyes), and, in many insects, over a very large angle of vision; surface properties of the substratum, by tactile antennal bristles and by trichobothria elsewhere on the body; taste, both on the lips and over the body surface and limbs in aquatic species; air vibrations, culminating in the acute hearing of "songs" by crickets and cicadas, by a variety of bristles and organs; gravity, by statocysts, etc., and the positions of limb and joints and the tensions set up within the sclerites and muscles are detected by simple and by elaborate proprioceptor organs. The optical and nervous equipment of bees enables them to navigate by their perception of the polarization of light of the sky, and they can see far into the ultraviolet range of the spectrum, rays to which man is blind. Vibrations akin in function to "radar" are probably used by some arthropods, and there are complex sense organs, such as the organs of Tomösvary, in land arthropods, whose function is as yet unknown.

Specialization in every class of Arthropoda is associated with elongation of limbs and a reduction in their number on the hind body segments, and with this there is a tendency toward concentration of the primitive ladderlike trunk nervous system. Larger masses of nervous tissue are formed by fusion of segmental ganglia from which longer nerves pass out to the segmental structures; for example, the ventral thoracic ganglionic mass of a crab and a fly. Elaboration of sense organs is associated with enlargement of the corresponding parts of the brain.

Nitrogenous waste matter is excreted by segmental excretory organs (some of which are converted to salivary glands), by Malpighian tubules or even by the midgut (*Peripatus*). Segmental organs are also concerned with osmoregulation, and possess longer ducts in freshwater species than in the corresponding marine ones. The end sac of these organs represents part of the coelom, as shown by the embryonic development. A long series of paired segmental organs is present in the Onychophora, and reduced numbers of these organs are present in chelicerates, myriapods, and crustaceans, culminating in their absence in the winged insects, where particulate excretion from the Malpighian tubules takes place. In the decapod crustaceans the end sac and duct of one pair of segmental organs is elaborated as the "green gland" or antennal gland, which forms an important excretory and osmoregulatory organ.

The sexes are usually separate, but there are many cases of hermaphroditism and of parthenogenesis. Reproductive organs and accessory glands may be very complex, but there is usually a median or one pair of external genital openings. Copulation is usual but not invariable, the eggs being fertilized in the female genital tract or externally just as they are laid. Great fecundity characterizes many arthropods, particularly some crustaceans and insects. Enormous numbers of lightly yolked eggs may be produced which quickly hatch into larvae and feed, grow, molt many times, and eventually assume the adult form; or few heavily yolked eggs, protected by a good shell or by parental care, may develop embryonically to hatch as miniature adults. The time interval between one generation and the next may be 3 days or less in some insects and small Crustacea, so that one pair, or one parthogenetic female reproducing without fertilization, may give rise to several million descendants in a few weeks. By contrast, well-armored, large arthropods, such as the lobster, become sexually mature at the age of 4 years and breed but every other year.

The form of the mouth parts (segmental head appendages) and trunk limbs of arthropods is enormously diverse, serving many different ways of feeding, running, and swimming. In aquatic species many ways of filtering food from the water exist, operated by head limbs alone or by trunk limbs in addition. Limbs also provide offensive, defensive, and copulatory aids and may bear the respiratory surfaces.

V. Evolution of Arthropodan Skeleton and Hemocoel

The manner in which the articulated exoskeleton, endoskeleton, and muscular systems of arthropods have contributed toward the success of these animals is very plain. Rapidity and precision of movements, either strong and slow, or very rapid, have thereby been achieved, and without these things flight could not have evolved. The great variety existing among the arthropods themselves gives ample indication as to how and why the most elaborate, rigid, mobile, or articulated skeletons evolved.

But the significance of the arthropodan hemocoel, the second major characteristic of this group, is far less clear. The blood functions much as in other phyla, even if great refinements obtain in the use of respiratory pigments. Blood transmits food material about the body and carries waste material to its sites of elimination as is usual. Much work has been done on these topics, but no textbook hazards a statement as to the major circumstances of the evolution of the arthropodan hemocoel, or of its basic assets. Lankester (1904) suggested that a swelling of venous spaces at the expense of the coelom was concerned with shape changes of the body. Local movements might be effected more easily by a flow of blood from one part to another and by the action of muscles at a distance. The feasibility of this suggestion has only recently emerged from comparisons between certain performances of annelids and arthropods.

Studies on functional morphology of terrestrial and certain aquatic arthropods have shown, during the last 20 years, how the structure and habits of these animals are correlated in great detail (e.g., Manton, 1950, 1952, 1954, 1956, 1958a, 1961, 1965, 1966, 1971). The several methods of moving about and of finding shelter and food appears to have been responsible in large measure for the evolutionary divergence of the several terrestrial classes and orders and for the establishment in each of their characteristic structural organization. And even more important may be the ability to put out a supreme effort or accomplishment occasionally, as circumstances demand, and to possess habits and structure capable of meeting occasional cataclysms, rather than the normal routine of life (Howell, 1944; Manton, 1956; Bidder, 1931).

Both annelids and arthropods comprise species which are capable of burrowing into the substratum. They initiate their burrows in a variety of ways, but the earthworm *Allolobophora,* the lugworm *Arenicola,* and the geophilomorph centipede *Orya* are all capable of exerting consider-able thrusts from the surface of their bodies on to the walls of their burrows. The maximum thrusts which can be exerted by individuals of these species of comparable sizes are very different. A septate earth-worm cannot generate as great a pressure from the body against the surrounding soil as can the anterior nonseptate part of the lugworm *Arenicola.* In the former, muscles and coelomic pressure of the group of segments actually pushing against the soil operate the thrust; in the latter, muscles situated at a distance from the site of the thrust also contribute by creating a higher coelomic pressure via the unimpeded coelomic space. The earthworm *Allolobophora* can exert its maximum thrust against the soil over and over again with no damage to itself. *Arenicola* can exert its much higher maximum thrust very few times because there is leakage of coelomic fluid and damage to gill capillaries at maximum exertions. But a burrowing geophilomorph centipede of comparable body proportions can put out 360 to 400 gm./cm.^{2} of the pushing area compared with the figures of 130 to 200 gm./cm.^{2} for *Arenicola* and 80 to 110 gm./cm.^{2} for *Allolobophora.* And the centipede *Orya* can exert its maximum thrust over and over again with no damage to itself (Manton, 1965, p. 352, Fig. 40).

It is clear that the maximum pushing ability of the centipede far exceeds those of the worms, and this is probably true also for their easy everyday movements. Can it be that the evolution of a hemocoel was associated with the need to burrow easily and safely into the surface layers of a sea floor? Shallow grubbing into the bottom must have been a widespread and primitive habit among marine animals, and anything which proved effective in facilitating this habit would be of survival value. The evolution of the hemocoel in the Mollusca possibly took place under similar circumstances. The archi-mollusk is usually consid-ered to have been a bottom crawler with perhaps moderate powers of grubbing into the detritus on which it fed.

If the origin of a hemocoel is bound up with effecting easy and safe changes in shape of the body and with better pushing abilities, then its appearance must have long antedated the evolution of sclerites and arthrodial membranes.

The mechanism of movement of a polychaete parapodium is very different from that of an onychophoran lobopodium (Manton, 1967), and the one could not readily have been derived from the other. More-over the hemocoel of the Onychophora plays an essential, if complex, part in the leg mechanism where hydrostatic isolation of each limb can be established. We know little concerning the supposed lobopod ancestors of, at any rate, the Onychophora-Myriapoda-Hexapoda assemblage of arthropods, but it is probable that such ancestors, if they possessed a lobopodium, also possessed a hemocoel. Modification of a lobopodium could readily lead to the jointed sclerotized limbs of arthropods. But the principles of movement of a parapodium are so divergent from those of arthropods as to preclude the origin of an articulated limb from that of the types of parapodia seen in present-day annelids.

The appearance of sclerites, joints, and arthrodial membranes would bring to an end an era in which body deformations and a pushing habit were all important. Precision and localization of movements leading to rapidity of action presumably then took precedence as striated muscle and sensory and nervous equipment were elaborated. With these advancements the original mechanical functions of the hemocoel would become less important, although a centipede devoid of hemocoelic pressure would be as amorphous as a sea anemone without coelenteric pressure. Many arthropodan movements still depend upon hydrostatic pressures, such as leg extensions when off the ground, jumping by paired legs working in similar phase, protraction of the head capsule of *Craterostigmus* in its feeding cycle, and extension of the cirri of barnacles, but the movements of the articulated exoskeleton of the larger and the most advanced arthropods become increasingly independent of hydrostatic pressure, antagonistic muscles alone being able to effect skeletal movements and to do it rapidly. Thus the fundamental assets of the arthropodan hemocoel appear to belong to the distant past and thereafter to have become progressively less important, but the physiological properties of the hemocoel remain.

VI. Classification and Relationships of Arthropods

Fossil remains do not demonstrate either the origin of Arthropoda or of its classes. When the fossil record provides no decisive evidence of interrelationships, classifications can be, at best, only working hypotheses. But such hypotheses must conform to the ever-growing body of evidence relating to past history of living animals which stems from all available sources. It is not surprising that some of the imperfectly known fossil arthropodan remains cannot be referred with certainty to any modern group and others appear to be decidedly unlike animals in any extant class. Classifications should be based upon facts and not upon speculations. The practical necessities of taxonomic and other work makes subdivision or classification of arthropods an imperative requirement.

A classification of arthropods should be based upon phylogeny, but in the absence of sufficient fossil evidence, taxonomic groupings must rest largely upon the comparative anatomy of living species, on embryology and life histories, and probably to some extent also on biochemistry and biophysics. The available evidence concerning the extinct arthropods is more limited and much less detailed. A very large measure of convergence is shown by the morphology and physiology of living arthropods whose past histories, it is inferred, must have been fundamentally different. An appreciation of such convergencies is of immense importance in the elucidation of arthropodan relationships. No simple scheme of classification which ignores convergence can provide a basis for the reconstruction of past history and relationships of arthropods. A review was given (Tiegs and Manton, 1958) of theories of arthropod phylogeny and classification which had been advanced up to that date. In recent years important new factual evidence concerning these matters has been obtained.

Abundant, and at first unexpected, evidence concerning the evolution and relationships of living arthropods has been provided by the increasing body of studies of functional anatomy and of the habits of life with which the morphology is intimately associated, a line of work not easy to apply to fossil material. Vast arrays of complex anatomy, such as those shown by crustacean limbs or the trunk skeleto-musculature of myriapods, takes on a new and ordered meaning. A differentiation of habits in very similar environments appears to have been of paramount importance in the evolutionary differentiation of many classes and orders. Our most detailed knowledge concerns the land fauna where a primitive divergence of habits must have accompanied the evolution of the trunk characteristics of major classes, for example (1) Pushing into the substratum by the motive force of the legs and herbivorous feeding has led to the Diplopoda, which burrow essentially by head-on shoving. (2) Faster running, a moderate ability to thicken and shorten the body momentarily, and carnivorous feeding have led to the Chilopoda, where further divergent specialization has conferred either extreme burrowing ability by body movements (not by legs), or fastest running and predatory habits. (3) Penetration of small and awkward crevices by twisting and turning of delicate bodies, without pushing, has led to the Symphyla, living in the protection of soil and litter. (4) The penetration of crevices by extreme and spectacular body deformations, again without pushing, thus gaining access to spaces where no sizeable predator could follow, has led to the Onychophora, with their retention of a soft body wall, unstriated muscles, primitive gaits, etc. (5) The penetration of crevices enabled by small size combined with hydrostatic and muscular rigidity of a short body and fast pattern of gaits has led to the Pauropoda (Manton, 1952, 1954, 1958b, 1965).

An understanding of the manner of working of different morphological systems, together with the circumstances under which they work, leads to two advances in our appreciation of arthropodan evolution. First, the different morphologies which characterize many of the larger groups of living arthropods have been shown to be related to habits of life which are not adaptations to particular environmental niches, as in the myriapod examples just given. Evolutionary advances in morphology and physiology can enable an animal to live better both in the same and in a variety of environmental circumstances. The end terms of evolution within a particular order or other category, on the contrary, often form adaptive radiations to particular niches, and these adaptations, superimposed upon the more basic characters of each group, have less far-reaching evolutionary significance, in that they do not give rise to new lines of evolutionary significance.

Second, when the functional advantages, or the mode of action, of various morphological set-ups are known, any postulated evolution from one to another which entails a functionally impossible intermediate or one which negates the functional advantages already achieved at once become apparent. The factual matters brought forward by this type of work are of basic and essential importance in any attempt to arrive at a natural classification of the Arthropoda. These lines of work are as yet in their infancy, and for their successful development the comparative approach is essential. Detailed study of one animal alone gives few clues, but a knowledge of the functional assets of animals showing either very different or closely similar habits at once becomes revealing as to the possible manners in which their evolution could have proceeded.

The outstanding convergencies among arthropods, which should be faced in any attempt at a natural classification, concern (1) *biramous limbs,* which differ basically in structure, at least in Crustacea and Trilobita, and which are insufficiently known in most fossil Arthropoda; (2) *mandibles,* which are entirely different in derivation in Crustacea and in the Onychophora-Myriapoda-Hexapoda assemblage. Even in the latter group the myriapod whole limb segmented mandible, utilizing a basic adductor-abductor movement, contrasts fundamentally with the hexapod whole limb unsegmented mandible. The basic movement of this latter mandible is a promotor-remotor roll giving a good grinding action and some cutting. A transition from this to mandibles which cut much more strongly in the transverse plane takes place by morphological changes which are parallel to those of some Crustacea which

also acquire transverse biting from a primitive rolling mandible
(Manton, 1964). (3) *Entognathy,* or the boxing in of the mandibles,
and sometimes of other mouth parts also, confers proximal freedom
of the mandible which permits protractor and retractor movements in
addition to the basic promotor-remotor roll giving grinding and cutting.
Entognathy has been evolved independently many times as shown in
Fig. 4, and the possession of this general feature, the details differing
in the several groups (Manton, 1964, 1965), is not indicative of close
affinity as has at times been suggested. (4) *Compound eyes* do not
appear to be basic in all classes. Trilobite compound eyes lacked the
refinements present in Hexapoda and in those Crustacea which possess
compound eyes; and such eyes appear to have been independently
evolved in the two latter groups. The eye structure in some crustacean
orders and in Hexapoda, although closely similar, is not identical; the
physiological requirements for this type of vision do not permit wide
deviation from the most suitable mechanism, which consequently appears as a parallel evolution in the two groups. (5) *Tracheal systems*
used in air breathing have evolved independently in Onychophora,
Myriapoda, Hexapoda, Arachnida, and in certain Crustacea. The fine,
almost unbranched tracheae of the Onychophora are not unique, as
has often been supposed. Similar tracheae are found in certain Chilopoda
(*Craterostigmus*) (see above). (6) *Uric acid excretion* and the conservation of water in the excretory processes in land forms are achieved
by Malpighian tubules in Arachnida and in Myriapoda and Hexapoda;
uric acid secretion is done very simply by the midgut in Onychophora
(Manton and Heatley, 1937); but the presence of Malpighian tubules
is not necessarily indicative of a uricotelic metabolism such as occurs
in pterygote insects (Bennett and Manton, 1962). (7) The *progoneate
condition* of the Symphyla and Pauropoda has been shown by Tiegs
(1940, 1947) to be secondary and probably related to anamorphosis.
Further convergencies could be noted.

No simple monophyletic scheme of arthropod classification can account for the distribution and morphology of the above features. Some
measure of polyphyletic evolution within the group seems inescapable.
At least three major groupings can be made, as shown diagrammatically
in Fig. 2, which are distinguishable by their tagmata and by their basic
structure of the jaws and trunk limbs. This grouping is endorsed by
Størmer (1944) who can find no bridging of the gaps between them.

The Onychophora are not separable from the other classes of Arthropoda by any characteristics of fundamental importance. There is no sound
evidence to justify the view that this class should be excluded from
the Arthropoda. Onychophoran structure is basically arthropodan in

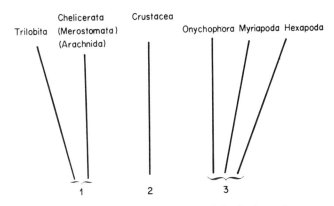

FIG. 2. (1) The form of limbs and tagmata of the body perhaps suggests distant affinity between the Chelicerata and Trilobita and a lack of affinity between these classes and the other Arthropoda. (2) The basic form of the biramous limbs and gnathobasic mandibles of Crustacea are so unlike the corresponding limbs of other Arthropoda as to preclude close affinity between them. (3) The Onychophora, Myriapoda, and Hexapoda have similar uniramous limbs and all bite with the tips, not bases, of the mandibles. Also similarities in the embryonic development of these groups contrast with chelicerate and crustacean developments. The three groups probably have had a roughly common origin, but the construction and mode of action of the segmented mandibles of the Myriapoda are so unlike those of the unsegmented hexapod mandibles as to indicate that the Hexapods have not descended from any one class of the Myriapoda.

great detail, and onychophoran peculiarities of structure are related to habits of life which are of survival value (Manton and Heatley, 1937, Manton, 1938, 1949, 1958b, 1959). Moreover, the Onychophora share many important features of structure and development with the myriapod classes in contrast to all other Arthropoda (Tiegs, 1940, 1947; Manton, 1949, 1965; Anderson, 1966b). The views to the contrary concerning the Onychophora and the classification and phylogeny of the Arthropoda in general, recently put forward by Sharov (1966), are not considered to be valid. The fallacy of the arguments and distortion of the facts in Sharov's book have been answered by Anderson (1966c), Manton (1967), and others.

The factual evidence provided by the jaws is summarized in Fig. 3, and it divides the Arthropoda into the same three groups, separated by the heavy vertical lines, as in Fig. 2. The gnathobases, used for cutting and squeezing, in the Chelicerata are fundamentally different in skeleto-muscular action from those of Crustacea, and the one could not have given rise to the other. The primitive rolling movement of the jaws of Crustacea and Hexapoda (Manton, 1964) must have arisen from the promotor-remotor swing of a walking or swimming limb, the actual mandibles in the two groups being quite different in derivation. Biting in the transverse plane is a secondary acquisition in many Crustacea and Hexapoda (shaded area in Fig. 3), but is a primitive movement for the gnathobasic limbs of the Chelicerata and mandibles of Myriapoda. However, the limb structure in Chelicerata and Myriapoda is quite different.

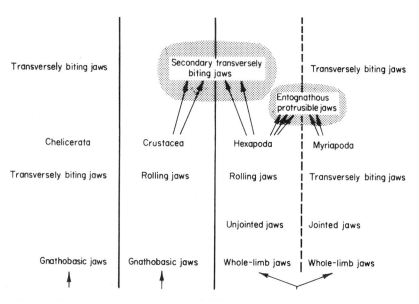

Fig. 3. Diagram showing the conclusions reached concerning the distribution of the principal types of mandibles or jaws (below) and the derivation of the jaw mechanisms (above). The heavy vertical lines indicate an entire absence of common ancestry between the jaws referred to on either side; an interrupted vertical line indicates separate evolutions of the jaw mechanisms of Hexapoda and Myriapoda which probably had a common origin; and the shaded areas indicate mandibular mechanisms showing convergent similarities derived from unlike origins. After Manton, 1964.

The similarity in the structure and movement of the mandibles in the myriapod classes, irrespective of the presence (Chilopoda and Pauropoda) or absence (Diplopoda and Symphyla) of entognathy, is of great importance (Fig. 3, right side). In all Myriapoda, the abductor mechanism of the mandible is provided in whole or in part by the mechanical action of a swinging anterior tentorial apodeme (Fechter, 1961; Manton, 1964). The hexapod mandibles are very different. No hexapod has a jointed mandible working in the myriapodan manner. The hexapod anterior tentorial apodeme does not swing and is never concerned directly with causing mandibular movements. No myriapod either possesses, or requires, a posterior tentorial apodeme such as is present in all hexapods. Even the superficially similar maxilla 1 and maxilla 2 of Symphyla and hexapods contrast in their skeleto-musculature and modes of action (Manton, 1964).

Tiegs (1940, 1947) showed that the progoneate condition of Symphyla and Pauropoda is secondary and probably related to anamorphosis. There is a community in structure of the leg and of the coxa-body joint in all myriapods which contrasts decisively with the several other types existing in hexapods, and the former could not have given rise to the conditions in the hexapod classes (Manton, 1966, 1971).

The above are the principal reasons for the reinstatement of the once discredited Myriapoda as a natural group (Manton, 1964, 1966). And they are the reasons for the destruction of the dream, so dear to entomologists, concerning a supposed close affinity between Symphyla and certain hexapods. The marked differences in head and trunk anatomy among the several classes of myriapods have been shown to be associated in considerable detail with divergent habits of life (Manton, 1954, 1956, 1961, 1965), and all could have evolved in parallel from a similar basic stock, although no one class could have given rise to any other.

The possession of only three pairs of legs born on a thorax is functionally advantageous in that it permits the use of long legs, capable of taking a long stride, with a wide range of gait patterns, as is impossible in Myriapoda which possess long and many legs (Manton, 1952, 1953, 1966). The advantages of walking or running on only three pairs of often longer legs have been acquired independently by many classes, notably certain Arachnida and Crustacea (Manton, 1952). It would therefore be conceivable that the six-legged state of the several hexapod classes might also be the result of independent and parallel evolutions.

The structure and mode of action of the coxa-body joint in the Collembola, Diplura, and Thysanura differ from one another and contrast decisively with these joints in the Myriapoda. In the latter the coxa derives its basic support from the sternite. There may be subsidiary support from a pleurite, but such pleurites are mobile, swinging with the coxa on the sternite. These features do not obtain in the Pterygota, Thysanura, Collembola, or even in the Diplura where there is sternal support of the leg bases. The apterygote classes differ greatly from one another in their modes of action of the coxa on the body. Only the Thysanura utilize tergo-pleural support for the leg base, and only this type of leg base could have the potentiality for the further evolution of flight. The swinging pleurite, so essential to the classes of fleeter myriapods, and the associated leg base musculature are not in the least appropriate for the evolution of flight muscles, and have committed the myriapods to a multilegged state.

The discovery of the decisive differences between the morphology and modes of action of the head endoskeleton and the jaws of all Myriapoda, on the one hand, and of the several groups of pterygote and apterygote hexapods, on the other, indicates that the hexapods are indeed more akin to one another than to any other classes of arthropods. This does not mean that the hexapods had a closely common origin, or that

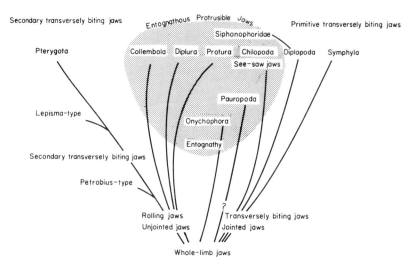

Fig. 4. Diagram showing the conclusions reached concerning the interrelationships and evolution of the jaw mechanisms of Onychophora, Myriapoda, Apterygota, and Pterygota. The shaded area indicates convergent evolution of entognathy and protrusible mandibles. The Pauropoda possess an unsegmented mandible, but there is no evidence as to whether this has been derived from a primitively segmented or unsegmented mandible. After Manton, 1964.

the hexapodous state was acquired once only in their past history. All it suggests is that the hexapods may have had several origins from an ancestral stock of animals which was quite distinct from the ancestral myriapods.

The same conclusion is indicated by a modern assessment of entognathy based upon accurate facts of morphology and function. The fundamental differences between the classes of entognathous Apterygota indicate that their entognathy has been convergently acquired (Fig. 4), just as the entognathy of certain Crustacea and of Myriapoda has been independently acquired (Manton, 1964).

Thus the factual evidence available to date suggests that the component classes of the Myriapoda and of the Hexapoda are more closely related to one another, within each of the two assemblages, than to any other Arthropoda; that none of the hexapod classes has a claim to close relationship with any myriapod class; and that the evolutionary history of the hexapodous classes has been distinct from each other, leading to convergent similarities, such as entognathy and the possession of three pairs of legs. The common segment number shown by some hexapods and Symphyla and the possession of a labiate maxilla 2 in both are also convergent similarities which do not outweigh the fundamental differences between these groups.

The Merostomata clearly comprise the Xiphosura and the Eurypterida as major groups, and probably other merostome taxa have become extinct and are insufficiently known (Simonetta, 1964). There is evidence suggesting the derivation of the Arachnida from aquatic chelicerates, but whether the transition to land occurred once or several times is unknown (Tiegs and Manton, 1958, pp. 304–307). There is no decisive evidence concerning the interrelationships of the several orders of either the Arachnida or of the Crustacea. The distinctions between the component orders of the Crustacea and of the Arachnida are just as profound as are those between the four myriapod classes and the several hexapod classes. But the reality of the Crustacea, Arachnida, Myriapoda, and Hexapoda as major groups seems clear.

Modern embryological studies, characterized by improved techniques and the use of the concept of fate maps, have thrown further light on distant arthropodan relationships (Anderson, 1966a,b, 1970, 1971). Among the annelids, the polycheates exhibit a basic pattern of spiral cleavage development, which is modified in a particular way in clitellate annelids in association with increased yolk. The Crustacea retain a modified total, spiral cleavage in a number of extant species, but they nevertheless have a unique pattern of embryonic development different from that of any annelid or other arthropod. The Chelicerata seem likely, as new evidence accumulates, to exhibit a second unique pattern of development. The Onychophora, Myriapoda, and Hexapoda, in contrast, share a common pattern of embryonic development seen in its most basic form in the Onychophora and in various derived forms in the myriapods and hexapods. Furthermore, the onychophoran mode of development appears to be clitellate-like, further modified in association with yolk. Comparative embryology thus supports the concept of an onychophoran-myriapod-hexapod assemblage of arthropods with antecedents close to the annelids and confirms the phylogenetic remoteness of the Crustacea and Chelicerata from this assemblage, from each other, and from known annelids. But the annelid-like lobopodial ancestors of the onychophoran-myriapod-hexapod group probably already possessed a hemocoel (see above) in contrast to the other extant classes of annelids. The phylogenetic origins of the Crustacea and Chelicerata cannot be identified embryologically.

Reference must be made to the concept of grades in arthropod evolution. Such terms were first applied by Tiegs (1947) to the Onychophora-Myriapoda-Hexapoda assemblage. The Monognatha (Onychophora) use one pair of postoral gnathal limbs, the Dignatha (Pauropoda and probably Diplopoda) use two pairs, the diplopod gnathochilarium may represent two pairs of limbs, and the Trignatha (Symphyla and Hexapoda) use three pairs. These terms do not indicate taxonomic groupings of affinity. They show, on the contrary, levels of organization reached independently by various classes (Fig. 5). The trignathy of the Sym-

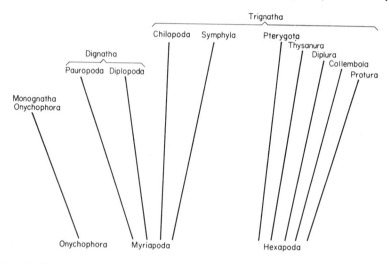

Fig. 5. The proximity of the roughly vertical lines indicates phylogenetic affinity. The grades of organization, Monognatha, Dignatha, and Trignatha, do not indicate relationship.

phyla does not separate this class from the other Myriapoda with which they have fundamental resemblances in the mandible, head endoskeleton, and in the structure of limbs and joints. Further, there is no reason to suppose that these grades have been acquired progressively. In any one phylogeny a monognathous state need not have preceded dignathy and the latter need not have come before a trignathous condition. These three states probably evolved directly from animals with undiversified limbs, as have the three or the one pair of maxillipedes in the eucaridan and pericaridan Crustacea. The absence of a dignathous hexapod or a monognathous myriapod probably means that no such animals ever existed. Similarly the term "Mandibulata" represents a grade of organization, of great functional importance, reached independently and by different means in Crustacea and in terrestrial myriapods and hexapods.

The above review of arthropodan classification is based rigidly upon the factual evidence available in 1969, and no speculations are offered concerning the ultimate origins of the groups of arthropods set out in the figures. But one further point may be made. The Arthropoda as a whole appear to be polyphyletic at least to the extent of the three main groups shown in Fig. 2, and there were probably more independent taxa which are now extinct. The basic unity of the Onychophora-Myriapoda-Hexapoda assemblage has been demonstrated by Tiegs (1940, 1947), Manton (1949, 1952, 1953, 1958b, 1959, 1964, 1965, 1967), and Anderson (1966b,c, 1970, 1971) but this does not imply just one ancestor for all. The probability that the Onychophora are primitively soft bodied, lacking surface sclerites, but not the ability for high levels of sclerotization, follows from the demonstration of the functional assets of onychophoran anatomy (Manton, 1950, 1958b). It is thus possible that the evolution of an armor of surface sclerites may have occurred more than once during the evolution of arthropods, taking place independently in the sea and on land, and that this most conspicuous characteristic of the phylum should be added to the list given above of major features which have arisen by convergence.

CLASSIFICATION

This classification embodies the recent work to which reference has been made above.

Class Crustacea

Head composed of acron fused with preoral preantennulary, antennulary, and antennal somites, the last two bearing paired antennule and antenna; and postoral somites bearing paired gnathobasic mandible, maxilla 1 and maxilla 2; thorax comprises a series of leg-bearing segments, some of which may be fused with the head, their limbs becoming feeding organs (maxillipedes); the abdomen may or may not bear limbs, and terminates in a telson. Legs often biramous, can be secondarily uniramous.

Class Trilobita

Palaeozoic, body molded longitudinally into 3 lobes; one pair of antennules; a head shield bearing eyes is followed by movable trunk segments, the hinder-most being immovably united to form a pygidium;

post-antennulary cephalic limbs and trunk limbs of a common type with two rami.

CHELICERATA

A taxon comprising at least the Merostomata and Arachnida. The most anterior limbs are a pair of chelate chelicerae used in feeding; the gnathobases present on some prosomal legs differ from those of crustacean mandibles.

Class Merostomata

Prosoma bearing preoral chelicera; five pairs of postoral walking legs and chilaria or metastoma; opisthosoma of 9 to 12 somites bearing genital operculum and five pairs of branchiate limbs or branchiae; the terminal telson forming a spine. Limbs biramous or secondarily uniramous.

Class Arachnida

Prosoma with embryonic precheliceral somite, preoral chelicerae and postoral pedipalps, and four pairs of walking legs; mesosoma bearing lung books or tracheae; limbless metasoma present or absent. Walking limbs presumed to be secondarily uniramous.

(MONOGNATHA)

A grade, not a taxon, with one pair of gnathal limbs (jaws) behind the mouth; it occurs only in the Onychophora.

Class Onychophora

Besides the unsegmented acron possessed by all Arthropoda, the head comprises the preoral antennal somite and the postoral jaw and the slime papilla somites, all bearing limbs; soft integument; a long series of trunk somites with short, paired uniramous legs. The jaw is a whole limb, biting with the tip, and gnathobases are absent.

MYRIAPODA

A taxon including Pauropoda, Diplopoda, Chilopoda, and Symphyla. Head comprises acron, preantennal (embryonic), antennal, and pre-mandibular (embryonic) somites in front of the mouth; only the antennal somite bears limbs, the paired antenna. Behind the mouth the head carries the mandibular, maxilla 1 and sometimes maxilla 2 somites, all of which typically carry limbs. The mandible is usually a jointed whole limb, biting with the tip, and gnathobases are absent. Paired anterior tentorial apodemes only are present, they swing within the head and serve mandibular abduction.

(DIGNATHA)

A grade, not a taxon, with two pairs of gnathal limbs behind the mouth. This grade comprises Pauropoda and possibly Diplopoda.

Class Pauropoda

Minute; paired antennae, entognathous unjointed mandible, and maxilla 1 present. Trunk with 9 or 10 limb-bearing somites; a reduction in every other tergite providing stability for the type of gaits employed.

Class Diplopoda

Head bearing preoral antenna and postoral segmented mandible and gnathochilarium, typically specialized herbivores burrowing by the motive force of their legs, large numbers (up to some 130 pairs) of which are obtained, without excessive body elongation, by the formation of diplo-segments along most of the trunk, each bearing two pairs of legs.

(TRIGNATHA)

A grade, not a taxon, with three pairs of gnathal limbs behind the mouth; it occurs in Chilopoda, Symphyla, and Hexapoda.

Class Chilopoda

Head bearing preoral antenna and postoral segmented mandible, maxilla 1 and maxilla 2; first trunk segment forms poison claws; followed by a variable number (15 to 177) of trunk somites bearing paired walking limbs.

Class Symphyla

Head bearing preoral antenna and postoral segmented mandible, maxilla 1 and maxilla 2; trunk composed of 14 somites, the anterior 12 bearing running legs. A duplication of tergites on segments 4, 6, and 8, and sometimes elsewhere also, enhances body flexibility.

HEXAPODA

Head with preoral somites as in the Myriapoda; the postoral composition is trignathan. The mandible is typically an unsegmented whole limb biting with the tip, whose mode of action, as well as structure, contrasts with that of all myriapodan mandibles. Two pairs of usually rigid tentorial apodemes are present in the head which do not push upon the mandibles causing abduction. Trunk differentiated into thorax, bearing three pairs of legs, and abdomen on which the legs are absent or reduced and serve purposes other than ambulation, except for their derivatives, the terminal springing organ of Collembola.

Class Collembola

Head bearing antenna, entognathous and protrusible mandible, and maxilla 1 and maxilla 2. Thorax bearing legs whose mode of suspension from the body is unlike all other hexapods and myriapods. The coxae are not articulated or directly supported by any sclerite, but by an elaborate internal suspensory system. Abodmen six-segmented, bearing hamula and furcula used for jumping.

Class Diplura

Head bearing antenna, entognathous protrusible mandibles, and maxilla 1 and maxilla 2, the entognathy contrasting with that of the Collembola. The bases of the thoracic legs are supported by the sternite, unlike the Pterygota and Thysanura, and differing in details and in principles of movement from the leg bases of myriapods. The pleural and endoskeletal features are also contrasting. Abdomen 10-segmented, bearing paired terminal filaments or forceps. Short, paired styli are present sometimes on most of the abdominal segments.

Class Protura

Head, lacking antennae, bears entognathous protrusible mandibles and maxilla 1 and maxilla 2 (labium). Thorax with legs 1 functionally and morphologically differentiated from the rest; abdomen 12-segmented with minute appendages on the first three segments and gonopods present posteriorly.

Class Thysanura

Head with antenna, ectognathous mandible, maxilla 1 and maxilla 2. At the leg base the coxa is supported by a pleuro-tergite complex entirely contrasting to the coxa-body joint of all Myriapoda, Diplura, Protura, and Collembola, but bearing some resemblance to the Pterygota. Abdomen 11-segmented, some of which sometimes bear styli; a median caudal filament and paired cerci arise from the last abdominal segment.

Class Pterygota (Insecta)

Typically, head bearing antenna, ectognathous whole limb mandible biting with the tip, maxilla 1, labium formed by maxilla, 2; trunk with

14 somites, the first 3 bearing thoracic legs with pleuro-tergal support of the leg base; 2 pairs of wings.

REFERENCES

Anderson, D. T. (1966a). *Acta Zool., Stockholm* **47**, 1–42.

Anderson, D. T. (1966b). *Proc. Linnean Soc. N.S. Wales* **91**, 10–43.

Anderson, D. T. (1966c). *Ann. Mag. Nat. Hist.* [13] 9, 445–456.

Anderson, D. T. (1970). *Phil. Trans. Roy. Soc. London* **B256**, 183–235.

Anderson, D. T. (1970). The development of the Hemimetabola, and The development of the Holometabola *in* "Developmental Systems—Insects" (S. J. Counce, ed.); in press. Academic Press, New York.

Anderson, D. T. (1971). "Annelid and Arthropod Embryology," in press. Pergamon Press, Oxford.

Bennett, D. S., and Manton, S. M. (1962). *Ann. Mag. Nat. Hist.* [11] **5**, 545–556.

Bidder, G. P. (1931). *Proc. Linnean Soc. London* **142**, 40–42.

Fechter, H. (1961). *Zool. Jahrb., Abt. Anat. Untog. Tiere* **79**, 479–582.

Fox, H. M., Gilchrist, B. M., and Phear, E. A. (1951). *Proc. Roy. Sc.* **B138**, 514–528.

Hinton, H. E. (1960a). *J. Insect Physiol.* **5**, 286–300.

Hinton, H. E. (1960b). *Nature* **188**, 336–337.

Hinton, H E. (1968). *Proc. Roy. Soc.* **B171**, 43–57.

Howell, A. B. (1944). "Speed in Animals: Their Specialization for Running and Leaping," pp. i–ix and 1–270. Univ. of Chicago Press, Chicago, Illinois.

Lankester, E. R. (1904). *Quart. J. Microscop. Sci.* **47**, 523–582.

Manton, S. M. (1938). *Phil. Trans. Roy. Soc. London* **B228**, 421–441.

Manton, S. M. (1949). *Phil. Trans. Roy. Soc. London* **B233**, 483–580.

Manton, S. M. (1950). *J. Linnean Soc. London, Zool.* **41**, Part 1, 529–570.

Manton, S. M. (1952). *J. Linnean Soc. London, Zool.* **42**, Part 2, 93–117; Part 3, 118–166.

Manton, S. M. (1953). *Soc. Exptl. Biol. Symp.* **7**, 339–376.

Manton, S. M. (1954). *J. Linnean Soc. London, Zool.* **42**, Part 4, 299–369.

Manton, S. M. (1956). *J. Linnean Soc. London, Zool.* **43**, Part 5, 153–187.

Manton, S. M. (1958a). *J. Linnean Soc. London, Zool.* **43**, Part 6, 487–556.

Manton, S. M. (1958b). *J. Linnean Soc. London, Zool.* **44**, 58–72.

Manton, S. M. (1959). *Systematics Assoc. Publ.* **3**, 23–32.

Manton, S. M. (1960). *Biol. Rev.* **35**, 265–282.

Manton, S. M. (1961). *J. Linnean Soc. London, Zool.* **44**, Part 7, 383–461.

Manton, S. M. (1964). *Phil. Trans. Roy. Soc. London* **B247**, 1–183.

Manton, S. M. (1965). *J .Linnean Soc. London, Zool.* **45**, Part 8, 251–484.

Manton, S. M. (1966). *J. Linnean Soc. London, Zool.* **46**, Part 9, 103–141.

Manton, S. M. (1967). *J. Nat. Hist.* **1**, 1–22.

Manton, S. M. (1971). *J. Linnean Soc. London, Zool.* (in preparation).

Manton, S. M., and Heatley, N. G. (1937). *Phil. Trans. Roy. Soc. London* **B227**, 411–464.

Needham, A. E. (1958). *Nature* **181**, 194–195.

Needham, A. E. (1960). *Comp. Biochem. Physiol.* **1**, 72–100.

Raymond, P. E. (1935). *Bull. Museum Comp. Zool. Harvard Coll.* **76**, 205–230.

Sharov, A. G. (1966). "Basic Arthropodan Stock, with Special Reference to Insects," pp. i–xii and 1–271. Pergamon Press, Oxford.

Simonetta, A. M. (1962). *Monitore Zool. Ital.* **69**, 172–185.
Simonetta, A. M. (1963). *Monitore Zool. Ital.* **70**, 97–108.
Simonetta, A. M. (1964). *Monitore Zool. Ital.* **72**, 215–231.
Størmer, L (1939). *J. Norsk. Geol. Tidsskr.* **19**, 143–273.
Størmer, L. (1944). *Skrifter. Norske Videnskaps. Akad. Oslo* No. 5.
Tiegs, O. W. (1940). *Quart. J. Microscop. Sci.* **85**, 1–225.
Tiegs, O. W. (1947). *Quart. J. Microscop. Sci.* **88**, 165–336.
Tiegs, O. W., and Manton, S. M. (1958). *Biol Rev.* **33**, 255–337.
Walshe, B. M. (1951). *J. Exptl. Biol.* **2**, 57–61.
Weis-Fogh, T. (1959). *Proc. 15th Intern. Congr. Zool., 1958.* pp. 393–395.

CHAPTER 2

Arthropod Nutrition

R. H. Dadd

I. Introduction

At the outset we must confront a disparity in knowledge of the several classes of arthropods. Insect nutrition, a widely studied specialty of some chemical sophistication, figures disproportionately. By contrast, information for other classes is fragmentary. As the emphasis of these volumes is chemical, I shall ignore purely dietetic work with natural foodstuffs. Nutrition in the narrow sense deals with chemically defined substances needed exogenously, and advances in nutrition studies depend on the development of artificial diets of increasing chemical definition. Dietetics and nutrition are intimately related, and where analysis allows some chemical definition of natural foods, nutritional inferences may be gleaned. Such inferences are usually the basis for formulating chemically defined diets for experimental use.

Nutrition, then, concerns the specific chemicals in food that maintain life, support growth, and eventuate in reproduction and the continuance of generations. The basic tool of nutrition studies is the deletion experiment. This requires the development of satisfactory artificial diets of sufficient definition to allow exclusion of chemicals whose nutritional functions are then assessed in growth studies. It tends to be assumed that fastest growth to the greatest size with highest fecundity is optimal; whether or not this is always so, in practice these criteria are variously taken as measures of optimal nutrition. Ideal diets would consist wholly of defined chemicals, but relative crudity is acceptable if levels of test nutrients may be specified.

Artificial diets are variously described as "crude," "semisynthetic," "synthetic," "chemically defined," etc. The usage is unsystematic, and to counter this, Dougherty (1959) introduced a terminology specifying degree of chemical definition: oligidic—consisting principally of crude natural materials; meridic—composed mainly of defined chemicals, but with one or more crude, natural, or ill-defined components (proteins, natural oils, plant extracts); holidic—consisting wholly of pure chemicals. The classificatory helpfulness of these terms is questionable however, for most diets used should strictly be classed as meridic. Dougherty and others (Hutner *et al.*, 1961) discuss the impossibility of achieving a truly holidic diet, even with the purest currently available biochemicals, if by this is implied total chemical definition.

Dougherty's terminology for diets is used only sporadically. However, his terms "xenic" and "axenic" achieved wide acceptance. "Axenic," equivalent to pure culture in bacteriology, denotes the condition of aseptic culture when only the experimental organism is present. It excludes otherwise aseptic culture of organisms having intracellular symbiotes. "Monoxenic," "dixenic," etc., denote conditions when other specified organisms are intentionally included in culture. Conditions such that unknown organisms are or may be present are designated "xenic." Aseptic culture is necessary with aqueous or agar-based diets in which microbial multiplication could change the composition of the diet and confound the interpretation of deletion tests; because of this, and because symbiotes may preclude detection of requirements for organic nutrients needed in minute amounts, axenic culture came to hold a touchstone position in rigorous nutritional work with insects (House, 1961, 1962). In fact, neither asepsis nor axenic culture are essential for much sound work with insects that take diets low in water (Fraenkel, 1959), not to mention the great bulk of vertebrate nutrition until the recent development of gnotobiological methods.

A primary interest in nutrition is the identification of those chemicals in food that may be utilized for growth or energy. Of many utilizable substances, those that must be provided are variously described as "essential," "required," "indispensable," etc. These terms tend to be used laxly, and some discussion of them is in order, especially with regard to what is meant by an essential nutrient.

Nutrients are essential if without them growth eventually ceases (even though this may take several consecutive generations), presumably because the nutrients cannot be synthesized in adequate amounts from other ingested material. Conversely, it is sometimes assumed that if a particular nutrient is synthesized, it is nonessential; but this will be true only if synthetic rates are high enough to provide a certain minimal requirement for survival and growth. Nutrients which are not essential, as defined by the criterion of eventual cessation of growth, but which are needed to maintain an optimal growth rate, may be termed "required," a convenient shorthand for "required for optimal performance though not, necessarily, essential." In these cases synthesis of the nutrient presumably occurs, but at so slow a rate that without exogenous augmentation it becomes the limiting factor in overall performance. The terms "essential," "indispensable," "required," or "necessary" are often applied indiscriminately when omission produces any adverse effect whatever, but when the status of a supposed nutrient is indefinite, a noncommittal term, such as "useful," is preferable.

Several factors can render interpretation of experiments ambiguous. The classic deletion method assumes equal ingestion of all diets being compared, for otherwise growth retardation consequent upon deletion might result from overall starvation rather than specific deficiency. With insects, this possible confusion is substantial, for many nutrients provide gustatory stimuli without which feeding behavior is impaired. Deletion of a phagostimulatory non-nutrient may lead to its erroneous designation as a needed nutrient; and deletion of a nutrient which at certain concentrations is phagoinhibitory may improve performances in the short term and lead to its designation as a non-nutrient.

Some limitations on interpretation are matters of practicability. Any adverse outcome of deletion from a satisfactory diet allows it to be definitely stated, in the context of the particular diet, that the deleted component is in some way necessary; but with no adverse effect, to assume dispensability is inappropriate without extended experimentation, particularly for putative nutrients, such as trace metals, known to function in minute amounts; for it is difficult to ensure that a deleted nutrient is not cryptically present as a contaminant of other dietary ingredients, thereby possibly masking the effect of deletion. In meridic diets contamination is particularly likely from crude components. Even with increasingly pure biochemicals available, contamination remains a frequent problem in studies of vitamins (Barlow, 1962), lipids (House, 1966a), and trace metals (Dadd, 1968). Furthermore, requirements may be obscured by reserves of nutrients sufficient to carry through several generations. Many arthropods, particularly insects, share to some extent with microorganisms the advantages of small size and brief life history that are conducive to experimentation over several generations. Even so, most studies span only one, or part of one, cycle of growth. It is now apparent that this period is inadequate for the expression of many vitamin and mineral deficiencies (Gordon, 1959; Forgash, 1958; Dadd, 1961, 1968; Dadd and Mittler, 1965; Dadd *et al.*, 1967; Ehrhardt, 1968a,b).

The main stumbling block in nutritional experimentation is the necessity first to produce an acceptable and readily modifiable artificial diet, and this has largely determined the historic sequence and range of animals studied. Those that are naturally unfastidious are most likely to feed readily on artificial diets. Such animals are the domesticated livestock that provide our knowledge of vertebrate nutrition. The first arthropods studied were insect pests of stored cereals, omnivorous roaches, and flies with larvae that are found in carrion or saprophytic environments. These situations involve more or less nonfastidious feeding and, further, have physical characteristics easily simulated in artificial diets. With improved understanding of feeding behavior, an array of both biting and suctorial phytophagous insects have become tractable to nutritional investigation in spite of their specialized natural dietaries.

The upsurge in insect nutrition studies stems from its economic importance to man. Crop pests compete directly for our food, and disease vectors feed upon us. Doubtless, information is meagre for other arthropods because of their relative economic insignificance; but also, their feeding habits make them difficult objects of nutritional study. Arachnids are largely suctorial predators, rendering the development of an artificial diet that will satisfy their complex preying and feeding behavior peculiarly difficult. Crustacea are principally aquatic, so that the development of artificial foods is inextricably linked with the problems of providing an artificial total environment. Since so much of our knowledge of arthropod nutrition relates to insects, it will be convenient to treat them separately, and then to relate the scattered information for other classes to the now substantial knowledge of insects.

II. Insect Nutrition

Insects may be found eating almost every type of organic material, including intractable stuffs such as wood, wool, and the bacteria of petroleum pools. Of the vast majority that appear less eccentric, many phytophagous and parasitic insects are restricted to particular food plants or host animals. Is this, one wonders, because they have special nutritional requirements that only their particular foods can satisfy? Where diet is narrowly restricted, and not very dissimilar foods are rejected even under stress of starvation, what specific mechanisms govern selection of the right food? In nutritional experimentation the two questions are interrelated. Early studies with nonfastidious insects generally revealed qualitative requirements essentially similar to those known from vertebrate nutrition. However, fastidious feeders, primarily larvae that normally feed on plant tissues, long were intractable to rearing on artificial diets unless augmented with plant material. Was failure due to lack of unknown growth factors present in plant tissues, or to starvation caused by the absence of whatever stimuli incited feeding on the natural dietary? In retrospect one can see that both causes were often operative.

Probably greatest weight was at first given to the notion of unknown growth factors, reasonably so at a time when there were many as yet uncharacterized growth factors in the parent disciplines of vertebrate and microbial nutrition. A lipid factor required by insects was early shown to be a sterol (Hobson, 1935), which is not a general vertebrate requirement, and vitamin "B_T," later shown to be carnitine, was needed only by certain tenebrionid beetles (Fraenkel and Friedman, 1957). Thus, there seemed every likelihood that more unknowns awaited discovery, some perhaps, like carnitine, peculiar to certain groups of insect.

With the development of apparently adequate, defined diets for many insects, the place for unrecognized nutrient factors diminished, and as many recalcitrant phytophagous insects clearly ate artificial diets reluctantly, the likelihood of a need for special phagostimulatory materials took on increasing prominence. Studies of feeding behavior proliferated, prompted by the need, in economic and medical entomology, for some insight into the food specificity that characterizes many important pests and parasites. Such studies were clearly relevant to attempts to rear restricted feeders on artificial diets, and it came to be recognized that information on feeding behavior would be generally necessary to prosecute successful nutritional work (Trager, 1953; Lipke and Frankel, 1956; Friend, 1958). We must therefore discuss the regulation of feeding before proceeding to the central topics of nutritional requirements.

It is convenient to list the many reviews on insect nutrition that have been published in recent years. I shall list them here, but subsequently just refer to them as "reviews"; I will refer to individual papers mainly for crucial points or recent material. General reviews that taken in sequence will provide a historic perspective are those of Wigglesworth (1939–1965, various revisions), Chauvin (1956), Trager (1953), Levinson (1955), Lipke and Fraenkel (1956), Gilmour (1961), House (1961, 1962, 1965a), and most recently, the extensive tabular summaries of qualitative requirements presented in the compendium of Altman and Dittmer (1968). In addition, special areas of insect nutrition have been reviewed: phytophagous insects (Friend, 1958); parasitic insects (House, 1958); honeybee nutrition (Haydak, 1970); silkworm nutrition (Legay, 1958; Shyamala and Bhat, 1962; Ito, 1967); aphids

(Auclair, 1963); grasshoppers and locusts (Dadd, 1963); mosquito nutrition (Clements, 1963); sterol requirements of insects (Clayton, 1964); relation of nutrition to insecticide resistance (Gordon, 1961); methods of insect nutrition (J. David, 1967); nutritional pathology (House, 1963); a recipe book of insect diets (House, 1967).

A. REGULATION OF FEEDING BEHAVIOR

Among insects, feeding involves a hierarchy of stereotyped behavioral components broadly distinguishable as: (a) orientation to food; (b) initiation of feeding; (c) maintenance of feeding and ingestion. To these some would add: (d) cessation of feeding, often followed by dispersal behavior. A predisposition to feed is brought about by intrinsic stimuli arising endogenously in some relation to fluctuations in the internal physiological state, and the sequence of overt feeding behavior may then be released by extrinsic stimuli from the food.

Since Dethier (1953) discussed insect feeding behavior in these terms, various designations have been proposed for the extrinsic stimuli that elicit these sequential responses (Thorsteinson, 1958, 1960; Dethier *et al.*, 1960; Dadd, 1963; Beck, 1965), but no generally agreed usage prevails, reflecting the fact that for various species the components into which feeding may be analyzed differ in number and often in modality of the sensory responses involved (visual, thermal, tactile, olfactory, gustatory). Three phases of feeding behavior may not be distinguishable in practice, for orientation to food and initiation of feeding often are inseparable. Location of food may be a matter of chance, as with many winged aphids, or may depend primarily on selection by the ovipositing mother for many phytophagous and parasitic larvae. In haustellate insects particularly, the initiation of feeding may itself be distinguishable into several distinct behavioral components.

The most generally useful designation for substances that release a feeding response is "phagostimulant," with "phagoinhibitant" denoting substances that deter feeding. "Attractant" and "repellant or deterrent" are often used synonymously with the foregoing, but "attractant" implies action at a distance, and should be so limited. "Arrestant" and "aggregant" are terms that have been used for orientation stimuli, emphasizing the inhibition of locomotion that may bring about aggregations of individuals at food, but the latter term is clearly inappropriate for single insects. "Biting stimulus," "acceptant," and "incitant" are terms for stimuli that initiate feeding, with "rejectant," "deterrent," or "suppressant" as their opposites. Substances stimulating continued feeding are referred to very broadly as "feeding or phagostimulants" or (Beck, 1965) just "stimulants."

The term "token factor or stimulant" occurs in discussions of phytophagous behavior. It denotes phagostimulant substances, usually secondary plant chemicals, that are essential for proper feeding, though not themselves nutritious. Token factors signal the particular food plants for some mono- or oligophagous species (species limited to one, or a restricted and usually botanically related group of food plants).

Terminologies of feeding behavior were proposed mostly to account for chemical stimuli concerned in host plant selection by phytophagous insects. It should nevertheless be remembered that stimuli other than chemical usually are involved, especially in carnivores, bloodsuckers, and parasites.

Water probably influences feeding behavior in many insects, particularly those, such as plant-feeders, that normally obtain it from their food; if desiccated, such insects may eat more, or unusual, food, largely for its water content (Dadd, 1963; Barton Browne, 1964). The quantities of cellulose-based artificial diets eaten by thirsty locusts increased with water content, up to the point that free water rendered the diets physically less acceptable (Sinoir, 1966, 1968). Murray (1968) showed that mealworms, given certain diets (bran or mixtures with high cellulose) with carbohydrate insufficient to provide the metabolic water that may otherwise, as on flour, be adequate for their needs, are then dependent on the water content of the diet, a function of ambient humidity, to maintain their feeding. Murray's discussion of why, in this case, water should not be considered a phagostimulant is valuable for clarifying that sensory/neural mediation is connoted by the definition of a substance as a phagostimulant; he suggests, rather, that mealworm larvae show gradual metabolic adaptation to protracted lack of water, involving no direct sensing of dietary water levels, though the avid ingestion of large quantities of free water by long dessicated individuals might suggest a definite sensory response. Pure water clearly functions as a phagostimulant for adult blowflies, for its rapid imbibition by dehydrated *Phormia* is mediated by specific receptors that are distinct from those sensitive to sugar (Barton Browne, 1964).

1. Intrinsic Regulation of Feeding

In simplistic terms, feeding is provoked by hunger and drinking by thirst. Though qualitatively recognizable sensations in humans, hunger and thirst in other animals can generally only be defined in terms of nonfeeding and starvation, nondrinking and dehydration. Such definitions are tautological, and use of the term *hunger* for insects has been decried (Dethier and Bodenstein, 1958). Nevertheless, discussion of feeding is helped by some such blanket term denoting, in the broadest way, the changed internal situation consequent upon food and water deprivation that predisposes to ingestion.

Since nutrients are ingested to replenish deficits arising from energy metabolism and tissue synthesis, it is logical to speculate that hunger would depend upon a feedback to centers regulating ingestion of information on changing levels of products absorbed from digested food. Evidence that may be so interpreted comes from experiments showing that dilution of the nutritive components of food by nutritionally inert material increases the absolute amount ingested. Locusts ate more synthetic diet the more it was diluted with cellulose powder; products of the dry weight of diet eaten and its percentage utilization were approximately constant for various dilutions, suggesting regulation of feeding to give a constant intake of metabolizable nutrient (Dadd, 1960a). Dilution of diet with cellulose likewise increased food intake with the silkworm (Mukaiyama and Ito, 1962), the sphinx moth larva, *Celerio euphorbiae* (House, 1965a), the grasshopper, *Melanoplus sanguinipes* (McGinnis and Kasting, 1967), and the roach, *Blattella germanica* (Gordon, 1968a), and it is apparent that in these cases the intake of food, overall, is somehow adjusted to metabolic need. Metabolic dependence is also indicated by the increased feeding or (in Diptera) change in type of food associated with egg development (Watson, 1967; L. Strong, 1967; Hill *et al.*, 1968; Orr, 1964).

The adult blowfly, *Phormia regina*, the only insect in which the mechanics of hunger have been resolved in any detail, presents an especially simple case in which to examine feeding, satiety, and the recurrence of feeding, since for maintenance it requires only solutions of sugar, which also provide the extrinsic phagostimuli essential to initiate feeding. In the hungry fly, stimulation of tarsal receptors by sugary solutions causes proboscis extension, and the consequent stimulation of oral receptors then induces sucking, the ingested fluid passing mainly to the crop, from whence, after feeding ceases, slugs of food are aperiodically passed via the foregut into the midgut. Feeding terminates when peripheral and central adaptation raise the threshold for extrinsic stimulation by food. Maintenance of central adaptation after the comparatively rapid disadaptation of the peripheral sensilla determines the interval to receptivity for the next meal (state of hunger). It might be anticipated that central adaptation (satiation), would be maintained by high levels of sugar in the midgut or absorbed into the hemolymph, but this is not necessarily so, for sugar injected into the midgut via the rectum, or into the hemolymph, does not prevent hunger (responsivity to external stimuli) in flies whose crop is already emptied. Elevated hemolymph osmotic pressure, however, does retard the emptying of crop contents into the midgut, and it is the continued sensing by stretch receptors of material traversing the foregut that, via the recurrent nerve, maintains central adaptation, and hence prevents the recurrence of hunger in flies whose crops still contain food (Evans and Barton Browne, 1960; Gelperin, 1966a,b, 1967; Dethier and Gelperin, 1967a). Thirst—readiness to drink pure water—was considered essentially dependent on blood volume (or pressure) in *Phormia* (Dethier and Evans, 1961), but complex determinants, including osmotic pressure and chloride concentrations specifically, as well as blood (or body) volume are operative in another blowfly, *Lucilia cuprina* (Barton Browne and Dudziński, 1968; Barton Browne, 1968). In no other insects have the events producing a readiness to feed been so thoroughly analyzed, but in a roach, *Periplaneta americana,* crop emptying is also controlled by sensory feedback based on osmotic pressure of the crop contents (Davey and Treherne, 1963, 1964).

Natural foods will always provide metabolizable materials for digestion and absorption, and so osmotic fluxes in the gut and hemolymph, and hence crop emptying and the consequent regulation of feeding-readiness (hunger) will be influenced by metabolic drain, as apparently occurs in the other insects discussed, and indeed is found to be generally so in the long run for various flies (Strangways-Dixon, 1961; Dethier, 1961; Dethier and Gelperin, 1967b). To the extent that the end products of digestion of all major nutrients, amino acids as well as sugars, affect osmotic pressure, they provide a general indicator of levels of all major utilizable metabolites.

Dethier and Gelperin (1967a), following earlier observations of Nuñez (1964) on *Lucilia* sp., latterly attributed a component of the central inhibition of ingestion in *Phormia* to a mechanical sensing of fullness by body wall stretch receptors, for section of the ventral nerve cord results in hyperphagia, and these insects then usually burst. Hyperphagia and bursting also occur in various mosquito species allowed to engorge blood following ventral nerve section, the degree of hyperphagia diminishing the farther back in the abdomen that the nerve is sectioned (Gwadz, 1969). Apart from considerations of efficiency of utilization of nutrients, these recent findings vindicate a common sense expectation that, in nature, some crudely mechanical induction of satiety would generally intervene to prevent self-immolation by gut rupture.

2. Phagostimulation in Plant-Feeding Insects

Many leaf-eating larvae feed only on groups of botanically related plants. Assuming that host plants are optimally nutritious, this "botanical instinct" might reside in an ability to discriminate nutrient properties. However, it is difficult to believe that optimal nutritiousness would coincide with botanical taxa. On the other hand, botanical taxa often have in common distinctive secondary plant substances (essential oils, flavonoids, alkaloids, etc.), suggesting that oligophagous insects might have evolved a need for such chemicals to release feeding behavior (Fraenkel, 1959).

The classic example is provided by insects infesting cruciferous and other plants containing mustard oil glycosides. Such is the moth, *Plutella maculipennis;* its larvae will feed on several nonhost plants painted with cabbage juice or solutions of the mustard oil glycoside, sinigrin, and agar gels are fed upon if they contain 0.1% of sinigrin—maximally if nutrients, particularly glucose, are also present. Mustard oil itself, allyl isothiocyanate, scarcely influences feeding, though it affects short-distance orientation to food (Thorsteinson, 1953). Sinigrin is thus a token phagostimulant for *Plutella,* and allyl isothiocyanate is an attractant that also leads the ovipositing mother moth to the appropriate larval food plant (Gupta and Thorsteinson, 1960). *Plutella* larvae respond with differing sensitivity to sinigrin, gluconapin, glucocheirolin, glucoerucin, glucotropaeolin, sinalbin, gluconasturtiin, progoitrin, and glucoringiin, and the occurrence of these mustard glycosides in different proportions in various Cruciferae doubtless contributes to differences in acceptability within the generally acceptable host-plant group (Nayar and Thorsteinson, 1963). Phagostimulant effects of sinigrin have been demonstrated in other Lepidoptera (W. A. L. David and Gardiner, 1966; Schoonhoven, 1967), aphids (Wensler, 1962; Wearing, 1968), and in coleopterous larvae (Tanton, 1965; Sugiyama and Matsumoto, 1959), though not all brassicaceous insects require sinigrin to feed normally (Gothilf and Beck, 1967).

Specific token chemicals are known for a few insects besides those on Brassicae: methyl chavicol and other components of essential oils of Umbelliferae for *Papilio* spp. that infest umbels (Dethier, 1953); hypericin for *Chrysomela brunsvicensis* feeding on *Hypericum* spp. (Schoonhoven, 1968); catalposides for *Ceratomia catalpae,* the catalpa sphinx moth (Nayar and Fraenkel, 1963a); curcurbitacins for the cucumber beetle (Chambliss and Jones, 1966); and the cyanogenetic glycosides, phaseolunatin and lotaustrin, for the Mexican bean beetle feeding principally on *Phaseolus* (Nayar and Fraenkel, 1963b). More usually, phagostimulant chemicals in extracts of host plants remain obscure, or, in attempts at their isolation, stimulant nutrients or substances of wide distribution, and therefore not tokens, come to light (Temple *et al.,* 1968).

This now seems so for some of the most fastidious of classic oligophages. Several workers have elucidated a hierarchy of responses to known chemicals in the silkworm, *Bombyx mori* (Beck, 1965). Leaf odor substances, among them β,γ-hexenol, α,β-hexenal, citral, terpinyl acetate, linalyl acetate, and linalool, attract the worm over distances of a few millimeters. Biting is incited by steroids, identical or closely related to β-sitosterol, and possibly esterified with C_{10}–C_{18} fatty acids; long-chain aliphatic alcohols of $C_{30}H_{62}O$ average composition, and the flavonoid glycoside, isoquercitrin, have also been implicated as biting stimuli. Stimulants found to maintain feeding are all nutrients: sucrose, raffinose, inositol, ascorbic acid, and phosphate. Although the silkworm is monophagous, none of the identified phagostimulants are specific to the host plant, mulberry, and even the steroids that Nayar and Fraenkel (1962) felt might include a specific token are more probably a mixture of rather ubiquitous plant chemicals.

The Colorado potato beetle, *Leptinotarsa decemlineata*, is also noteworthy for the many nutrients that individually stimulate biting and feeding, including twelve sugars, eleven amino acids, lecithin, inositol phosphatide, phosphatidyl serine, phosphatidyl ethanolamine, cholesterol, and β-sitosterol (the steroids purely as biting stimulants); salts alone were ineffective, but several had a synergistic action with sucrose and amino acids. Indeed, various mixtures of nutrients at individually subliminal levels were stimulatory, and a judicious mixture of the most stimulant nutrients enabled last instar larvae to grow as well on artificial diet as on potato leaves (Hsiao and Fraenkel, 1968a). Both *Leptinotarsa* and *Protoparce sexta*, a hornworm likewise limited to species of Solanaceae, feed maximally on agar gels containing sucrose together with extracts of tomato plant thought to contain a glycosidic token (Yamamoto and Fraenkel, 1959, 1960). Attempts to identify the putative token yielded a phagostimulant substance, chlorogenic acid, but this is a ubiquitous plant chemical that could hardly characterize Solanaceae (Hsiao and Fraenkel, 1968b). The flavonoid glycoside, isolated from fresh leaves only, was preferred in choice tests, but since old and fresh leaf powders were both effective stimulants of feeding, its role as a token would appear minor, perhaps initiating orientation, or inducing oviposition predominantly on the host plant.

It seems, then, that the principal phagostimulants for some oligophagous insects may be those nutrients also found active with polyphagous insects such as some grasshoppers, aphids, and wireworms (Thorsteinson, 1960; Dadd, 1963; Thorsteinson and Nayar, 1963; Nayar, 1964; Mittler and Dadd, 1964, 1965; Mittler, 1967a,b,c; Davis, 1965). A sugar, often sucrose, is generally most effective, with auxiliary stimulation variously provided by amino acids, peptides, phospholipids, certain vitamins, and some salts, often acting, in concert, with greatly increased effectiveness (Gothilf and Beck, 1967).

Nutrients invariably are necessary to stimulate normal feeding even where a token is indubitably required. This suggests that feeding behavior, generally, is released by patterns of stimuli from various ubiquitous nutrient and non-nutritive chemicals, the patterns for oligo- and monophagous species being presumably more specific and sometimes including token components. Fastidiousness may be reinforced by phagoinhibitant chemicals in nonhost plants, a particularly well-documented case being that of the potato beetle, which rejects many solanaceous species because of deterrent saponins and alkaloids (Stürckow and Low, 1961). Host differentiation between two bark beetles, *Scolytus quadrispinatus* and S. *multistriatus*, depends on 5-hydroxy-1,4-naphthoquinone in bark of *Carya orata* acting as a feeding deterrent for S. *multistriatus* (B. L. Gilbert and Norris, 1968). The importance of inhibitors has been demonstrated by using maxillectomized larvae, in which sense receptors responsive to inhibitory chemicals are removed; silkworms thus treated feed on the nonhosts, cabbage and cherry, and the tobacco hornworm on dandelion (Beck, 1965; Schoonhoven, 1968).

Interest in the phagostimulant action of nutrients received impetus from the "dual discrimination theory" of Kennedy and Booth (1951); while recognizing the importance of botanically characteristic stimuli, this theory proposed that choice of feeding site by aphids, once on an appropriate host, hinged on nutritional factors. The role of nutrients in stimulating *Myzus persicae* to feed on synthetic diet supports this view. Sucrose solutions stimulate initial probes of short duration and maximal depth, whereas sucrose with amino acids provokes prolonged but shallow insertions (Mittler and Dadd, 1964, 1965). Both sucrose and amino acids are necessary for substantial ingestion (Mittler, 1967a), and as the natural food, phloem sap, is essentially such a mixture, it perhaps provides a "probe arrestant" stimulus signaling location of food, in nature, in the deep-lying sieve tubes. Corn plant tissues on which larvae of *Pyrausta nubilalis* concentrate their feeding tend to have high levels of sucrose with low resistance factor A (6-methoxybenzoxazolinone), respectively attractant and repellent in agar gel choice tests (Beck, 1965). Feeding-site selection by the spruce budworm, *Choristoneura fumiferana*, also involves balanced stimulation and inhibition, for the larvae select vegetative tissues high in sugar, proline, shikimic and caffeic acids, all phagostimulants, and low in pungenin, a phagoinhibitant concentrated in the older, uneaten needles (Heron, 1964).

Because of the often striking dependence of feeding on token factors, early studies tended to dwell unduly on their importance, covertly implying that nutritional considerations had little direct part in regulating feeding or in choice of host. It is now apparent that all insects, including those dependent upon tokens, require nutrients to maintain proper feeding, and the implications of this for the development of artificial diets and their use in nutritional studies are considered by Davis (1968d). Clearly, if a token is essential for feeding, no progress is possible until it is included in the diet. With most situations involving complex patterns of stimuli, omission of single slightly phagostimulant substances does not greatly affect overall ingestion; fortunately, many of the stimulatory nutrients are in this category, for otherwise it would be difficult to draw unambiguous nutritional conclusions from deletion experiments.

3. Phagostimulation in Bloodsuckers

Parasitic insects display host specializations equaling those of phytophagous insects and, one may suppose, likewise dependent on characteristic patterns of stimuli. Host selection occurs when the mother oviposits, and its basis is in great part olfactory and "ovipositor gustatory"; little is known of the chemical stimuli involved (see bibliography of Hocking, 1960), though ammonium compounds and indole appear to act as attractants and oviposition stimulants with some flesh flies (Barton Browne, 1965). Among predatory carnivorous insects, stimuli denoting movement, to a great extent visual and tactile, orient them to suitable prey and induce attack and biting. Continued feeding would then doubtless hinge upon the presence of gustatory stimulants and inhibitants in the prey tissues. Several sugars and lipid nutrients, particularly linoleic acid, stimulate feeding of predatory fire ants, *Solenopis saevissima* (Vinson *et al.*, 1967), but otherwise knowledge of specific phagostimulants is confined to a specialized type of predator, the bloodsucking insects, principally adult, female Diptera.

Two distinct kinds of feeding occur in these adult Diptera. For normal longevity, both males and females require only sugar and water, often obtained in nature by nectar feeding. Male fertility generally demands nothing further (exceptionally, proteinaceous food is necessary, as in tsetse and stable flies). Females, however, usually, require protein to allow normal egg development: vertebrate blood in most biting flies and carrion or saprophytic materials for flesh and filth flies.

Sugar feeding, particularly by flesh flies, has been intensively studied for several decades (Dethier, 1966) and the stimuli that regulate ingestion once contact is made with sugary material are well understood and have already been discussed. Though non-nutrient sugars such as fucose may be stimulatory, and nutrient sugars do not always stimulate, it is noteworthy that the common, naturally occurring sugars (sucrose, glucose, fructose) both provide needed nutriment and are phagostimulant. In its main outlines, sugar feeding and its regulation in mosquitoes is similar to the situation found in flesh flies (Owen, 1963, 1965). Recent study of two species of mosquito compares the phagostimulant and nutrient properties of 39 sugars and related substance and the inhibitory effects of various common electrolytes (salts, acids, bases) and organic alcohols (Salama, 1966a,b, 1967).

Factors stimulating blood feeding have been studied principally in mosquitoes. Orientation to prey is influenced by vision and by heat, carbon dioxide, water vapor, and olfactory stimuli emanating from the prey. The relative significance of these has been contended (Clements, 1963), but recent choice experiments with *Aedes aegypti* suggest an overriding influence of olfactory stimuli from the skin (Khan *et al.*, 1966, 1967; Khan and Maibach, 1966). Many have argued that attraction resided in sweat, and among substances proposed to account for this are steroid lipids and various amino acids, particularly lysine (the latter because of its ability to absorb CO_2 or form carbaminolysine) (Skinner *et al.*, 1965; Roessler and Brown, 1964; Lipsitz and Brown, 1964). Attempts to isolate attractants from human sweat lipids revealed only repellent unsaturated hydrocarbons (Skinner *et al.*, 1967); other olfactometer studies provide strong evidence that the principal human sweat attractant for *Aedes* is L-lactic acid (Acree *et al.*, 1968; Müller, 1968), but contrarily, Skinner *et al.* (1968) present evidence showing lactic acid to be repellent.

Turning to the maintenance of feeding, in mosquitoes a difference must be noted in the destination of meals; sugary foods are generally taken into the foregut diverticula, whereas blood is engorged directly to the midgut. This difference has been thought to depend upon tactile factors involved in feeding through skin on fluid that contains particles (blood corpuscles), but the weight of evidence now points to a gustatory differentiation. Hosoi (1959) showed that *Culex pipiens* engorged fluids directly to the midgut if the fluids lacked sugar and contained substances fractionated from erythrocytes. Muscle adenylic acid (adenosine 5'-phosphate) proved to be the principal erythrocyte-derived phagostimulant, active at 10^{-3} to 10^{-5} M in the presence of 0.15 M NaCl, the latter providing an osmotic pressure comparable to that of blood. Adenosine di- and triphosphates, and deoxyadenosine 5'-phosphate were weaker gorging stimuli; yeast adenylic acid (adenosine 2'- and 3'-monophosphates) was probably ineffective. Various nucleotides have subsequently been found to stimulate gorging in other mosquitoes (Rutledge *et al.*, 1964; Mason *et al.*, 1965). In *Aedes*, adenosine mono-, di-, tri-, and tetraphosphates are effective phagostimulants, while phosphates of inosine, guanosine, and cytidine are not (Galun *et al.*, 1963), the effect again depending upon NaCl, in this case with a specific requirement for sodium ion (Galun, 1967). In contrast, it should be noted that 5-adenylic acid and adenosine di- and triphosphates failed to induce significant gorging of saline in *Culiseta inornata* (Owen and Reinholz, 1968). Since ticks have recently been found to respond to nucleotides only if glucose is also present (Galun and Kindler, 1968) perhaps a similar synergism might also be necessary for some mosquitoes. The bloodsucking bug, *Rhodnius prolixus*, is stimulated to engorge by many nucleoside phosphates, the effect being less specific than in mosquitoes, since 10^{-3} M concentrations (again with 0.15 M NaCl) of di- and triphosphates of adenosine, guanosine, cytosine, inosine, and uridine are all active (Friend, 1965). In the female housefly, *Musca domestica*, the protein-type feeding related to egg development (as distinct from sugar-maintenance feeding) is stimulated by several amino acids, notably L-leucine, and by guanosine mono- (2′, 3′, or 5′), di-, and triphosphates, but not by adenosine, cytosine, or uridine phosphates, although some of these latter stimulated proboscis extension when applied to the tarsi (Robbins *et al.*, 1965; Yamamoto and Jensen, 1967).

Clearly, nutritional study of bloodsucking insects is likely to involve prior clarification of their position with respect to substances like nucleotides acting as "tokens" for blood. Even if ingestion of synthetic food seems normal, in flies its destination may not be, and this may effect digestive and absorptive efficiency and the subsequent utilization of the nutrients in egg production.

B. NUTRITIONAL REQUIREMENTS

A prime impetus behind nutritional studies was the need for bulk standardized diets to rear continually available, uniform, experimental insects for the burgeoning research concerned with pest control (Smith, 1966). An empirical knowledge of requirements and balances for compounding diets has thus been a major and often sole aim. Because so many pestilential insects demand study, many species from the main orders are now characterized nutritionally, allowing an exceptionally broad base for an appreciation of the class as a whole, but direct studies on the metabolic fate of absorbed nutrients are few when compared with the emphasis this aspect receives in the corresponding vertebrate and microbial disciplines. Indeed, for insects, such important explicative extensions of nutrition are for the most part conjectures that assimilate metabolic schemes elucidated primarily in vertebrates and microorganisms and are hopefully assumed to have general application.

The formulations listed in Table I give an overall impression of the nutrients commonly required by insects. The examples selected cover the range of larval types that have developed on synthetic diets with something approaching normality. *Phormia* is a flesh fly whose naturally

TABLE I

Components of Synthetic Diets for Diverse Larval Insects Expressed
as Percentages of Total Dry Ingredients of Diet

	Tribolium confusum[a]	Phormia regina[a]	Argyrotaenia velutinana[a]	Bombyx mori[a]
Water	nil[b,c]	1400.0[c]	800.0[c]	300.0[c]
Inert materials	nil[c]	52.7[c]	26.6[c]	49.2[c]
Agar	–	37.9	26.6	15.0
Cellulose powder	–	–	–	34.2
D-Amino acids[e]	–	14.8	–	
Lipids	3.4[c]	1.5[c]	6.7[c]	3.5[c]
Tween 80	–	–	2.5	–
Sterol	0.4[d]	1.5[d]	1.7[d]	0.5[d]
Oil (essentially $C_{18:2}$ and $C_{18:3}$ fatty acids)	3.0	–	2.5[d]	3.0[d]
Minerals[f]	3.5[c,d]	3.6[c,d]	4.1[c,d]	4.5[c,d]
Carbohydrate	72.5[c,d]	nil[c]	44.1[c,d]	20.0[c,d]
Starch	72.5	–	–	7.5
Sucrose	–	–	–	12.5
Glucose	–	–	44.1	–
L-Amino acids	20.0[c]	40.6[c]	17.9[c]	20.0[c]
Alanine	–	2.0	1.3	1.4
Arginine	0.9[d]	1.6[d]	2.7[d]	1.2[d]
Aspartate	–	2.3	0.9	2.5
Cysteine/cysteine	2.0	0.5[g]	0.4	0.2
Glutamate	4.5	8.3	0.9	2.4
Glycine	4.5	1.1	1.3	1.0
Histidine	0.6[d]	1.1[d]	0.7[d]	0.5[d]
Isoleucine	1.2[d]	2.3[d]	1.0[d]	1.1[d]
Leucine	1.4[d]	4.2[d]	1.5[d]	1.7[d]
Lysine	1.3[d]	2.7[d]	1.0[d]	1.6[d]
Methionine	0.6[d]	1.4[g]	0.7[d]	0.5[d]
Phenylalanine	0.8[d]	2.1[d]	1.3[d]	1.1[d]
Proline, hydroxy-proline	–	3.8[d]	0.4	0.8[d]
Serine	–	–	0.4	1.0
Threonine	0.9[d]	1.4[d]	0.7[d]	1.0[d]
Tryptophan	0.2[d]	0.7[d]	0.9[d]	0.4[d]
Tyrosine	–	2.5	0.4	0.4
Valine	1.1[d]	2.6[d]	1.2[d]	1.2[d]
Growth Factors	0.7[c]	1.8[c]	1.2[c]	2.5[c]
Thiamine	0.0012[d]	0.0075[d]	0.005[d]	0.002[d]
Riboflavin	0.0018[d]	0.023[d]	0.009[d]	0.002[d]
Nicotinic acid	0.01[d]	0.023[d]	0.054[d]	0.03[d]
Pyridoxine	0.0016[d]	0.023[d]	0.054[d]	0.003[d]
Pantothenic acid	0.004[d]	0.023[d]	0.018[d]	0.015[d]

TABLE I   (Continued)

	Tribolium confusum[a]	Phormia regina[a]	Argyrotaenia velutinana[a]	Bombyx mori[a]
Folic acid	0.0005[d]	0.0075[d]	0.009[d]	0.0004
Biotin	0.00006[d]	0.00004[d]	0.0002[d]	0.0004[d]
Inositol	0.2[d]	0.15[d]	–	0.2[d]
Choline	0.4[d]	0.15[d]	0.9	0.15[d]
Cobalamin	0.00005	–	0.00002	–
p-Aminobenzoic acid	0.05	0.023	–	–
Carnitine	0.001[d]	–	–	–
Menadione	0.0001	–	–	–
α-Tocopherol	–	–	0.13	–
Ribonucleic acid	–	1.5	–	–
Ascorbic acid	0.001	–	–	2.0[d]
Phagostimulants[h]	–	–	–	**1.3[c]**
Citric acid	–	–	–	0.5
Morin (isoquercitrin)	–	–	–	0.3
Mulberry leaf fraction	–	–	–	0.5

[a] Percentages calculated from: *Tribolium* (M. W. Taylor and Medici, 1966); *Phormia* (McGinnis *et al.*, in House, 1967); *Argyrotaenia* (Rock and King, 1967a); *Bombyx* (Ito and Arai, 1967).

[b] Diets as dispensed would contain some water after equilibration with ambient humidity.

[c] Numbers in boldface represent totals.

[d] Essential, based on information from many sources besides those quoted for dietary composition.

[e] The diet for *Phormia* used some racemic amino acids, of which D forms, taken to be 50%, are here considered inert.

[f] All mineral mixtures contain Ca, K, Na, Mg, Mn, Fe, Cl, PO_4, SO_4, and various minor ions; though certain requirements have been demonstrated for *Tribolium* and *Bombyx*, nothing is known in detail of the needs of *Phormia* and *Argyrotaenia*.

[g] Either cystine or methionine essential.

[h] In addition to various nutrients that also are phagostimulatory.

necrophilous larvae need a semiliquid, largely proteinaceous diet. *Tribolium confusum*, a pest of stored cereals, needs dry diets high in carbohydrate, from which it derives its water metabolically. The leaf-eating caterpillars, *Argyrotaenia velutinana* and *Bombyx*, require diets fairly high in water content but of firm texture, and additional growth factors must be provided; the silkworm apparently needs inert "roughage" and phagostimulant substances to ensure adequate feeding. Qualitatively the diets are similar, outstanding differences being in the relative proportions of the constituents, especially carbohydrates, nonutilized solids, and water.

Since water is generally required by insects and usually constitutes 60% to 80% of their tissue weight, one may ask why it is absent from formulations of artificial diets for several species. Sometimes, as for roaches and grasshoppers, water is separately provided ad lib. Where this is not so, as for stored-products insects of which *Tribolium* is an example, a special facility for utilizing metabolic water and minimizing excretory and respiratory water loss must be presumed, augmented by such water as is cryptically present in the diet after hygroscopic equilibration with ambient water vapor. The importance of the latter source is evident from a detailed study of the water economy of the mealworm showing that on diets deficient in carbohydrate, and thus limiting with respect to the production of metabolic water, growth depends critically on a high ambient relative humidity that is able to raise the actual water content of the diet (Murray, 1968). Water content for a given relative humidity was shown to vary with the composition of the diet, and similar observations on "dry" artificial diets for the waxworm suggested that, in part, the beneficial effect of very high levels of sugar could be ascribed to their hygroscopic properties, since a proportion of utilizable sugar could be spared by the nonutilizable carbohydrate, inulin (Dadd, 1964).

1. Carbohydrates and Other Energy-Producing Nutrients

In heterotrophic organisms, a major part of the ingested nutriment is used to provide energy, directly or potentially, in the storage form of glycogen and fat. For animals generally, three categories of organic materials may provide molecular species suitable for eventual entrainment in the cycles of energy-producing reactions: carbohydrates, fats, proteins. Though carbohydrate is the main, and probably a required, energy nutrient for most insects, all three sources are doubtless utilized as available, with differing facilities that will have evolved in relation to the constitutions of the natural dietaries.

Except for a few Diptera, carbohydrate is a major component in all diets designed for larval insects. However, it is often difficult to judge quite how stringent the need for it is, even if clearly well utilized, unless calorifically equivalent sources have been tested. This generally has not been done. Sugar was included in larval diets in all early nutritional studies of the mosquito *Aedes*, and its omission from a completely synthetic diet prevented pupation (Singh and Brown, 1957); yet the most recent study indicates that sugar is dispensable so long as the diet, overall, provides sufficient calories, in this case as protein (Akov, 1962a). Carbohydrate requirements of dipterous larvae are generally low, and often omission merely slows growth. Where a requirement is indicated on the basis of diets using amino acid mixtures rather than protein, caloric inadequacy may often be suspected, since an upper restriction on the concentration of free amino acids may be imposed by the inability of larvae in wet diets to tolerate high levels of these small molecules (House and Barlow, 1964). Carbohydrate is entirely dispensable from the larval diet of the housefly and certain flesh flies. For *Phormia*, sugar in any concentration adversely affects growth (Cheldelin and Newburgh, 1959), and these larvae must obtain energy from protein or amino acids, since no lipid (other than small amounts of sterol) is needed or advantageous.

Although many insects doubtless draw on dietary fats for a contribution to their energy nutrition [as inferred from the prevalence of lipolytic enzymes in digestive juices, direct observation of fat uptake, and from studies showing an effect of dietary fatty acids on the constitution of body fats (Fast, 1964; Gilby, 1965; L. I. Gilbert, 1967)], the possibility of dietary fat as a major or exclusive energy source is largely unexamined. There are particular difficulties in making such studies by the usual deletion and subsitution techniques. When carbohydrate is not needed, and the main energy source is protein, growth failure upon substitution of fat for part of the protein will be difficult to distinguish from failure due to suboptimal structural amino materials. Where carbohydrate is necessary, failure upon substitution of lipid may result from reduced edibility, considering the frequent dependence on phagostimulant effects of sugars and changes in the texture of diets on substituting fats as a bulk constituent.

For larvae of the locusts *Schistocerca gregaria* and *Locusta migratoria*, oils and fatty acids were totally inadequate substitutes for the substantial levels of carbohydrate (approximately 30% by weight) needed in the diet (Dadd, 1963). Lipids can certainly be the principal energy nutrient for larvae of the wax moth, *Galleria mellonella*, which infest old honeycombs of bees (Young, 1964). Despite this natural waxy diet, the larvae are generally cultured on cereal and honey, which are largely devoid of lipids, and the larvae grow optimally on a semisynthetic diet which includes casein, cellulose, and glucose as the bulk ingredients; about 30% by weight of glucose (or dextrin) was required, but could be replaced entirely by purified beeswax or myricin, a fraction of wax consisting principally of esters of palmitic acid and the C_{30} myricyl alcohol (Dadd, 1964, 1966).

Startling changes in food requirements sometimes occur in holometabolous insects at metamorphosis. In many Diptera, which generally have low carbohydrate requirements as larvae, the only nutrient necessary for full adult longevity is a suitable sugar (augmented by periodic protein intake purely for the maturation of eggs in the females). The nutrition of adult Lepidoptera and Hymenoptera, male and female, is often similarly restricted, and in many cases, for example the wax moth, no adult food whatever is taken. However, oviposition requirements in Hymenoptera may include amino acids, salts, and many vitamins (Bracken, 1965, 1966), and *Drosophila* females need choline (Geer *et al.*, 1970).

Because adult flies and bees require only sugar and water for optimal maintenance, they have been favored in studies of sugar and carbohydrate utilizability, readily assessed in terms of longevity without the complication of possibly alternative energy sources (lipids and amino acids) that are present in the complete diets needed for the growing stages. With larval growth it is sometimes difficult to decide between low, partial utilization and complete inadequacy, especially where the absence of carbohydrate merely retards growth, as with dipterous larvae. Often little account has been taken of the different phagostimulatory powers of sugars, and further uncertainties arise from the possibility of considerable impurity in some sugars tested.

Data on sugar and carbohydrate utilization for some 40 species are tabulated by Altman and Dittmer (1968). Bearing in mind the foregoing cautionary provisos, and that in this context utilization means major, facile utilization approximating that of glucose, a few generalizations are in order. Glucose is always well utilized. All pentoses, and the hexose, sorbose, generally are utilized poorly or not at all. All the adult insects studied, and all except a few stored-product species among the larvae, utilize fructose well. Several adult cyclorrhaphous Diptera utilize both galactose and mannose, but the mosquito and bee utilize neither, nor, with a few exceptions for one or another sugar, do most larvae. Ability to utilize oligo- and polysaccharides is generally ascribed to the possession of digestive enzymes able to degrade them to simple sugars that may then be absorbed and metabolized. For example, the general ability to utilize maltose well argues the widespread occurrence of a digestive α-glucosidase. Carbohydrate utilization studies have been much used to deduce the carbohydrases in the digestive juices of various insects (see Chapter 4), but such deductions are weakened by recent demonstrations that oligosaccharides sometimes pass into or through the gut epithelium without prior digestion to their component simple sugars (Hansen, 1964; Maurizio, 1965).

2. Protein and Amino Acids

At first sight it is not clear how insects that feed on wood, paper, and similar materials obtain amino nitrogen. Either nitrogenous compounds must be present in minute amounts and the insects adapted to a slow rate of growth commensurate with this, as in many wood borers; or amino acids must be obtained from the fungi and microorganisms cryptically associated with the apparent food (e.g., ambrosia beetles), or symbiotic within the insect (e.g., termites). However, most insect dietaries are more obvious sources of protein or its degradation products, the peptides and amino acids, and much effort has been directed to determining which of the twenty or so amino acids ultimately resulting from the digestion of proteinacous food are necessary.

The reviews cited earlier summarize and discuss the mass of data now accumulated on amino acid requirements, covering about thirty species by the most recent tabulation (Altman and Dittmer, 1968). For continued growth, nearly all require an extraneous source of ten amino acids: arginine, histidine, isoleucine, leucine, lysine, methionine, phenylalanine, threonine, tryptophan, and valine. Similar requirements are found for optimal egg production in some Diptera (Singh and Brown, 1957; Lea *et al.*, 1958; Sang and King, 1961), and the boll weevil, *Anthonomus grandis* (Vanderzant, 1963a). The same ten amino acids are essential for the rat, and with occasional exceptions or additions, for other vertebrates studied, as well as for several of the more biochemically animallike protozoa (see Volume I of this treatise). Generally only L-amino acids are utilizable, but the D forms of phenylalanine, methionine, and histidine are readily used by *Drosophila* (and some other insects), while D-arginine, lysine, and valine may partially spare the corresponding L forms (Geer, 1966).

Most apparent exceptions to this core of essential amino acid requirements can generally be discounted as probably the result of carry-over of reserves (especially if eggs are large compared to fully grown larvae), contamination of other dietary components by the test amino acid, or a definite, though inadequate, synthetic capability. Requirements can also be masked in insects harboring symbiotic microorganisms. For example, normal larvae of the beetle *Stegobium paniceum* were little affected by single deletion of most amino acids, but aposymbiotic larvae failed to grow on omission of any of the ten essential amino acids (Pant *et al.*, 1960).

Minor variations on this generally uniform pattern of essentiality occur. The roach *Blattella*, subject of several studies, is an instructive example, for it shows several anomalous features discussed at length by Gordon (1959). Several of the ten usually essential amino acids seem dispensable—lysine, methionine, tryptophan, phenylalanine, threonine—the number so considered differing in different studies, using different basal diets, with or without asepsis. This apparent dispensability probably stems from masking effects due to both intracellular symbiotes and a rich gut flora, only the latter being eliminated by asepsis. Methionine and cysteine are moderately interconvertible in the aseptic roach, rapidly so if undeflorated, when both are readily synthesized from a variety of sulfur-containing organic substances or from sulfate. Unlike most insects, in which phenylalanine can spare tyrosine but not the reverse (Davis, 1968a,e), these two aromatics are interconvertible in *Blattella,* and in the septic insect can be derived from dietary tryptophan; indeed both can be derived from other aromatics such as shikimic acid. These interconversions were most marked in septic roaches and to that extent are probably largely functions of microorganisms. However, microorganisms could play no part in the interconvertability of cysteine and methionine in the axenic blowfly *Phormia* (Cheldelin and Newburgh, 1959).

Besides these examples of dispensable "essential" amino acids, the literature carries recurring claims for the essentiality to *Blattella* of proline, serine, and alanine, which are generally considered dispensable. Proline, said to be needed by male roaches only, may well be on the borderline of essentiality; it undoubtedly is essential for *Phormia,* and its deletion impaired growth of the mosquito larva, *Aedes* (Singh and Brown, 1957), and more recently it proved essential for the screwworm, *Cochliomyia hominivorax,* (Gingrich, 1964) and the silkworm (Arai and Ito, 1967; Inokuchi *et al.,* 1967). It is most unlikely that serine or alanine would be essential; they are amongst the labile amino acids of central importance in metabolic interchanges, certainly so in *Blattella* (Gordon, 1959) and might well be required contingently in particular basal diets deficient in alternative labile amino acids and with many amino acids supplied in DL form.

It is usually found that a mixture solely of essential amino acids is inadequate or useless (Reviews). With only essential amino acids in the diet, others occurring in the tissues must derive amino fragments from some or other of the essentials provided, leaving unutilized surplus fragments, disposal of which is likely to impose a strain on metabolism, reflected in poor growth. Basal diets are always provided with amino acids that individually are dispensable, and much recent interest centers on the relative importance of these. Besides the ten essentials and one or other of the sulfur-containing alternates, *Phormia* requires only glutamic or aspartic acid. Septic *Blattella* fails on a mixture solely of essentials but grows optimally if glutamic acid is added, with alanine, aspartic acid, or serine as good alternatives in descending order of efficacy. Gordon (1959) found growth to be excellent if glutamic acid constituted 80% of such a mixture, and considered it perhaps the most important amino acid for *Blattella,* even though it is not considered essential. For several other insects one dispensable amino acid combined with all essentials allows nearly as good growth as a complete mixture of about twenty. For the silkworm, whose eleven essential amino acids (the usual ten plus proline) alone support little growth, addition of either glutamic or, best, aspartic acid allows nearly optimal performance; the remaining dispensables, together or individually, allow further, but slight, improvement (Arai and Ito, 1964; Ito and Arai, 1965b, 1966, 1967). The aphid *Myzus* cannot grow on a mixture of the ten essentials plus cysteine, but supplementation with large amounts of serine, alanine, or glutamate supports good growth, nearly optimal with serine (Dadd and Krieger, 1968). The beetles, *Anthonomus* and *Tribolium,* and the lepidopteran, *Argyrotaenia,* are unusual in that essential amino acids alone support fair growth, but optimal performances demand supplementation respectively with glutamic acid (Vanderzant, 1965), glutamic or aspartic acids (Naylor, 1963; M. W. Taylor and Medici, 1966), and glutamic acid, aspartic acid, alanine, or serine (Rock and King, 1967a,b).

Questions of balance, which are of increasing interest in insect nutrition, involve especially amino acids, the most numerous nutrient category. Studies with several species show that changes in the proportions of single or small groups of amino acids may markedly affect performances (Reviews; Davis, 1967a, 1968a,b,c, 1969a,b; Naylor, 1963; Taylor and Medici, 1966; Rock and King, 1967b). The protein chosen for most early synthetic diets was casein, which was readily available in a highly purified form, and when attempts were made to replace it by amino acid mixtures, their proportions were based on casein analyses. Conservatism clung to the casein pattern for amino acid mixtures until their failure in work with plant-feeding insects suggested that proportionalities approximating those of natural food proteins would be more logical. The pink bollworm, *Pectoinphora gossypiella,* failed to grow with casein amino acids (even though it grew well with whole casein), but grew well with a mixture based on the amino acid composition of cotton plant proteins (Vanderzant, 1958), and proportionalities have since been based whenever possible on those of the natural food protein, especially for phytophagous insects (Ishii and Hirano, 1955; Ito and Arai, 1965a; Dadd and Mittler, 1965).

It might seem that a diet providing all amino acids in their tissue proportions would be optimal, and this is apparently so for *Argyrotaenia* (Rock and King, 1967b). However, this takes no account of the probability of continual flux in overall tissue requirements, nor does it allow for synthesis of nonprotein, nitrogenous tissue components such as nucleic acid bases, which are also in flux. No single dietary balance is likely to be optimal at all times, and dispensable amino acids are important as a readily transmuted reserve for adjusting dietary intake to changing tissue requirements. For this, the more labile and generally interconvertible the better, and the evidence shows that in insects, as in other organisms, glutamic and aspartic acids, alanine, and serine are of prime importance in this respect.

The tolerance of insects for imbalances in dietary amino acids varies widely. The mealworm, *Tenebrio molitor*, among the first insects studied nutritionally and able to grow well on casein diets, still cannot be reared with amino acid mixtures (Leclercq and Lopez-Francos, 1964, 1967), supposedly because an exceptionally critical balance has not yet been met. Similar failure attended work with the rat flea, *Xenopsylla cheopis;* this also touched on another aspect of the balance problem, well known in vertebrate nutrition, that single amino acids in excess may inhibit growth; for the addition, individually, of thirteen amino acids to an otherwise satisfactory casein diet inhibited growth of the flea larva (Pausch and Fraenkel, 1966).

It is difficult to believe that where amino acids fail to replace protein, faulty balance is always the whole answer. At one time it was thought that incompletely digested peptide fragments, such as the strepogenins, might be needed (Lipke and Fraenkel, 1956), and this view is still echoed, though no positive improvement has been demonstrated in the few cases where di- and tripeptides have been tested in attempts to improve amino acid mixtures (Leclercq and Lopez-Francos, 1964, 1966; Kasting *et al.*, 1962). The possibility cannot be excluded, particularly if it should transpire that peptides can be ingested through the gut epithelium without prior digestion, but one might equally well surmise that high levels of free amino acids adversely affected ingestion, either directly, as phagoinhibitants, or in some indirect way involving unusual osmotic relationships in the gut.

It is generally supposed that strictly essential nutrients are those the organism is unable to synthesize in adequate amounts from dietary precursors. A method based on this supposition has been much in vogue for determining the essential amino acids of insects. Labile, isotopically tagged intermediates are introduced into the insect, usually by feeding or injecting glucose-U-^{14}C, and tissue amino acids are subsequently separated and the incorporated radiocarbon measured. Those lacking radioactivity are considered essential, those with activity, nonessential. First introduced to entomology in work with *Phormia*, the method gave results in agreement with classic deletion studies (Kasting and McGinnis, 1958, 1960). It provides the only means of studying amino acid requirements in insects that cannot be reared on synthetic diets, and has been so used with several plant-feeding, bloodsucking, or parasitic species (Kasting and McGinnis, 1962, 1964, 1966; Shyamala and Bhat, 1965; Schaefer, 1964; Pickett and Friend, 1965; Kasting *et al.*, 1962; Alikhan, 1968).

However, deletion and isotopic methods gave contrary results for proline in studies on *Argyrotaenia;* proline proved dispensable in deletion studies, yet had low specific activity in larvae reared on a medium containing glucose-U-^{14}C (Rock and King, 1968), accounted for by dilution of the ^{14}C label during the synthetic route from glucose to proline. More extensive discrepancies emerged from work on the aphid, *Myzus.* Before this insect could be reared on synthetic diet, the radioisotope method indicated at least nine essential amino acids (F. E. Strong and Sakamoto, 1963), yet with the deletion technique, only methionine, histidine, and isoleucine could be shown definitely essential, with lysine and threonine probably required for optimal performances (Dadd and Krieger, 1968). This unusually low number of essentials is probably a result of synthetic activity by the aphid's symbiotes, for in larvae with reduced symbiotes following maternal antibiotic treatment, deletion affects growth adversely for all ten essential amino acids. All ten can be shown to be essential in normal pea aphids without recourse to aposymbiosis (Retnakaran and Beck, 1968). Dadd and Krieger suggested that low specific activities for amino acids synthesized by the aphid or its symbiotes probably resulted from preferential routing of the sugar-derived ^{14}C through some synthetic pathways at the expense of others, coupled with inadequate time to allow dispersal through all eventually possible pathways. A full discussion of the pitfalls involved in interpreting the radioisotope method is given by Kasting and McGinnis (1966). We may note here that the final arbiter of essentiality in dubious cases remains the classic deletion method.

3. Water-Soluble Vitamins and Growth Factors

Much early interest in insect nutrition focused on the need for growth factors supplied by yeast or liver extracts, subsequently augmented by plant extracts in attempts to rear phytophagous insects. Following their identification in vertebrate and microbial studies, most of the water-soluble vitamins historically grouped as the B complex were found essential for several insect species. At this time a distinctive insect requirement for sterol was already established, though no requirement was apparent for any of the vertebrate fat-soluble vitamins A, D, and E, nor for vitamin C, the antiscorbutic factor in human nutrition. It was clear, however, that all known B vitamins did not fully account for the growth-promoting potential of the yeast and liver extracts they sometimes could replace.

With the extension of tests to cover more than one larval cycle, and with increasing study of phytophagous species, it became apparent that additional growth factors were often essential (Reviews).

The vitamin needs of approximately forty species have now been determined (Altman and Dittmer, 1968), and it may fairly be generalized that all require seven water-soluble vitamins: thiamin, riboflavin, nicotinic acid or its amide, pyridoxine (or pyridoxal phosphate or pyridoxamine), pteroylglutamic (folic) acid, pantothenic acid or a pantothenate, and biotin. These substances have in common the function of cofactors for enzymes of basic vital importance. Their metabolic essentiality may therefore be assumed, and, evidently, insects, like vertebrates, cannot synthesize them, or can do so only inadequately, as perhaps in some cases for folic acid. Some closely related substitutions may be possible. Besides the general alternatives for nicotinic acid and pyridoxine, desthiobiotin and pimelic acid are claimed as alternates for biotin with some insects. In contrast to the ability of vertebrates to synthesize nicotinic acid from tryptophan via kynurenine, this pathway is absent in the few insects examined, though the conversion of tryptophan to kynurenine is presumably widespread in those many, perhaps all, insects that synthesize ommochrome pigments. Choline, sometimes classified with the vitamins, but more appropriately distinguished as a lipogenic factor and methyl donor, is also essential for most insects studied (Reviews).

Quantitative requirements for many species are summarized in various reviews (Trager, 1953; House, 1965c). The usefulness of these data is diminished by the fact that dosages are mostly expressed on a weight basis proportional to the whole diet (the diets ranging from aqueous or agar media of high water content to dry powders). Since the amounts of diet eaten are generally not known, comparisons of absolute requirements are excluded, and molar comparisons between dietary components, of most interest for considerations of metabolic function, are difficult to calculate. These shortcomings in quantitative work are critically discussed by Sang (1959), Gordon (1959), and others.

Apparent exceptions to requirements for the principal B vitamins can usually be accounted for on the basis of symbiosis, reserves, or dietary contamination. Normal larvae of the beetles *Stegobium* and *Lasioderma* are scarcely affected by a lack of dietary vitamins, but aposymbiotic larva show extensive vitamin and sterol requirements (Reviews; Pant and Kapoor, 1963). Similarly, various bloodsucking insects depend upon symbiotes for adequate supplies of some vitamins (Gumpert and Schwartz, 1963; Lake and Friend, 1968; Ehrhardt, 1968c). Some anomalous findings concern folic acid and biotin; deletion sometimes has little or no effect, merely retarding growth or impairing pupation or adult emergence. For example, lack of folic acid scarcely affected larval growth of *Tribolium castaneum,* though causing heavy pupal mortality (Applebaum and Lubin, 1967). These two vitamins are active in amounts an order or two of magnitude less than the "major" B vitamins, so there is a heightened possibility that impurities in diets or maternally derived reserves might mask requirements. In general, meridic and agar-containing diets are likely to have significant levels of many vitamins as impurities. A case requiring special comment concerns pyridoxine. The initial claim tends to recur that it is not essential for the parasitoid Dipteran, *Agria affinis,* even though it was subsequently shown that the supposedly pyridoxine-deficient diets used with this fly contained, as unintended impurity, sufficient pyridoxine to account for its function in the transaminase systems of the insect (Barlow, 1962). The apparent absence of a requirement for pyridoxine in *Cochliomyia* (Gingrich, 1964) perhaps has a similar explanation. Masking of dietary deficiencies by vitamin reserves was strikingly demonstrated in the aphid *Myzus.* Deletion of all vitamins together had little effect on larvae whose mothers were maintained on complete diet, yet in larvae from mothers subjected to vitamin deprivation for a few days preceding parturition, requirements for nine B vitamins and ascorbic acid were individually demonstrable, which was a surprising result in view of the possession by the aphid of abundant symbiotes (Dadd and Mittler, 1965; Dadd *et al.,* 1967). In another aphid, *Neomyzus circumflexus,* ten generations have been reared in the absence of riboflavin, pantothenic acid, biotin, and choline, though the aphids required ascorbic acid and five other vitamins for continued growth beyond two to four generations (Ehrhardt, 1968b).

Probably maternally derived reserves account in part for the belated recognition of mesoinositol as a growth factor for insects. The pioneering studies of Fraenkel and Blewett (1943) hinted at a need for inositol for *Ptinus tectus,* but this was subsequently discounted in view of the general failure of inositol to influence other insects subsequently studied. However, with the roaches *Periplaneta* and *Blattella* an inositol requirement emerged in tests covering reproducing adults or a second larval generation (Forgash, 1958, 1962; Gordon, 1959). Since plant-eating insects became tractable to study, several, from various orders, have proved to require inositol (Vanderzant, 1959; Dadd, 1963; Dadd *et al.,* 1967; Ehrhardt, 1968b; Vanderzant, 1968). This proliferation tempts one to wonder how many previous judgments of dispensability might be faulted on grounds of inositol-contaminated basal diets, or too abbreviated an experimental period. The silkworm was first judged not to need inositol (Horie and Ito, 1963) because, one might conjecture, of impurities in soybean meal, replaced by casein in later studies (Horie *et al.*, 1966). The cutworm, *Agrotis orthogonia*, grew well without inositol (Kasting and McGinnis, 1967), but a tendency for the pupae to be undersized hints that study for two generations might unmask a requirement.

A majority of known inositol-requiring insects normally eat plants, and thus an appreciation of the widespread importance of inositol hinged on the recent efflorescence of studies of phytophagous species. This applies most forcibly to the recognition of ascorbic acid as an insect vitamin, for it has so far been found essential only for insects that in nature feed on plants. Speculations on a nutritional role for ascorbic acid first occur in the silkworm literature (Legay, 1958; Shyamala and Bhat, 1962). Fraenkel and Blewett (1946) found that it improved the growth of *Ephestia,* but as other antioxidants (gallates or tocopherol) did likewise, it was deemed that it functioned merely to protect linoleic acid, an essential growth factor for this moth. The first insects unequivocally shown to require ascorbic acid were locusts; without it, growth was retarded in the later instars and death occurred, often during the final molt. Hemolymph of 4th and 5th instar larvae reared on deficient diet contained no ascorbic acid, whereas larvae reared on diet containing ascorbic acid had hemolymph levels comparable to those of grass-reared larvae. In normal larvae, ascorbic acid disappeared from the hemolymph at the molt, suggesting that it was in some way involved with the events of ecdysis (Dadd, 1960b). Ascorbic acid proved essential for the boll weevil, the bollworm, *Heliothis zea,* and the salt-marsh caterpillar, *Estigmere acrea,* all of which had reduced ascorbic acid tissue levels when reared on ascorbic-deficient diets (Vanderzant *et al.,* 1962); it was also found to be essential for several other phytophagous caterpillars (Chippendale and Beck, 1964; Chippendale *et al.,* 1965; Ito and Arai, 1965b; Levinson and Navon, 1969) and aphids (Dadd *et al.,* 1967; Ehrhardt, 1968b). It is now invariably included in the formulation of diets for any insect that in nature feeds on living plant tissues, though it is by no means always essential (Vanderzant *et al.,* 1962; Rock and King, 1967).

Several other water-soluble substances have been considered growth factors for particular insects, but in most cases their status is equivocal. *p*-Aminobenzoic acid, one of the original B complex factors that affected growth of some microorganisms, was included in most early insect diets, but no subsequent work has shown any need for it. Coenzyme A and thioctic (α-lipoic) acid slightly improved growth of the onion maggot, *Hylemyia antiqua* (Friend and Patton, 1956). Since pantothenic acid is a constituent of coenzyme A, possibly the effect of the latter resulted from inadequate uptake or utilization of dietary pantothenic acid.

Thioctic acid, essential for the ciliate *Tetrahymena,* has not proved essential or beneficial for any insect other than *Hylemyia.*

Glutathione was judged essential for *Aedes* (Singh and Brown, 1957), and was considered to improve growth of *Agria,* but no other insect requires it, and subsequent studies of *Aedes* (Akov, 1962a) discount its significance. Since glutathione is a tripeptide, it possibly might have had a crucially beneficial effect on amino acid balance in the marginal diet of Singh and Brown. Glutathione is a feeding stimulant for some coelenterates (Volume II of this treatise), and a gorging factor for certain argasid ticks (Galun and Kindler, 1965); as amino acids and peptides are sometimes phagostimulant, effects on growth attributable to glutathione perhaps stem from changes in feeding behavior.

Singh and Brown (1957) also considered carnitine necessary for *Aedes,* but this, too, was subsequently discounted. Carnitine, is, however, essential for six species of tenebrionid beetles. Of wide occurrence in animal tissues, carnitine (*p*-hydroxy-γ-butyrobetaine) is involved in fatty acid and phospholipid metabolism. The pathology of carnitine deficiency in *Tenebrio* and *Tribolium* larvae is characterized by degeneration of midgut epithelium and fat body, and imperfections in the molting process (Fraenkel and Friedman, 1957; Naton, 1967). A carnitine requirement is restricted to Tenebrionidae and perhaps a related sylvanid beetle, *Oryzaephilus* (Davis, 1964), a uniquely narrow taxonomic requirement.

Though not required, carnitine can replace dietary choline for several Diptera. Choline is considered to have three general functions: as a constituent of lecithins (phosphatidylcholines) in structural and transport phospholipids (Thomas and Gilbert, 1967); as acetylcholine in nervous transmission; and as a metabolic donor of labile methyl groups. With exceptions to be noted for Diptera, attempts to spare dietary choline by related methyl-donating substances such as methionine, betaine, ethanolamine, and carnitine are generally negative, though partial sparing was achieved with mono- and dimethylaminoethanol in *Tribolium* and roaches, and complete sparing by betaine in *Blattella* (Gilmour, 1961; Gordon, 1959; Vanderzant, 1963b).

Larvae of *Phormia* and *Musca* grow apparently normally if choline is entirely replaced by carnitine, β-methycholine, γ-butyrobetaine, and mono- or dimethylaminoethanol; with the first two substances, the lecithin of their tissue phospholipids then contain β-methylcholine in place of choline; the methylaminoethanols are incorporated unchanged into both lecithins and cephalins (Bieber *et al.,* 1963; Hodgson and Dauterman, 1964; Bridges *et al.,* 1965). Cephalins normally are phosphatidyl ethanolamines, in which the ethanolamine can be synthesized from serine, glycine, or via formate (J. F. Taylor and Hodgson, 1965). In *Musca,* a large number of amino alcohols and their N-alkyl derivatives can be incorporated from diet into phospholipids instead of choline and ethanolamine (Bridges and Ricketts, 1967). Analysis of the phospholipid of adult *Musca,* reared, as larvae, with dietary carnitine, shows that choline (presumably from the egg) occurs preferentially in brain tissue, and that choline subsequently provided to adults displaces the β-methylcholine derived from the larval dietary carnitine (Bridges *et al.,* 1965). This suggests that choline is ultimately essential for certain specialized functions, such as in nerve transmission phenomena, but that for much of the membrane-structural and lipid-transport functions the precise composition of the phospholipids is immaterial in certain Diptera, a situation with analogies to "essential" and "sparing" sterols.

For insects, the status of cobalamine (vitamin B_{12} of vertebrate nutrition) is uncertain. It was without effect in most studies, but slightly improved growth with *Aedes* and *Drosophila* (Reviews); most interestingly, second generation *Blattella* needed it (Gordon, 1959). Vitamin B_{12} is effective in minute amounts, so there would be every expectation that an imposed dietary deficiency might be masked by contamination or reserves, the latter being indicated for the second-generation effect with *Blattella.* Larvae of *Argyrotaenia* grow at a normal rate without B_{12} in the diet, but mortality is unusually high, especially among pupae, suggesting that a deficiency might become apparent in subsequent generations (Rock, 1969).

Among substances tested as substitutes for the yeast used as a source of accessory growth factors, ribonucleic acid (RNA) proved of nutritional importance to *Aedes, Drosophila,* and *Musca;* DNA (deoxyribonucleic acid) was ineffective in promoting larval growth, and sometimes impaired pupation. Though they had little effect on larval growth of *Phormia,* RNA slightly, and DNA markedly improved pupation. In contrast, both RNA and DNA promote larval growth of *Agria.* Various combinations of nucleic acid components (purine and pyrimidine bases, nucleosides, nucleotides) are more or less effective substitutes for RNA and DNA in these various insects (Reviews). For example, in *Drosophila,* dietary nucleotides, both ribose and deoxyribose, can be utilized, as also can their corresponding nucleosides and bases; the ribose nucleotides can be precursors of the deoxynucleotides, but not the converse; however, the only dietary *requirement* is for adenine, adenosine, or adenylic acid (Burnet and Sang, 1963). In *Agria,* four ribonucleotides, but not their corresponding nucleosides or bases, are effective replacements for RNA (House, 1964).

Excepting certain *Drosophila* mutants for which particular nucleic acid components are essential (Hinton, 1959), nucleic acid seems merely to accelerate growth, for development is generally completed without it, at least as shown by single generation studies. This led to the concept that although insects, generally, can synthesize the small molecule units and assemble complete nucleic acids, certain synthetic steps are rate-limiting in Diptera, a limitation removed by the dietary provision of the particular slowly synthesized components. However, *Cochliomyia* ceases growth without RNA or appropriate combinations of precursors in the diet, some of which are therefore evidently essential (Gingrich, 1964).

Until recently, dietary nucleic acid seemed advantageous only for Diptera, except for an early, generally discounted report of improved growth in a beetle, *Scobius granulosus*. It now appears that growth of another beetle, *Oryzaephilus*, is improved by dietary RNA, replaceable by a combination of guanine and cytosine (Davis, 1966a).

In analyzing the crude RNA requirement of *Oryzaephilus* it emerged that certain polyamines may be growth factors, as they are for some bacteria, vertebrate tissue culture cells, and the crustacean *Artemia salina* (Provasoli and D'Agostino, 1962). Putrescine and spermidine had subtle beneficial effects on overall development of *Oryzaephilus* (Davis, 1966b). As with nucleic acid, the polyamines affected growth, pupation, and emergence in different and sometimes contradictory ways; since they showed no regular dosage pattern and were not essential, it is questionable whether they are to be regarded as vitamins. Their effects resemble "hormetic" stimulation by suboptimal levels of dietary sodium observed in crickets (Luckey and Stone, 1960), which is a type of metabolic stimulation brought about by minute concentrations of various substances that are not required in the usual nutritional sense.

Antimetabolites. Usually these are structural analogs of metabolites, whose function they specifically block, perhaps competing for reaction sites on enzymes, or, by combining specifically with the metabolites, sequestering them from use. Characteristically, but not invariably, their antagonism can be overcome by an excess of the blocked metabolite. However, unless reversibility obtains, there is no certainty that antagonism is specific rather than that of a general toxicant. It was early appreciated that antimetabolites might reveal certain nutritional requirements of an organism for which no defined diet was available; the procedure involves determining whether administration of a supposed antimetabolite with the normal food results in toxicity that can be counteracted by concurrent or subsequent administration of the putatively essential nutrient. For example, reversible antagonism of pyrithiamine and deoxypyridoxine for thiamine and pyridoxin was recently demonstrated with naturally fed Mexican bean beetles (Gothilf and Waites, 1968). Growth inhibition by various D-amino acids, such as

D-serine for *Drosophila* and *Phormia* (Reviews) perhaps is to be regarded as an antimetabolite effect. The well known toxicity of mannose for bees and wasps is probably in this category, since it depends on the relative amount of glucose-producing sugar (e.g., sucrose) concurrently administered, suggesting a competition between structurally similar D-mannose and D-glucose for glycolytic enzymes (Wyatt, 1967). A powerful antagonism of 5-thio-D-glucopyranose for D-glucose in *Drosophila* and *Periplaneta* appears to have a similar explanation (Shankland *et al.*, 1968).

Analogs are claimed to demonstrate requirements for B vitamins and cholesterol in *Chilo*, *Periplaneta*, and *Musca* (Reviews). However, inconsistencies have emerged that stress the uncertainties of the method as a nutritional tool. A supposed antimetabolite function of cholesteryl chloride against cholesterol could not be substantiated (Monroe *et al.*, 1963; Clayton *et al.*, 1964). In silkworms, 3-acetylpyridine fed with mulberry leaves apparently produced niacin deficiency (Shyamala and Bhat, 1958), but on synthetic diet no antagonism of 3-acetylpyridine for niacin was observed (Horie and Ito, 1965). A comprehensive evaluation of the function of many structural analogues of the major B vitamins was made with the mosquito, *Aedes* (Akov, 1962b, 1967; Akov and Guggenheim, 1963a,b,c). Reversible (or partially reversible) antagonism was found for 2-amino-2-methyl-1-propanol against choline; 3-acetylpyridine against niacin; 4-deoxypyridoxine against pyridoxine; pyrithiamine against thiamine; and aminopterin or amethopterin against folic acid; but with many other supposed structural antimetabolites, toxicity was irreversible, and therefore not necessarily due to interference specifically with the vitamin in question.

Much recent work on antimetabolite function aims to discover controlling agents for pests as alternatives to insecticides, and is thus more closely linked with the study of antibiosis (Gordon, 1961), chemosterilants (Smith *et al.*, 1964; J. David, 1966), and hormone mimetics (Spielman and Skaff, 1967; Suchy *et al.*, 1968; Robbins *et al.*, 1968). From a nutritional point of view the latter field assumes pertinence since so many plants are now found to contain insect hormones (ecdysones), or hormone mimetics (juvabione, etc.), and this raises fascinating ecological questions of their intervention in the nutritional regulation of insects to possible host plants (Staal, 1968; Williams and Robbins, 1968).

4. Lipid Growth Factors

a. Sterol. Dietary sterol is probably essential for all insects if judgment is reserved on exceptions noted for aphids (Dadd and Mittler, 1966; Dadd and Krieger, 1967), where apparent inessentiality probably depends on synthesis of sterol by intracellular symbiotes (Ehrhardt, 1968d). Symbiotic yeasts are known to provide adequate sterol for the beetles *Stegobium* and *Lasioderma* (Pant and Kapoor, 1963). Hence there is a presumption that the pathways of sterol biogenesis so prominent in vertebrates are absent or greatly reduced, and this has been demonstrated isotopically in *Dermestes, Calliphora, Musca,* and the beetle *Oulema melanopus* (Clayton, 1964; Lamb and Monroe, 1968a). Since aseptic roaches, though requiring dietary sterol, still had isotopically demonstrable residual cholesterogenesis, and substantial radiocarbon, from acetate, appeared in the sterol fraction of the silverfish *Ctenolepisma*, it seemed that primitive insects, at least, might retain vestigial synthetic capabilities. However, critical reappraisal of the situation in another primitive, *Thermobia domestica,* afforded no evidence of sterol synthesis (Kaplanis *et al.*, 1963), and the concensus is that no insect *devoid of symbiotes* can synthesize sterol (L. I. Gilbert, 1967). Lack of synthetic capability is evident quite early in the pathways from acetate to sterol, for such intermediates in vertebrate cholesterogenesis as squalene, farnesol, and mevalonic acid are ineffective in growth or as sterol precursors in several Lepidoptera (Ishii and Hirano, 1964; Ito and Horie, 1966; Sridara and Bhat, 1965; L. I. Gilbert, 1967) and a sawfly, *Neodiprion pratti* (Schaeffer *et al.*, 1965). Many earlier cases are cited in the comprehensive review of Clayton (1964), a prime source for unattributed information given below.

Much interest centers on the range of utilizable steroids and the structural features that make them so. With a single exception discussed later, cholesterol completely fulfills the requirement of all species studied. As a broad generalization, sterols that can wholly replace cholesterol (as distinct from sparing sterols—see below) must have an intact, planar nucleus, a 3β-hydroxy group, free or esterified, and a hydrocarbon side chain at C-17 such that the whole molecule has 27, 28, or 29 carbons (Clayton and Bloch, 1963). Within these restrictions, the twenty or so species of insects tested with a range of sterols vary in their ability to manage minor structural modifications, such as the degree of unsaturation of the B ring (cholestanol, cholesterol, 7-dehydrocholesterol), the presence or absence of unsaturation at C-22 (ergosterol compared with 7-dehydrocholesterol, Δ^{22}-cholesterol with cholesterol), or alkylation of the side chain (β-sitosterol, stigmasterol, ergosterol). Since cholesterol is generally completely adequate dietarily, and is usually the principal tissue sterol, it, or a related C_{27} sterol, is presumed to be metabolically required by all insects, and differences in ability to utilize alternatives for the essential requirement are thought to hinge on the presence of absence of dealkylating and B-ring-modifying enzymes. In considering the extensive literature on sterols and analogs that have been tested (Reviews), the cautionary remarks of Clayton (1964; also see Altman and Dittmer, 1968) need re-emphasis. Commercial sterols often contain substantial amounts of other sterol impurities (Svoboda *et al.*, 1968), perhaps enough to satisfy the essential requirement, and some $\Delta^{5,7}$-sterols are prone to oxidation; hence reports of both utilization and nonutilization (e.g., 7-dehydrocholesterol) carry more than the usual uncertainty.

A distinction between essential and sparing sterols is now well substantiated. *Dermestes* (Clark and Bloch, 1959), and subsequently many other insects, grew well if cholesterol, in amounts that alone would be subminimal, was provided together with a major sterol that alone failed to support growth. Such findings suggested that sterol subserved two functions, "metabolic" and "structural," the metabolic function involving cholesterol specifically, while the structural function, accounting for most of the total requirement, was less specific and could be spared by a variety of steroids. Subsequent evidence suggests that most of the essential sterol function is also structural (Clayton, 1964; Lasser and Clayton, 1966; Lasser *et al.*, 1966), and in the housefly larva, at any rate, it can be fulfilled by certain sterols (e.g., campesterol) other than cholesterol (Kaplanis *et al.*, 1965). If the idea of a distinct metabolic function is still retained [and this must be so in view of the demonstration that cholesterol is a precursor of the polar steroid hormone, ecdysone (Karlson and Hoffmeister, 1963)], then it becomes necessary to postulate three distinguishable functions: relatively nonspecific structural, specific structural, and specific metabolic. Sparing sterols, studied as such with *Dermestes*, exhibit a wider variety of structural possibilities than the essential sterol requirement; assuming that the many partially effective substituent sterols fulfilled only the nonspecific structural function, this would account for the wide range utilizable by *Musca vicina* (Levinson and Bergmann, 1957; Bergmann and Levinson, 1966).

With regard to versatility in utilizing sterols, a distinction has been made between two purely carnivorous dermestid beetles, *Dermestes* and *Attagenus*, and all other insects studied, the latter loosely termed "phytophagous," though this group includes feeders on microphyta and cereal products. The carnivores utilized cholesterol and 7-dehydrocholesterol, but not plant and yeast sterols (β-sitosterol, stigmasterol, ergosterol, and analogs), though these latter are readily utilized, often better than cholesterol, by the "phytophagous" species. On the assumption that insect carcass sterols generally were cholesterol and 7-dehydrocholesterol, it was supposed that carnivorous insects, acquiring these directly from their food, lacked enzymes whereby phytophagous insects were assumed, variously, to dealkylate C_{28} and C_{29} plant and yeast sterols to the C_{27} series. Use of an ingenious biological method extended this proposition to several truly phytophagous species. *Dermestes*, unable to grow with plant sterols, grew well on the dried carcasses of a variety of plant-feeding insects that ingested only phytosterols, indicating that the plant-feeders converted some phytosterol to cholesterol or related sterols; chromatography of the phytophagous insects' sterols confirmed that in addition to, or in place of, their food plant phytosterols, all contained cholesterol (Levinson, 1962). This method has serious flaws stemming from the distinction between essential and sparing sterol, for it would require only minor contamination by cholesterol to allow growth of *Dermestes* in the event of no conversion of phytosterol. Furthermore, several plants are now known to contain small amounts of cholesterol; preferential absorption of traces of optimally utilizable sterol has been demonstrated (Kaplanis *et al.*, 1965); and the dependence of *Dermestes* on cholesterol may not be so absolute as earlier thought in view of its ability to utilize 22-dehydrocholesterol, 27-norcholesterol, and Δ^7,Δ^9-cholesterol isomers (Bergman and Levinson, 1966). In spite of these cautionary strictures, Levinson's work can be taken to show a general ability of phytophagous insects to convert phytosterols to cholesterol, and this is supported by the unequivocal demonstration, tracing isotopic conversions, of dealkylation of β-sitosterol (and perhaps campesterol) to cholesterol in *Neodiprion* and *Locusta* (Schaefer *et al.*, 1965; Allais and Barbier, 1966) and via the intermediate desmosterol (24-dehydro-cholesterol), in *Protoparce* (Svoboda *et al.*, 1967). In the latter insect, brassicasterol, fucasterol, stigmasterol, 22,23-dihydrobrassicasterol, and 24-methylene cholesterol also are converted to cholesterol via desmo-sterol (Svoboda and Robbins, 1968).

An early assumption that utilizable food sterols are always largely converted to cholesterol and 7-dehydrocholesterol as in the German roach (Robbins *et al.*, 1962) and the phytophagous species just discussed, is called into question by extensive studies on the housefly. Larvae reared on purely vegetable media have no detectable tissue cholesterol, but instead contain principally campesterol, which is a minor, but selectively absorbed C_{28} sterol in the medium, with lesser amounts of β-sitosterol, the principal medium sterol. If provided, choles-terol is absorbed in preference to campesterol, but no conversion of β-sitosterol to either cholesterol or campesterol occurs (Kaplanis *et al.*, 1965). Evidently the housefly larva can use dietary cholesterol and campesterol facultatively for both specific and nonspecific functions, just as it can use cholestanol or cholestenone, the latter being metabolized to cholestanol (Dutky *et al.*, 1967). The adult, however, requires cholesterol specifically for production of viable eggs (Robbins and Shortino, 1962); in the egg considerable metabolism to 7-dehydrocholesterol occurs, and is suggested to be on the route of synthesis of hormones such as the ecdysones (Monroe *et al.*, 1967, 1968). It may be conjectured that if larval growth involves a requirement for cholesterol or its 7-dehydroderivative for hormone production (the "metabolic" function of sterols earlier discussed), then this must be adequately provided for by reserves built up in the egg.

Metabolism of cholesterol to 7-dehydrocholesterol occurs in the roach *Blattella* and several other insects (Robbins *et al.*, 1964), generally taking place throughout growth rather than restricted to embryogenesis as in the fly; these authors speculate that production of 7-dehydrocholesterol may be the first step in metabolism of cholesterol to ecdysone, or alternatively (in view of its function as provitamin D_3 in vertebrates), that vitamin D-like compounds may have some function in insects, though there is otherwise no evidence for this. In *Tribolium*, a variety of vertebrate sex hormones (dehydroepiandrosterone, pregnenolone, progesterone) have been identified as metabolites derived from cholesterol, but the significance of this for the insect is unknown (Smissman *et al.*, 1964). When vertebrate steroid hormones or calciferol (vitamin D) have been tested as dietary substitutes for cholesterol they have always been completely useless.

Sterol nutrition in insects has been pursued in some metabolic depth, promoted a decade ago by the expectation that the major insect endocrines of central importance in insect physiology would be steroid in nature, or at least of isoprenoid affinities. Cholesterol has been shown to be a precursor of ecdysone (Karlson and Hoffmeister, 1963). The claim was made that brain hormone was cholesterol (Kirimura *et al.*, 1962), but though various sterols mimic certain of its effects, this now seems unlikely (L. I. Gilbert, 1967). A few years back Levinson (1962) speculated that cholesterol might be a precursor of juvenile hormone, neotenin, and recently he demonstrated some curious interactions between cholesterol and neotenin-mimetic substances on the ability of these latter to delay development in *Dermestes* (Levinson, 1966). However, since mevalonate is converted to farnesol in the silkworm (Schmialek, 1963), it seems more likely that neotenin can be synthesized via the acetate–mevalonate route.

It remains to comment on the so far unique case of *Drosophila pachea*, the only insect studied that apparently can utilize neither cholesterol nor the common plant sterols, stigmasterol, β-sitosterol, or ergosterol (Heed and Kircher, 1965). This species, in nature restricted to feeding on the senita cactus, *Lophocereus schottii*, cannot utilize Δ^5-sterols, but requires the Δ^7 structure, as in Δ^7-stigmasten-3β-ol (identical or very similar to the cactus sterol schottenol), Δ^7-cholesten-3β-ol (7-dehydrocholestanol), and $\Delta^{5,7}$-cholestadien-3β-ol (7-dehydrocholesterol). Other commonly studied species of *Drosophila* utilize cholesterol, and *D. melanogaster* utilizes ergosterol well and β-sitosterol and stigmasterol partially, so this case represents a remarkably specific metabolic adaptation whereby the host-plant relationship is most narrowly circumscribed, the more so since it is reinforced by immunity to toxic glycosides (pilocereine and lophocereine) peculiar to the senita cactus and lethal to other species of desert *Drosophila* (Kircher *et al.*, 1967).

b. *Fatty Acid Requirements.* Polyunsaturated fatty acid was first noted as essential for successful adult emergence in the moth *Anagasta* (*Ephestia*) *kuhniella* (Fraenkel and Blewett, 1946). Similar requirements have since been demonstrated in other Lepidoptera, several Orthoptera, and a beetle (Fast, 1964; Dadd, 1963, 1964; Nayar, 1964; Vanderzant and Richardson, 1964; Ito and Nakasone, 1966; Rock *et al.*, 1965). Since fatty acid deficiency tends to affect larval growth only slightly, it is manifest in moths most noticeably by faulty pupal emergence, a lesion ranging from noneclosion to emergence with characteristically scaleless or malformed wings. Wing deformity also characterizes the deficiency in locusts and grasshoppers. In the German roach, deficiency became apparent only in a second experimental generation (Gordon, 1959), and in the boll weevil the effect was reduced fecundity that worsened with subsequent generations (Earle *et al.*, 1967). Generally both linoleic and linolenic (dienoic and trienoic C_{18}) acids satisfy the requirement. The tetraenoic arachidonic acid is ineffectual for adult emergence, though it sometimes (locusts, some Lepidoptera) apparently alleviates retardation in larval growth; however, in view of the uncertain purity of the fatty acids used and the low levels of linolenic acid that could bring about partial improvement, a growth function of arachidonic acid may be questionable.

Though both linoleic and linolenic acids were individually satisfactory for *Pectinophora* (Vanderzant *et al.*, 1957), different minimal requirements were found, suggesting perhaps differing functions. Recent studies indicate that for several Lepidoptera, linolenic acid, specifically, is required to allay the failure in pupal eclosion (Chippendale *et al.*, 1964, 1965; Vanderzant, 1967, 1968; Levinson and Navon, 1969), and one wonders whether in earlier studies the linoleic acid used might have contained linolenic acid as a contaminant.. However, in many cases, gas-chromatographic analysis shows that without dietary linoleic or linolenic acids the corresponding tissue acids are low or absent, in contrast to stearic, oleic, and palmitic acids, etc., which appear in substantial amounts whether present or not in the diet (Schaefer, 1968; Nakasone and Ito, 1967; Rock *et al.*, 1965; Lambremont *et al.*, 1965; Nelson and Sukkestad, 1968; Ito and Nakasone, 1969). That this is so for linoleic as well as linolenic suggests that both acids are essential for growth, but that linolenic acid has an additional specific function in connection with molting, a situation analogous to that for essential and sparing sterols.

The radioisotope method of indicating essentiality (discussed in connection with amino acids) has been applied to fatty acid studies; usually acetate-1-^{14}C is fed, and the specific activities of the acids isolated by gas chromatography are compared. In a roach, *Eurycotis floridana* (Bade, 1964), and the beetle *Oulema* (Lamb and Monroe, 1968b), very little activity found its way into the $C_{18:2}$ and $C_{18:3}$ acids, indicating little synthesis; in *Oulema*, a major proportion of fatty acid was nonlabeled linolenic acid, derived directly from the food. Radioactivity from glucose-U-^{14}C, given to silkworms, appeared in palmitic, palmitoleic, stearic, and oleic acids of their fat body, but not in linoleic or linolic acids (Horie and Nakasone, 1968). The uncertainties of the radioisotope method for delineating nutritional requirements is again shown in studies with the aphid *Myzus;* since only little activity from ingested acetate-1-^{14}C or glucose-U-^{14}C appeared in tissue linoleic acid, and it appeared to be selectively absorbed from sugar beet juice (F. E. Strong, 1963a,b), it was tentatively suggested that it might be required, but subsequent growth studies over many generations revealed no need for any dietary lipid (Dadd, 1967).

Many insects seem to require no dietary unsaturated fatty acids, and their synthesis has been shown in *Tenebrio* and *Dermestes* (Reviews). All Diptera studied dispense with dietary polyunsaturated fatty acids, and one would suppose they must synthesize them, assuming a probable need, at least as components of phospholipid. But analyses of *Agria, Musca, Aedes sollicitans,* and *Drosophila* indicate no more than traces of linoleic or linolenic acids unless they are provided in the diet (Barlow, 1964, 1966; Van Handel and Lum, 1961; Keith, 1967). Possibly Diptera, which as a group have an unusual fatty acid spectrum characterized by large proportions of palmitoleic acid ($C_{16:1}$), may have an exceptionally low functional need for the di- and triunsaturated C_{18} acids. However, since few growth studies with Diptera cover more than one larval cycle, and bearing in mind that an unsaturated fatty acid requirement became manifest in the roach and boll weevil only in second generation development, perhaps this is a case for caution before assuming inessentiality.

Although only linoleic and linolenic acids have proved essential for some insects, growth-improving effects are sometimes noted when certain other fatty acids, especially in combinations (myristic, stearic, palmitic and particularly oleic), are included in diets (Barlow, 1966; Ito and Nakasone, 1967, 1969; G. R. F. Davis, 1967c). Chromatographic analysis shows that saturated and monoenoic acids are synthesized when absent from the diet, and these effects are clearly different in nature from those of the polyunsaturated acids. They probably are further examples of the optimalization of growth brought about by a variety of fine adjustments to nutrient balance.

c. *Fat-Soluble Vitamins.* As recently as House's review (1965c) it was still a fair generalization that no fat-soluble vitamins were essential for insects. This can no longer be maintained in view of mounting evidence of functions in growth, vision, and reproduction for vitamins A and E.

Carotene (provitamin A) was early known to contribute to pigmentation of phytophagous insects and was presumed to be derived unchanged from their food. The silkworm literature contains early claims that vitamin A as well as β-carotene could be detected in larval tissues, and conjectures of nutritional function for carotenoids appear (Shyamala and Bhat, 1962; Legay, 1958), but without suitable artificial diets the means to test these speculations were lacking. Since vitamin A could not be unequivocally identified in any insect tissues at this time, and as all early tests for a dietary effect were negative, it was believed that no insects required carotenoid vitamins. Yellow pigmentation was shown to depend upon dietary intake of β-carotene in the locust *Schistocerca*. Initially it, or vitamin A, seemed necessary for good growth, but with improved diets this was not confirmed. However, using larvae from parents reared on carotene-deficient diets (so as to deplete carotene normally stored in the egg), growth of both *Schistocerca* and *Locusta* was then found to be retarded unless the diet contained β-carotene; not only were carotenoid pigments lacking with deficient diet, but the pink, brown, and black ommochrome pigments characteristic of gregariously reared locusts were largely replaced by a blue pigment, mesobiliverdin, usually present in locusts of phase *solitaria* reared in isolation or in gregarious locusts implanted with extra corpora allata (Dadd, 1961). Though not proving a vitamin A requirement, these experiments demonstrated that dietary carotene was involved in physiological functions that went beyond the mere adventitious presence or absence of pigment. Carotene is necessary for proper pigmentation of the grasshopper *Melanoplus bivittatus*, though it has no effect on its growth over one larval cycle (Nayar, 1964). A mixture of carotene, vitamin E, and vitamin K improved egg production in the boll weevil, but which of the three was effective was not determined (Vanderzant and Richard-son, 1964). Recently, vitamin A acetate, but not the acid, was reported to improve larval growth and to cure the reproductive failure that had plagued a decade of nutritional analysis of the fly, *Agria* (House, 1965b). This proved a classic case of confounding by contamination, for the effect on reproduction was subsequently traced to α-tocopherol (vitamin E), a contaminant of the acetate but not the acid. Nevertheless, vitamin A was thought to improve growth and emergence (House, 1966a).

Dadd (1961) pointed out that if insect visual pigments were caroteno-proteins as they are in vertebrates, crustaceans, and mollusks, then caro-tenoids would be a dietary necessity, unless it were supposed that in-sects, alone amongst animals, could accomplish their synthesis. Several workers have now identified retinol (vitamin A) or retinal (retinene) in bees, flies, and a locust; flies reared on carotene-deficient media have defective vision, becoming effectively blind after three generations if microbial contamination is rigorously excluded from both adults and larvae (Cohen and Barker, 1963; Goldsmith *et al.*, 1964; Goldsmith and Fernandez, 1966). Besides visual failure in *Aedes* reared without caro-tenoids, abnormalities in ommatidial microstructure occur, as was also noted in some moths (Brammer, 1969; Carlson *et al.*, 1967). The occur-rence of vitamin A in diverse orders indicates that for its visual function, at least, it is probably needed exogenously by most insects.

As noted above, α-tocopherol (vitamin E), the "antisterility" factor of vertebrate nutrition, is essential, in the context of reproduction, for *Agria*. Tocopherol is also essential for reproduction in a beetle, *Crypto-laemus monstrousieri* (Chumakova, 1962), and in a cricket, *Acheta* (Meikle and Mcfarlane, 1965); but whereas in *Agria* and *Cryptolaemus* it acts primarily on the female, in *Acheta* the male is sterile without it. Fraenkel and Blewett (1946) showed that α-tocopherol improved growth of *Ephestia* (ascribing this to a generalized antioxidant protec-tion of essential unsaturated fatty acids rather than to a specific vitamin effect). The substance has since been tested with several insects, until recently with negative results. In few of these studies was fecundity considered, and hence a vitamin E action would probably be missed even if present. House (1966a) notes that exceptionally minute quanti-ties of fat-soluble vitamins exert their effects with insects. Low-level contamination of other dietary lipids is most likely, and this, together with the possibility of egg reserves where the effective dose is so small, makes it especially difficult to judge the significance of apparent non-requirement in single generation growth studies. To date, no insects have shown any dietary need for the phylloquinones (vitamin K) (Winteringham, 1965), or the ubiquinones [see, however, speculations on their uptake in food (L. I. Gilbert, 1967)], but it would be rash to assert that this will remain the position.

5. *Mineral Nutrition*

The reviews reveal a marked neglect of inorganic nutrition in insects. Most workers merely determined suitable concentrations of a standard vertebrate salt mixture for inclusion in their diets. Given the reasonable presumption that all animals require a qualitatively similar set of inorganic elements and radicals for basic enzyme, homeostatic, and nervous functions, then interest would attach only to quantitative differences. But since inorganic elements often are needed in trace amounts no greater than those occurring as contaminants of dietary chemicals, inherent practical difficulties in preparing sufficiently purified basal diets dissuade from attempting their study.

Where the attempt is made, the necessity of substantial potassium, magnesium, and phosphate is readily demonstrated. This was so in early studies with *Drosophila,* and, with more purified diets, a requirement for low levels of sodium was shown, but not of calcium. In contrast, several mosquito larvae require substantial calcium, but no sodium above the level of dietary impurities. Potassium, magnesium, and phosphate requirements were demonstrated for the roach *Blattella,* but again sodium and calcium requirements were below levels of dietary impurities, though a need for iron was shown. A zinc requirement was first demonstrated in *Tenebrio* (Reviews). Requirements for K, Mg, and phosphate were quantitated for *Tribolium;* Na requirements could not be demonstrated, Fe in concentrations exceeding those of whole tissue was toxic, and in early studies, Ca deficiency only became manifest in poor adult emergence (Huot *et al.,* 1958; Chaudhary and Lemonde, 1962; Lemonde and Chaudhary, 1966); using a purer basal diet, requirements for Fe, Zn, and Mn were quantitated (Medici and Taylor, 1966). With careful attention to purity of dietary protein, recent silkworm studies quantitated requirements for K, Mg, phosphate, Ca, Fe, Zn, and Mn, but dietary impurities precluded demonstration of a sodium deficiency (Ito and Niimura, 1966; Horie *et al.,* 1967).

It seems that in insects generally, sodium, calcium, and, probably, chloride (Dadd, 1968), are required only in minor or trace amounts, in marked contrast to the vertebrate situation where they constitute the principal inorganic nutrients. Presumably exceptions would be found with respect to calcium in insects whose larvae or pupae have a heavily calcified cuticle (e.g., Stratiomyidae), and the cricket, *Acheta,* requires more sodium for optimal growth than can be supplied by certain unsupplemented natural foods (Luckey and Stone, 1968). The inappropriateness of assuming good growth with standard vertebrate salt mixtures that are grossly unbalanced in relation to insects' needs is now realized, for although such mixtures suffice for many species that apparently are indifferent to large excesses of various salts, notably improved performances have often followed the adoption of low calcium, low sodium mixtures (House and Barlow, 1965; Beck et al., 1968).

Aphids are especially sensitive to trace metal deficiency. Besides the usual substantial requirement for K, phosphate, and Mg, Myzus has critical requirements for Fe, Zn, Mn, and probably Cu, the last requiring two or three generations of deprivation for the deficiency to become apparent (Dadd, 1967, 1968). The same four metals, and also calcium, proved essential for Neomyzus, taking up to five generations of deprivation to halt growth completely in the case of copper (Ehrhardt, 1968a). Besides K, Mg, phosphate, and Ca (Ehrhardt, 1965), a mixture of four trace metals is needed by Aphis fabae, although individual requirements were not determined (Dadd and Krieger, 1967, 1968). The evidence for Acyrthosiphon is contradictory, for although Markkula and Laurema (1967) found iron necessary, Retnakaran and Beck (1967) obtained no response in one generation to any trace metals, but found that reproduction depended upon a critical calcium–phosphate balance. Dadd (1967) speculated that sensitivity to dietary trace metals in aphids might be connected with the occurrence of intracellular symbiotes, analogously to the dependence of symbiote transmission on dietary Mn, Zn, and Ca balance in the roach (Brooks, 1960). Distortion and loss of symbiotes associated with trace metal deficiencies in Neomyzus (Ehrhardt, 1968a) lend strong support to this conjecture.

In Myzus, inorganic sulfate improves growth, even when cysteine, which it can spare, is also present (Dadd and Krieger, 1968; Dadd, 1968). It is not absolutely essential, since generations continue indefinitely in its absence (Dadd and Krieger, 1967, 1968); it probably subserves some balancing function in relation to the sulfur-containing amino acids, as sparing of both cysteine and methionine by sulfate is indicated also in Acyrthosiphon (Retnakaran and Beck, 1968).

6. Nutrient Balance

Undoubtedly the diversity of insects' foods is dictated partly by nutrition. Special nutrients may characterize certain feeding types, as ascorbic acid does many leaf-eaters. However, qualitative requirements of insects as a whole are too uniform to offer much explanation of food diversity. Hence a concept of balance assumes prominence in speculation on the nutritional basis of natural dietetics, for any number of nutrient balances may be envisaged to distinguish the most diverse dietaries.

For any insect, characteristic limits to concentrations of nutrients will circumscribe foods on which survival is possible. This, in conjunction with whatever phagostimulant factors regulate feeding, and the ecological circumstances governing possible food encounters, would account for observed dietaries.

The nutrient proportionalities of artificial diets clearly reflect gross differences between natural foods, as already discussed in connection with Table I. At a subtler level, small quantitative differences in requirements distinguish taxonomically related insects with apparently similar diets that nevertheless are not mutually optimal. Species of *Drosophila* differ in ability to develop on single types of yeast from among several that constitute adequate natural dietaries, perhaps reflecting the different levels of protein, nucleic acids, and vitamins needed in artificial diets by different species, strains, and mutants (Sang, 1959, 1964; Royes and Robertson, 1964; Erk and Sang, 1966). For some aphids, 5% to 15% of sucrose in a synthetic diet is optimal, whereas others require 25% or more, a difference that doubtless reflects the suitability of their particular host phloem saps (Dadd and Mittler, 1965; Auclair, 1965, 1967). Crucial balances among amino acids, nucleic acids, and minerals are touched on in previous sections. Work with the beetle, *Oryzaephilus*, reveals that many subtle effects on growth and development at different life cycle stages hinge on delicately balanced relationships involving RNA, guanine, cytosine, putrescine, spermidine, arginine, proline, alanine, and aspartic acid (Davis, 1966a,b, 1967a,b, 1968b,c). In *Drosophila* and *Musca* the expression of tumor-producing genes is sensitive to shifts in balance of dietary amino acids and nucleic acids (Sang and Burnet, 1963; Bodnaryk, 1968).

Though, within limits, particular balances may characterize an insect, in actuality *optimal* balance is probably always subject to flux. Changes in nutrient balance at different stages of growth are seen at their most extreme in the radically different needs of larvae and adults of many holometabolous insects. Within the adult stage, such changes occur in relation to ovarian development, exemplified by the fluctuating carbohydrate and protein needs of female flies (Strangways-Dixon, 1961; Orr, 1964; Wilkens, 1968). Gross utilization of natural foods, a large area of insect nutrition critically reviewed by Waldbauer (1968), may change within larval instars and over the sequence of instars, pointing to changing metabolic demands that probably entail varying exogenous requirements. Some larval Lepidoptera and Orthoptera have a higher protein requirement in the early instars and increased carbohydrate requirement, perhaps associated with fat deposition, in the late instars (Dadd, 1963; Ito and Tanaka, 1962; Hirano, 1964). Particular growth-factor and amino acid deficiencies often become manifest at characteristic phases of development (Reviews), suggesting particular demands in some relation to such times; the expression of linolenic acid deficiency principally as a failure of pupal eclosion is a ˜ase in point. Gordon (1959) and Sang (1959) discuss at length how interdependent metabolic functions can result in various optimal nutrient balances. For example, minimal levels of nucleic acid and several vitamins involved in amino acid metabolism differ between *Drosophila* reared on high or low protein diets that allow equally good growth (Sang, 1962; Geer, 1963). In another fly, *Agria*, optimal growth at different temperatures involves differing proportionalities between protein, salts, and some vitamins (House, 1966b,c). Most probably the beneficial effect for *Oryzaephilus* of aspartic acid in a diet containing guanine and cytosine in place of RNA (with which aspartic acid has no effect) stems from its use as a precursor of purines and pyramidines that must be synthesized if it is not provided preformed in RNA (Davis, 1967b).

Nutrients required for optimal performance but not essential have a balancing function. Apart from the amino acid and nucleic acid components discussed, the occasional beneficial effect of a generally inessential growth factor may come into this category; for example, the beneficial effect of coenzyme A on *Hylemyia* (Friend and Patton, 1956) was perhaps due to inadequate intake of pantothenic acid, and sparing of biotin by oleic acid (Gilmour, 1961) by its function in fatty acid synthesis (Miura *et al.*, 1967; Horie and Nakasone, 1968). Growth-promoting effects sometimes noted with saturated and monoenoic fatty acids, particularly oleic acid (House and Barlow, 1960; Ito and Nakasone, 1966, 1969; Yamada and Kato, 1967; Davis, 1967c), may be viewed in this light. In no case are these essential, and indeed there is abundant evidence of their substantial and facile synthesis, as distinct from the sometimes essential linoleic and linolenic acids. Insect fats often contain fatty acids in taxonomically characteristic proportions (Barlow, 1964) that presumably are physiologically optimal in some respect. Excepting linoleic and linolenic acids, such proportionalities are largely independent of diet, reflecting the ability of insects to synthesize most of their fatty acids. Nevertheless, if an optimal proportionality is more readily attained by incorporating or modifying particular exogenous fatty acids, then the ingestion of these in food might well improve growth.

In recent silkworm studies, sparing by dietary fatty acids of β-sitosterol was noted (Ito and Nakasone, 1967). Interactions between β-sitosterol, fatty acids, and tocopherol were also reported for *Oryzaephilus* (Davis,

1967c). Interrelations between fatty acid and sterol metabolism were suggested in explanation of these balance effects, but since fatty acids and oils may influence the efficiency of absorption of other lipids from the gut, differential intake rather than nutrient balance may be in question. Oily or fatty components often alter the physical characteristics of diets profoundly, thereby altering the mechanics of ingestion, digestion, and absorption, and they may have unsuspected phagostimulant or inhibitant properties that could alter feeding rates. One wonders to what extent some of the minor effects on growth here discussed as nutrient balance may find their explanation in such essentially non-nutritional terms.

III. Arthropods Other Than Insects

Paucity of chemical information on the food requirements of Crustacea and Arachnida stems from the largely unsurmounted problems of rearing representative species on defined diets (Rodriguez, 1966). While this remains so, our knowledge of their nutrition tends to conjecture, leaning heavily on circumstantial evidence from dietetics, digestive capabilities, and metabolic studies. Such coverage as there is centers on a few groups of economic significance: among Arachnida, the ticks of medical and veterinary importance and a spider mite pest; among Crustacea, fishery research supports extensive dietetic and growth studies of planktonic copepods, and considerable metabolic studies on the large decapods.

A. ARACHNIDS

Over many decades the need for artificial feeding techniques in studies of disease transmission by ticks has prompted interest in the stimuli that aid them to attain and feed upon their hosts. The literature is conveniently abstracted in the comprehensive bibliography of Hocking (1960). Sensory physiology involved in host-attaining (Dethier, 1957; Arthur, 1965) has analogies with that of biting flies. Odor plays a prominent part in locating the host [e.g., the "questing" of ixodid larvae in response to cattle odor (Wilkinson, 1953)], but little is known of the identity of the attractive or activating odor components.

Phagostimuli that induce and maintain gorging have received attention principally in the rapidly bloodsucking argasid ticks, which can often be induced to feed from capillary tubes or, more usually, via membranes (mostly animal skins or mesenteries) on warmed blood (Tarshis, 1958). Starved *Ornithodorus tholozani* will probe through a membrane of Parafilm (a wax and rubber material) into water, saline isotonic with blood,

blood, or a hydrolysate of washed erythrocytes, if the temperature is maintained at 33°, but gorging occurs only with blood or the laked erythrocytes. However, isotonic saline is engorged if it contains 10^{-2} M reduced glutathione; oxidized glutathione, S-methylglutathione, and the constituent amino acids of glutathione (glycine, cysteine, glutamic acid) are inneffective, glutamic acid being an inhibitant if present with glutathione. Several other Argasidae occasionally engorged on saline alone, but all engorged heavily in response to reduced glutathione (Galun and Kindler, 1965).

Since glutathione occurs in blood at a much lower concentration than that necessary to induce gorging on saline, other stimulants are presumeably involved in natural feeding. Glucose, at blood concentrations (1 mg./ml.) or greater, is barely stimulating, but in isotonic sucrose rather than saline it is partially stimulating, though sucrose alone, and also fructose, galactose, and arabinose are not so. However, glucose in saline in combination with blood levels of reduced glutathione (10^{-4} M) induces gorging optimally. Further, with 1 mg./ml. of glucose, adenosine tri- or diphosphates, inosine or guanine triphosphates, or reduced diphosphopyridine nucleotide all induce gorging, although all are totally inactive without glucose; adenosine monophosphate is effective only if inorganic phosphate is additionally present. No amino acids alone in saline induce gorging, but with glucose (but not sucrose) several, in particular leucine, are active with ticks previously starved for 6 or more months (Galun and Kindler, 1968). Evidently these ticks have evolved a recognition pattern for vertebrate blood that shares with the response pattern of bloodsucking insects the use of stimuli from nucleoside phosphates. They differ from the insects studied in requiring the blood sugar, glucose, as a part of the pattern, and in addition have developed a second recognition response based on glutathione.

With this understanding of tick engorging stimuli, the means are at hand to administer artificial diets with some confidence of the uniform feeding necessary for nutritional study. Among other arachnids, techniques for feeding and maintaining a scorpion on liquid and agar gel diet have been used to show that a complex diet (but incomplete with respect to amino acids, supplied only by gelatin) allowed slight weight increment over 2 months, as compared with no increment on water or sucrose gel alone (Bender, 1959). Quantitative studies relating the dry weight and numbers of prey eaten, and the utilization of prey tissue, to growth (dry weight increments) and development (progression of instars) have been made with the spider, *Linyphia triangularis* (Turnbull, 1962), and application of radioisotope metabolic studies indicates absence of sterol synthesis in spiders (Zandee, 1964). But apart from some early attempts purporting to demonstrate vitamin requirements in the ixodid tick *Boophilus moubata* in terms of reduced egg production by females fed on vitamin-deficient rats (DeMeillon and Golberg, 1947; DeMeillon *et al.*, 1947), essentially no information is yet available on specific nutrient requirements of any arachnid except for some tentative results recently obtained with spider mites.

The phytophagous mite, *Tetranychus urticae*, can be reared from protonymph to adult on sterilized liquid synthetic diet presented via a delicate collodion membrane. Though no deletion experiments are reported, the radioisotope method has been used to determine probable essential amino acids (Rodriguez and Hampton, 1966). Eight of the usual ten essential amino acids derived little radiocarbon from diet-administered glucose-U-^{14}C, and are therefore considered essential; tyrosine was unlabeled, as would be expected, if, as in some insects studied, it could be synthesized only from phenylalanine. Threonine was substantially labeled and therefore considered possibly inessential. However, bearing in mind that threonine is particularly difficult to separate completely and therefore prone to give misleading results with the isotope method (Kasting and McGinnis, 1966; Rock and King, 1968), it can be tentatively accepted that the essential amino acid requirements of this mite differ little from those of insects and other animals.

The synthetic diet for *Tetranychus* contains a complex mixture of lipids, including an array of fatty acids, apparently helpful in stimulating ingestion. Fatty acid analysis of the mite reveals an unusual predominance of linolenic acid, comparable to that occurring in phytophagous Lepidoptera (rather than in the few other arachnids—spiders and a trombidiid mite—for which data are available). Since in phytophagous Lepidoptera polyunsaturated fatty acids usually are essential and must be concentrated from the food plant, the same might be expected of *Tetranychus*. However, in mites maintained on lipid-free diet, tritiated acetate was incorporated substantially into linoleic and linolenic acids, though markedly less so than in stearic and oleic acids (Walling *et al.*, 1968), and this was considered probable evidence for the inessentiality of fatty acids.

A plant-feeder like *Tetranychus* would be expected to utilize carbohydrate for its major energy source, and the diets referred to above do indeed include substantial amounts of sugar. Though nutritional need has not been explicitly demonstrated, extracts of whole *Tetranychus* contain an extensive complement of carbohydrases able to hydrolyze starch, maltose, sucrose, trehalose, melibiose, lactose, melezitose, and raffinose, though not cellulose, cellobiose, or pectic substances (Ehrhardt and Voss, 1961).

B. CRUSTACEA

Echoing an earlier review of Beerstecher (1952), Marshall and Orr (1960) began: "Strictly speaking there is as yet no physiology of feeding and nutrition in Crustacea." The situation has changed only marginally so far as chemical definition of nutritional requirements is concerned, though peripheral work on natural dietetics and food utilization efficiency, particularly of filter-feeding planktonic forms, is substantial. A recent review (Conover, 1968) considers such topics as efficiency of utilization in relation to temperature, plankton density, ash content of plankton, food value of different microphyta, and seasonal changes affecting the foregoing; attempts to infer the principal energy substrate (fat, protein, carbohydrate) in terms of O:N ratios (oxygen uptakes: nitrogen excretion rates); and the development of mathematical models relating growth, food intake, and metabolic and execretory loss. A basic assumption of such studies, doubtless in the main justified, is that natural foods comprise, qualitatively, all essential nutrients, for otherwise utilization of the bulk food components would be quite erratic and not amenable to predictive formulation. Conover comments on the need for, and present lack of, nutritional analysis using defined diets to justify this assumption.

Beerstecher *et al.* (1954a) attempted nutritional growth studies with a terrestrial isopod, *Oniscus asellus,* using artificial diets of casein, starch, cellulose, and yeast. Though avoiding the problems of an aquatic environment, *Oniscus* survives for weeks without food and is unsuitably slow-growing for experimental convenience. However, yeast was shown to be slightly beneficial, 20% of protein (casein) detrimental, and survival was as good without as with any casein, taken to indicate that microorganisms in the gut supplied minimal nitrogen requirements. Since oils and fat-soluble vitamins failed to improve performances, they were considered of no nutritional import, an unwarranted conclusion in view of the near stasis in growth on all diets tested. Antimetabolites were used to gain some insight into B vitamin and amino acid requirements, but though analogs of niacin, phenylalanine, and methionine were inhibitory, some reversibly, results generally were inconclusive (Beerstecher *et al.*, 1954b).

Hints at particular nutritional requirements come from studies of planktonic Crustacea maintained in cultures that are inadequate without supplementation. *Daphnia* reared with the alga, *Chlamydomonas,* had a tripled life span and a tenfold increase in egg production on supplementation with pantothenic acid (Fritsch, 1953), and trace minerals improved cultures of *Euchaeta japonica* (Lewis, 1967). That microphyta, even at the species level, differ critically in their adequacy as food, is well illustrated by the idiosyncrasies of *Artemia salina* and *Tigriopus* spp. in mono- and dixenic culture, variously, with ten algal species (Provasoli *et al.*, 1959). *Tigriopus japonicus* soon dies out in monoxenic culture with *Isochrysis* or *Chromomonas* (though it survives in dixenic culture with both), but may be cultured indefinitely on supplementing either with a B vitamin mixture or glutathione alone (Shiraishi and Provasoli, 1959). In these studies of supplemented live foods it cannot be said whether the supplement is an immediate nutrient for the animal, or acts indirectly by altering the cultured food organism. From the differing effects of supplements (glucose, liver or yeast extracts, vitamins) on growth of two races of *Artemia* reared in dixenic culture (two species of algae, *Dunaliella*) at salinities between 0.5% and 20.0% total salts, D'Agostino and Provasoli (1968) conclude that organic enrichment most likely acts indirectly on *Artemia* by affecting the metabolism and consequent nutrient value of the algae.

Though results gained with supplemented living food are inherently ambiguous, growth stimulation on augmenting a dead basal diet shows reasonably certainly that the supplement is a needed nutrient, as a B vitamin mixture proved to be for *Daphnia* reared aseptically on artificial organic detritus (Rodina, 1963). Among Crustacea, only the brine shrimp, *Artemia*, has been successfully reared axenically on semisynthetic diets suitable for rigorous nutritional study (Provasoli and Shiraishi, 1959). Particulate material is required to ensure proper feeding, and, in a formulation used to determine vitamin requirements, is provided as a starch slurry, with heat-precipitated globulins and albumin providing solid protein, not replaceable by amino acids. Deletion experiments with such diets showed thiamine, riboflavin, nicotinic acid, pantothenic acid, folic acid, biotin, and putrescine to be essential for development to adults; carnitine, inositol, and choline may also be necessary, for though not preventing development, their omission reduced the numbers of egg-carrying females (Provasoli and D'Agostino, 1962). The vitamin requirements of this crustacean are akin to those of insects, but the clear requirement for putrescine is remarkable among higher animals, notwithstanding the recent evidence that putrescine and spermidine influence growth rates in the beetle *Oryzaephilus* (Davis, 1966b).

Oblique nutritional insights may be gleaned from metabolic studies. Huggins and Munday (1968) review evidence (from respiratory quotient studies, production of $^{14}CO_2$ from various isotopic substrates, relative transformations of different substrates by enzymes of the tricarboxylic acid cycle, etc.) earlier interpreted to indicate that carbohydrate is comparatively unimportant in the crustacean energy economy. Even with expanded information these areas remain equivocal, but it was tentatively concluded that while Crustacea, generally, probably utilize carbohydrate, lipid, and protein as ultimate energy sources, as the extensive arrays of digestive enzymes, particularly polysaccharases, from the hepatopancreas of some species would suggest, carbohydrate is of rather minor importance as an immediate substrate source for oxidative metabolism, except during molting.

The radioisotope method has been used to indicate essential amino acids and lipids. With the crayfish, *Astacus astacus,* radiocarbon from injected acetate appeared in glutamic acid, aspartic acid, alanine, glycine, and serine, but not in valine, leucine, isoleucine, threonine, lysine, histidine, phenylalanine, and tyrosine, though tyrosine became active if 3-^{14}C-phenylalanine was supplied (Zandee, 1966c). These results are similar to those obtained with insects, and, so far as they go, accord with the amino acids generally found essential for insects and vertebrates. Radiocarbon, also from acetate, appeared in many fatty acids in *Astacus,* heaviest labeling occurring with oleic and palmitic acids; of particular interest in the context of nutrition is the recovery of label from several, long, polyunsaturated fatty acids characteristic of Crustacea ($C_{20:2}$, $C_{20:3}$, $C_{20:4}$), but *not* from linoleic ($C_{18:2}$) acid, hinting that in some Crustacea, as in many insects, linoleic acid may be a dietary essential (Zandee, 1966a). In several decapods (*Astacus, Homarus, Cancer*), isotope studies show no incorporation of radiocarbon from acetate or mevalonate into cholesterol (van den Oord, 1964; Gosselin, 1965; Zandee, 1966b, 1967), and it seems likely that, like insects, crustaceans, generally, require a dietary sterol.

IV. Concluding Remarks

Meagre coverage allows little to be said of arachnid and crustacean nutrition. Excepting the need for putrescine in *Artemia,* no notable departures from the generalities applicable to insects have yet emerged. Assuming the putrescine requirement is unambiguous (i.e., that there was no possibility of contamination by some more ordinary micronutrient), one wonders if it is widespread among Crustacea, or merely a taxonomical quirk, as the carnitine requirement of Tenebrionidae is among insects. The dependence on exogenous sterol in all insects studied, taken with the lack of sterol synthesis in several Crustacea, a spider, and a Diplopod, has generated the doctrine of a sterol requirement as an arthropod characteristic (Winteringham, 1965). This seems most likely; but one would wish for evidence from a wider base in taxonomy and feeding habit for arachnids and crustaceans (not to mention the several minor classes), bearing in mind that among mollusks, sterol synthesis appears sporadically, possibly associated with phytophagy (Voogt, 1968).

Turning to insects, the contrast between basic uniformity in qualitative requirements and extreme diversity in natural dietetics is most striking. The most unpromising diets are made adequate by widespread co-opting of the nutritional versatility of microorganisms; diversity otherwise depends on wide variation within the class in the predominant food substrates used for energy, and related to this, variable dependence on metabolic rather than exogenous water. These features determine major differences in nutritional requirements, differences largely in proportionalities between water and the classes of bulk nutrients. Insect requirements are not, on the whole, so different from those of vertebrates, though they are sharply distinguished by the former's need for dietary sterol, but another hitherto made distinction—apparent indifference to fat-soluble vitamins—has become eroded of late with the demonstration that a few species require vitamins A and E. The list may well be extended, since a feature of recent insect studies is the attribution of erstwhile "special" requirements to more and more species as experiments improve in rigor and are prolonged over successive generations.

This has notably been the case with ascorbic acid, inositol, and polyunsaturated fatty acid, but here the explanation may lie, rather, in the recent proliferation of studies of phytophagous species. This is certainly so of ascorbic acid; inositol and fatty acid requirements are not so consistently tied to phytophagy, but they are nevertheless found predominantly among plant feeders. That such requirements should characterize plant feeders is not surprising, for the ubiquitous distribution of these substances in food would favor an evolutionary loss of mechanisms for their synthesis.

Though qualitative requirements are now defined for many types of insects, certain lacunae remain. Virtually nothing is known of parasites and little of predators, unless we count among the latter the screwworm, *Cochliomyia*, and the parasitoid, *Agria*. With living animal food one might anticipate some loss of synthetic capabilities and some special requirements, and it is perhaps significant that nucleic acid components are essential for *Cochliomyia*, rather than merely an aid to rapid growth as in other Diptera studied.

A quite different area of qualitative need is adumbrated by the unique sterol requirements of *Drosophila pachea*. Are other such plant-specific variants on a basic nutritional requirement commonplace among monophagous insects? This case exemplifies additionally one of the main lines in which future advances may be anticipated. In ecological nutrition, the aim will be to relate qualitative and quantitative nutritional requirements to the abilities of potential ecosystems to satisfy them, and thus depends much on complementary biochemical information about the normal food. Questions of phagostimulation are here interwoven with nutrition per se, particularly so in the phytophagous and biting pest insects which offend humans and are most likely to receive attention.

So far as mainline nutrition is concerned, future development, one hopes, will take the form of metabolic and quantitative sophistication. Knowing most requirements empirically, and something of their optimal dietary proportionalities, the transformation of nutrients into metabolites, their subsequent interdependences and cyclings, and their ultimate physiological functions next solicit investigation. Work at these levels expands apace, with bridgeheads already established to such central physiological fields as amino acid metabolism, lipid function in membranes, and endocrine synthesis. Good nutrition is assessed as growth, and, in vertebrates, a major concern has been to quantitate relationships between growth and nutrient consumption. Thus far, with arthropods, this approach has been restricted almost entirely to overall utilization studies of natural foods; such work has dealt in the main with chemically undefined material and has received only passing mention, but recent comprehensive reviews are available for insects (Waldbauer, 1968) and Crustacea (Conover, 1968). It has been suggested (Sang, 1959; Gordon, 1959) that the fundamental question to pose for any nutrient is: how efficiently is it utilized, and how much, absolutely, is needed to allow unit increment in substance of the growing organism? Because this would have involved much painstaking additional work, inordinately so when basic requirements were still being worked out, the question has largely gone by default in work with defined diets.

In strong advocacy of this approach, Gordon (1968b) presents the ultimate ideal of nutritional research as the formulation of equations to describe numerically the ingestion and conversion of all nutrients to the feeding organism; from simplifying postulates and hypotheses he formulated preliminary growth equations and applied them to describe growth events in adult male cockroaches allowed specified diets of yeast, sucrose, and cellulose (Gordon, 1968a). The use of adults avoided irregularities that might issue from developmental needs as distinct from those of straightforward accretion of substance; use of males skirted possible complexities from ovarian maturation; and the skeleton diets were presumed to provide all adult requirements, with three variables for energetics (sucrose), for tissue-building protein (yeast), and for nonutilizable diluent (cellulose), with water provided separately ad lib. Gordon's equations, really at this stage a speculative model, fitted much of the data reasonably well, though complexities were fore-shadowed in connection with irregular phagostimulant responses to utilizable sugars other than sucrose. To extend such a treatment to cover all nutrients in food for complete cycles of growth and development might seem forbiddingly complex, and the necessary multivariate equations only manageable by a computer. However, the ideal is worthy, even if unlikely to be realized in full plenitude in the near future.

REFERENCES

Acree, F., Turner, R. B., Gouk, H. K., and Beroza, M. (1968). *Science* **161**, 1346.
Akov, S. (1962a). *J. Insect Physiol.* **8**, 319.
Akov, S. (1962b). *J. Insect Physiol.* **8**, 337.
Akov, S. (1967). *J. Insect Physiol.* **13**, 913.
Akov, S., and Guggenheim, K. (1963a). *Biochem. J.* **88**, 182.
Akov, S., and Guggenheim, K. (1963b). *Comp. Biochem. Physiol.* **9**, 61.
Akov, S., and Guggenheim, K. (1963c). *J. Nutr.* **81**, 419.
Alikhan, M. A. (1968). *Entomol. Exptl. Appl.* **11**, 43.
Allais, J. P., and Barbier, M. (1966). *Compt. Rend.* **263**, 1252.
Altman, P. L., and Dittmer, D. S. (1968). *In* "Metabolism," Committee on Handbooks, pp. 148–167. Federation Am. Soc. Exptl. Biol., Washington, D.C.
Applebaum, S. W., and Lubin, Y. (1967). *Entomol. Exptl. Appl.* **10**, 23.
Arai, N., and Ito, T. (1964). *J. Sericult. Sci. Japan* **33**, 107.
Arai, N., and Ito, T. (1967). *Bull. Sericult. Expt. Sta. (Tokyo)* **21**, 373.
Arthur, D. R. (1965). *Advan. Parasitol.* **3**, 249.
Auclair, J. L. (1963). *Ann. Rev. Entomol.* **8**, 439.
Auclair, J. L. (1965). *Ann. Entomol. Soc. Am.* **58**, 855.
Auclair, J. L. (1967). *J. Insect Physiol.* **13**, 431.
Bade, M. L. (1964). *J. Insect Physiol.* **10**, 333.
Barlow, J. S. (1962). *Nature* **196**, 193.
Barlow, J. S. (1964). *Can. J. Zool.* **43**, 337.
Barlow, J. S. (1966). *Can. J. Zool.* **44**, 775.
Barton Browne, L. (1964). *Ann. Rev. Entomol.* **9**, 63.
Barton Browne, L. (1965). *J. Insect Physiol.* **11**, 1131.
Barton Browne, L. (1968). *J. Insect Physiol.* **14**, 1603.
Barton Browne, L., and Dudziński, A. (1968). *J. Insect Physiol.* **14**, 1423.
Beck, S. D. (1965). *Ann. Rev. Entomol.* **10**, 207.
Beck, S. D., Chippendale, G. M., and Swinton, D. E. (1968). *Ann. Entomol. Soc. Am.* **61**, 459.
Beerstecher, E. (1952). *Vitamins Hormones* **10**, 69.
Beerstecher, E., Cornyn, J., Volkmann, C., Cardo, L., and Harper, R. (1954a). *Texas Rept. Biol. Med.* **12**, 207.
Beerstecher, E., Cornyn, J., and Volkmann, C. (1954b). *Texas Rept. Biol. Med.* **12**, 212.
Bender, G. L. (1959). *Ann. N.Y. Acad. Sci.* **77**, 262.
Bergmann, E. D., and Levinson, Z. H. (1966). *J. Insect Physiol.* **12**, 77.
Bieber, L. L., Cheldelin, V. H., and Newburgh, R. W. (1963). *J. Biol. Chem.* **238**, 1262.
Bodnaryk, R. P. (1968). *J. Insect Physiol.* **14**, 223.

Bracken, G. K. (1965). *Can. Entomologist* **97**, 1037.

Bracken, G. K. (1966). *Can. Entomologist* **98**, 918.

Brammer, J. D. (1969). *Science* **163**, 821.

Bridges, R. G., and Ricketts, J. (1967). *J. Insect Physiol.* **13**, 835.

Bridges, R. G., Ricketts, J., and Cox, J. T. (1965). *J. Insect Physiol.* **11**, 225.

Brooks, M. A. (1960). *Proc. Helminthol. Soc. Wash., D.C.* **27**, 212.

Burnet, B., and Sang, J. H. (1963). *J. Insect Physiol.* **9**, 553.

Carlson, S. D., Steeves, H. R., Vande Berg, J. S., and Robbins, W. E. (1967). *Science* **158**, 268.

Chambliss, O. L., and Jones, C. M. (1966). *Science* **153**, 1392.

Chaudhary, K. D., and Lemonde, A. (1962). *Can. J. Zool.* **40**, 375.

Chauvin, R. (1956). "Physiologie de l'Insecte; le comportement, les grandes fonctions, écophysiologie." Inst. Natl. Rech. Agron., Paris.

Cheldelin, V. H., and Newburgh, R. W. (1959). *Ann. N.Y. Acad. Sci.* **77**, 373.

Chippendale, G. M., and Beck, S. D. (1964). *Entomol. Exptl. Appl.* **7**, 241.

Chippendale, G. M., Beck, S. D., and Strong, F. M. (1964). *Nature* **204**, 710.

Chippendale, G. M., Beck, S. D., and Strong, F. M. (1965). *J. Insect Physiol.* **11**, 211.

Chumakova, B. M. (1962). *Vop. Ekol. Kievsk.* **8**, 133; *Biol. Abstr.* (1964). **45** (No. 44, 502), 3613.

Clark, A. J., and Bloch, K. (1959). *J. Biol. Chem.* **234**, 2583.

Clayton, R. B. (1964). *J. Lipid Res.* **5**, 3.

Clayton, R. B., and Bloch, K. (1963). *J. Biol. Chem.* **238**, 586.

Clayton, R. B., Hinkle, P. C., Smith, D. A., and Edwards, A. M. (1964). *Comp. Biochem. Physiol.* **11**, 333.

Clements, A. N. (1963). "The Physiology of Mosquitoes." Pergamon Press, Oxford.

Cohen, C. F., and Barker, R. J. (1963). *J. Cellular Comp. Physiol.* **62**, 43.

Conover, R. J. (1968). *Am. Zoologist* **8**, 107.

Dadd, R. H. (1960a). *Entomol. Exptl. Appl.* **3**, 283.

Dadd, R. H. (1960b). *Proc. Roy. Soc.* **B153**, 128.

Dadd, R. H. (1961). *Bull. Entomol. Res.* **52**, 63.

Dadd, R. H. (1963). *Advan. Insect Physiol.* **1**, 47.

Dadd, R. H. (1964). *J. Insect Physiol.* **10**, 161.

Dadd, R. H. (1966). *J. Insect Physiol.* **12**, 1479.

Dadd, R. H. (1967). *J. Insect Physiol.* **13**, 763.

Dadd, R. H. (1968). *Bull. Entomol. Soc. Am.* **14**, 22.

Dadd, R. H., and Krieger, D. L. (1967). *J. Econ. Entomol.* **60**, 1512.

Dadd, R. H., and Krieger, D. L. (1968). *J. Insect Physiol.* **14**, 741.

Dadd, R. H., and Mittler, T. E. (1965). *J. Insect Physiol.* **11**, 717.

Dadd, R. H., and Mittler, T. E. (1966). *Experientia* **22**, 832.

Dadd, R. H., Krieger, D. L.. and Mittler, T. E. (1967). *J. Insect Physiol.* **13**, 249.

D'Agostino, A. S., and Provasoli, L. (1968). *Biol. Bull.* **134**, 1.

Davey, K. G., and Treherne, J. E. (1963). *J. Exptl. Biol.* **40**, 763.

Davey, K. G., and Treherne, J. E. (1964). *J. Exptl. Biol.* **41**, 513.

David, J. (1966). *Arch. Sci. Physiol.* **20**, 281.

David, J. (1967). *Ann. Nutr. Aliment.* **21**, 25.

David, W. A. L., and Gardiner, B. O. C. (1966). *Entomol. Exptl. Appl.* **9**, 247.

Davis, G. R. F. (1964). *Arch. Intern. Physiol. Biochim.* **72**, 70.

Davis, G. R. F. (1965). *Arch. Intern. Physiol. Biochim.* **73**, 610.

Davis, G. R. F. (1966a). *Can. J. Zool.* **44**, 781.

Davis, G. R. F. (1966b). *Comp. Biochem. Physiol.* 19, 619.
Davis, G. R. F. (1967a). *J. Nutr.* 91, 255.
Davis, G. R. F. (1967b). *J. Insect Physiol.* 13, 1737.
Davis, G. R. F. (1967c). *Rev. Can. Biol.* 26, 119.
Davis, G. R. F. (1968a). *Can. J. Zool.* 46, 469.
Davis, G. R. F. (1968b). *Comp. Biochem. Physiol.* 24, 395.
Davis, G. R. F. (1968c). *J. Insect Physiol.* 14, 1247.
Davis, G. R. F. (1968d). *Bull. Entomol. Soc. Am.* 14, 27.
Davis, G. R. F. (1968e). *J. Insect Physiol.* 14, 1693.
Davis, G. R. F. (1969a). *Can. Entomologist* 101, 27.
Davis, G. R. F. (1969b). *Comp. Biochem. Physiol.* 28, 741.
DeMeillon, B., and Golberg, L. (1947). *J. Exptl. Biol.* 24, 41.
DeMeillon. B., Thor, J. M., and Hardy, F. (1947). *S. African J. Med. Sci.* 12, 111.
Dethier, V. G. (1953). *Trans. 9th Intern. Congr. Entomol., Amsterdam, 1951* Vol. 2, p. 81. Junk, The Hague, Netherlands.
Dethier, V. G. (1957). *Exptl. Parasitol.* 6, 68.
Dethier, V. G. (1961). *Biol. Bull.* 121, 456.
Dethier, V. G. (1966). *3rd Symp. Roy. Entomol. Soc., London, 1965*, p. 46.
Dethier, V. G., and Bodenstein, D. (1958). *Z. Tierpsychol.* 15, 129.
Dethier, V. G., and Evans, D. R. (1961). *Biol. Bull.* 121, 108.
Dethier, V. G., and Gelperin, A. (1967a). *J. Exptl. Biol.* 47, 191.
Dethier, V. G., and Gelperin, A. (1967b). *Physiol. Zool.* 40, 218.
Dethier, V. G., Barton Browne, L., and Smith, C. N. (1960). *J. Econ. Entomol.* 53, 134.
Dougherty, E. C. (1959). *Ann. N.Y. Acad. Sci.* 77, 27.
Dutky, R. C., Robbins, W. E., Shortino, T. J., Kaplanis, J. N., and Vroman, H. E. (1967). *J. Insect Physiol.* 13, 1501.
Earle, N. W., Slatten, B., and Burks, M. L. (1967). *J. Insect Physiol.* 13, 187.
Ehrhardt, P. (1965). *Z. Vergleich. Physiol.* 50, 293.
Ehrhardt, P. (1968a). *Z. Vergleich. Physiol.* 58, 47.
Ehrhardt, P. (1968b). *Z. Vergleich. Physiol.* 60, 416.
Ehrhardt, P. (1968c). *Z. Parasitenk.* 31, 38.
Ehrhardt, P. (1968d). *Experientia* 24, 82.
Ehrhardt, P., and Voss, G. (1961). *Experientia* 17, 307.
Erk, F. C., and Sang, J. H. (1966). *J. Insect Physiol.* 12, 43.
Evans, D. R., and Barton Browne, L. (1960). *Am. Midland Naturalist* 64, 282.
Fast, P. G. (1964). *Mem. Entomol. Soc. Can.* 37, 1.
Forgash, A. J. (1958). *Ann. Entomol. Soc. Am.* 51, 406.
Forgash, A. J. (1962). *Ann. Entomol. Soc. Am.* 55, 703.
Fraenkel, G. (1959). *Science* 129, 1466.
Fraenkel, G., and Blewett, M. (1943). *Biochem. J.* 37, 687.
Fraenkel, G., and Blewett, M. (1946). *J. Exptl. Biol.* 22, 172.
Fraenkel, G., and Friedman, S. (1957). *Vitamins Hormones* 15, 73.
Friend, W. G. (1958). *Ann. Rev. Entomol.* 3, 57.
Friend, W. G. (1965). *Can. J. Zool.* 43, 125.
Friend, W. G., and Patton, R. L. (1956). *Can. J. Zool.* 34, 152.
Fritsch, R. H. (1953). *Z. Wiss. Zool.* 157, 35.
Galun, R. (1967). *Bull. World Health Organ.* 36, 590.
Galun, R., and Kindler, S. H. (1965). *Science* 147, 166.

Galun, R., and Kindler, S. H. (1968). *J. Insect Physiol.* **14**, 1409.
Galun, R., Avi-Dor, Y., and Bar-Zeev, M. (1963). *Science* **142**, 1674.
Geer, B. W. (1963). *J. Exptl. Zool.* **154**, 353.
Geer, B. W. (1966). *J. Nutr.* **90**, 31.
Geer, B. W., Olander, R. M., and Sharp, P. L. (1970). *J. Insect Physiol.* **16**, 33.
Gelperin, A. (1966a). *J. Insect Physiol.* **12**, 331.
Gelperin, A. (1966b). *J. Insect Physiol.* **12**, 829.
Gelperin, A. (1967). *Science* **157**, 208.
Gilbert, B. L., and Norris, D. M. (1968). *J. Insect Physiol.* **14**, 1063.
Gilbert, L. I. (1967). *Advan. Insect Physiol.* **4**, 69.
Gilby, A. R. (1965). *Ann. Rev. Entomol.* **10**, 141.
Gilmour, D. (1961). "Biochemistry of Insects." Academic Press, New York.
Gingrich, R. E. (1964). *Ann. Entomol. Soc. Am.* **57**, 351.
Goldsmith, T. H., and Fernandez, H. R. (1966). *Proc. Intern. Symp. Functional Organ. Compound Eye, Stockholm, 1965* p. 125, Pergamon, New York.
Goldsmith, T. H., Barker, R. J., and Cohen, C. F. (1964). *Science* **146**, 65.
Gordon, H. T. (1959). *Ann. N.Y. Acad. Sci.* **77**, 290.
Gordon, H. T. (1961). *Ann. Rev. Entomol.* **6**, 27.
Gordon, H. T. (1968a). *J. Insect Physiol.* **14**, 41.
Gordon, H. T. (1968b). *Am. Zoologist* **8**, 131.
Gosselin, L. (1965). *Arch. Intern. Physiol. Biochim.* **73**, 543.
Gothilf, S., and Beck, S. D. (1967). *J. Insect Physiol.* **13**, 1039.
Gothilf, S., and Waites, R. E. (1968). *Entomol. Exptl. Appl.* **11**, 261.
Gumpert, J., and Schwartz, W. (1963). *Z. Allgem. Mikrobiol.* **3**, 1.
Gupta, P. D., and Thorsteinson, A. J. (1960). *Entomol. Exptl. Appl.* **3**, 305.
Gwadz, R. W. (1969). *J. Insect Physiol.* **15**, 2039.
Hansen, O. (1964). *Biochem. J.* **92**, 333.
Haydak, M. H. (1970). *Ann. Rev. Entomol.* **15**, 143.
Heed, W. B., and Kircher, H. W. (1965). *Science* **149**, 758.
Heron, R. J. (1964). *Can. J. Zool.* **43**, 247.
Hill, L., Luntz, A. J., and Steele, P. A. (1968). *J. Insect Physiol.* **14**, 1.
Hinton, T. (1959). *Ann. N.Y. Acad. Sci.* **77**, 366.
Hirano, C. (1964). *Bull. Natl. Inst. Agr. Sci.* **C17**, 103.
Hobson, R. P. (1935). *Biochem. J.* **29**, 2023.
Hocking, B. (1960). "Smell in Insects: A Bibliography with Abstracts," E P Tech. Rept. No. 8. Defence Research Board, Ottawa.
Hodgson, E., and Dauterman, W. C. (1964). *J. Insect Physiol.* **10**, 1005.
Horie, Y., and Ito, T. (1963). *Nature* **197**, 98.
Horie, Y., and Ito, T. (1965). *J. Insect Physiol.* **11**, 1585.
Horie, Y., and Nakasone, S. (1968). *J. Insect Physiol.* **14**, 1381.
Horie, Y., Watanabe, K., and Ito, T. (1966). *Bull. Sericult. Expt. Sta.* (*Tokyo*) **20**, 393.
Horie, Y., Watanabe, K., and Ito, T. (1967). *Bull. Sericult. Expt. Sta.* (*Tokyo*) **22**, 181.
Hosoi, T. (1959). *J. Insect Physiol.* **3**, 191.
House, H. L. (1958). *Exptl. Parasitol.* **7**, 555.
House, H. L. (1961). *Ann. Rev. Entomol.* **6**, 13.
House, H. L. (1962). *Ann. Rev. Biochem.* **31**, 653.
House, H. L. (1963). *In* "Insect Pathology: An Advanced Treatise" (E. A. Steinhaus, ed.), Vol. 1, pp. 133–160. Academic Press, New York.

House, H. L. (1964). *Can. J. Zool.* **42**, 801.

House, H. L. (1965a). *Can. Entomologist* **97**, 62.

House, H. L. (1965b). *J. Insect Physiol.* **11**, 1039.

House, H. L. (1965c). *In* "The Physiology of Insecta" (M. Rockstein, ed.), Vol. 2, pp. 769–813. Academic Press, New York.

House, H. L. (1966a). *J. Insect Physiol.* **12**, 409.

House, H. L. (1966b). *J. Insect Physiol.* **12**, 299.

House, H. L. (1966c). *J. Insect Physiol.* **12**, 1493.

House, H. L. (1967). "Artificial Diets for Insects: A Compilation of References and Abstracts," Inform. Bull. No. 5. Res. Inst., Can. Dept. Agr., Belleville, Ontario.

House, H. L., and Barlow, J. S. (1960). *J. Nutr.* **72**, 409.

House, H. L., and Barlow, J. S. (1964). *J. Insect Physiol.* **10**, 255.

House, H. L., and Barlow, J. S. (1965). *J. Insect Physiol.* **11**, 915.

Hsiao, T. H., and Fraenkel, G. (1968a). *Ann. Entomol. Soc. Am.* **61**, 44.

Hsiao, T. H., and Fraenkel, G. (1968b). *Ann. Entomol. Soc. Am.* **61**, 476.

Huggins, A. K., and Munday, K. A. (1968). *Advan. Comp. Physiol. Biochem.* **3**, 271.

Huot, L., Bernard, R. and Lemonde, A. (1958). *Can. J. Zool.* **36**, 7.

Hutner, S. H., Provasoli, L., and Baker, H. (1961). *Microchem. J., Symp. Ser.* **1**, 95.

Inokuchi, T., Horie, Y., and Ito, T. (1967). *Bull. Sericult. Expt. Sta.* (*Tokyo*) **22**, 195.

Ishii, S., and Hirano, C. (1955). *Bull. Natl. Inst. Agr. Sci.* **C5**, 35.

Ishii, S., and Hirano, C. (1964). *Japan. J. Appl. Entomol. Zool.* **8**, 84.

Ito, T. (1967). *Proc. Japan Acad.* **43**, 57.

Ito, T., and Arai, N. (1965a). *Bull. Sericult. Expt. Sta.* (*Tokyo*) **19**, 345.

Ito, T., and Arai, N. (1965b). *Bull. Sericult. Expt. Sta.* (*Tokyo*) **20**, 1.

Ito, T., and Arai, N. (1966). *J. Insect Physiol.* **12**, 861.

Ito, T., and Arai, N. (1967). *J. Insect Physiol.* **13**, 1813.

Ito, T., and Horie, Y. (1966). *Annotationes Zool. Japan.* **39**, 1.

Ito, T., and Nakasone, S. (1966). *Bull. Sericult. Expt. Sta.* (*Tokyo*) **20**, 375.

Ito, T., and Nakasone, S. (1967). *J. Insect Physiol.* **13**, 281.

Ito, T., and Nakasone, S. (1969). *Bull. Sericult. Expt. Sta.* (*Tokyo*) **23**, 295.

Ito, T., and Nümura, M. (1966). *Bull. Sericult. Expt. Sta.* (*Tokyo*) **20**, 361.

Ito, T., and Tanaka, M. (1962). *Bull. Sericult. Expt. Sta.* (*Tokyo*) **18**, 1.

Kaplanis, J. N., Robbins, W. E., Vroman, H. E., and Bryce, B. M. (1963). *Steroids* **2**, 547.

Kaplanis, J. N., Robbins, W. E., Munroe, R. E., Shortino, T. J., and Thompson, M. J. (1965). *J. Insect Physiol.* **11**, 251.

Karlson, P., and Hoffmeister, H. (1963). *Z. Physiol. Chem.* **331**, 298.

Kasting, R., and McGinnis, A. J. (1958). *Nature* **182**, 1380.

Kasting, R., and McGinnis, A. J. (1960). *Can. J. Biochem. Physiol.* **38**, 1229.

Kasting, R., and McGinnis, A. J. (1962). *J. Insect Physiol.* **8**, 97.

Kasting, R., and McGinnis, A. J. (1964). *Can. Entomologist* **96**, 1133.

Kasting, R., and McGinnis, A. J. (1966). *Ann. N.Y. Acad. Sci.* **139**, 98.

Kasting, R., and McGinnis, A. J. (1967). *Can. J. Zool.* **45**, 787.

Kasting, R., Davis, G. R. F., and McGinnis, A. J. (1962). *J. Insect Physiol.* **8**, 589.

Keith, A. D. (1967). *Comp. Biochem. Physiol.* **21**, 587.

Kennedy, J. S., and Booth, C. O. (1951). *Ann. Appl. Biol.* **38**, 25.

Khan, A. A., and Maibach, H. I. (1966). *J. Econ. Entomol.* **59**, 902.

Khan, A. A., Maibach, H. I., Strauss, W. G., and Fenley, W. R. (1966). *J. Econ. Entomol.* **59**, 690.

Khan, A. A., Strauss, W. G., Maibach, H. I., and Fenley, W. R. (1967). *J. Econ. Entomol.* **60**, 318.

Kircher, H. W., Heed, W. B., Russell, J. S., and Grove, J. (1967). *J. Insect Physiol.* **13**, 1869.

Kirimura, J., Saito, M., and Kobayashi, M. (1962). *Nature* **195**, 729.

Lake, P., and Friend, W. G. (1968). *J. Insect Physiol.* **14**, 543.

Lamb, N. J., and Monroe, R. E. (1968a). *Ann. Entomol. Soc. Am.* **61**, 1164.

Lamb, N. J., and Monroe, R. E. (1968b). *Ann. Entomol. Soc. Am.* **61**, 1167.

Lambremont, E. N., Stein, C. I., and Bennett, A. F. (1965). *Comp. Biochem. Physiol.* **16**, 289.

Lasser, N. L., and Clayton, R. B. (1966). *J. Lipid Res.* **7**, 413.

Lasser, N. L., Edwards, A. M., and Clayton, R. B. (1966). *J. Lipid. Res.* **7**, 403.

Lea, A. O., Dimond, J. B., and DeLong, D. M. (1958). *Proc. 10th Intern. Congr. Entomol., Montreal, 1956,* Vol. 3, p. 793.

Leclercq, J., and Lopez-Francos, L. (1964). *Arch. Intern. Physiol. Biochim.* **72**, 276.

Leclercq, J., and Lopez-Francos, L. (1966). *Arch. Intern. Physiol. Biochim.* **74**, 397.

Leclercq, J., and Lopez-Francos, L. (1967). *Arch. Intern. Physiol. Biochim.* **75**, 89.

Legay, J. M. (1958). *Ann. Rev. Entomol.* **3**, 75.

Lemonde, A., and Chaudhary, K. D. (1966). *Rev. Can. Biol.* **25**, 21.

Levinson, Z. H. (1955). *Riv. Parassitol.* **16**, 113.

Levinson, Z. H. (1962). *J. Insect Physiol.* **8**, 191.

Levinson, Z. H. (1966). *Riv. Parassitol.* **27**, 47.

Levinson, Z. H., and Bergmann, E. D. (1957). *Biochem. J.* **65**, 254.

Levinson, Z. H., and Navon, A. (1969). *J. Insect Physiol.* **15**, 591.

Lewis, A. G. (1967). *Limnol. Oceanog.* **12**, 147.

Lipke, H., and Fraenkel, G. (1956). *Ann. Rev. Entomol.* **1**, 17.

Lipsitz, E. Y., and Brown, A. W. A. (1964). *Bull. Entomol. Res.* **54**, 675.

Luckey, T. D., and Stone, P. C. (1960). *Science* **132**, 1891.

Luckey, T. D., and Stone, P. C. (1968). *J. Insect Physiol.* **14**, 1533.

McGinnis, A. J., and Kasting, R. (1967). *Can. J. Zool.* **45**, 365.

Markkula, M., and Laurema, S. (1967). *Ann. Agr. Fenniae* **6**, 77.

Marshall, S. M., and Orr, A. P. (1960). In "The Physiology of Crustacea" (T. H. Waterman, ed.), Vol. 1, pp. 227–258. Academic Press, New York.

Mason, J. O., Frothingham, T. E., Spielman, A., and Weller, T. H. (1965). *Proc. Soc. Exptl. Biol. Med.* **118**, 736.

Maurizio, A. (1965). *J. Insect Physiol.* **11**, 745.

Medici, J. C., and Taylor, M. W. (1966). *J. Nutr.* **88**, 181.

Meikle, J. E. S., and McFarlane, J. E. (1965). *Can. J. Zool.* **43**, 87.

Mittler, T. E. (1967a). *Entomol. Exptl. Appl.* **10**, 39.

Mittler, T. E. (1967b). *Entomol. Exptl. Appl.* **10**, 87.

Mittler, T. E. (1967c). *Nature* **214**, 386.

Mittler, T. E., and Dadd, R. H. (1964). *Entomol. Exptl. Appl.* **7**, 315.

Mittler, T. E., and Dadd, R. H. (1965). *Entomol. Exptl. Appl.* **8**, 107.

Miura, K., Takaya, T., and Koshiba, K. (1967). *Arch. Intern. Physiol. Biochim.* **75**, 65.

Monroe, R. E., Robbins, W. E., Chamber, D. L., and Tabor, L. A. (1963). *Ann. Entomol. Soc. Am.* **56**, 124.

Monroe, R. E., Hopkins, T. L., and Valder, S. A. (1967). *J. Insect Physiol.* **13**, 219.

Monroe, R. E., Polityka, C. S., and Lamb, N. J. (1968). *Ann. Entomol. Soc. Am.* **61**, 292.

Mukaiyama, F., and Ito, T. (1962). *J. Sericult. Sci. Japan* **31**, 398.
Müller, W. (1968). *Z. Vergleich. Physiol.* **58**, 241.
Murray, D. R. P. (1968). *Entomol. Exptl. Appl.* **11**, 149.
Nakasone, S., and Ito, T. (1967). *J. Insect Physiol.* **13**, 1237.
Naton, E. (1967). *J. Stored Prod. Res.* **3**, 49.
Nayar, J. K. (1964). *Can. J. Zool.* **42**, 11.
Nayar, J. K., and Fraenkel, G. (1962). *J. Insect Physiol.* **8**, 505.
Nayar, J. K., and Fraenkel, G. (1963a). *Ann. Entomol. Soc. Am.* **56**, 119.
Nayar, J. K., and Fraenkel, G. (1963b). *Ann. Entomol. Soc. Am.* **56**, 174.
Nayar, J. K., and Thorsteinson, A. J. (1963). *Can. J. Zool.* **41**, 923.
Naylor, A. F. (1963). *Can. J. Zool.* **41**, 1127.
Nelson, D. R., and Sukkestad, D. R. (1968). *J. Insect Physiol.* **14**, 293.
Nuñez, J. A. (1964). *Naturwissenschaften* **17**, 419.
Orr, C. W. M. (1964). *J. Insect Physiol.* **10**, 53.
Owen, W. B. (1963). *J. Insect Physiol.* **9**. 73.
Owen, W. B. (1965). *Proc. 12th Intern. Congr. Entomol., London, 1964* p. 793.
Owen, W. B., and Reinholz, S. (1968). *Exptl. Parasitol.* **22**, 43.
Pant, N. C., and Kapoor, S. (1963). *Indian J. Entomol.* **25**, 311.
Pant, N. C., Gupta, P., and Nayar, J. K. (1960). *Experientia* **16**, 311.
Pausch, R. D., and Fraenkel, G. (1966). *Physiol. Zool.* **39**, 202.
Pickett, C., and Friend, W. G. (1965). *J. Insect Physiol.* **11**, 1617.
Provasoli, L., and D'Agostino, A., (1962). *Am. Zoologist* **2**, Abstr. No. 12. p. 439.
Provasoli, L., and Shiraishi, K. (1959). *Biol. Bull.* **117**, 347.
Provasoli, L., Shiraishi, K., and Lance, J. R. (1959). *Ann. N.Y. Acad. Sci.* **77**, 250.
Retnakaran, A., and Beck, S. D. (1967). *J. Nutr.* **92**, 43.
Retnakaran, A., and Beck, S. D. (1968). *Comp. Biochem. Physiol.* **24**, 611.
Robbins, W. E., and Shortino, T. J. (1962). *Nature* **194**, 502.
Robbins, W. E., Dutky, R. C., Monroe, R. E., and Kaplanis, J. N. (1962). *Ann. Entomol. Soc. Am.* **55**, 102.
Robbins, W. E., Thompson, M. J., Kaplanis, J. N., and Shortino, T. J. (1964). *Steroids* **4**, 635.
Robbins, W. E., Thompson, M. J., Yamamoto, R. T., and Shortino, T. J. (1965). *Science* **147**, 628.
Robbins, W. E., Kaplanis, J. N., Thompson, M. J., Shortino, T. J., Cohen, C. F., and Joyner, S. C. (1968). *Science* **161**, 1158.
Rock, G. C. (1969). *Ann. Entomol. Soc. Am.* **62**, 611.
Rock, G. C., and King, K. W. (1967a). *J. Insect Physiol.* **13**, 59.
Rock, G. C., and King, K. W. (1967b). *J. Insect Physiol.* **13**, 175.
Rock, G. C., and King, K. W. (1968). *J. Nutr.* **95**, 369.
Rock, G. C., Patton, R. L., and Glass, E. A. (1965). *J. Insect Physiol.* **11**, 91.
Rodina, A. G. (1963). *Limnol. Oceanog.* **8**, 388.
Rodriguez, J. G. (1966). *Ann. N.Y. Acad. Sci.* **139**, 53.
Rodriguez, J. G., and Hampton, R. E. (1966). *J. Insect Physiol.* **12**, 1209.
Roessler, P., and Brown, A. W. A. (1964). *Bull. Entomol. Res.* **55**, 395.
Royes, V. W., and Robertson, F. W. (1964). *J. Exptl. Zool.* **156**, 105.
Rutledge, L. C., Ward, R. A., and Gould, D. J. (1964). *Mosquito News* **24**, 407.
Salama, H. S. (1966a). *J. Insect Physiol.* **12**, 1051.
Salama, H. S. (1966b). *J. Insect Physiol.* **12**, 583.
Salama, H. S. (1967). *Mosquito News* **27**, 32.
Sang, J. H. (1959). *Ann. N.Y. Acad. Sci.* **77**, 352.

Sang, J. H. (1962). J. Nutr. 77, 355.

Sang, J. H. (1964). Genet. Res. 5, 50.

Sang, J. H., and Burnet, B. (1963). Genetics 48, 235.

Sang, J. H., and King, R. C. (1961). J. Exptl. Biol. 38, 793.

Schaefer, C. H. (1964). J. Insect Physiol. 10, 363.

Schaefer, C. H. (1968). J. Insect Physiol. 14, 171.

Schaefer, C. H., Kaplanis, J. N., and Robbins, W. E. (1965). J. Insect Physiol. 11, 1013.

Schmialek, P. (1963). Z. Naturforsch. 18b, 462.

Schoonhoven, L. M. (1967). Koninkl. Ned. Akad. Wetenschap., Proc. C70, 556.

Schoonhoven, L. M. (1968). Ann. Rev. Entomol. 13, 115.

Shankland, D. L., Stark, J. H., and Whistler, R. L. (1968). J. Insect Physiol. 14, 63.

Shiraishi, K., and Provasoli, L. (1959). Tohoku J. Agr. Res. 10, 89.

Shyamala, M. B., and Bhat, J. V. (1958). J. Insect Physiol. 2, 137.

Shyamala, M. B., and Bhat, J. V. (1962). J. Sci. Ind. Res. (India) 21A, 26.

Shyamala, M. B., and Bhat, J. V. (1965). Indian J. Biochem. 2, 201.

Singh, K. R. P., and Brown, A. W. A. (1957). J. Insect Physiol. 1, 199.

Sinoir, Y. (1966). Compt. Rend. 262, 2480.

Sinoir, Y. (1968). Entomol. Exptl. Appl. 11, 195.

Skinner, W. A., Tong, H., Pearson, T., Strauss, W., and Maibach, H. (1965). Nature 207, 661.

Skinner, W. A., Tong, H. C., Pearson, T. R., and Maibach, H. I. (1967). J. Econ. Entomol. 60, 927.

Skinner, W. A., Tong, H., Johnson, H., Maibach, H., and Skidmore, D. (1968). Experientia 24, 679.

Smissman, E. E., Jenny, N. A., and Beck, S. D. (1964). J. Pharm. Sci. 53, 1515.

Smith, C. N. (1966). "Insect Colonization and Mass Production." Academic Press, New York.

Smith, C. N., LaBreque, G. C., and Børkovec, A. B. (1964). Ann. Rev. Entomol. 9, 269.

Spielman, A., and Skaff, V. (1967). J. Insect Physiol. 13, 1087.

Sridhara, S., and Bhat, J. V. (1965). Life Sci. 4, 167.

Staal, G. B. (1968). Koninkl. Ned. Akad. Wetenschap., Proc. C70, 409.

Strangways-Dixon, J. (1961). J. Exptl. Biol. 38, 225.

Strong, F. E. (1963a). Science 140, 983.

Strong, F. E. (1963b). Hilgardia 34, 43.

Strong, F. E., and Sakamoto, S. S. (1963). J. Insect Physiol. 9, 875.

Strong, L. (1967). J. Insect Physiol. 13, 495.

Stürckow, B., and Low, I. (1961). Entomol. Exptl. Appl. 4, 133.

Suchy, M., Slama, K., and Sorm, F. (1968). Science 162, 582.

Sugiyama, S., and Matsumoto, Y. (1959). Nogaku Kenkyu 46, 150.

Svoboda, J. A., and Robbins, W. E. (1968). Experientia 24, 1131.

Svoboda, J. A., Thompson, M. J., and Robbins, W. E. (1967). Life Sci. 6, 395.

Svoboda, J. A., Thompson, M. J., and Robbins, W. E. (1968). Steroids 12, 559.

Tanton, M. T. (1965). Entomol. Exptl. Appl. 8, 74.

Tarshis, I. B. (1958). Ann. Entomol. Soc. Am. 51, 294.

Taylor, J. F., and Hodgson, E. (1965). J. Insect Physiol. 11, 281.

Taylor, M. W., and Medici, J. C. (1966). J. Nutr. 88, 176.

Temple, C., Roberts, E. C., Frye, J., Struck, R. F., Shealy, Y. F., Thompson, A. C., Minyard, J. P., and Hedin, P. A. (1968). J. Econ. Entomol. 61, 1388.

Thomas, K. K., and Gilbert, L. I. (1967). *J. Insect. Physiol.* **13**, 963.
Thorsteinson, A. J. (1953). *Can. J. Zool.* **31**, 52.
Thorsteinson, A. J. (1958). *Entomol. Exptl. Appl.* **1**, 23.
Thorsteinson, A. J. (1960). *Ann. Rev. Entomol.* **5**, 193.
Thorsteinson, A. J., and Nayar, J. K. (1963). *Can. J. Zool.* **41**, 931.
Trager, W. (1953). *In* "Insect Physiology" (K. D. Roeder, ed.), pp. 350–386. Academic Press, New York.
Turnbull, A. L. (1962). *Can. Entomologist* **94**, 1233.
van den Oord, A. (1964). *Comp. Biochem. Physiol.* **13**, 461.
Vanderzant, E. S. (1958). *J. Econ. Entomol.* **51**, 309.
Vanderzant, E. S. (1959). *J. Econ. Entomol.* **52**, 1018.
Vanderzant, E. S. (1963a). *J. Insect Physiol.* **9**, 683.
Vanderzant, E. S. (1963b). *J. Econ. Entomol.* **56**, 357.
Vanderzant, E. S. (1965). *J. Insect Physiol.* **11**, 659.
Vanderzant, E. S. (1967). *Ann. Entomol. Soc. Am.* **60**, 1062.
Vanderzant, E. S. (1968). *Ann. Entomol. Soc. Am.* **61**, 120.
Vanderzant, E. S., and Richardson, C. D. (1964). *J. Insect Physiol.* **10**, 267.
Vanderzant, E. S., Kerur, D., and Reiser, R. (1957). *J. Econ. Entomol.* **50**, 606.
Vanderzant, E. S, Pool, M. C., and Richardson, C. D. (1962). *J. Insect Physiol.* **8**, 287.
Van Handel, E., and Lum, P. T. (1961). *Science* **134**, 1979.
Vinson, S. B., Thompson, J. L., and Green, H. B. (1967). *J. Insect Physiol.* **13**, 1729.
Voogt, P. A. (1968). (1968). *Comp. Biochem. Physiol.* **25**, 943.
Waldbauer, G. P. (1968). *Advan. Insect Physiol.* **5**, 229.
Walling, M. V., White, D. C., and Rodriguez, J. G. (1968). *J. Insect Physiol.* **14**, 1445.
Watson, J. A. L. (1967). *J. Insect Physiol.* **13**, 1689.
Wearing, C. H. (1968). *New Zealand J. Sci.* **11**, 105.
Wensler, R. J. D. (1962). *Nature* **195**, 830.
Wigglesworth, V. B. (1939–1965). "The Principles of Insect Physiology," various eds. Methuen, London.
Wilkens, J. L. (1968). *J. Insect Physiol.* **14**, 927.
Wilkinson, P. R. (1953). *Australian J. Zool.* **1**, 345.
Williams, C. M., and Robbins, W. E. (1968). *BioScience* **18**, 791.
Winteringham, F. P. W. (1965). *Biochem. Soc. Symp. (Cambridge, Engl.)* **25**, 29–37.
Wyatt, G. R. (1967). *Advan. Insect Physiol.* **4**, 287.
Yamada, H., and Kato, M. (1967). *Proc. Japan Acad.* **43**, 230.
Yamamoto, R. T., and Fraenkel, G. (1959). *Nature* **194**, 206.
Yamamoto, R. T., and Fraenkel, G. (1960). *Ann. Entomol. Soc. Am.* **53**, 499.
Yamamoto, R. T., and Jensen, E. (1967). *J. Insect Physiol.* **13**, 91.
Young, R. G. (1964). *Ann. Entomol. Soc. Am.* **57**, 325.
Zandee, D. I. (1964). *Nature* **202**, 1335.
Zandee, D. I. (1966a). *Arch. Intern. Physiol. Biochim.* **74**, 614.
Zandee, D. I. (1966b). *Arch. Intern. Physiol. Biochim.* **74**, 435.
Zandee, D. I. (1966c). *Arch. Intern. Physiol. Biochim.* **74**, 35.
Zandee, D. I. (1967). *Comp. Biochem. Physiol.* **20**, 811.

CHAPTER 3

Digestion in Crustacea

P. B. van Weel

I. Introduction

The physiology of digestion in crustaceans has been studied extensively in only a few genera (*Astacus, Procambarus,* a few crabs, *Homarus*). Of others, comparatively few data have been published lately. Excellent reviews of the older literature have been given by Mansour-Bek (1954a,b) and Vonk (1960, 1964), to which the reader is referred.

All crustaceans have in common a relatively simple intestinal tract: a straight gut (coiled ones are rare) showing three main divisions, the foregut (stomodaeum), midgut (mesenteron), and hindgut (proctodaeum). Only the midgut arises from the endoderm and is not lined by a chitinous layer. This layer is found, often conspicuously so, in the ectodermal fore- and hindgut. The short esophagus opens into a wider part, the so-called stomach, which is ectodermal and strongly chitinized in malacostracans only. In nonmalacostracans it is endodermal and lacks a chitinous lining. In malacostracans the stomach often has a "gastric mill," the proventriculus, in its anterior part, whereas the posterior pyloric part then contains a press and filter apparatus. Crustaceans having these gastric structures do not masticate their food. The mechanical trituration occurs in the gastric mill. Press and filters allow only the smallest particles to enter the midgut gland. Larger particles are either pushed back into the mill, or they may be passed on directly to the midgut, which as a rule is very short.

Those crustaceans with a reduced mill structure, or lacking such an apparatus entirely, either feed on particulate matter suspended in the water (copepods for instance), or they have mouth parts with sharp teeth which enable them to chew and triturate the food mechanically before swallowing it (Macrura and Natantia).

As mentioned before, the midgut is often quite short. It has no glands in its wall and seems to serve only as a structure to resorb digested food material. Small groups of glands may be found in the walls of maxillae, maxillulae, esophagus, and hindgut. They open into the intestinal lumen by means of ducts through the chitinous exoskeleton, but their function in digestion is poorly understood. Whether they really produce an amylase (Yonge, 1924) is uncertain. They do seem to secrete mucus. All crustaceans do have, however, one pair to many glandular appendages (tubules, diverticula), which form the midgut gland. This gland produces at least the bulk, maybe all, of the true digestive juices.

The midgut gland is recently generally called the hepatopancreas in favor of the more "neutral" term midgut gland. Vonk (1960) pointed out that this gland, like the vertebrate liver, seems to play a central role in the metabolic processes: it stores glycogen, fat, and calcium. Because of the presence of adenosine deaminase and guanase it may play a part in the purine metabolism (Roush and Betz, 1956). "Bile acids" may also be produced in this gland. The production of digestive enzymes, supposedly by specialized cells in the gland epithelium, gives, of course, rise to the second part of the name.

Against these considerations certain objections can be raised:

a. Calcium storage is not the exclusive function of the midgut gland. Storage occurs chiefly during the premolt stage, whereas Ca content is lowest during intermolt. The increase in Ca content during premolt is "probably due to storage of some constituents dissolved from the exoskeleton" (Sather, 1967). This increase is, however, small compared to the loss of Ca by the exoskeleton during this stage. Hence storage does not seem to be excessive. It is much more pronounced in the exoskeleton.

b. Glycogen is indeed stored in the gland and again shows fluctuations during inter- and premolt stages. This would therefore point toward a liver function. But the muscles also store much glycogen, its quantity seeming to follow closely that of the midgut gland fluctuations during the molt cycle (Sather, 1967). Glycogen storage is, therefore, apparently not an exclusive property of this "liver." What is more, it is well known that apart from muscles, other tissues such as connective tissue in *Branchiostoma lanceolatus* (van Weel, 1937) can do the same.

c. The gland often does contain sizeable amounts of fat, often so much as to make a cytological analysis of cyclic changes impossible. *Thalamita crenata* shows such a fat accumulation in this gland particularly during starvation, while its glycogen contents then seem to decrease greatly. In freshly caught, supposedly well-fed crabs the gland contains fewer fat droplets in its epithelial cells (van Weel, unpubl.). Whether this fat accumulation should be considered a true storage phenomenon, or an expression of a certain phase of metabolism, is unknown. Furthermore, although storage of fat may be one of the liver functions, it is certainly not exclusively typical for a liver, and demonstrating the presence of fat in an organ does not imply it to be a liver.

d. With respect to Vonk's claim (1947) of the presence of bile acids in the secretion of this gland (which would indeed strongly support the concept of it being a liver), more recent work by van den Oord *et al.* (1965), van den Oord (1966), and by Yamasaki *et al.* (1965) has demonstrated the absence of common bile acids. It seems, therefore, still too early to attach the term "hepar" to the name of this gland and it will be more prudent to use the "neutral" term midgut gland for the time being.

II. Sites of Digestion and Resorption

Because the midgut gland seems to be the only major gland to produce digestive secretions, and since these secretions appear in the stomach as gastric juice (antiperistaltic movements of the gut cause the secretions to move into the stomach in a great many crustaceans), it would be expected that the main site of digestion would be the stomach. This is certainly true with respect to predigestion. However, the food *brei* appears after a short while in the diverticula of the midgut gland (Matthews, 1955; van Weel, 1955; Vonk, 1960) where the final breakdown appears to occur. Hence this gland must also be a main site of digestion. In malacostracans the resorption of digested food occurs mainly in the midgut gland diverticula (the often very short midgut does not seem to play an important part in this respect). In the other crustaceans the midgut is in all probability of more importance to resorption, because it is much longer and the midgut gland usually much smaller, but convincing observations are lacking. Yonge (1924) found osmiophilic droplets in the midgut epithelium cells of *Nephrops* 1 to 3 days after force-feeding with a suspension of olive oil, none in the cells lining fore- or hindgut. The very long time it takes for the fat droplets to appear in the epithelium makes one wonder whether they represent directly resorbed fat. Because phagocytosis has never been reported to occur either in midgut, or in midgut gland of crustaceans, resorption seems to occur only at the molecular level. According to

Krijgsman (1953), true resorption does not happen in the chitinous stomach and hindgut, but diffusion through the wall is possible in these parts of the intestinal tract. Peptone and glucose do not seem to permeate the walls of these intestinal parts in *Astacus*.

III. Digestive Juice and Its Enzymes

A. GASTRIC AND INTESTINAL JUICES

Only comparatively small amounts seem to be produced at a time, even in the larger crustaceans. Because of this, the gastric juice has chiefly been investigated in the malacostracans (decapods). Its color in these animals varies from yellowish-brown (*Thalamita*, starved) to light brown (*Thalamita*, fed; *Procambarus*) to dark brown (*Astacus*). It has a low surface tension (Table I) and foams easily when shaken. It appears to be slightly acidic, particularly in starved animals. After feeding, the pH rises slightly (Table I). An exception seems to be the neutral juice of the fiddler crab, *Uca*, which has a pH 7.0 to 7.2 when starved and a pH 7.4 to 7.6 after feeding (Altevogt, 1957).

In *Astacus* some protein (2.38% to 5.46%) can always be found in the gastric juice, even after prolonged starvation (Mansour-Bek, 1954b). The most conspicuous ions present are Na^+, Ca^{++}, Cl^-, and PO_4^{---}. Krüger and Graetz (1927, cited from Vonk, 1960) ascribed the slightly acid properties either to NaH_2PO_4, $CaH_4(PO_4)_2$, or both. Typical for the investigated gastric juices is their clearing action on emulsions of oleic acid and fat (see also Section III,B,3).

B. ENZYMES

The digestive enzymes of crustaceans have again been studied most extensively in decapods, particularly in *Astacus* and *Maja*, although lately data from other crustaceans (*Orchestia, Carcinus, Orconectes, Procambarus*) have also been published. For a complete list of species investigated before 1953 the reader is referred to Mansour-Bek's paper (1954a).

1. Carbohydrases

All crustaceans usually secrete a very strongly acting amylase with a pH optimum ranging from about pH 5.0 to pH 7.8 (Table II). The enzyme is most probably an α-amylase (Blandamer and Beechney, 1964, 1966), although there is some evidence that a β-amylase may also be present in some crustaceans (Vonk, 1960). The enzyme is activated by chloride ions. Whether a specific "glycogenase" occurs (Agrawal,

TABLE I

pH AND PHYSICAL PROPERTIES OF THE DIGESTIVE JUICE

Species	Digestive juice	pH	Physical properties	Reference
Daphnia magna	Intestinal	6.0–6.2	—	Mansour-Bek (1954b)
Calanus finmarchicus	Intestinal	6.0–8.0	—	Mansour-Bek (1954b)
Ligia oceanica	Intestinal, starved	6.4	—	Mansour-Bek (1954b)
	Intestinal, fed	6.3	—	Mansour-Bek (1954b)
Marinogammarus	Gastric	6.1	—	Martin (1966)
obtusatus	Intestinal	6.2	—	Martin (1966)
Orchestia gammarella	Intestinal, starved	6.2	—	Agrawal (1964a)
	Intestinal, fed	6.4	—	Agrawal (1964a)
Homarus vulgaris	Gastric	—	Brown, foaming, low ST^a	Mansour-Bek (1954b)
Astacus fluviatilis	Gastric, starved	4.7–5.0	Dark brown, foaming, low ST^a	Mansour-Bek (1954b)
	Gastric, fed	5.8–6.6	Dark brown, foaming, low ST^a	Mansour-Bek (1954b)
A. macrodactylus	Gastric, starved	5.01	—	Mansour-Bek (1954b)
	Gastric, fed	5.6	—	Mansour-Bek (1954b)
A. leptodactylus	Gastric	5.0	Dark brown, strongly foaming, low ST^a	Mansour-Bek (1954b)
Procambarus clarkii	Gastric, starved	5.05–5.3	Light brown, foaming	Fingerman *et al.* (1967)
Thalassina anomala	Gastric	5.1	—	Mansour-Bek (1954b)
Maja squinado	Gastric, starved	6.1	Low ST^a	Mansour-Bek (1954b)
	Gastric, fed	6.3	—	Mansour-Bek (1954b)
Cancer pagurus	Gastric	5.8–6.0	Yellowish to green, strongly foaming, low ST^a	Mansour-Bek (1954b)
C. productus	Gastric	6.4	—	Mansour-Bek (1954b)
Carcinus maenas	Gastric	6.42	Low ST^a	Mansour-Bek (1954b)
Uca marionis and *U. annulipes*	Gastric, starved	7.1	—	Altevogt (1957)
	Gastric, fed	7.5	—	Altevogt (1957)
Thalamita crenata	Gastric	5.3	Brownish, foaming	James (1968)

[a] ST = surface tension.

1962, 1963) is questionable. The difference in pH optimum between the amylase and the "glycogenase" (pH 5.9 and 6.1 respectively) is so small that it does not seem very significant.

Maltase (α-glucosidase) is also generally present with an optimum pH 5.62 (*Procambarus*) and a pH 4.43 to 5.02 (probably closer to pH 5.02) in *Thalamita* (Table II). A β-glucosidase (amygdalinase) has been

TABLE II

Carbohydrases in Gastric Juice and Midgut Gland[a]

Species	Enzyme	pH optimum	Gastric juice (g.j.)	Midgut gland extract (m.g.)	Reference
Orchestia gammarella	Amylase	5.9 (m.g.)		+	Agrawal (1962)
	"Glycogenase"	6.1 (m.g.)		+	Agrawal (1962)
	Maltase			+	Agrawal (1962)
	Saccharase	6.0 (m.g.)		+	Agrawal (1962)
	Amygdalinase	5.6 (m.g.)		+	Agrawal (1962)
Corophium volutator	Amylase	5.8 (m.g.)		+	Agrawal (1963)
	"Glycogenase"			+	Agrawal (1963)
	Maltase			+	Agrawal (1963)
	Lactase			+	Agrawal (1963)
Marinogammarus	Amylase	5.6–6.3			Martin (1966)
	Saccharase	5.4–6.2			Martin (1966)
	Arbutinase	5.3			Martin (1966)
	Raffinase	5.0–5.6			Martin (1966)
Limnoria lignorum	Cellulase			+	Ray and Julian (1952)
Procambarus clarkii	Amylase	5.18–6.05 (m.g.)	+	+	Fingerman *et al.* (1967); Yasumasu *et al.* (1965); Yee (1968)
	Maltase	5.62 (m.g.)	+	+	Fingerman *et al.* (1967); Yasumasu *et al.* (1965); Yee (1968)
	Saccharase		+	+	Fingerman *et al.* (1967); Yasumasu *et al.* (1965); Yee (1968)
	Cellulase			+	Fingerman *et al.* (1967); Yasumasu *et al.* (1965); Yee (1968)
Astacus fluviatilis	Cellobiase		+	+	Kooiman (1964)
	α-Galactosidase		+	−	Kooiman (1964)
	Saccharase		+	+	Kooiman (1964)

	Enzyme	pH optimum			Reference
	Lactase		+	+	Kooiman (1964)
	α-Xylosidase		+	−	Kooiman (1964)
	Maltase		+	+	Kooiman (1964)
	Isomaltase		+	+	Kooiman (1964)
	β-1,3-glucanase		+	+	Kooiman (1964)
	Cellulase	4.0–4.5 (m.g.)	+	+	Kooiman (1964)
	Mannase		+	+	Kooiman (1964)
	Chitinase	3–4	+	+	Kooiman (1964)
Astacus sp.	Amylase				Vonk (1937)
	Maltase				Vonk (1937)
	Saccharase	5.7–6.0 (m.g., g.j.)			Vonk (1937)
Palinurus japonicus	Cellulase			+	Vonk (1937)
Homarus vulgaris	Amylase		+?	+	Takahashi *et al.* (1964); Yokoe and Yasumasu (1964)
	Cellulase		+?	+	Takahashi *et al.* (1964); Yokoe and Yasumasu (1964)
	Amylase			+	Takahashi *et al.* (1964); Yokoe and Yasumasu (1964)
	Cellulase			+	Takahashi *et al.* (1964); Yokoe and Yasumasu (1964)
Calappa	Cellulase			+	Yokoe and Yasumasu (1964)
Pachygrapsus	Cellulase			+	Yokoe and Yasumasu (1964)
Haplogaster	Cellulase			+	Yokoe and Yasumasu (1964)
Penaeus	Cellulase			+	Yokoe and Yasumasu (1964)
Eriocheir sinensis	Chitinase	4.9–5.5 (m.g.)	+	+	Jeuniaux (1960, 1963)
	Chitinase	5.2 (g.j.)		+	Jeuniaux (1960, 1963)
Thalamita crenata	Amylase	7.74–7.87 (m.g.)		+	van Weel (1960)
	Maltase	6.97 (m.g.)		+	van Weel (1960)
	Saccharase	7.87 (m.g.)		+	van Weel (1960)
Carcinus maenas	Amylase	6.17–7.25 (m.g.)	+	+	James (1968)
	Maltase	4.43–5.02 (m.g.)	+	+	James (1968)
	Saccharase	5.91–6.52 (m.g.)	+	+	James (1968)
	α-Amylase			+	Blandamer and Beechey (1963, 1964)

a For earlier literature, see Mansour-Bek (1954a).

reported to occur in the intestinal juice of the amphipod *Orchestia* (Agrawal, 1962, 1964b) with an optimum pH 5.8.

Saccharase, although usually less strong than amylase, seems also to be generally secreted by the midgut gland (Agrawal, 1962, 1964a,b; Martin, 1966; Yee, 1968; Kooiman, 1964; James, 1968; van Weel, 1960). *Marinogammarus* appears to secrete also a raffinase (optimum pH 5.0 to 5.6), splitting the trisaccharide raffinose, and an arbutinase (optimum pH 5.3, Martin, 1966).

It is generally believed that lactase (β-galactosidase) is not secreted by the midgut gland of crustaceans. However, Agrawal (1963) claimed to have found this enzyme in midgut gland extracts of *Corophium volutator* (amphipod), and Kooiman (1964) found this enzyme in *Astacus*. According to Kooiman the negative results by other investigators were obtained because the digestion periods used were too short. However, neither Yee (1968) nor James (1968) could demonstrate lactase in *Procambarus* and *Thalamita* even after an incubation period of 24 hours. The presence of lactase is therefore still a point of dispute, and even if it were extruded, its concentration in the gastric juice must then be so low as to be of no practical use to the animal.

Kooiman's investigation (1964; see also Table II) revealed an impressive list of carbohydrases produced by *Astacus fluviatilis*. It is quite possible that an equally extensive investigation in other crustaceans will disclose the presence of many more carbohydrases.

Until quite recently, it was considered questionable whether cellulase and chitinase are indeed secreted by the midgut gland of certain crustaceans (Vonk, 1960). However, there was some evidence that the wood-boring isopod, *Limnoria,* possesses a cellulase, because no cellulolytic microorganisms could be found in the gut (Ray and Julian, 1952). More recent investigations also strongly suggest that both cellulase (β-1,4-glucanase) [*Astacus* (Kooiman, 1964), *Panulirus japonicus* (Yokoe and Yasumasu, 1964), *Procambarus clarkii* (Yasumasu and Yokoe, 1965), *Calappa, Pachygrapsus* (Yokoe and Yasumasu, 1964] and chitinase [*Astacus fluviatilis* (Kooiman, 1964), *Eriocheir sinensis* (Jeuniaux, 1960, 1963)]] can be produced. More data, however, are needed to clear up this point definitely.

2. Proteases

Proteases, amino- and carboxypolypeptidases, and dipeptidases have been found in the gastric juice and midgut gland extracts of all crustaceans investigated (Mansour-Bek, 1954a; Vonk, 1960; see also Table III). Whether catheptic proteases are secreted is still a moot point. As a rule it can be said that the pH optima of the proteolytic enzymes

TABLE III
Proteases

Species	Enzyme	pH optimum	Gastric juice	Midgut gland extract	Reference
Orchestia gammarella	Protease		Total animal extracts	+	Agrawal (1964a)
Corophium volutator	Protease	(?)3.6–4.0	Total animal extracts	+	Agrawal (1963)
Calanus finmarchicus	Cathepsin	8.0–8.49			Bond (1934)
	Protease				
Lirceus sp.	Tryptic protease; also cathepsin?			+	DeVillez and Buschlen (1967)
Synurella sp.	Tryptic protease; also cathepsin?		+	+	DeVillez and Buschlen (1967)
Balanus sp.	Tryptic protease; also cathepsin?			+	DeVillez and Buschlen (1967)
Orconectes virilis	Tryptic protease	7.5–8.5	+		DeVillez (1965)
	Carboxypeptidase	6.0(?) and 8.0	+		DeVillez (1965)
Procambarus clarkii	Protease		+		Fingerman *et al.* (1967)
	Protease	5.0 (peptone)	+	+	Yee (1968)
	Protease	6.52 (gelatin)	+	+	Yee (1968)
Astacus astacus	Tryptic protease			± inactive	Kleine (1966)
	Chymotryptic protease		+ (trace)	± inactive	Kleine (1966)
	Carboxypeptidase A		+	± inactive	Kleine (1966)
	Aminopeptidase		+	± inactive	Kleine (1966)
Astacus sp.	Protease			+	Rosén (1937)
Homarus vulgaris	Protease	6.5	+	+	Engel (1938)
	Aminopeptidase		+	+	Engel (1938)
	Dipeptidase		+	+	Engel (1938)
Palinurus japonicus	Proteases			+	Takahashi *et al.* (1964)
Carcinus sp.	Cathepsin	5.12–6.70		−	Takahashi *et al.* (1964)
Thalamita crenata	Protease	8.53		+	James (1968)
	Protease			+	van Weel (1960)

fall in the range of pH 5.0 to 7.0, although DeVillez (1965) reported
an optimum pH 7.5 to 8.5 for the tryptic protease of *Orconectes*. Using
total animal extracts of *Calanus finmarchicus,* Bond (1934) found a
pH optimum 8.0 to 8.49, apart from a second very low one at pH 3.6
to 4.0. The question may be asked whether the latter is cathepsin from
tissues other than those that form digestive juice. Van Weel (1960)
arrived at very high values (pH 8.53) in midgut gland extracts of
Thalamita. Careful reinvestigation carried out by James (1968) could
not confirm this. She found an optimum range of pH 5.12 to 6.70, which
fits much better in the general picture (for a discussion of this discrepancy, see Section V).

3. Fat-Splitting Enzymes and Emulsifiers

a. *Lipases and Esterases.* Fat-splitting enzymes have been demonstrated to occur in all crustaceans investigated. Although most enzymes
seem to be esterases rather than lipases, *Homarus* and *Panulirus* seem
to digest fats better than they do esters of lower alcohols and lower
fatty acids (Vonk, 1960). Agrawal (1963, 1964a) described digestion
of olive oil and of milk by the midgut gland extracts of *Corophium
volutator* and *Orchestia gammarella*. Martin (1966) found both a nonspecific lipase and an esterase in *Marinogammarus*. According to Kleine
(1966), lipolytic and esterolytic activity are practically nonexistent in
the gastric juice of *Astacus astacus,* but midgut gland extract of this
species contains a highly active esterase and lipase, with a pH optimum
of 8.0! This value is very high compared with those data for other
members of the genus compiled by Mansour-Bek (1954a), where an
optimum range of pH 5.2 to 6.5 has been found. Takahashi *et al.* (1964)
found a good esterolytic activity in the intestinal juice and midgut gland
extract of *Panulirus japonicus*. Van Weel (1960) reported an esterase
(optimum pH 6.97) in the midgut gland extract of *Thalamita crenata*.

b. *Emulsifiers.* Although they are not enzymes, and hence are incapable of digesting fatty substances, emulsifying agents play a very
distinctive and important role in fat digestion and resorption. They act
to reduce the particle size of fatty substances, thus tremendously enlarg-
ing their total surface area exposed to lipolytic and esterolytic attack,
and consequently the rate of digestion is very strongly increased. Vonk
(1935a,b) had shown that milk or an oleic acid suspension, when shaken
with the gastric juice of *Potamobius* (*Astacus*) *leptodactylus,* became
a practically optically clear "solution." Vonk *et al.* (1938) demonstrated
that such "solutions" are in fact submicroscopic colloidal suspensions that
cannot pass parchment membranes. Although fatty acids in colloidal

suspension become resorbed, this is in all probability not true for colloidally suspended fats. These have to be broken down into their basic components before resorption is possible.

It is obvious that the presence of bile salts and bile acids was first looked for in the gastric juice. Vonk (1962) pointed out that the properties of these surface-active compounds in decapod crustacean gastric juice are indeed comparable to those of bile acids and bile alcohols. He had suggested the presence of bile acids in the juice (Vonk, 1947). However, van den Oord *et al.* (1964) and Yamasaki *et al.* (1965) proved that bile acids and bile alcohols do not occur in the gastric juice of either *Cancer* or *Procambarus*. According to van den Oord *et al.* (1965) the emulsifiers of *Cancer* must be assigned the general structure of acylsarcosyltaurine, whereas Yamasaki *et al.* (1965) found taurochenodeoxycholic acid in the gastric juice of *Procambarus*. These substances are in all probability produced by the midgut gland (van den Oord, 1966).

IV. Production of Digestive Juices

As mentioned before (Sections I and II) the midgut gland is in all probability the chief, if not the only (in malacostracans), source of digestive secretion. This gland consists of a number (2 to many) of blind tubules or diverticula (ceca) which open into the midgut (and stomach of the malacostracans). These tubules are lined with a simple epithelium consisting of various cell types. Extrusion is either holocrine (*Astacus*) or merocrine (*Orconectes*, Loizzi, 1966; *Atya*, van Weel, 1955), which explains the presence of proteins in the gastric juice. Whether the various cell types represent (a) different types, each with its own specific properties (resorption, storage, extrusion), or (b) actually only one cell type, but with the cells showing various cyclic stages of restitution, storage of "ripe" secretion, and extrusion of the secretion material, is still a point of dispute. Those accepting the first possibility distinguish between B-cells (*Blasenzellen*) as the true secretory cells and the R-cells (*Restzellen*) as storage and resorption cells. Loizzi (1966) separates "absorption cells" from "fibrillar cells," the latter being prestages of the secretory B-cells.

Histological and enzymic studies of the midgut gland of *Astacus*, *Orconectes*, *Thalamita*, and *Atya* have suggested that this gland undergoes cyclic changes of restitution and extrusion, at least after a period of starvation. Gland extracts, following starvation, made at various time intervals after feeding, showed maxima and minima of enzymic activity.

Histological analysis in the course of time after feeding, demonstrated "waves" of the various cell types. The maxima found for the B-cells more or less coincided with the maxima in enzymic activity of the extracts. This indeed suggests a cyclic restitution, "ripening," and extrusion of the secretion that contains the active digestive enzymes. Vonk (1960) correctly pointed out, however, that such a cyclic and rhythmic activity of the gland, although occurring in such highly artificial conditions of a long starvation period followed by only one short feeding period, need not happen under natural conditions where feeding is supposedly more or less continuous.

V. Resorption of Digested Substances

Resorption of the extracellularly digested food occurs in the midgut gland and the midgut. In the chitinized fore- and hindgut true resorption is impossible, but diffusion of certain small-molecular solutions may happen here. Krijgsman (1953) pointed out, however, that peptone and glucose do not seem to penetrate the walls of these parts of the intestinal tract. In *Nephrops* fat droplets appear 1 to 3 days after force-feeding with olive oil suspensions in the midgut epithelium (Yonge, 1924), whereas no trace of fat could be found in the fore- and hindgut epithelium. Iron appears in the midgut gland cells after feeding with iron lactate and iron saccharate.

In decapods the midgut is, as a rule, extremely short, so that resorption here cannot play a role of importance. In these animals the midgut gland must be considered the sole organ of resorption. Iron and fat droplets (after feeding with Fe saccharate and fat, respectively) appear in the gland cells in *Atya* (van Weel, 1955). In *Astacus* Fe resorption could also be demonstrated here. Because of its high fat contents resorption of fat could not be conclusively demonstrated to occur in the crayfish. Lehman and Scheer (1956) showed uptake of ^{32}P by this gland in *Hemigrapsus*. This is a true resorption according to these authors.

VI. Factors Affecting Secretion

Apart from its effect on cyclic restitution and extrusion in the midgut gland, starvation seems also to have an effect on the constituents of the secretion material, other than enzymes. This becomes visible in a change in pH of the gastric juice. The rather few data available suggest that during prolonged starvation the pH of the juice is somewhat lower than that in freshly caught, or well-fed animals: *Astacus fluviatilis,* starved: pH 4.7 to 5.0, fed: pH 5.8 to 6.6; *A. macrodactylus,* starved:

pH 5.01, fed: pH 5.6; *Maja squinado,* starved: pH 6.1, fed: pH 6.3; *Orchestia gammarella,* starved: pH 6.2, fed: pH 6.4; *Uca marionis* and *U. annulipes,* starved: pH 7.0 to 7.2, fed: pH 7.4 to 7.6 (see also Table I). An exception to this "rule" may be *Ligia oceanica:* the intestinal juice of starved animals shows a pH 6.4, that of fed ones pH 6.3 (Table I). Whether this slight difference in pH is a significant one needs further investigation, however. Fingerman *et al.* (1967) also reported a slight increase in pH of the gastric juice of *Procambarus clarkii* after starvation up to 10 days. Since it is believed that the pH of the digestive juice is caused by NaH_2PO_4 and $CaH_4(PO_4)_2$ (Section III,A), starvation may have its effect on the liberation of these inorganic compounds.

Martin (1966) observed a definite rhythm in feeding (these animals do not therefore feed continuously) which appears to be related to the tides, in *Marinogammarus,* which apparently only feeds during high tides. The tidal rhythm has therefore a definite effect on feeding, and consequently in all probability also on digestion. It would be interesting to study intestinal juice and secretion in these animals in connection with the tides.

Temperature has also been found to have a definite effect on secretion, although there are few data. Mews (1957) found in *Eriocheir sinensis* that the proteolytic activity of the intestinal juice is higher in crabs kept at 20°C than in those acclimated to 15°C. It seems therefore that at higher acclimation temperatures more enzymes (in any case, more proteases) are secreted than at lower temperatures.

Fingerman *et al.* (1967) finally pointed out that neuroendocrines may have a marked effect. Removal of the eyestalks from starved *Procambarus clarkii* resulted in a decrease in total nitrogen content, a marked increase in pH, and a decrease in amylolytic activity of the gastric juice. The midgut gland suffered a loss of RNA under these conditions. Starvation of normal crayfish resulted in a slight increase in amylase activity in the midgut gland. Since a neuroendocrine substance of the eyestalk stimulated the RNA synthesis in the midgut gland, it was concluded that RNA is responsible for the amylase synthesis here.

Lehman and Scheer (1956) found a marked increase in the rate of resorption of ^{32}P by the midgut gland of *Hemigrapsus nudus* upon eyestalk ablation during the C_3 and C_4 stages of the intermolt. In a later stage (D_2, preparatory to molt), a decrease of phosphate resorption occurs in eyestalk-ablated crabs. Thus the eyestalk endocrine component not only has an (inhibitory) effect on phosphate resorption, but the molt stage (again under influence of endocrines) has also a definite effect. The males seem to resorb phosphates less rapidly than the females, so that sex hormones appear to be a factor affecting resorption also.

Whether this is a direct effect, or whether male sex hormones affect the eyestalks in producing more of the inhibitory eyestalk endocrine than female sex hormones do, is unknown.

VII. Conclusions and Comments

Except for the filter feeders, nonmalacostracan crustaceans triturate their food mechanically by means of their mouth parts before ingesting it, whereas the malacostracans use their gastric mill for this purpose. The secretion of the midgut gland, the chief, possibly even the exclusive source of digestive fluid, is either poured directly into the stomach, or it appears first in the midgut and is subsequently passed on into the more anterior parts of the digestive tract by antiperistaltic movements of the gut. In malacostracans chemical trituration occurs, therefore, parallel to and simultaneous with mechanical size reduction of the food. A few cases have been reported where one or more digestive enzymes, found in midgut gland extracts, seem to be lacking in the intestinal or gastric juices: Agrawal (1964a) could not detect maltase in *Orchestia* intestinal juice. Kooiman (1964) missed α-galactosidase and α-xylosidase in the gastric juice of *Astacus* and *Homarus*. Whether these enzymes are only produced in such small quantities that their concentration in the intestinal or gastric juice is too low to detect, or whether they are intracellular enzymes, cannot be ascertained at the moment. If they are intracellular enzymes, then intracellular digestion (of a few substances) would occur in the midgut gland and this would imply that maltose, or α-galactose and α-xylose, would be resorbed by the midgut gland cells. This possibility cannot a priori be excluded.

Upon considering the enzymic picture, crustaceans seem to have a protease complement, more or less (but not completely) comparable to that of vertebrates, with the exception of pepsin which is never produced. A definite tryptic enzyme has been found in the crayfish *Orconectes* (DeVillez, 1965), *Lirceus* (isopod), and the amphipod *Synurella* (DeVillez and Buschlen, 1967). These authors did not find a tryptic enzyme in *Balanus nubilus*. Kleine (1966) also failed to find one in *Astacus*. Chymotrypsin seems to be absent (DeVillez, 1965; Kleine, 1966). Carboxypeptidase, but no aminopeptidase, was found in *Orconectes* (DeVillez, 1965), but the gastric juice of *Astacus* contains both carboxy- and aminopeptidases (Kleine, 1966). Mansour-Bek (1932) demonstrated the presence of carboxy-, amino-, and dipeptidase in *Maja*. The scarcity of data concerning these enzymes is without doubt the result of not testing midgut gland extracts and gastric juices for these enzymes in most of the cases.

Kleine (1966) pointed out the interesting fact that the midgut gland extract of *Astacus* contains ". . . practically inactive exo- and endopeptidases," whereas their activity in the gastric juice was much higher and that for tryptic activity very much higher. A surprisingly low (for such supposedly carnivorous animals) proteolytic activity of midgut gland extracts was also found in *Atya* and *Thalamita* by van Weel (unpubl.) who did not attach any special meaning to it at the time. Yee and James (1968) also found a much lower proteolytic activity in gland extracts than in the gastric juice of *Procambarus* and *Thalamita*. Kleine (1966) suggested that, in all probability, the proteolytic enzymes secreted are inactive, but that they become activated in an unknown way in the stomach. Mansour-Bek (1932) had shown that *Maja* protease can be activated by purified pig's enterokinase. Engel (1938) demonstrated that the protease of *Homarus* can be activated by (reduced) glutathione. Although no specific activator has as yet been isolated in crustaceans (and if present, nothing is known as to where such an activator is produced), these few data indicate that protease activation does seem to occur, or is at least possible in certain crustaceans. Investigation in this area is needed. It is possible that protease activity will be strongest in the stomach, but it will, no doubt, also occur in the diverticula of the midgut gland, because the food *brei* from the stomach (therefore mixed with active gastric juice) is passed on to them. Carboxy-, amino-, and dipeptidase activity might be of more importance in the gland tubules, however.

With respect to the carbohydrases, the general consensus seems to be that lactase is lacking completely in this group of enzymes. Only Kooiman (1964) has reported its presence in the gastric juices of *Astacus*, but a very long incubation period was needed to disclose its activity. This would mean that, if present, it is apparently produced in only minute quantities. One wonders whether the secretion of so little of this enzyme has any biological meaning, because digestion in the crayfish does not seem to take such a long time. Agrawal (1963) claimed its presence in *Corophium* midgut gland extracts. No lactase was found in gastric juice or midgut gland extract of *Procambarus clarkii* and of *Thalamita crenata*, even after incubation of up to 24 hours at 36°C (Yee and James, 1968). The "lactase problem" in crustaceans should certainly be looked into again.

The problem as to whether chitinase and cellulase are produced by (certain) crustaceans or whether they are of (symbiotic) bacterial origin seems to be solved: Jeuniaux (1960) was not yet completely certain, but Kooiman (1964) was very definite in his opinion that neither enzyme is of bacterial origin, but that they are secreted by the midgut gland of *Astacus*. Ray and Julian (1952) were also convinced that cellulase was produced by the diverticula (midgut gland) of the isopod *Limnoria*. Yasumasu and Yokoe (1965) found cellulase bound to microsomes isolated from the midgut gland of *Procambarus*. In this state the enzyme is inactive, but upon release from the microsomes by ATP its activity is manifested. Yokoe and Yasumasu (1964) also reported cellulolytic activity of midgut gland extracts (the cellulase was believed to be a secretory product under normal conditions) in *Calappa, Pachygrapsus,* and *Panulirus*.

Since Kooiman found such an extensive carbohydrase complement in *Astacus* (its gastric juice contains cellobiase, α-galactosidase, saccharase, presumably a little lactase, α-xylosidase, maltase, isomaltase, β-1,3-glucanase, cellulase, mannase, and chitinase!), one wonders whether the crayfish should not be considered an omnivore, rather than a carnivore. Immediate analysis of the stomach contents of a large number of freshly caught crayfish should give an answer to this question. It is quite possible that many crustaceans may depend more on plant (algal) material for food than has been thought possible.

With respect to fat digestion, it seems that crustaceans produce esterases rather than lipases, although *Homarus* and *Panulirus* seem to produce a stronger lipase. Fat emulsifiers are present in the gastric juice and are in all probability secreted by the midgut gland (van den Oord, 1966). They are not bile acids or bile alcohols, but have apparently the general structure of acylsarcosyltaurine (in *Cancer*, van den Oord *et al.*, 1965). Their presence is of utmost importance for rapid fat digestion and resorption because in emulsifying these substances to submicroscopical dimensions the total surface area open to lipolytic or esterolytic attack increases dramatically, with the result that the rate of fat digestion and resorption of fatty acids strongly increases. Since even the submicroscopically small fat droplets do not pass a parchment membrane, resorption of nondigested fat does not seem very possible.

With respect to the pH optimum ranges of the various enzymes there is at least one report which does not fit in the overall picture. As a rule the slightly acid reaction of the gastric and intestinal juices falls in the range of the pH optima (although certain peptidases seem to have an optimum of about pH 8.0): the optimum range of carbohydrases is from pH 5.0 to 6.8, that of proteases from pH 5.0 to 7.0, that of lipases (esterases) from pH 5.2 to 6.5 (Kleine, however, found a pH optimum in midgut gland extracts of *Astacus* of 8.0). In a study on certain enzymes in midgut gland extracts of *Thalamita* (van Weel, 1960) an optimum pH range of 6.97 to 7.87 for carbohydrases (Table II), of pH 8.53 for protease (Table III), and an optimum pH 6.97 for esterase were found. These figures appear to be exceptionally high. A recent careful study by James (1968) could not confirm these data. She found for carbohydrases an optimal range from pH 4.43 to 7.25 (Table II) and for proteases pH 5.12 to 6.70. The discrepancy between these two sets of data collected from the same species cannot be explained satisfactorily. It is felt that for the time being James' data should be accepted as valid ones, unless new data become available which could support van Weel's older results.

Whether the rhythms in secretion of digestive juices as found by various investigators (Vonk, 1960; van Weel, 1955) also occur under normal conditions of life, cannot be ascertained as yet. Vonk (1960) does not believe so, because crustaceans are thought to be "continuously" feeding organisms. However, one must be careful in making such assumptions because many animals, originally thought to be continuous feeders, have subsequently been shown to feed intermittently. They often show distinct feeding periods, alternated with nonfeeding periods, even when food is available all the time. Thus the normal activity may very well result in a rhythmic extrusion and restitution of the secretions. More investigations in this direction are needed before it can be stated whether such rhythmical secretion processes are normal.

Resorption of the digested food occurs primarily in the midgut gland, although in nonmalacostracans with their relatively long midgut and their "reduced" midgut gland, resorption in the midgut may play a very important part. According to Roche (1953, cited from Vonk, 1960) the midgut of *Asellus* is of more importance to digestion (and presumably also to resorption) than that of *Ligia* and decapods.

Finally, it should be pointed out that certain factors can and do affect the rate of secretion by the midgut gland and the composition of the secretion material. This may be particularly true for neuroendocrines and maybe also for sex hormones. It is quite possible that studies of digestive juice and midgut gland extracts in the same species, undertaken at different stages of the molt cycle, will lead to different results. This has not been recognized until recently. More data on hormonal effects on digestion and resorption are urgently needed. We cannot exclude the possibility that such hormonal effects may change our concepts of pH optima ranges, existing pH's of digestive juice, digestive activity of these juices, secretion and restitution, resorption, etc., in crustaceans.

REFERENCES

Agrawal, V. P. (1962). *Enzymologia* **25**, 173–177.
Agrawal, V. P. (1963). *J. Marine Biol. Assoc. U.K.* **43**, 125–128.
Agrawal, V. P. (1964a). *J. Zool.* **143**, 133–141.

Agrawal, V. P. (1964b). *J. Zool.* **143**, 545–551.
Altevogt, R. (1957). *Z. Morphol. Öekol. Tiere* **46**, 1–110.
Blandamer, A., and Beechey, R. B. (1963). *Nature* **197**, 591–592.
Blandamer, A., and Beechey, R. B. (1964). *Comp. Biochem. Physiol.* **13**, 97–105.
Blandamer, A., and Beechey, R. B. (1966). *Biochim. Biophys. Acta* **118**, 204–206.
Bond, R. M. (1934). *Biol. Bull.* **67**, 461–465.
DeVillez, E. J. (1965). *Comp. Biochem. Physiol.* **14**, 577–586.
DeVillez, E. J., and Buschlen, K. (1967). *Comp. Biochem. Physiol.* **21**, 541–546.
Engel, C. (1938). *Acta Brev. Neerl. Physiol., Pharmacol., Microbiol.* **8**, 28–29.
Fingerman, M., Dominiczak, T., Miyawaki, M., Oguro, C., and Yamamoto, Y. (1967). *Physiol. Zool.* **40**, 23–30.
James, M. L. (1968). Unpublished data.
Jeuniaux, C. (1960). *Arch. Intern. Physiol. Biochim.* **68**, 684–685.
Jeuniaux, C. (1963). *Arch. Intern. Physiol. Biochim.* **71**, 307–309.
Kleine, R. (1966). *Naturwissenschaften* **53**, 201–202.
Kooiman, P. (1964). *J. Cellular Comp. Physiol.* **63**, 197–201.
Krijgsman, B. J. (1953). *Tabul. Biol.* (*Hague*) **21**, No. 2, 203–239.
Lehman, R., and Scheer, B. T. (1956). *Physiol. Comparata Oecol.* **4**, 164–171.
Loizzi, R. F. (1966). *Dissertation Abstr.* **27**, 1329B.
Mansour-Bek, J. J. (1932). *Z. Vergleich. Physiol.* **17**, 153–208.
Mansour-Bek, J. J. (1954a). *Tabul. Biol.* (*Hague*) **21**, 75–367.
Mansour-Bek, J. J. (1954b). *Tabul. Biol.* (*Hague*) **21**, 368–382.
Martin, A. L. (1966). *J. Zool.* **148**, 515–525.
Matthews, D. C. (1955). *Pacific Sci.* **9**, 382–386.
Mews, H. H. (1957). *Z. Vergleich. Physiol.* **40**, 345–355.
Ray, D. L., and Julian, J. R. (1952). *Nature* **169**, 32–33.
Roche, A. (1953). *Ann. Sci. Nat. Zool. Biol. Animale* [11] **15**, 347–359.
Rosén, B. (1937). *Z. Vergleich. Physiol.* **24**, 602–612.
Roush, A. H., and Betz, R. F. (1956). *Biochim. Biophys. Acta* **19**, 579–580.
Sather, B. T. (1967). *Pacific Sci.* **21**, 193–209.
Takahashi, T., Morishita, T., and Tachino, S. (1964). *Rept. Fac. Fisheries, Prefect. Univ. Mie* **5**, 127–135.
van den Oord, A. H. A. (1965). Ph.D. Dissertation, Utrecht, Netherlands.
van den Oord, A. H. A. (1966). *Comp. Biochem. Physiol.* **17**, 715–718.
van den Oord, A. H. A., Danielson, H., and Ryhage, R. (1964). *Nature* **203**, 301.
van den Oord, A. H. A., Danielson, H., and Ryhage, R. (1965). *J. Biol. Chem.* **240**, 2242–2247.
van Weel, P. B. (1937). *Pubbl. Staz. Zool. Napoli* **16**, 221–272.
van Weel, P. B. (1955). *Physiol. Zool.* **28**, 40–54.
van Weel, P. B. (1960). *Z. Vergleich. Physiol.* **43**, 567–577.
Vonk, H. J. (1935a). *Z. Vergleich. Physiol.* **21**, 717–738.
Vonk, H. J. (1935b). *Koninkl. Ned. Akad. Wetenschap., Proc.* **38**, 210–215.
Vonk, H. J. (1937). *Biol. Rev.* **12**, 245–284.
Vonk, H. J. (1947). *Bull. Soc. Chim. Biol.* **29**, 94–96.
Vonk, H. J. (1960). In "The Physiology of Crustacea" (T. H. Waterman, ed.), Vol. 1, pp. 291–316. Academic Press, New York.
Vonk, H. J. (1962). *Arch. Intern. Physiol. Biochim.* **70**, 67–85.
Vonk, H. J. (1964). *Comp. Biochem.* **6**, 377–398.
Vonk, H. J., Engel, C., and Engel, C. (1938). *Biochem. Z.* **295**, 171–182.

Yamasaki, K., Usui, T., Iwata, T., Nakasone, S., Hozumi, M., and Takatsuki, S. (1965). *Nature* **205,** 1326–1327.
Yasumasu, I., and Yokoe, Y. (1965). *Sci. Papers Coll. Gen. Educ., Univ. Tokyo* **15,** 95–98.
Yee, H. W. W. (1968). Unpublished data.
Yee, H. W. F.. and James, M. L. (1968). Unpublished data.
Yokoe, Y., and Yasumasu, I. (1964). *Comp. Biochem. Physiol.* **13,** 323–338.
Yonge, C. M. (1924). *Brit. J. Exptl. Biol.* **1,** 343–389.

CHAPTER 4

Digestion in Insects

R. H. Dadd

I. Anatomic Considerations

Food is predominantly macromolecular, whereas its passage into tissues generally necessitates material of small molecular dimensions, a reduction accomplished by digestion. Though absorption of nutrients may occur via the general body surface in soft-bodied aquatic animals (Stephens and Schinske, 1961), and necessarily does so in gutless internal parasites (Volume II of this treatise), in most terrestrial animals having an impervious integument, digestion and absorption are restricted to the alimentary tract. This sequence of organs has other important functions in metabolism and excretion, but it primarily is adapted to reduce food to absorbable form. This entails mechanical operations here dealt with only summarily. The following points, amplified in the reviews of Day and Waterhouse (1953), House (1965), and Wigglesworth (1965), may be noted.

The functions of the alimentary tract can be thought of as comprising several steps, though in particular insects not all are evident or discrete. Grasping, breaking, sucking in, etc., of food and its preliminary trituration is performed with endless variety by variously modified external mouthparts, buccal, and pharyngeal organs. Often lubrication and preliminary chemical degradation is effected by secretions from morphologically various salivary glands. Ingested food may be stored in a crop, an enlargement or outgrowth of the foregut following the pharynx and esophagus. Salivary digestion may here continue, perhaps assisted by digestive juices passed forward from the midgut. Often, particularly in larvae, a crop is absent or insignificant. Further trituration of food may occur in a proventriculus or gizzard, a division of the foregut following the crop, prominent in insects taking hard food, but often absent, or apparent only as a toothed or sievelike valve separating the stomodeal regions from the midgut, ventriculus, or mesenteron. All regions of the foregut are ectodermal and lined with a heavy chitinous intima, suggesting that absorption is unlikely.

The midgut is the principal digestive organ. Basically a tube whose epithelium is one cell-layer thick and unlined by cuticle, it secretes most digestive enzymes, and supposedly absorbs most products of digestion. It often has a variety of outgrowths or ceca, and these, as well as variously differentiated regions of the main ventriculus, may subserve special functions. As is usual in animal epithelia concerned in transport functions, on a microscopic scale the lumen surface of midgut cells consists of minute villi, the striated or brush border, which enormously increase the surface available for the ingress or egress of materials. In many insects, food in the midgut is ensheathed by a delicate, chitinous, peritrophic membrane, a coagulated secretory product formed either by special cells adjacent to the esophageal invagination and passed back as a tube investing the entering food, or formed by delamination of successive membranelles condensing at the striated border of the whole midgut epithelium. Peritrophic membranes are generally assumed to protect the epithelium from abrasive foods, since insects that take liquid food tend to lack them; but this is by no means always so, for they are commonly found in bloodsucking mosquitoes (Waterhouse, 1953; Freyvogel and Staubli, 1965; Freyvogel and Jaquet, 1965; Gander, 1968), and are said to occur in the sap-feeding leafhopper, *Cicandella viridis* (Gouranton and Maillet, 1965). Waterhouse (1957) surmised that peritrophic membranes might facilitate the passage of soluble digested materials to absorptive sites independently of the rearward movement of undigested food within the membrane, as, e.g., in mosquito larvae (Clements, 1963). Such a functional separation is implied by the finding that membranes of some dipterous larvae are readily permeable to small molecules (hexoses and amino acids) but not to polysaccharides and proteins (Zhuzikov, 1964); food would presumably remain within until digested, requiring that enzymes traverse the membrane, which apparently amylase could do in one direction only, from outside in.

Following the midgut, the ectodermal hindgut, cuticle-lined, though usually less heavily chitinized than the foregut, comprises various regions named after analogous parts of vertebrate guts—intestine, ileum, colon, rectum, etc. Since the cuticular intima is often very delicate, the hindgut may well be an additional seat of absorptive processes. About its juncture with the midgut, the excretory Malpighian tubules empty into it. Excreta of insects thus comprise mixed urinary and fecal products, and this material, in its passage through the rectum to be processed into fecal pellets, probably undergoes considerable re-absorption of inorganic ions and water, the rectal pads or papillae being active sites for these important conservational exchanges.

The main concern of this chapter is with the chemical degradation of food during digestion, essentially the functions of salivary and midgut secretions. It needs to be emphasized again that the actual sites of digestion vary among insects. Though saliva generally functions in the buccal cavity and foregut regions, it frequently is ejected externally into or onto the food, as in many adult Diptera and plant-sucking Heteroptera. Similarly, though most other digestive enzymes are secreted by the midgut epithelium, the actual site of maximal digestion may be in the crop, as in some cockroaches and adult dytiscids, or external to the insect, as in dytiscid larvae that inject digestive fluid into their prey via specially modified mandibles.

Five reviews (Day and Waterhouse, 1953; Waterhouse, 1957; Gilmour, 1961; House, 1965; Wigglesworth, 1965) will be drawn on as a convenient summary source of most early information. To conserve space, in what follows these five core references will be cited together simply as: (Reviews).

II. Conditions for Digestive Action

Digestive efficiency is conditional upon the time enzymes and their substrates together occupy a suitable reaction environment and hence on the progress of food through the alimentary tract. This has been studied in many insects by following the movement of colored, X-ray opaque, or isotope-tagged food (Reviews). It is convenient to compare insects that have a large storage organ, usually the crop but sometimes the midgut, with those whose gut is essentially a nonstorage tube. In the former (e.g., cockroaches, carnivorous beetles, adult Diptera) the storage organ tends to be filled or added to by distinct, markedly discontinuous meals. Nonstorage guts are characteristic of so-called continuous feeders, notably many larvae; when critically observed these often prove also to feed intermittently but more frequently and with a relatively high proportion of time spent actually feeding. It is more realistic, therefore, to distinguish between occasional and frequent, rather than discontinuous and continuous feeders.

At optimal temperatures, the passage of food from mouth to hindgut tends to be faster in nonstorage feeders, 1 to 3 hours being usual in various lepidopterous, coleopterous and dipterous larvae and in Orthoptera (Acridids and Phasmids) having reduced crops and simple tubular guts (Reviews; Waterhouse, 1954; Goodhue, 1963; Gangwere, 1966). Filter-feeding mosquito larvae move food rearward by packing more in anteriorly (Dadd, 1968), with clearance times of less than an hour. Transit times for starved storage feeders may initially be as rapid, but thereafter translocation tends to be protracted. The plant bug *Dysdercus* retains sugar solution in its first ventriculus for about 3 to 4 hours and requires 12 to 16 hours for the bulk of the sugar to pass completely through to the rectum (Khan and Ford, 1962). Unfed cockroaches, with an "in line" crop, may at first pass food through to the rectum in 2 hours; in normal feeding, transit times of 8 to 24 hours are recorded for various species, and on starvation food may be retained in the crop for periods up to 2 days (Gangwere, 1966; Englemann, 1968). The carnivorous water beetle *Dytiscus marginalis* may still retain material in its crop a week after feeding to repletion (Dadd, 1956). Biting flies engorge blood directly into the midgut, which then functions both as storage organ and digestion site; in mosquitoes and tsetse flies, single blood meals may be retained, undergoing digestion for several days (Langley, 1966; Staubli *et al.*, 1966). One full meal lasts the blood-sucking bugs *Rhodnius prolixus* and *Cimex lectularius* a whole larval instar of several days duration (Friend *et al.*, 1965; Tawfik, 1968).

Presumably digestive efficiency would be greater the slower the translocation of food through the alimentary canal, but data specifically on this point are lacking. Digestibility coefficients, determined for whole natural foods with many insects, depend on many factors besides efficiency and duration of enzyme action. Certainly no pattern connecting apparent digestibility with frequent, as opposed to occasional, feeders can readily be inferred from the data exhaustively tabulated and discussed by Waldbauer (1968). However, there is little doubt that digestion must be very inefficient in many frequently feeding larvae having rapid food transit times, since much apparently unchanged food material is often noted in the feces of various caterpillars, grasshoppers, and mosquito larvae (Wigglesworth, 1965; Gangwere, 1966; Clements, 1963).

The sensitivity of enzymes to hydrogen-ion concentration has prompted many measurements of pH in the various regions of insect alimentary tracts. Of the two methods commonly employed, the inclusion of indicators with food provides a complete pH map of the undisturbed contents of the gut, but it is imprecise, and inapplicable with colored gut contents; potentiometric measurement with a microelectrode offers precision, but, if not recorded rapidly, exposure of gut fluid entrains errors due to changes in composition. Bearing in mind that these faults make for approximations, the pH data, recorded from the alimentary tracts of about 150 species, discussed, and partially tabulated by House (1965), allow certain generalizations.

The majority of all recordings fall within the range pH 6–8. Foregut pH varies considerably between and within species, from a mild acidity of about pH 4.5 to slight alkalinity, largely reflecting the differing pH of foodstuffs, or the action on particular foods of foregut bacteria, such as those that ferment starchy foods in the roach crop. In most insects the midgut pH is stable and generally unaffected by food, indicating efficient buffering by the midgut secretion. However, in mosquitoes the well-buffered blood meal maintains its own pH against that of the unfed midgut for long periods. Of the scores of species examined, most have midgut pH values near neutrality, excepting lepidopterous larvae, whose midguts are highly alkaline (about pH 10), in accord with the characteristically high pH optima of their midgut digestive enzymes. Insects with morphologically subdivided midguts (e.g., many plant-feeding Hemiptera) may have different pH reactions in the various zones (Khan and Ford, 1967). Some dipterous larvae (*Stomoxys, Phormia, Sarcophaga, Musca,* and *Calliphora*) possess an unusually acid (pH 2.8–4.0) midgut zone, doubtless related to the possession of an acid-acting proteinase (Labremont *et al.,* 1959; Greenberg, 1968); as neither food pH nor the presence of bacteria affected pH values in *Stomoxys* and *Calliphora,* acidity is evidently maintained by an intrinsic buffering system in the digestive secretion, probably involving phosphoric acid. Clear-cut differences in pH sometimes occur within midguts that are apparently simple in structure; the anterior acid and posterior alkaline regions of the *Tenebrio molitor* larval midgut are associated with histological differences and differential secretion of proteolytic and amylolytic enzymes (Dadd, 1954). Early attempts to identify buffering systems in the insect midgut are discussed by Day and Waterhouse (1953). Phosphates occur substantially in the digestive fluids of some insects, and buffering systems involving them were considered operative in the bee, but in several lepidopterous larvae buffering is not associated with phosphates, even if they are substantially present. In general, buffering probably depends on complex systems of weak organic and amino acids, various salts besides phosphates, and proteins.

Though a few insects can digest wool or feathers, proteinases of keratin-digesting larvae exhibit few unusual features, except for a relative insensitivity to cysteine inhibition, and, *in vitro,* attack wool poorly or not at all. The strong alkalinity of the midgut of the clothes moth larva *Tineola bisselliella* might weaken the stability of the cystine disulfide linkages between polypeptide chains that account for the indigestibility of keratin. However, as dermestid larvae with neutral midguts also digest keratin, alkalinity clearly is not crucial, but merely an incidental lepidoteran feature. The many studies contributing to an understanding of keratin digestion are summarized by Waterhouse (1957). A common feature of the tineids, dermestids, and bird-infesting Mallophaga that alone digest hair or feathers is the unusual reducing condition maintained in the midgut. Whereas other insects tested have slightly positive redox potentials, the keratin-digesters all have negative potentials in the range −100 to −300 mV. This is associated with poor midgut tracheation, although the precise factors that maintain the low potential are unknown. With such negative redox potentials, disulfide bonds in keratin are rapidly reduced and the unstabilized protein is then attacked readily by ordinary tryptic proteinases.

III. Digestive Enzymes

Since most organic materials are eaten by insects of some sort, and in contrast to such groups as the arachnids, digestion is mainly if not entirely extracellular (Barrington, 1962), an extensive listing of digestive enzymes is attributed to the class as a whole. Their characterization has generally been primitive, often no more than the demonstration that selected substrates were lysed by crude homogenates or extracts of gut tissues, enzymes being designated according to the substrate. It is not always clear whether digestive exoenzymes, endogenous tissue enzymes, or enzymes of the food are in question. Nor does measured lytic activity necessarily denote just one enzyme; unrefined homogenates or extracts will contain multiple enzymes, and the degradation product finally recorded may result from a sequence of hydrolyses.

The core reviews amply confirm that insects do indeed possess complements of digestive enzymes capable of lysing the main classes of nutrients in their various foods. On the whole, enzymes detected, and their relative strengths, reflect reasonably well the type of food normally taken. Larval insects and adults that eat complete foods tend to have full complements of proteinases, lipases, and carbohydrases, in contrast to the meager complement of some holometabolous adults of limited diet, such as nectar-feeding Lepidoptera possessing only a sucrase. Carnivores generally have predominantly proteolytic and lipolytic digestive fluids deficient in amylases and saccharases, whereas omnivores and herbivores usually possess powerful and varied carbohydrases, sometimes including unusual enzymes (pectinases, hemicellulases, cellulases) capable of hydrolyzing various structural polysaccharides of plant origin, particularly notable in wood-eating insects.

In spite of a general complementarity between enzymes and food there are many anomalies. Phytophagous Hemiptera and lepidopterous larvae may be deficient in amylase and thus unable to utilize the starch commonly occurring in their food (Ito *et al.*, 1962; Mukaiyama *et al.*, 1964; Khan and Ford, 1967). Sucrase and protease are predominant enzymes in female biting flies that take both nectar and blood meals, yet the nonblood-feeding males may also possess protease (Yang and Davies, 1968a). Some apparent anomalies can be rationalized. Wood-eating insects that do not secrete cellulase often have cellulolytic symbionts (Rössler, 1961). Substantial amylolytic activity in the guts of bloodsucking flies may derive from enzymes of the ingested blood (Yang and Davies, 1968b). The amylase sometimes detected in aphids, whose food, phloem sap, lacks polysaccharides, is almost certainly produced by bacteria that adventitiously enter from the plant surface (Srivastava and Auclair, 1962a, 1963a). Phloem sap contains free amino acids and lacks proteins, and in accord with this, most aphids examined lack proteinases (though they may have di- and tripeptidases); an exception, *Viteus vitifolii*, feeds on parenchyma cells, not phloem tissue (Ehrhardt, 1962; Srivastava and Auclair, 1963b; Schäller, 1968).

Besides defining the gross lytic capabilities of various digestive organs, crude determinations have adequately measured relative secretory activity in relation to feeding, metamorphosis, egg development, differential secretion, and mechanisms regulating secretion. However, without further characterization, little can be said about specific enzymes in the context of general enzymology. Purified or crystalline enzymes have scarcely been approached with insect material other than for trehalase, which is probably not a true digestive enzyme (Wyatt, 1967). Otherwise, partial characterization may be achieved with standardized extracts in terms of pH and temperature optima, inhibitor and activator effects, kinetic data, and the narrowing of substrate specificities. Increasing use of such criteria in recent years allows a more precise characterization of some of the commoner types of insect enzymes.

Most digestive enzymes are secreted by the midgut epithelium and the following sections on enzyme characteristics largely concerns them. However, in much work that used whole gut extracts (i.e., gut tissue plus its contents) salivary enzymes may quite possibly have been accounted to the midgut. In Orthoptera particularly, the crop or its contents has often been studied, probably yielding mixtures of salivary and midgut enzymes. Salivary enzymes of special interest are considered in a subsequent section.

A. AMYLASES

Two major categories of amylases are recognized. Saccharogenic, exo- or β-amylases remove maltose from the ends of the poly-1,4-glucosidic chains of starch and are best known from plants and yeasts. Amyloclastic, dextrinogenic, endo- or α-amylases randomly attack glucosidic links and disrupt the interior of the starch molecule, only comparatively slowly increasing maltose concentration. Few attempts have been made to distinguish α- and β-amylases in insects. The frequent observation of chloride activation, an α characteristic, suggest that insect enzymes, like the better studied salivary and pancreatic amylases of mammals, are predominantly of the endoamylase type (Gilmour, 1961; Evans and Payne, 1964), though both α- and β-amylases are considered to occur in silkworm digestive juice (Ito *et al.*, 1962; Mukaiyama *et al.*, 1964). Attempts to characterize *Tenebrio* amylase in terms of temperature optima, chloride activation, and effects of known inhibitors of β-amylase (cysteine, glutathione, $HgCl_2$, $CuSO_4$, and ascorbic acid) were inconclusive (Applebaum *et al.*, 1961), but action-pattern studies with amylopectin, β-amylase limit dextrin, and glycogen indicated a typical α-amylase; curiously, when *Tenebrio* feeds on wheat grain, this enzyme is largely inhibited by a wheat α-amylase inhibitor, the major digestion of starch then depending on the β-amylase of the ingested wheat (Applebaum, 1964). The same wheat inhibitor completely suppressed *in vitro* activity of *Prodenia litura* amylase (Applebaum *et al.*, 1964b). Most insect amylases have slightly acid to neutral pH optima, but those of Lepidoptera, whose midguts characteristically are alkaline, function optimally at about pH 10. Salivary amylases of three of several Heteroptera recently studied had markedly acid pH optima between 3.5 and 5.0; chloride activated most, but not all, of these amylases, tending to have most effect at nonoptimal pH and thereby changing the pH optimum (Hori, 1968, 1969a,b, 1970).

B. GLYCOSIDASES

Current classifications of sugar-splitting enzymes are based on the view that specificity depends largely on the nature of the monosaccharide contributing its reducing group to the glycosidic bond, and the α or β form of this linkage. Thus, D-glucose donating a reducing group in α linkage to a complex sugar or glucoside would be detached by an α-D-glucosidase, galactose in β linkage by an β-galactosidase, and so on. This concept implies that a single enzyme may split many substrates;

α-glucosidase, for example, might hydrolyze all α-glucosides regardless of the moiety to which glucose was linked. Though an oversimplification, digestive glycosidases in insects are often so interpreted.

The commonest oligosaccharides of foods are sucrose and maltose (the latter principally a product of digestion of food starch or glycogen). Both have α-glucosidic bonds (as also do trehalose, turanose, melezitose) and might therefore be hydrolyzed by the same α-glucosidases. Such an enzyme is commonly demonstrated in insect digestive juices, and can be inferred from tests of the nutritive values of sugars (see Chapter 2). However, evidence in many cases indicates α-glucosidases of narrower specificity. Gut extracts of *Tenebrio* and *Lucilia* hydrolyzing maltose, sucrose, and trehalose were inactive with α-methylglucoside, and glycerol differentially inhibited maltase and sucrase activity of roach gut extracts (Gilmour, 1961). Specific trehalases unable to attack maltose and sucrose are well characterized from midgut tissue extracts (Wyatt, 1967). Work with the locust *Schistocerca gregaria* exemplifies the critical use of this approach to glycosidase identification (Evans and Payne, 1964). Besides a specific trehalase, four oligosaccharidases are postulated on the basis of substrates hydrolyzed: a general α-glucosidase (hydrolyzing maltose, sucrose, trehalose in part, melezitose, isomaltose, α-methylglucoside); a β-glucosidase (cellobiose, gentiobiose, salicin); an α-galactosidase (melibiose, raffinose); and a β-galactosidase (lactose, o-nitrophenol-galactoside. Hydrolysis of sucrose and raffinose by a β-fructofuranosidase is refuted by several arguments: a single pH optimum for sucrose hydrolysis the same as that for α-glucosidase action on α-methylglucoside and melezitose; no action on inulin, which probably would be cleaved by a β-fructosidase; competitive inhibition of sucrose hydrolysis by added glucose or α-glucosides but not by fructose or raffinose; and no hydrolysis of raffinose by extracts (of salivary glands) deficient in α-galactosidase. Locusts also possess a β-glucuronidase in their crop fluid, but its function is not clearly digestive and it may derive from bacteria. Similar groups of saccharases are inferred in the scarabaeid larvae *Sericesthis geminata* (Soo Hoo and Dudziński, 1967), in five species of grasshopper (Davis, 1963) (with the suggestion that sucrase, maltase, and trehalase may all be specific α-glucosidases), in the silkworm (Horie, 1959), and in various species of roach (Ehrhardt and Voss, 1962; Fisk and Rao, 1964). In these and other (Banks, 1963) roaches, β-fructosidase is said to be present, as it reasonably surely is in silkworms (inulin lysis) and the adult blowfly, *Calliphora erythrocephala,* showing double pH optima for sucrose hydrolysis (Evans, 1956).

With these few exceptions, insect sucrases (invertases), like those of other animals, are considered α-glucosidases, as distinct from the plant and yeast β-fructosidase invertases (Waterhouse, 1957). Gilmour (1961) places greatest weight on the nature of the transglycolyzation observed with insect invertase preparations. Transglycolyzation oligosaccharides were first noted for insects in excreta of aphids, coccids, and a blowfly (Auclair, 1963) and have since been extensively studied *in vitro* using enzyme preparations from aphids, heteropterous plant bugs, biting flies, and grasshoppers (Srivastava and Auclair, 1962b; Saxena and Gandhi, 1966; Payne and Evans, 1964; Yang and Davies, 1968c). Unlike plant transglycolysis, in which fructoinvertase transfers fructose units onto sucrose, the insect invertases transfer glucose units. With sucrose as substrate, the commonest products are the trisaccharide glucosucrose (= maltosyl fructoside = fructomaltose), formed by addition of glucose to the C-4 position of the glucose end of the parent sucrose, and melezitose, formed by the attachment of glucose at the C-3 of the fructose end. Higher saccharides may then be formed by successive addition of glucose units. Although insect transglycolyzation indicates the presence of α-glucosidases only, the existence of two series of products clearly denotes functionally different α-glucosidases.

Few other insect glycosidases have been characterized beyond their optimal pH for lysing an appropriate substrate (Reviews). Kinetics and pH criteria indicate similarities between β-glucosidase from silkworm and the better known plant enzymes (Ito and Tanaka, 1959). Using a sensitive fluorimetric technique, Robinson (1964) found β-glucosidase, β-glucuronidase, β-galactosidase, and α-arabinosidase activities in insects of several orders, and he discussed whether these activities really represent different enzymes. Except for crop fluid from locusts and roaches the enzyme extracts were from whole insects, and thus not necessarily pertinent to alimentary digestion.

C. OTHER CARBOHYDRASES

Cellulose is undoubtedly utilized by many wood-eating insects, and controversy centers on how digestion occurs. Some beetles (mainly Cerambycidae) and the silver fish *Ctenolepisma* secrete cellulase, which otherwise comes from symbiotic or associated microorganisms (Rössler, 1961; Soo Hoo and Dudziński, 1967). Davis (1963) detected no cellulase in five species of grasshopper, but Evans and Payne (1964) considered that the locust *Schistocerca* secreted low levels of both a true cellulase and a β-1,4-polyglucosidase (acting only on partially degraded cellulase products) in its gut tissues, though bacterial commensals admittedly contributed to the overall cellulolytic action. The work of several authors on various roaches has been critically reviewed by Wharton *et al.*

(1965), who consider that except for salivary secretion of cellulase in *Periplaneta*, all other cellulolytic activities are probably ascribable to bacteria. Cellobiase (β-glucosidase), needed to complete the breakdown of cellulose to glucose, commonly occurs in these insects.

As all insects digest their chitinous cuticle during ecdysis, a priori they must produce a chitinase in the ecdysial fluid. Chitinase of nonbacterial origin has recently been demonstrated in the midgut of the roach, *Periplaneta*, together with a β-acetylglucosaminidase (lysing chitobiose and phenyl acetylglucosaminide) distinguishable from the various glucosidases of the midgut (Powning and Irzykiewicz, 1963, 1964). The function of these enzymes is equivocal; if they are digestive, and secreted into the gut lumen, it is difficult to conceive how the delicate chitinous peritrophic membranes could survive.

D. Proteases

Proteolytic activity is generally detected if suitable tests are applied to insect midgut extracts. Associated peptidases undoubtedly, in many cases, contribute to "proteinase" activity, especially when determined by methods that measure increases in end products of overall proteolysis. Hence, many attempts to characterize "proteinase" in terms of inhibitors and activators known to have characteristic effects with defined mammalian enzymes are of dubious meaning. Most studies, however, agree in finding optimal proteolysis at neutral to alkaline pH, to this extent, more closely resembling the tryptic and chymotryptic, rather than peptic activity of mammalian digestive proteinases (Gilmour, 1961). This general finding was confirmed in an extensive early study of midgut proteinases of several insects (measured by a method based on disappearance of substrate and therefore more definitely dealing with proteinases as such), a supporting criterion being insensitivity to cyanide inhibition, a characteristic of trypsins (Powning *et al.*, 1951).

The difficulties inherent in attempting characterization of proteinases in unpurified, nonfractionated, gut extracts will be apparent from the electrophoretic demonstration of multiple proteolytic enzymes in single preparations. Electrophoretic proteinase zymograms showed six distinct bands for silkworm digestive juice (Yoshitake, 1967). In both *Stomoxys* and *Musca*, three different trypsin-like enzymes were separated (Patterson and Fisk, 1958; Patel and Richards, 1960). Three distinct enzymes were concentrated chromatographically from *Tenebrio* protease; two exopeptidases were considered (substrate specificity and activation tests) to be a carboxypeptidase B (hydrolyzing terminal lysine and arginine residues only) and an aminotripeptidase; the third, a proteinase, had pH, kinetic, inhibition, and activation characteristics, and an activity pattern with polylysine, all essentially similar to bovine trypsin (Applebaum *et al.*, 1964a). Both *Tenebrio* and *Tribolium* proteinases are, like trypsin, inactivated by soybean proteinase inhibitors (Birk and Applebaum, 1960; Birk *et al.*, 1962). Crop fluid of *Locusta migratoria* was submitted to electrophoresis, and the separated proteins were tested for enzyme activity with substrates considered indicative for mammalian trypsin, chymotrypsin, and leucine aminopeptidase (benzoylarginine nitranilide, carboxypropionylphenylalanine *p*-nitranilide, leucine *p*-nitranilide, respectively) yielding two different tryptic proteinases and the dipeptidase (Freeman, 1967); a dipeptidase acting on glycylglycine had previously been noted free in *Locusta* gut fluid (Khan, 1962). Proteolytic optima at pH 5.5, 7.5, and 9.5, for midgut extracts of two species of adult mosquito, suggest multiple enzymes, and positive hydrolysis of N-benzoyl-L-arginine ethyl ester and N-benzoyl-L-tyrosine ethyl ester indicated esterase specificities resembling those of mammalian trypsin and chymotrypsin, respectively (Gooding, 1966a). With the carnivorous beetle *Pterostichus melanarius* the same esterase specificity tests and partial chromatographic separation in various systems indicated at least one chymotryptic and two tryptic proteinases that, in terms of inhibitor sensitivities, were similar to bovine chymotrypsin and trypsin (Gooding and Huang, 1969). Rao and Fisk (1965), in work on the roach, *Nauphoaeta cineria*, and Yang and Davies (1968a), in a comparison of proteinase activities in various species of black flies (Simuliidae), used *p*-tosyl-L-arginine methyl ester·HCl as substrate, standardized against crystalline mammalian trypsin; by taking advantage of the highly specific esterase activity of trypsin for this substrate, they singled out for measurement only proteinases having this particular trypsin-like feature. Besides substrate specificity, most recent studies include data on pH and temperature optima, kinetic (Michaelis) constants, and tests of various potential inhibitors and activators. Excepting the high pH optima for the enzymes of Lepidoptera, about pH 11 for the silkworm proteinase (Horie *et al.*, 1963), the data are, in general, consonant with the view that the principal insect proteinases are close in character to mammalian trypsins (Gooding and Huang, 1969). Bearing in mind the evident complexity of the "protease" content of insect enzyme extracts, attempts at closer characterization of insect "trypsins" seem pointless without separation and purification of individual enzymes.

Occasionally proteolysis at rather acid pH has been detected. For example, a gut extract of the water scorpion *Laccotrephis maculatus* had a proteolytic pH optimum at 5.5 as well as at the more usual 8.5 (Khan, 1964b). The intracellular catheptic proteinases of mammals function at pH 4–5, and such findings in insects are generally ascribed, purely on this account, to similar "cathepsins." Until recently it appeared that no proteinases active in the extremely acid conditions (pH 2–3) essential for mammalian pepsin occurred in insects. However, proteolysis by midgut extracts acting on substrate buffered at pH 2–3 has been demonstrated for certain dipterous larvae (*Musca, Stomoxys, Calliphora*), in one case for axenically reared larvae that could not have been contaminated by microorganisms (Lambremont *et al.*, 1959; Fraser *et al.*, 1961). All these flies have been shown to have an acid midgut region of about pH 3 (Greenberg, 1968). Without further characterization it cannot be said whether these enzymes resemble true pepsins other than in the pH at which they function optimally.

Collagen and keratin are structural proteins resistant to mammalian trypsins but are digested by certain insects. The excreta of sterile blowfly maggots lyse collagen, apparently due to a collagenase separable chromatographically from their principal proteinase (Gilmour, 1961). The dependence of the keratin-digesting ability of certain insects upon their negative midgut redox potential has already been discussed. Under reducing conditions ordinary proteinases can hydrolyze wool, and conversely, in the early studies, *Tineola* proteinase failed to hydrolyze wool in aerobic incubations. However, using partially purified enzyme preparations from *Tineola*, slow digestion of wool occurs *in vitro* (about 30% in 24 hours, as compared with 80% in 2 hours with reducing agents such as thioglycolic acid present), indicating that this proteinase does, in fact, possess unusual "keratinase" properties (Powning and Irzykiewica, 1962).

E. LIPASES

Little can be added to Gilbert's account (1967) of fat digestion in insects. Midgut and salivary extracts frequently contain lipases or esterases; the distinction between enzymes cleaving insoluble long-chain glycerides (e.g., triolein) and those acting on short-chain esters (e.g., tributyrin, ethyl butyrate) is not absolute, and, in the early work particularly, was not considered. Thus, supposed digestive lipases may sometimes be among the several esterases known from insect midgut tissues (Gouranton, 1968; Eguchi and Sugimota, 1965) and of uncertain, not necessarily digestive, function. The best characterized of insect digestive lipases, from the roach, shows both acid and alkaline pH optima (Gilbert, 1967). This indication that there is more than one enzyme was subsequently supported by the recent separation of six carboxylic esterases by zone electrophoresis of *Periplaneta* gastric secretion, of which one was purified and shown to hydrolyze tripalmitin at rates comparable with the lipolytic activity of Gilbert's work (Cook *et al.*, 1969).

A still unsolved problem concerns the unique ability of waxmoth larvae to digest and utilize beeswax. Reviewing much early work, Niemierko (1959) notes that in *Galleria mellonella* about half the rapidly emulsified ingested wax is utilized, both saponifiable (fatty acids) and unsaponifiable components (largely alcohols from wax esters). This is broadly confirmed by recent comparative chromatographic analyses of ingested wax and excreta (Young, 1964). In the gut, alcohols supposedly are converted to fatty acids, whose absorption is thought to involve their conversion to phospholipid, which appears substantially in the emulsified gut contents though absent from wax. Niemierko considers these transformations to be accomplished by larval enzymes, though others ascribe them to cerolytic bacteria. Enzymes hydrolyzing olive oil, lecithin, cholesterol esters, and tributyrin are reported from *Galleria* gut extracts, but *in vitro* hydrolysis of wax, affirmed by some, is denied by others (Waterhouse, 1957). Pure beeswax or myricin (a wax fraction consisting of esters of palmitic acid and myricyl alcohol) is a sufficient energy source in synthetic diets for *Galleria*. Assuming utilization involves hydrolysis to fatty acids and alcohols, these would be expected to replace adequately wax or myricin in diets; yet simple acids (palmitic, stearic, etc.), alcohols (cetyl, ceryl, myricyl), or palmitic acid esters (palmityl palmitate, tripalmitin) were not effective substitutes for wax (Dadd, 1966), suggesting some highly specific condition (or enzyme) requiring the presence of long-chain esters for proper absorption.

F. Salivary Enzymes

With the scant tissues available, work on salivary digestion tends to be comparatively perfunctory and enzymes little characterized beyond the lysing of particular substrates. Though information is slight beside that for the midgut, it should be noted that enzymes attributed to other gut regions sometimes may have come from ingested saliva. Strong amylase in the roach crop is largely salivary (Wigglesworth, 1965), and much ventricular digestion is due to salivary enzymes in *Dysdercus* (Saxena, 1963). Besides those insects (e.g., many Coleoptera) that lack or have vestigial salivary glands, some salivas, as in many biting flies, lack digestive enzymes (Wigglesworth, 1965). Others have complements approaching the complexity of the midgut secretions; the silkworm, for example, has proteinase, amylase, and saccharases able to hydrolyze sucrose, maltose, trehalose, cellobiose, mellibiose, and lactose (Mukaiyama, 1961). However, salivary enzymes tend to be fewer than those of the midgut, even allowing for the likelihood of some being missed by tests too insensitive for the small quantities of material available. It is usually possible to relate enzyme pattern to the type of food taken, as in the correlation of salivary amylase with fungus eating in various ants (Ayre, 1967). A view once current held that enzymes might occur sequentially with proteinases and polysaccharases in the saliva, and a full range of glycosidases and peptidases only in the midgut; with strong salivary amylase, and glycosidases only in the midgut, carbohydrate digestion in *Periplaneta* can be so interpreted, but there is otherwise little sustaining evidence.

Because the feeding of plant-sucking Hemiptera often results in characteristic phytopathologies (toxic lesions, galls, virus diseases), their salivas have engendered a special interest. Miles' recent review on insect secretions in plants (1969) deals substantially with this topic. Extensive complements of digestive enzymes are found in some phytophagous Hemiptera. *Oncopeltus fasciatus* has proteinase, amylase, esterase (lipase), and an invertase (Salkeld, 1960; Feir and Beck, 1961); and peptidases (but not proteinases), lipase, amylase, and α- and β-glucosidases are recorded for *Dysdercus* spp. (Saxena, 1958; Ford, 1962; Khan and Ford, 1967), but commonly a more limited number are present, especially in phloem-feeding aphids and leafhoppers whose food requires little digestion (Nuorteva, 1958; Auclair, 1963; Schäller, 1968). During feeding, saliva is pumped into the plant tissues, suggesting preoral digestion, especially if, as with *Oncopeltus*, dry seed material is reduced rapidly to a mush (Miles, 1959, 1967a). From a study of rates of ingestion by *Dysdercus* from solutions, gels, and seeds, Saxena (1963) concluded that breakdown of plant tissues was principally mechanical, significant digestion starting only in the first midgut ventriculus after reingestion of saliva and plant debris. Whatever the location, the salivary enzymes of these lygaeids clearly are potent in digestion, and it is noteworthy that with a high fat content in the seeds which are their food, they have a strong salivary lipase.

Although poorly supplied with digestive enzymes, many aphids possess a salivary pectinase, specifically α-1,4-polygalacturonase. Species with pectinase penetrate the host plant intercellularly, suggesting that the enzyme might hydrolyze pectic components of the middle lamella to facilitate stylet insertion (McAllen and Adams, 1961). Pectinases are recorded in one other homopteran, a lygaeid, and several species of Miridae, but are absent from the majority of Homoptera Aucchenorrhyncha and Heteroptera examined (Laurema and Nuorteva, 1961). Strong and Kruitwagen (1968) consider *Lygus* "macerating enzyme" to include a pectinase complex of exo- and endopolygalacturonases and pectin methylesterases. Presumably pectinases have evolved sporadically as an aid to the mechanical problems haustellate insects may have in penetrating or liquefying plant tissues, and a similar function may be ascribed to the factor that digests cellulose in the saliva of some aphids (Adams and Drew, 1965).

Certain other specialized salivary components are also connected with mechanical peculiarities of haustellate feeding. When plant bugs insert their stylets, many (Homoptera, Heteroptera Pentatamorpha, but not Cimicomorpha) deposit rapidly coagulating proteinaceous material to form a collar supporting the rostrum where it abuts on the plant surface, and often an internal tube, the salivary sheath, which solidifies around the stylets as they penetrate the plant tissues, supposedly preventing exudation of plant juices from the stylet insertion (Auclair, 1963). A watery saliva which can be ejected independently contains the digestive enzymes, if present, secreted from the posterior lobe of the complex salivary gland, and sometimes, especially in high humidity, diluted by the "excretion" of water from the accessory gland. Lipoprotein sheath material arises in separate lobes, and coagulation depends on the formation of hydrogen and disulfide bonding upon ejection, such bonding being prevented within the intact gland, supposedly by delicately balanced dielectric and reducing conditions poised by a variety of "companion materials" (nongelling protein, many free amino acids), assisted by spatial separation of sulfhydryl-donating compounds, an equilibrium that is lost upon ejection and exposure to air. This outline is based mainly on studies on Heteroptera (Miles, 1959, 1960, 1964a, 1967a,b), but essentially similar mechanisms are indicated for aphids (Miles, 1965). Additional stability is perhaps conferred upon the coagulum by quinone tanning, the quinones being formed, by polyphenol oxidase secreted from the accessory gland, from tyrosine and dihydroxyphenylalanine occurring among the "companion materials." However, phenoloxidase occurs also in the salivary glands of many Cimicomorpha that produce no sheath material or are carnivorous (Miles, 1964b), prompting the speculation that perhaps salivary phenoloxidases preceded the evolution of the stylet sheath and had as their basic function the production of pharmacologically active substances—toxic neuroamines in predators, auxins in plant bugs—that might variously immobilize or improve potential food.

Many have sought gall-producing substances in plant bug salivas. Free amino acids, often found in substantial amounts, were said to be cecidogenic (Anders, 1958), but their occurrence and galling effects are variable and dependent upon diet (Schäller, 1960, 1963; Kloft, 1960; Nuorteva and Laurema, 1961a; Miles, 1967b); nonmetabolizable materials such as D-amino acids appear preferentially in saliva if fed or injected, suggesting a subsidiary excretory function for the salivary gland (Schäller, 1968). Certain amino acids, given the presence of phenoloxidase, could give rise to the plant auxin, 3-indoleacetic acid, known to occur in the salivas of some plant bugs (Nuorteva, 1962; Schäller, 1965), supposedly derived from ingested plant material. Synthesis of indoleacetic acid from tyrosine and tryptophan is accomplished by salivary tissue of a lygaeid *Elasmolomus sordidus,* and this normally noncecidogenic insect was rendered temporarily cecidogenic by injecting excess precursors of indoleacetic acid (Miles and Lloyd, 1967; Miles, 1968). Miles postulates that quinones formed from tyrosine and dopa by salivary polyphenoloxidase react with tryptophan, also commonly present in salivas, to produce indoleacetic acid, and suggests that all Hemiptera potentially have the apparatus for auxin production.

IV. Regulation of Secretion

Early ideas about secretory regulation rested on histological features interpreted as digestive secretion. Though such interpretations may be invalid, they nevertheless led to a widely held view that many insects, particularly frequent (continuous) feeders, secreted digestive enzymes continuously and automatically, while others, typified by predatory dragonfly nymphs and beetles, were held to secrete only in response to their more occasional meals. A related question was whether foods of different composition might induce differential secretion of enzymes patterned to the substrates available, a phenomenon now known to oc-cur, in some mammals, with pancreatic trypsin and amylase (Schramm, 1967).

The following discussion will show that diverse mechanisms for regu-lating digestive secretion are to be found among insects. Unfortunately comparisons are fogged by a general failure to distinguish between synthesis of enzymes in the tissues and discharge. Digestive juices will usually be complex mixtures of several enzymes, buffering substances, peritrophic membrane precursors, etc., synthesis and discharge of which might be variously interlinked and under various regulatory control mechanisms. Day and Powning (1949) provide a critique of speculations on secretion and their histological basis. Although correlated enzyme and histological study of the beetle *Dytiscus* showed that feeding-in-duced discharge of proteolytic enzymes from the midgut epithelium was accompanied by profound cellular disruption (Duspiva, 1939), in the roach *Blattella,* Day and Powning found maximal protease and amy-lase to coincide with a histological picture of an apparently quiescent midgut epithelium; apparent disruption, hitherto considered secretion, coincided with low enzyme activity in unfed roaches, and was ascribed to cell senescence. Subsequent work correlating histology and enzyme measurements confirms that histological appearances, alone, are a poor guide to enzyme production (Khan and Ford, 1962; Couch and Mills, 1968), although in particular cases histological and cytological characteristics can be related to secretion (Day, 1951; Dadd, 1954; Bertram and Bird, 1961; Staubli *et al.*, 1966; Gander, 1968).

A sharp distinction between automatic secretion in frequent feeders and discontinuous secretion in insects taking occasional meals cannot be sustained, for all quantitative enzyme studies that have sought a relationship between secretion and feeding show elevated enzyme activity after taking food. Once it is understood that so-called continuous feeders do not usually feed all the time (it is their *option* to feed that is continuous), the evolution of some degree of secretory regulation in relation to food ingestion might be expected as generally making for efficiency.

Frequent feeders often exhibit limited and gradual fluctuations in enzyme activity, largely because substantial enzyme activity occurs in their midgut at all times (excluding pupation) whether fed or not (Day and Powning, 1949; Khan and Ford, 1962; Applebaum *et al.*, 1964b; Rao and Fisk, 1965). Where tissue enzyme and that in the midgut contents are distinguished, most is found in the gut contents, persisting during starvation even when tissue activity becomes low. This was so for amylase in *Prodenia* (Applebaum *et al.*, 1964b), protease in *Tenebrio* and *Locusta* (Dadd, 1956; Khan, 1963), and invertase in *Locusta* (Khan, 1964a), suggesting that synthesis of enzyme within the epithelium and discharge of definitive digestive fluid into the gut lumen are interdependent processes. In sharp contrast, *Dytiscus* accumulates substantial intracellular protease during starvation, at which time the gut lumen is devoid of enzyme, to be discharged, on feeding, with massive cellular disruption (Duspiva, 1939; Dadd, 1956).

Most other occasional feeders that have been studied are adult flies, attention being centered on protease secretion in response to the proteinaceous meals necessary for egg development. The moderate level of protease in the midgut of female *Calliphora* maintained on sugar-water is markedly increased when meat is fed (Thomsen and Møller, 1963). Midgut proteinase increases in several biting flies on taking a blood meal. In the mosquitoes *Aedes aegypti* and *Culex fatigans*, unfed adults have essentially no midgut proteinase; a blood meal rapidly stimulates its secretion to maximal levels in 18 to 24 hours, depending on temperature (Fisk and Shambaugh, 1952; Gooding, 1966b). Proteinase is absent from the newly emerged tsetse fly *Glossina morsitans*, but it automatically develops to a low level in the teneral fly; a blood meal raises the level fourfold during the day following feeding (Langley,

1966). It is not known how proteinase is distributed between midgut tissue and lumen in the mosquitoes, but in *Glossina*, at no time could activity be found in tissue, suggesting either that it is discharged continuously as synthesized, as in the frequent feeders, or that an inactive zymogen occurs in the tissues, requiring activation by a kinase from elsewhere. Against the latter view, it should be noted that none of the several attempts to show activation of insect proteinases, analogous to the activation of trypsinogen to trypsin, have succeeded, whether using mammalian enterokinase or extracts of various parts of the insect (Fisk, 1950; Fisk and Shambaugh, 1952; Gilmour, 1961). Several species of blackfly (Simuliidae) already have proteinase in the midgut 1 hour after emerging from the pupa; a blood meal trebles the level in 6 to 9 hours (Yang and Davies, 1968a).

In blackflies, meals of sucrose fail to raise the level of protease above that which develops automatically on emergence from the pupa, and though sucrose slightly increases proteinase in *Aedes*, the effect is transient and negligible after a few hours. This might be considered evidence of differential secretion elicited only by the appropriate substrate, the proteins of blood, but in both *Aedes* and simuliids no increase in sucrase occurs on feeding sucrose solutions, though definite sucrase secretion follows blood feeding, transient in *Aedes*, but elevated for the duration of blood digestion in simuliid females (Fisk and Shambaugh, 1954; Yang and Davies, 1968c). These effects in the blackflies can be accounted for by supposing that midgut secretion of both enzymes is a unified process, intensified in response to a stimulus given only by some component(s) of blood. In *Aedes*, however, the different time courses for the elevation of proteinase and sucrase indicate differential secretion, but not, apparently, in response to substrate differences, for blood, again, stimulates secretion of both enzymes. Since blood meals generally proceed straight to the midgut in bloodsucking flies, whereas sucrose solutions are stored in the diverticula for later gradual release, it seems possible that the stimulus releasing midgut secretion is dependent on events that bring about the selection of direct midgut routing, amongst them being gustation of specific blood chemicals, identified for several mosquitoes as adenylic acid or related nucleotides (see Chapter 2). It would be of interest to determine whether salines containing adenylic acid that were engorged directly to the midgut result in enzyme secretion similar to that following blood ingestion.

Though providing evidence of differential enzyme secretion, the mosquito studies scarcely support the idea of substrate induction of specific enzymes, and this is in accord with what little other information is available, largely gained in roach studies that showed no relative increase of amylase after feeding on starchy foods (Day and Powning, 1949); on the contrary, activity sometimes decreased, perhaps because of depletion by excessive substrate. *Tenebrio* midgut protease increased on ingesting water, cellulose powder, or flour, and parallel fluctuations of amylase and protease were noted (Dadd, 1956). In *Prodenia,* increased amylase followed feeding on diets high in starch but not with maltose (Applebaum *et al.,* 1964b), and salivary protease was detected in a pentatomid only after feeding on high protein diets (Nuorteva and Laurema, 1961b), but in neither case is it clear that this was more than a reflection of overall increase in digestive secretion. Similarly, without data on the parallel activity of other enzymes, the recent demonstration in the roach *Leucophaea* (Englemann, 1969) that 4 of 14 proteins tested (or a contaminant in common?), but not starch or charcoal, elicit proteinase secretion, does not of itself prove substrate-induced differential secretion.

Some studies of peritrophic membrane formation are pertinent to the question of differential secretion. Where membrane precursors and digestive enzymes must traverse the same epithelial surface, one might suppose that the membrane is merely a solidifying component of a single digestive fluid secreted as a whole. This clearly does not apply to the anteriorly produced membranes of dipterous larvae, yet secretion of both these and the more general delaminated membranes is increased by feeding (Waterhouse, 1954), just as is enzyme secretion. In unfed mosquitoes the midgut lacks both membranes and proteinase, while both appear on feeding, and increase in proportion to the quantity of blood ingested (Freyvogel and Jaquet, 1965). Though far from final, the weight of current evidence seems against the hypothesis of substrate-induced differential secretion.

Day and Powning (1949) envisaged three modes of secretory regulation: neural, hormonal, and secretogogue (direct stimulation of the secretory epithelium by food chemicals). In the absence of suitable midgut innervation neural regulation was discounted for *Blattella* and *Periplaneta;* enzyme production was associated with increased mitosis in the midgut regenerative cells, and as mitosis in adult *Tenebrio* was increased by injection of blood from fed, but not from unfed donors, it was circuitously argued that secretion, generally, might be controlled by a blood-borne hormonal factor. In *Tenebrio,* automatic, postemergence build-up of protease can be progressively restrained by head ligature or decapitation at progressively earlier times before completion of sclerotization, suggesting enzyme synthesis related to the hormonal events governing ecdysis; hormonal regulation is further indicated by the ability of injections of blood from fed or newly emerged donors, but not from those starved, to elevated protease in starved adults (Dadd, 1961). Recently the brain neurosecretory cells were shown to be the source of this hormone (Mordue, 1967). In the fly *Calliphora*, regulation of midgut protease is also attributed specifically to hormone from medial neurosecretory cells since their excision prevented the increase in proteinase (and also midgut cell esterase) normally induced by a meat meal (Thomsen and Møller, 1963; Thomsen, 1966). The same operation interferes with growth of ovaries, corpora allata, and oenocytes, prompting the suggestion that increased midgut proteinase is but one aspect of an overall stimulation of protein synthesis coordinated by the medial neurosecretory cells. It is perhaps relevant to this idea that increased enzyme production is associated with increased weight of midgut tissue in *Tenebrio* and *Locusta* (Dadd, 1956; Khan, 1964a), in turn correlating with increased regenerative cell mitosis in *Tenebrio* (Day and Powning, 1949). Hormonal regulation of midgut proteinase seems also to obtain in *Glossina*, for the automatic development of proteinase in teneral flies is prevented by head ligature, but can then be restored by injection of brain extracts (Langley, 1967). The level of proteinase in *Glossina* 24 hours after a meal is proportional to the volume of fluid ingested, whether whole blood, or blood diluted with up to 90% saline; but saline alone, or washed erythrocytes suspended in saline, caused no elevation, so evidently some plasma component is essential to activate secretion, even though the magnitude of secretion is unrelated to its concentration (Langley, 1966). Since automatic secretion by teneral flies is prevented if they are unable to expand themselves on emergence, Langley supposes that in *Glossina*, midgut secretion is regulated by a brain-derived hormone whose production is controlled neurally in response to gut distension.

A proportionality between amount of food ingested and the level of midgut proteinase secreted holds also for *Aedes, Sarcophaga*, and the roach *Leucophea maderae*, but, in these, hormonal regulation is considered unlikely. The failure of injected blood from fed donors to elevate proteinase in starved *Aedes*, coupled with the ability of various blood components, principally plasma or plasma proteins, but not erythrocytes (cf. *Glossina*), to induce maximally elevated enzyme activity, was considered indicative of secretogogue regulation (Shambaugh, 1954); however, it is not clear whether all blood substitutes were ingested equally, so that in view of the dependence of secretion on volume intake of whole blood, there remains some question as to whether the supposed specific substrate effects might really have been volume effects. Gooding (1966b) found that decapitation of *Aedes* shortly after feeding prevented the usual elevation of protease, suggesting a secretion-regulating factor from the head. In starved *Leucophaea*, midgut proteinase is scarcely detectable (contrasting in this respect with *Blattella*), but 24 hours after feeding, activity is directly proportional to the size of meal taken. This relationship holds for roaches deprived variously of brain, corpora cardiaca, and corpora allata, thus excluding hormonal in favor of secretogogue regulation (Engelmann, 1965, 1966, 1969). Extirpation of brain neurosecretory cells in *Blatta orientalis* curtails ovarian development, but is without effect on feeding or on midgut protease levels (Gordon, 1968). Like *Calliphora*, another fleshfly, *Sarcophaga*, secretes more proteinase when fed on meat and has reduced proteinase following extirpation of the medial neurosecretory cells; but since proteinase levels are directly correlated with meal size regardless of the presence or absence of neurosecretory cells, and low proteinase is due largely to diminished feeding, Engelmann and Wilkens (1969) conclude that secretogogues regulate secretion without endocrine involvement. These authors argue that as proteinase secretion is now known to depend on meal size in several species, failure to quantitate ingestion invalidates the argument for direct hormonal regulation in much previous work.

Direct nervous regulation of midgut secretion has been considered unlikely not only for lack of suitable innervation, but also because of the time lag between feeding and increased enzyme levels. On the latter basis, the very rapid discharge of protease in *Dytiscus*, within minutes of pouncing on food, suggests immediate nervous control, though evidence for this is lacking. Since salivation, in insects generally, accompanies feeding, neural control is undoubtedly involved in some aspect of the process, though it might merely regulate mechanical discharge from salivary reservoirs rather than actual secretion from glandular tissues. In roaches, both reservoirs and salivary acini are well innervated. In the acini of *Periplaneta*, zymogen cells synthesize salivary amylase, and "ductule" cells are conceived to transfer enzyme to cells lining the salivary ducts from which the definitive saliva is expelled, to be passed either to the buccal cavity or the salivary reservoirs. Zymogen cells pass through histologically distinct phases related to feeding and a consequent synthesis of amylase, and the histological picture of "no secretion" prevailing on starvation, when amylase is minimal, became the permanent condition following section of the salivary nerves. Injection of roaches with pilocarpine induced "histological secretion" in zymogen cells, but electrical stimulation of salivary nerves failed to do so (Day, 1951).

Synthesis of enzymes and elaboration of the ejected saliva, not to mention reservoir emptying, could be under separate and various control. However, the amount of saliva in the reservoirs and its amylase content tend to be proportional in *Periplaneta* (Sutherland and Chillseyzn, 1968), suggesting that enzyme synthesis and elaboration of the definitive saliva are interlinked. It has now been shown that electrical stimulation of the salivary nerves of *Periplaneta* can induce and maintain fluid secretion from the salivary glands for as long as 3 hours continuously, though whether saliva so produced has a normal enzyme content is not known (Whitehead, 1969). Whitehead further found that 10^{-6} M pilocarpine or acetylcholine induces transitory secretion from excised salivary glands, while 10^{-9} M 5-hydroxytryptamine maintains copious secretion for hours. Interestingly, 10^{-10} M 5-hydroxytryptamine induces secretion from the excised salivary glands of the blowfly *Phormia;* 10^{-3} M cyclic adenosine monophosphate, but not pilocarpine or acetylcholine, also induces secretion in this case (Berridge and Patel, 1968). 5-Hydroxytryptamine occurs in nervous tissue of several insects and is perhaps involved as a neurotransmitter mediating the nervous stimulation of salivation demonstrated in the roach.

V. Digestion, Absorption, and Nutrition

Products of digestion are in a sense external to the insect, and unavailable for utilization until absorbed from the gut lumen. Absorption was until recently a matter of circumstantial speculation drawing heavily on histochemical localization in gut epithelia of food-derived substances, particularly fats and metal ions (Reviews), a recent example being the deposition of various metals in particular regions of an aphid midgut (Ehrhardt, 1965). But localization of material does not necessarily indicate its normal absorptive route; excess nutrients or abnormal marker substances might atypically load the epithelium by a sort of facultative storage excretion. Concentrations of glycogen have been taken to indicate regions of absorption of sugar and amino acids, supposedly converted en route through the midgut epithelium, but absorption could well occur elsewhere and the visualized deposits be merely subsequent storage sites.

Quantitative studies of the movement of radiolabeled nutrients from the gut lumen are comprehensively reviewed by Treherne (1962, 1967), a principal contributor to such work. Movement of water and inorganic ions across the gut wall, as an aspect of osmoregulation, is dealt with elsewhere in this volume. Treherne followed the egress of sugars, amino acids, and fats from the alimentary tracts of *Periplaneta* and *Schistocerca* by recording in various regions of the gut lumen changes in relative concentration of radiolabeled nutrients and a nonabsorbed dye, amaranth. All nutrients diminished rapidly at the fore-midgut and ceca,

evidently the principal absorptive sites, a cecal function already suspected on circumstantial grounds in many insects.

Absorption of hexose sugars (glucose, fructose, mannose) is passively
diffusive, contrasting with active sugar transport in the mammalian intestine; diffusion is facilitated by a rapid conversion of absorbed hexose
to hemolymph trehalose (accomplished by fat body investing the midgut), thus maintaining a glucose diffusion gradient across the gut wall.
Rates of absorption are proportional to hexose concentration in the gut,
and relative rates for glucose, fructose, and mannose depend on the
facility with which they are converted to trehalose. Essentially similar
facilitated diffusion occurs in the silkworm (Shyamala and Bhat, 1965)
and hexose absorption in the blowfly *Phormia* is also diffusive (Gelperin,
1966). Wyatt (1967) suggests that the frequent occurrence of endocellu-
lar midgut trehalase in so many insects whose food lacks trehalose might
be a means of countering the tendency of hemolymph trehalose to diffuse
back through the rather pervious midgut, reconverting it to glucose
and thus further assisting the appropriate diffusion gradient.

Treherne found no active transport of amino acids (glutamine, glycine,
serine) in *Schistocerca*, net movement from ceca to hemolymph being
diffusive and assisted by a proportionately more rapid removal of water
from the gut, so concentrating materials in the lumen as to enhance
the lumen/hemolymph diffusion gradient. Transport of amino acids
across isolated silkworm intestine is also metabolically inactive, as indicated by indifference to dinitrophenol and cyanide (Shyamala and Bhat,
1966); however, in this and other insects (Bhatnagar, 1962; Bragdon
and Mittler, 1963) characteristic differential absorption of amino acids
is noted.

Fat absorption has a long history of study by histological methods,
particularly in roaches, where the appearance of oil droplets in epithelial
cells of the crop following ingestion of fatty food led to the assumption
that the crop was the principal site of lipid absorption. Though some
fat unquestionably traverses the crop intima, Treherne recorded quanti-
tatively insignificant loss of radioactive tripalmitin from *Periplaneta* crop,
maximal absorption being again associated with the midgut ceca. This
suggests the crop is unimportant in the bulk absorption of fats, but
it may be a major site for the absorption of minor lipids since tracer
studies show that cholesterol is absorbed in roaches mainly via this
route (Clayton *et al.*, 1964).

It is widely assumed that absorption of carbohydrates and proteins
in insects necessitates their reduction to monosaccharides and amino
acids (Gilmour, 1961), yet in the silkworm, amylase, alone of the carbohydrases, occurs in the digestive juice, glycosidases being restricted to

the epithelial tissue (Horie, 1959). It is argued from this that carbohydrate digestion here occurs in two phases, polysaccharides being cleaved in the gut lumen, and the resultant and other oligosaccharides being cleaved only after absorption into the epithelial tissue (Horie, 1961; Mukaiyama *et al.*, 1964). How widespread such phenomena may be is not known, though recent reports (Hansen, 1964; Maurizio, 1965; Wyatt, 1967) indicate that considerable absorption of disaccharides may be more common than has been generally supposed. A similar division of labor has long been mooted for protein digestion, hinging on the possibility that peptide fragments might be absorbed as such, and their digestion completed within the gut epithelium or elsewhere (Reviews). A recent example is the detection of dipeptidase in midgut tissue but not in digestive juice of the silkworm (Horie *et al.*, 1963).

The possibility that partially cleaved macromolecules might normally be substantially absorbed has considerable relevance to the relative nutritive value of polysaccharides compared with sugars, and particularly, proteins with amino acids. One might suppose that an amino acid mixture based on the amino acid composition of a protein should be its nutritional equivalent, but this frequently is not so (see Chapter 2). This has prompted speculation that particular peptide fragments might be required intact, but there is thus far no real evidence. More likely an osmotic problem is in question. If, as the admittedly meager current information suggests, absorption of both sugars and amino acids is essentially diffusive in insects, it must be very dependent on relative concentrations of absorbed entities in hemolymph and gut lumen, in contrast to active transport mechanisms that in mammals have been shown to allow absorption of both sugars and amino acids against concentration gradients. The possibility then arises that, faced with unnaturally high free amino acids in the gut lumen, excessive and uncontrolled egress to the hemolymph might saturate the capacities of subsequent metabolism, at the same time upsetting internal osmotic relationships by the withdrawal of water from the hemolymph.

This, and indeed the general bearing of the digestion of whole carbohydrates and proteins typical of natural foods on their nutritive values is a border area bridging digestion, absorption, and nutrition that demands serious study rather than the occasional speculation thus far accorded it. The utilization of natural foods, reviewed comprehensively by Waldbauer (1968), is usually subsumed under the mantle of nutrition. However, the older term for its most measured parameter, "coefficient of digestibility," indicates the probable complexity of the functions embraced. Such measures of overall utilization of a food depend on the individual digestibility of each nutrient, the digestive capability of the particular animal for each nutrient, the efficiency of absorption for the several products of digestion, and the extent to which such absorbed products may be utilized in metabolism. Further, since insect excreta are mixed fecal and urinary products, considerations devolving from excretion also enter the parameter. These several functions making up overall food utilization are doubtless integrated by variously delicately balanced gustatory, secretogogue, humoral, neural, and hormonal links, ultimately driven by the metabolic needs of survival, growth, and reproduction, and directly set rolling by the acts of feeding. Such interrelationships, barely touched on as yet, provide the more enticing vistas of alimentary physiology.

REFERENCES

Adams, J. B., and Drew, M. (1965). Can. J. Zool. 43, 489.
Anders, F. (1958). Experientia 14, 62.
Applebaum, S. W. (1964). J. Insect Physiol. 10, 897.
Applebaum, S. W., Janković, M., and Birk, Y. (1961). J. Insect Physiol. 7, 100.
Applebaum, S. W., Birk, Y., Harpaz, I., and Bondi, A. (1964a). Comp. Biochem. Physiol. 11, 85.
Applebaum, S. W., Harpaz, I., and Bondi, A. (1964b). Comp. Biochem. Physiol. 13, 107.
Auclair, J. L. (1963). Ann. Rev. Entomol. 8, 439.
Ayre, G. L. (1967). Can. Entomologist 99, 408.
Banks, W. M. (1963). Science 141, 1191.
Barrington, E. J. W. (1962). Advan. Comp. Physiol. Biochem. 1, 1.
Berridge, M. J., and Patel, N. G. (1968). Science 162, 462.
Bertram, D. S., and Bird, R. G. (1961). Trans. Roy. Soc. Trop. Med. Hyg. 55, 404.
Bhatnagar, P. (1962). Indian J. Entomol. 24, 66.
Birk, Y., and Applebaum, S. W. (1960). Enzymologia 22, 318.
Birk, Y., Harpaz, I., Ishaaya, I., and Bondi, A. (1962). J. Insect Physiol. 8, 417.
Bragdon, J. C., and Mittler, T. E. (1963). Nature 198, 209.
Clayton, R. B., Hinkle, P. C., Smith, D. A., and Edwards, A. M. (1964). Comp. Biochem. Physiol. 11, 333.
Clements, A. N. (1963). "The Physiology of Mosquitoes." Pergamon Press, Oxford.
Cook, B. J., Nelson, D. R., and Hipps, P. (1969). J. Insect Physiol. 15, 581.
Couch, E. F., and Mills, R. R. (1968). J. Insect Physiol. 14, 55.
Dadd, R. H. (1956). J. Exptl. Biol. 33, 311.
Dadd, R. H. (1954). Ph.D. Thesis, Universtiy of London.
Dadd, R. H. (1961). J. Exptl. Biol. 38, 259.
Dadd, R. H. (1966). J. Insect Physiol. 12, 1479.
Dadd, R. H. (1968). Mosquito News 28, 226.
Davis, G. R. F. (1963). Arch. Intern. Physiol. Biochim. 71, 166.
Day, M. F. (1951). Australian J. Sci. Res. B4, 136.
Day, M. F., and Powning, R. F. (1949). Australian J. Sci. Res. B2, 175.
Day, M. F., and Waterhouse, D. F. (1953). In "Insect Physiology" (K. D. Roeder, ed.), pp. 273–349. Wiley, New York, Chapman and Hall, London.

Duspiva, F. (1939). *Protoplasma* **32**, 211.
Eguchi, M., and Sugimoto, T. (1965). *J. Insect Physiol.* **11**, 1145.
Ehrhardt, P. (1962). *Z. Vergleich. Physiol.* **46**, 169.
Ehrhardt, P. (1965). *Z. Vergleich. Physiol.* **50**, 293.
Ehrhardt, P., and Voss, G. (1962). *J. Insect Physiol.* **8**, 165.
Engelmann, F. (1965). *Arch. Anat. Microscop. Morphol. Exptl.* **54**, 387.
Engelmann, F. (1968). *Naturwissenschaften* **53**, 113.
Engelmann, F. (1968). *J. Insect Physiol.* **14**, 1525.
Engelmann, F. (1969). *J. Insect Physiol.* **15**, 217.
Engelmann, F., and Wilkens, J. L. (1969). *Nature* **222**, 798.
Evans, W. A. L. (1956). *Exptl. Parasitol.* **5**, 191.
Evans, W. A. L., and Payne, D. W. (1964). *J. Insect Physiol.* **10**, 657.
Feir, D., and Beck, S. D. (1961). *Ann. Entomol. Soc. Am.* **54**, 316.
Fisk, F. W. (1950). *Ann. Entomol. Soc. Am.* **43**, 555.
Fisk, F. W., and Rao, B. R. (1964). *Ann. Entomol. Soc. Am.* **57**, 40.
Fisk, F. W., and Shambaugh, G. F. (1952). *Ohio J. Sci.* **52**, 80.
Fisk, F. W., and Shambaugh, G. F. (1954). *Ohio J. Sci.* **54**, 237.
Ford, J. B. (1962). *Ann. Appl. Biol.* **50**, 355.
Fraser, A., Ring, R., and Stewart, R. (1961). *Nature* **192**, 999.
Freeman, M. A. (1967). *Comp. Biochem. Physiol.* **20**, 1013.
Freyvogel, T. A., and Jaquet, C. (1965). *Acta Trop.* **22**, 148.
Freyvogel, T. A., and Staubli, W. (1965). *Acta Trop.* **22**, 118.
Friend, W. G., Choy, C. T. H., and Cartwright, E. (1965). *Can. J. Zool.* **43**, 891.
Gander, E. (1968). *Acta Trop.* **25**, 133.
Gangwere, S. K. (1966). *Rev. Espan. Entomol.* **41**, 247.
Gelperin, A. (1966). *J. Insect Physiol.* **12**, 331.
Gilbert, L. I. (1967). *Advan. Insect Physiol.* **4**, 69.
Gilmour, D. (1961). "Biochemistry of Insects." Academic Press, New York.
Goodhue, D. (1963). *Nature* **200**, 288.
Gooding, R. H. (1966a). *Comp. Biochem. Physiol.* **17**, 115.
Gooding, R. H. (1966b). *J. Med. Entomol.* **3**, 53.
Gooding, R. H., and Huang, C. T. (1969). *J. Insect Physiol.* **15**, 325.
Gordon, R. (1968). *Gen. Comp. Endocrinol.* **11**, 284.
Gouranton, J. (1968). *J. Insect Physiol.* **14**, 569.
Gouranton, J., and Maillet, P. L. (1965). *Compt. Rend.* **261**, 1102.
Greenberg, B. (1968). *Ann. Entomol. Soc. Am.* **61**, 365.
Hansen, O. (1964). *Biochem. J.* **92**, 333.
Hori, K. (1968). *Appl. Entomol. Zool.* **3**, 198.
Hori, K. (1969a). *J. Insect Physiol.* **15**, 2305.
Hori, K. (1969b). *Entomol. Exptl. Appl.* **12**, 454.
Hori, K. (1970). *J. Insect Physiol.* **16**, 373.
Horie, Y. (1959). *Bull. Sericult. Expt. Sta. (Tokyo)* **15**, 365.
Horie, Y. (1961). *Bull. Sericult. Expt. Sta. (Tokyo)* **16**, 287.
Horie, Y., Tanaka, M., and Ito, T. (1963). *J. Sericult. Sci. Japan* **32**, 8.
House, H. L. (1965). *In* "The Physiology of Insecta" (M. Rockstein, ed.), Vol. 2, pp. 815–858. Academic Press, New York.
Ito, T., and Tanaka, M. (1959). *Biol. Bull.* **116**, 95.
Ito, T., Mukaiyama, F., and Tanaka, M. (1962). *J. Sericult. Sci. Japan* **13**, 228.
Khan, M. A. (1962). *Comp. Biochem. Physiol.* **6**, 167.

Khan, M. A. (1963). *Entomol. Exptl. Appl.* **6**, 181.
Khan, M. A. (1964a). *Entomol. Exptl. Appl.* **7**, 125.
Khan, M. A. (1964b). *Entomol. Exptl. Appl.* **7**, 335.
Khan, M. R., and Ford, J. B. (1962). *J. Insect Physiol.* **8**, 597.
Khan, M. R., and Ford, J. B. (1967). *J. Insect Physiol.* **13**, 1619.
Kloft, U. (1960). *Z. Angew. Entomol.* **45**, 337; **46**, 42.
Lambremont, E. N., Fisk, F. W., and Ashrafi, S. (1959). *Science* **129**, 1484.
Langley, P.A. (1966). *J. Insect Physiol.* **12**, 439.
Langley, P. A. (1967). *J. Insect Physiol.* **13**, 1921.
Laurema, S., and Nuorteva, P. (1961). *Ann. Entomol. Fennici* **27**, 89.
McAllen, J. W., and Adams, J. B. (1961). *Can. J. Zool.* **39**, 305.
Maurizio, A. (1965). *J. Insect Physiol.* **11**, 745.
Miles, P. W. (1959). *J. Insect Physiol.* **3**, 243.
Miles, P. W. (1960). *J. Insect Physiol.* **4**, 209.
Miles, P. W. (1964a). *J. Insect Physiol.* **10**, 147.
Miles, P. W. (1964b). *J. Insect Physiol.* **10**, 121.
Miles, P. W. (1965). *J. Insect Physiol.* **11**, 1261.
Miles, P. W. (1967a). *Australian J. Biol. Sci.* **20**, 785.
Miles, P. W. (1967b). *J. Insect Physiol.* **13**, 1787.
Miles, P. W. (1968). *J. Insect Physiol.* **14**, 97.
Miles, P. W. (1969). *Ann. Rev. Phytopathol.* **6**, 137.
Miles, P. W., and Lloyd, J. (1967). *Nature* **213**, 801.
Mordue, W. (1967). *Gen. Comp. Endcrinol.* **9**, 406.
Mukaiyama, F. (1961). *Nippon Sanshigaku Zasshi* **30**, 1.
Mukaiyama, F., Horie, Y., and Ito, T. (1964). *J. Insect Physiol.* **10**, 247.
Niemierko, W. (1959). *Proc. 4th Intern. Congr. Biochem., Vienna, 1958*, Vol. 12, p. 185. Pergamon Press, Oxford.
Nuorteva, P. (1958). *Entomol. Exptl. Appl.* **1**, 41.
Nuorteva, P. (1962). *Ann. Zool. Soc. Zool.-Botan. Fennicae Vanamo* **23**, 1.
Nuorteva, P., and Laurema, S. (1961a). *Ann. Entomol. Fennici* **27**, 57.
Nuorteva, P., and Laurema, S. (1961b). *Ann. Entomol. Fennici* **27**, 93.
Patel, N. G., and Richards, A. G. (1960). *J. Insect Physiol.* **4**, 146.
Patterson, R. A., and Fisk, F. W. (1958). *Ohio J. Sci.* **58**, 299.
Payne, D. W., and Evans, W. A. L. (1964). *J. Insect Physiol.* **10**, 675.
Powning, R. F., and Irzykiewicz, H. (1962). *J. Insect Physiol.* **8**, 275.
Powning, R. F., and Irzykiewicz, H. (1963). *Nature* **200**, 1128.
Powning, R. F., and Irzykiewiez, H. (1964). *Comp. Biochem. Physiol.* **12**, 405.
Powning, R. F., Day, M. F., and Irzykiewiez, H. (1952). *Australian J. Sci. Res.* **B4**, 49.
Rao, B. R., and Fisk, F. W. (1965). *J. Insect Physiol.* **11**, 961.
Robinson, D. (1964). *Comp. Biochem. Physiol.* **12**, 95.
Rössler, M. E. (1961). *J. Insect Physiol.* **6**, 62.
Salkeld, E. H. (1960). *Can. J. Zool.* **38**, 449.
Saxena, K. N. (1958). *Physiol. Zool.* **31**, 129.
Saxena, K. N. (1963). *J. Insect Physiol.* **9**, 47.
Saxena, K. N., and Gandhi, J. R. (1966). *Comp. Biochem. Physiol.* **17**, 765.
Schäller, G. (1960). *Entomol. Exptl. Appl.* **3**, 128.
Schäller, G. (1963). *Zool. Jahrb., Abt. Allgem. Zool. Physiol. Tiere* **70**, 399.
Schäller, G. (1965). *Zool. Jahrb., Abt. Allgem. Zool. Physiol. Tiere* **71**, 385.
Schäller, G. (1968). *Zool. Jahrb., Abt. Allgem. Zool. Physiol. Tiere* **74**, 54.

Schramm, M. (1967). *Ann. Rev. Biochem.* **36**, 307.

Shambaugh, G. F. (1954). *Ohio J. Sci.* **54**, 151.

Shyamala, M. B., and Bhat, J. V. (1965). *Indian J. Biochem.* **2**, 101.

Shyamala, M. B., and Bhat, J. V. (1966). *J. Insect Physiol.* **12**, 129.

Soo Hoo, C. F., and Dudziński, A. (1967). *Entomol. Exptl. Appl.* **10**, 7.

Srivastava, P. N., and Auclair, J. L. (1962a). *J. Insect Physiol.* **8**, 349.

Srivastava, P. N., and Auclair, J. L. (1962b). *J. Insect Physiol.* **8**, 527.

Srivastava, P. N., and Auclair, J. L. (1963a). *J. Insect Physiol.* **9**, 469.

Srivastava, P. N., and Auclair, J. L. (1963b). *Ann. Soc. Entomol. Quebec* **8**, 24.

Staubli, W., Freyvogel, T. A., and Suter, J. (1966). *J. Microscopie* **5**, 189.

Stephens, G. C., and Schinske, R. A. (1961). *Limnol. Oceanog.* **6**, 175.

Strong, F. E., and Kruitwagen, E. C. (1968). *J. Insect Physiol.* **14**, 1113.

Sutherland, D. J., and Chillseyzn, J. M. (1968). *J. Insect Physiol.* **14**, 21.

Tawfik, M. S. (1968). *Quaest. Entomol.* **4**, 225.

Thomsen, E. (1966). *Z. Zellforsch. Mikroskop. Anat.* **75**, 281.

Thomsen, E., and Møller, I. (1963). *J. Exptl. Biol.* **40**, 301.

Treherne, J. E. (1962). *Viewpoints Biol.* **1**, 201.

Treherne, J. E. (1967). *Ann. Rev. Entomol.* **12**, 43.

Waldbauer, G. P. (1968). *Advan. Insect Physiol.* **5**, 229.

Waterhouse, D. F. (1953). *Australian J. Zool.* **1**, 299.

Waterhouse, D. F. (1954). *Australian J. Biol. Sci.* **7**, 59.

Waterhouse, D. F. (1957). *Ann. Rev. Entomol.* **2**, 1.

Wharton, D. R. A., Wharton, M. L., and Lola, J. E. (1965). *J. Insect Physiol.* **11**, 947.

Whitehead, A. T. (1969). Ph.D. Thesis, University of California, Berkeley, California.

Wigglesworth, V. B. (1965). "The Principles of Insect Physiology." Methuen, London.

Wyatt, G. R. (1967). *Advan. Insect Physiol.* **4**, 287.

Yang, Y. J., and Davies, D. M. (1968a). *J. Insect Physiol.* **14**, 205.

Yang, Y. J., and Davies, D. M. (1968b) *J. Med. Entomol.* **5**, 9.

Yang, Y. J., and Davies, D. M. (1968c). *J. Insect Physiol.* **14**, 1221.

Yoshitaki, N. (1967). *Nature* **214**, 843.

Young, A. G. (1964). *Ann. Entomol. Soc. Am.* **57**, 321 and 325.

Zhuzhikov, D. P. (1964). *J. Insect Physiol.* **10**, 273.

CHAPTER 5

Carbohydrate Metabolism in Crustaceans

Lyle Hohnke and Bradley T. Scheer

I. Introduction

Studies on carbohydrate metabolism in crustaceans have been essentially conventional in approach. Investigators have concentrated primarily on ascertaining the presence of classic carbohydrate pathways and on identification of the major components found in the body fluids. Studies pertaining to control mechanisms are limited in scope, pending the purification of regulatory factors. This review aims to locate the common denominator of recent inquiries in crustacean carbohydrate metabolism and will be limited to material not treated in earlier reviews (Waterman, 1960; Scheer and Meenakshi, 1961; Huggins and Munday, 1968).

II. Body Fluids

Careful analysis of the internal medium[1] of an organism often allows certain inferences to be made regarding its physiological and biochemical behavior. Prerequisite to this, however, is the establishment of a norm which forms a basis of comparison for future work. Investigators in their search for "normal" levels of organic constituents have met with extreme variability in measurements, and this limits any inferences that can reasonably be made concerning other concurrent activities of the organism (Florkin, 1960).

[1] The internal medium of crustaceans is equivalent to the terms hemolymph, blood, and body fluids often found in the literature, since the circulatory fluids are not completely separated from interstitial fluids by a membrane.

Early studies were limited to the use of the reducing power of the aldehyde group as an indicator of the presence of sugars. Total reducing power was partially "fractionated" by the use of fermentation tests as a criterion for the presence of glucose. None of these tests is specific for glucose, however, so the fermentable fraction described in early investigations is of uncertain identity. Glucose determinations are routinely performed now with the use of glucose oxidase enzyme preparations, marketed, for example, under the trade name Glucostat. These determinations enjoy the specificity of all enzyme-catalyzed reactions, but commercial glucose oxidase may be contaminated with other enzymes. It is also of current interest to identify the other blood sugars composing the reducing and nonreducing fractions. Chromatography has found great utility in this area, and the subtle differences among species will undoubtedly require this type of refined analysis.

A spectrum of saccharides has been identified by Telford (1965) in the hemolymph of *Homarus americanus.* Table I gives representative "normal" values for a few intermolt crustaceans with similar lab histories.

As evidenced by Table I, glucose is the major component of blood carbohydrates. In *Hemigrapsus nudus* glucose levels are very low and the significance of this has not been determined. Many parameters have been shown to influence blood sugar determinations; among these are (1) stress of handling (Telford, 1968b); (2) stage of molt cycle (Telford 1968a; McWhinnie and Scheer, 1958; Riegel, 1960; Telford, 1968c); (3) stage of reproductive cycle (Dean and Vernberg, 1965a); (4) time of sampling (Dean and Vernberg, 1965a); (5) acclimation temperature (Dean and Vernberg, 1965b). Attention to variables is thus essential to this type of analysis. C. M. Wang and Patton (1969) have summarized values for blood sugar contents of numerous groups of insects in their study of *Acheta domesticus,* the house cricket. Adult glucose levels are invariably higher in all groups than corresponding crustacean values with trehalose levels being one hundred to several hundred times greater. The physiological significance of crustacean trehalose is presently questionable but is a subject of current research. Clegg (1965) noted trehalose accumulation only in the embryos of *Artemia salina* that were "programmed" to enter dormancy and found that maternal tissues lacked the ability to synthesize this disaccharide. The possible involvement of trehalose in the dormancy of encysted embryos has been suggested.

The presence of the oligosaccharides maltose, maltotriose, and maltotetrose is also a biochemical-physiological curiosity. These oligosaccharides were first observed in our laboratory by Hu (1958) and since have been reported in several other crabs (Telford, 1968c) following chromatographic identification. Meenakshi and Scheer (1961) have

TABLE I

BLOOD SUGARS OF CRUSTACEA

Species	Component	Concentration (mg./100 ml.)	Reference
Homarus americanus	Reducing sugars	12.3 ♂	Telford (1968b)
	Reducing sugars	11.9 ♀	Telford (1968b)
	Glucose	7.9	Telford (1968b)
	Trehalose	2.5[a]	Telford (1968b)
	Unidentified disaccharide	2.0[a]	Telford (1968b)
	Maltotriose	Trace	Telford (1968b)
	Maltose	Trace	Telford (1968b)
	Galactose	Trace	Telford (1968b)
	Fructose	Trace	Telford (1968b)
Hemigrapsus nudus	Glucose	1.28–2.55	McWhinnie and Scheer (1958)
Orconectes virilis	Total reducing substance	2.06–75.62	McWhinnie and Saller (1960)
	Glucose	1.0–19.77	McWhinnie and Saller (1960)
Pacifasticus leniusculus	Glucose	15–39	Riegel (1960)
Artemia salina	Glucose	48–51[b]	Clegg (1965)
Cancer magister	Total carbohydrate	44.3	Meenakshi and Scheer (1961)
	Oligosaccharides	10.9	Meenakshi and Scheer (1961)
	Glucose 6-P	7.2	Meenakshi and Scheer (1961)
	Glycoprotein	13.2	Meenakshi and Scheer (1961)
	Glucose	5.7	Meenakshi and Scheer (1961)
Hepatus ephelitus	Glucose	17.92	Dean and Vernberg (1965a)
Libinia emarginata	Glucose	12.74[c]	Dean and Vernberg (1965a)
Nephrops norvegicus	Total Cu reducing	14.1	Robertson (1961)
Orconectes limosus	Glucose	94.6	Andrews (1967)
Panopeus herbstii	Glucose	6.57	Dean and Vernberg (1965a)
Callinectes sapidus	Glucose	15.87	Dean and Vernberg (1965a)
Carcinus[d] maenas	Reducing sugar	13.8	Telford (1968c)
	Glucose	9.9	Telford (1968c)
	Maltotriose	2	Telford (1968c)
	Trehalose	1.5	Telford (1968c)
	Maltose	3	Telford (1968c)
	Disaccharide	5	Telford (1968c)
	Fructose	1.5	Telford (1968c)

[a] Approximate values.
[b] Female, eggs just visible.
[c] Female, early spring.
[d] Blood sugar values of *C. irroratus* and *C. borealis* were very similar for all sugars.

shown that glucose is a precursor of the oligosaccharide fraction and that the circulating levels are very responsive to the diet. Labeling experiments also showed that injection of labeled maltose was not followed by appearance of radioactivity in the glucose fraction. Such experiments suggested that the maltose oligosaccharides are intermediates of glycogen synthesis, and·carbon from ^{14}C-maltose is found in glycogen shortly after administration to crabs (Meenakshi and Scheer, 1961). The participation of nucleotides in this biosynthesis has been inferred but not demonstrated. Clarification of the functional significance of these oligosaccharides is still pending further analysis.

III. Body Composition

Vonk (1960) has summarized total body composition for *Cancer pagurus*. These figures provide little direct information aside from their general orientation to the gross structural features. Scant information is available with regard to the biochemical constitution of each body component, and correspondingly fewer data exist on the biochemical behavior of constituent organ systems. Muscle and hepatopancreas are the main tissues utilized for most biochemical preparations. These tissues constitute 72% to 80% and 10% to 17% respectively of the total soft tissue in *Cancer magister* (Giese, 1966). Other tissues excluding hemolymph constitute less than 5% of the total soft tissue weight, making preparations from these sources correspondingly more difficult.

Since the comprehensive study of Renaud (1949), considerable effort has been expended to determine the metabolic role of glycogen. Following the utilization of blood sugar, mammals and most insects mobilize (1) glycogen, (2) lipids, and (3) proteins, in that order. This pattern is not ubiquitous, however. Gilmour (1965) reports that butterflies utilize fats preferentially, and the tsetse fly uses amino acids as sources of energy in flight. Beenakkers (1969) has identified three different types of flight muscles in insects: (1) dependent on carbohydrate, (2) dependent on fatty acids, and (3) capable of oxidizing both substrates. Comparable information is not available for crustaceans and would be of interest.

Steeves (1963) has followed changes in the glycogen reserves of the hepatopancreas following starvation and concluded that major portions were being utilized as a metabolic substrate in the isopod, *Lirceus brachyurus* (Harger). Barnes (1965) cites utilization of carbohydrate, nitrogen, and lipid during the development of cirripede eggs (Table II).

Numerous histological studies appear to support Renaud's concept that glycogen is a focal point of crustacean intermediary metabolism (Travis, 1955; Martin, 1965; Adiyodi, 1969), but this evidence still lacks chemical confirmation. Neiland and Scheer (1953), moreover, arrived at a somewhat divergent view of glycogen's role. Their studies with *Hemigrapsus nudus* (Dana) revealed no change in glycogen or fat content following 23 days of fasting. This result has been recently supported by Jungreis (1968). His investigation centered on oxygen consumption associated with metabolic temperature adaptation in starved crayfish. Glycogen levels of heart, abdominal muscle, and hepatopancreas were analyzed to determine their dependence on glycogenolysis. Calculations

TABLE II

LOSS OF MAJOR COMPONENTS DURING THE DEVELOPMENT OF EGGS[a]

Species	Percentage Lost		
	Carbohydrate	Nitrogen	Lipid
Balanus balanoïdes	74.6	25.6	11.5
Balanus balanus	79.8	35.2	17.3

[a] Barnes (1965).

showed that only "1% of the differential oxygen consumption associated with MTA (metabolic temperature adaptation) between 1 and 45 days of acclimation could be accounted for on the basis of total body glycogen changes. It was concluded that *O. virilis* is not dependent upon glycogen as a source of energy (ATP) during long term starvation." Jungreis (1968) does note, however, that changes in glycogen content of the heart muscle can account for 36% to 42% of the altered oxygen uptake, supporting some dependence on glycogenolysis for this tissue. These data, *in toto*, advance a concept of "tissue personality" concerning substrate preference for metabolic purposes. It might be prudent to think first of the functional position of an organ in the animal, then suggest the substrate(s) most feasible for meeting these requirements rather than postulating preferred substrates for the whole animal based on data from single tissue or whole animal analyses.

IV. Dynamics of Metabolism

The presence of the glycolytic pathway in most cells is well established as the major route of glucose metabolism. It is interesting that skeletal muscles utilize this pathway anaerobically for ATP production, heart muscle uses it aerobically for high ATP demands, and microbes ferment glucose to ethanol, all utilizing essentially the same pathway. This diversity has probably contributed to the great interest manifest in this series of reactions. Figure 1 is a diagrammatic presentation of carbohydrate metabolism as it is presently being viewed in crustaceans. It will serve primarily to orient the following discussion and to depict some important relationships between major carbohydrate cycles.

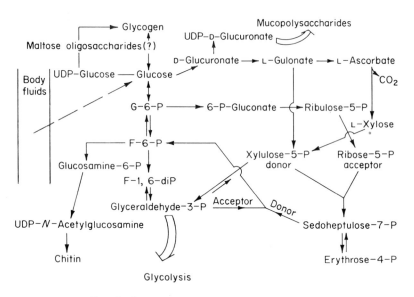

FIG. 1. Crustacean carbohydrate metabolism.

The early doubts concerning the presence of the Embden-Meyerhof (EM) pathway raised by Scheer and Scheer (1951) and Scheer *et al.* (1952) have been clarified more recently in Scheer's laboratory and elsewhere. Table III summarizes some of the data presently available that support the presence of the EM catabolic pathway. Although the functional presence of the pathway has been established, there is presently some question concerning the contribution of the pathway in relation to other possible routes such as the pentose phosphate pathway [also designated the hexose monophosphate shunt (HMS)].

Also of interest in the discussion of glycolysis is the assessment of possible ancillary sequences. Both anabolism and catabolism cause attrition of metabolic intermediates and these are restored via anapleurotic sequences. Specifically, it would be of interest to know if tricarboxylic

TABLE III
EVIDENCE SUPPORTING CRUSTACEAN GLYCOLYSIS

Organism	Tissue	Technique	Reference
H. nudus	Whole animal	1. Isolation of glycolytic intermediates	Hu (1958)
		2. Respirometric	Hu (1958)
H. nudus C. magister	Whole animal	Respirometric	Meenakshi and Scheer (1961)
H. americanus	Hepatopancreas	Stimulate O_2 uptake following addition of EM and TCA intermediates	Hochachka et al. (1962)
O. virilis	Hepatopancreas	Metabolic inhibition	McWhinnie and Kirchenberg (1962)
C. affinis, Say	Antennal gland Gills Hindgut Testes Stomach Hypodermis Abdominal muscle Heart Cerebral ganglion Blood serum	Enzymology	Keller (1965a)
P. leniusculus	Whole animal	Respirometric	Puyear et al. (1965)
A. astacus	Whole animal	Respirometric	Zandee (1966)
C. maenas	Hepatopancreas Gill Muscle	Glucose conversion to sugar phosphates and lactate	Huggins (1966)
E. modestus	Whole animal	Glucose conversion to sugar phosphates and lactate	Boulton et al. (1967)
U. pugnax	Whole animal	1. Glycogen depletion	Teal and Carey (1967)
		2. Lactate production	Teal and Carey (1967)
P. polymerus	Embryos	Enzymology	Eastman (1968)
A. salina	Whole animal	Glucose conversion to lactate and alanine	Huggins (1969)

acid cycle (TCA) intermediates such as oxalacetate can be decarboxylated to phosphoenolpyruvate, thus promoting carbohydrate biosynthesis. Additionally this would aid conversion of amino acids and other metabolites involved in steady-state exchange with TCA intermediates into carbohydrates when this is desirable. Studies on carbohydrate biosynthesis in crustaceans have largely been limited to glycogen and chitin, while glycogenesis and gluconeogenesis are completely unexplored in crustaceans.

Hochachka *et al.* (1962) established the presence of the pentose cycle by observing stimulated oxygen uptake following the addition of ribose, ribose 5-phosphate, and xylose in lobster hepatopancreas; 6-phosphogluconate also had this effect when substrates were enriched with added NADP and methylene blue. It was further shown that the pentose and EM pathways are located extramitochondrially, a feature congruent with their location in other organisms.

McWhinnie and Kirchenberg (1962) and McWhinnie and Corkill (1964) demonstrated an apparent differential use of glycolytic and pentose phosphate routes linked to the stage of molting activity. Differential sensitivities to metabolic inhibitors suggested that the hepatopancreas of the crayfish *Orconectes virilis* may depend on the pentose pathway during intermolt and glycolysis during premolt activities. Puyear *et al.* (1965) arrived at a similar conclusion following respirometric analyses of glucose utilization in whole animals (*Pacifastacus leniusculus*) and further reported the operation of the glucuronate pathway. McWhinnie and Corkill (1964) have proposed that the HMS may function in two capacities: (1) lipid metabolism and (2) protein synthesis. The HMS, in addition to supplying a variety of carbon skeletons, also replenishes reducing power in the form of NADPH, and anabolic processes often have exclusive requirements for this coenzyme. One such process is fatty acid biosynthesis. Zandee (1966) has shown in *Astacus astacus* that fatty acid biosynthesis is more prevalent in "December animals" than in "April animals," i.e., intermolt rather than premolt. This finding supports HMS participation in lipid metabolism. Skinner (1968), in studies related to nucleic acid metabolism in *Gecarcinus lateralis* has observed a fivefold increase in ribosomal ribonucleic acid (rRNA) by late D_2 stage in the epidermis, a doubling of rRNA during premolt in the midgut gland, and a four- to fivefold elevation in rRNA levels in muscles that extends well past ecdysis. Such evidence does not support widespread involvement of the HMS in protein synthesis via formation of pentose sugars. Further speculation is presently contraindicated until experimental evidence becomes available.

Studies designed to relate low temperature acclimation to changes in overall metabolism have introduced another factor governing substrate pathways. McWhinnie and O'Connor (1967) demonstrated that whole animal respiration and tissue metabolism is modified in the temperate crayfish *Orconectes virilis* when exposed to low temperature. Specifically, it was observed that substrate flow through both the glycolytic and the pentose pathway was augmented and that the ratio of HMS/EM activity increased during the premolt stages D_0 to D_1. This contrasts with their earlier finding of reduced HMS activity during the premolt stages.

Indication has also been given by Eastman (1968) that the pentose pathway may be a major route of glucose oxidation during embryogenesis of the barnacle *Pollicipes polymerus*. His conclusion was based on a low ratio of aldolase/G-6-P dehydrogenase activity in early embryonic stages, followed by a high ratio at hatching.

The pentose cycle as presented in Fig. 1 is intimately associated with yet another pathway, the glucuronic acid circuit. Initially demonstrated in the hepatopancreas of the crayfish *Pacifasticus leniusculus*, it has since been found operative in ventral nerve cord preparations of the lobster *Homarus vulgaris* (M. Edw.) and the crayfish *Astacus fluviatilis* F. (Gilles and Schoffeniels, 1969a). Current studies indicate that the glucuronic acid pathway probably functions in the main to produce mucopolysaccharides, since ascorbic acid has not been identified as a dietary requirement in crustaceans. Puyear (1969) views the synthesis of glycogen, chitin, and mucopolysaccharides as being controlled by a triumvirate of nucleotide pyrophosphatases. Nucleotide pyrophosphatase catalyzes the following type of reaction:

$$NuDP\text{-sugar} \longleftrightarrow sugar\ 1\text{-phosphate} + NuMP$$

Since polysaccharide biosynthesis proceeds through nucleotide diphosphate sugar (NuDP-sugar), intermediate regulation of this precursor pool would allow substrate control over synthetic activities. Puyear (1969) proposed the scheme shown in Fig. 2.

Evidence for the proposed system is based on the occurrence of differing levels of pyrophosphatase activity in the hepatopancreas at various

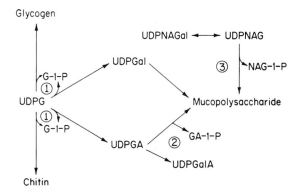

FIG. 2. Nucleotide pyrophosphate control points. Abbreviations: UDP = uridine diphosphate; UDPG = UDP glucose; UDPGA = UDP glucuronic acid; UDPNAG = UDP-*N*-acetylglucosamine; UDPGal = UDP. galactose; UDPGalA = UDP galacturonic acid; UDPNAGal = UDP-*N*-acetylgalactosamine; NAG-1-P = *N*-acetylglucosamine 1-phosphate; G-1-P = glucose 1-phosphate. Puyear (1969).

intervals of the molt cycle. Nucleotide pyrophosphatase activity increased until intermolt (C) or premolt (D_1–D_2), then fell rather sharply. The inverse relationship between these enzyme activities and polysaccharide biosynthesis complements current concepts regarding carbohydrate metabolism. Further comments regarding the significance of the glucuronic acid cycle will be deferred until the discussion of mucopolysaccharides.

A. CHITIN

Chitin is a structural polysaccharide widely distributed throughout the invertebrate series. Functionally it forms part of a complex barrier isolating the organism from the environment. The notion that chitin is a supporting element is largely based on its occurrence in tissues that contribute to the structural integrity of the organism. Crustacean exoskeletons yield considerable chitin; it constitutes 64% to 74% of the organic material in brachyurans (Drach and Lafon, 1942). It is the purpose of the following discussion to elucidate the important contributions made by study of crustaceans to our present knowledge of the chitin molecule.

Phylogenetically, chitin enjoys an extensive distribution among the invertebrate series with an abrupt absence in the vertebrates. Jeuniaux (1965), Hyman (1966), Florkin (1966), and Tracy (1968) have all presented current data relative to chitin phylogeny. Here it is important to note that there are no reported instances of a crustacean lacking chitin as an organic constituent of the cuticle. Its presence in the cuticle, coupled with the cyclic nature of the crustacean life cycle, makes chitin a cardinal feature in the metabolic economy of these organisms.

The chemistry of chitin has been deftly reviewed by Kent (1964). Chitin is an unbranched homopolysaccharide chain of N-acetyl-D-glucosamine residues linked by β-1,4-glycosidic bonds. Hackman (1960), using *Scylla serrata* preparations, found protein covalently bound to chitin, forming stable glycoprotein complexes. Further support for the presence of complexes was derived from chitin preparations of insect cuticle, cuttlefish shell, and skeletal pen of the squid. The protein-chitin complex appeared bound through aspartyl or histidyl residues. These findings led Hackman to propose the following nomenclature: (a) native chitin = protein-bound chitin complexes, and (b) chitin = high molecular weight polymers of N-acetyl-D-glucosamine. Jeuniaux (1965) has recently developed an enzymic tool for the specific quantitative determination of both the free and the bound chitin. The extreme insolubility of chitin makes it less than amenable to chemical studies, yet very suitable as a component of the external skeleton.

As stated earlier, Drach and Lafon (1942) reported 64% to 74% of the organic material in brachyuran exoskeletons to be chitin. Jeuniaux (1965) states that 58% to 85% of the decalcified cuticle is chitin in crustaceans and diplopods. Considered as a polysaccharide that must be synthesized from precursor molecules, chitin biosynthesis represents a substantial drain on the animal's organic reserves. Classically the stored glycogen has been considered as the pre-existing pool of chitin precursor molecules. Evidence for this is largely based on the cyclic appearance and disappearance of glycogen in the hepatopancreas as reported by Renaud (1949). This utilization of glycogen occurs at a time when the animal is known to be synthesizing chitin (late D). Travis (1955) has also given histochemical evidence that growth periods in *Panulirus argus* Latreille are accompanied by cyclical alterations in the epidermis, subepidermis, and hepatopancreas. Zaluska (1959), however, upon examining metabolism of both glycogen and chitin in the silkworm *Bombyx mori* L. has concluded that the total amount of glycogen utilized in the postdiapause period of development is not sufficient to account for the amount of chitin present. He suggests that other substances, "possibly lipids," contribute to chitin formation. Barnes (1965), in a study of the biochemistry of cirripede eggs, concurs with Zaluska's observation that glycogen is not the only carbon source of chitin hexose units. In cirripedes, a material is secreted by the oviducts that encloses the eggs in a neatly packaged egg-mass. This material, presumably chitin, eventually breaks down. A second burst of chitin synthesis follows, presumably in the development of the stage II nauplius within stage I before the latter is hatched (Barnes, 1965). It was noted that in this period carbohydrate depletion was not adequate to supply sufficient glucose for the amount of chitin synthesized. This implicates hexose synthesis from other metabolites. Porter and Jaworski (1965) have suggested that the presence of isocitrate lyase activity concurrent with peak chitin synthetase activity would be ideal for converting fat reserves into carbohydrate at a time when demands are especially acute. Isocitratase activity has been demonstrated in the insect *Prodenia eridania* (Carpenter and Jaworski, 1962) but not in crustaceans. Activities were low and the significance is equivocal at the present time.

Meenakshi and Scheer (1961) have shown glucose to be incorporated into chitin during early postmolt but not during intermolt. Hu (1958) also reported that administration of uniformly labeled glucose resulted in no incorporation into chitin in intermolt animals. Since it is now axiomatic that an animal's metabolism and its control must be interpreted in an enzymic framework, some studies have been performed at this level. Glaser and Brown (1957) have reported a particulate enzyme from *Neurospora crassa* capable of chitin synthesis directly from uridine diphosphate-*N*-acetylglucosamine (UDPNAG). The enzyme is a glucosyl donor and has an absolute primer requirement. Candy and Kilby (1962) demonstrated the presence of enzymes leading from glucose to UDPNAG the immediate chitin precursor, in the epidermis of the desert locust, *Schistocerca gregaria*. Their study was unsuccessful in demonstrating chitin synthetase activity. Chitin synthetase activity was first shown in animals by Porter and Jaworski (1965) in extracts of the southern armyworm, *Prodenia eridania*. Carey (1965) has further shown chitin synthetase activity in the epidermis of the molting blue crab, *Callinectes sapidus*, and 3-day larvae of *Artemia salina*. Chitodextrins also appear necessary for chitin synthetase activity in crustaceans.

The scanty literature available on chitin synthesis in general and in crustaceans in particular shows similarities to the metabolism of oligosaccharides and polysaccharides in other organisms. As with other polysaccharides, chitin synthesis appears to have a primer requirement; biosynthesis proceeds through enzymic utilization of phosphorylated monosaccharide intermediates; complex saccharide formation occurs through the use of nucleoside diphosphate sugar donors; and the catabolic pathway is not a simple reversal of the anabolic route. There is no indication of any unusual character of the pathway to date. It should be pointed out that because chitin synthetase is terminal to the chitin biosynthetic pathway it may be a very important control point.

The enzymology is virtually unexplored. It is also not known to what extent uracil can be replaced by the other bases in the sugar nucleotide donors. More analysis is needed to document and complete the chemical story of this carbohydrate in the crustacean economy.

Before concluding this discussion of chitin metabolism, mention should be made of the site of its biosynthesis. It is generally acknowledged that the epidermis is the site of chitin biosynthesis. No definitive work is available, however, which specifies the type of cell responsible. Studies on insects (Philogene and McFarlane, 1967; Ritter and Bray, 1968) have implicated oenocytes in the extracellular deposition of chitin. It would be of interest to extend and enlarge upon these findings in crustaceans.

B. Mucopolysaccharides

In vertebrates, acid mucopolysaccharides form one component of the intercellular substance commonly surrounding loose ordinary connective tissue cells. This jellylike amorphous intercellular fabric has important assignments in vertebrates. Among these are (1) facilitation of material transfer between capillaries and cells through ready diffusion of dissolved materials; (2) nutrient and fluid transfer between cells and capillaries; (3) body defense against infection; and (4) as a lubricant in synovial joints. It is obvious that certain of these postulated functions are not possible in the invertebrates. Mathews (1967) cites the extrusion of marcromolecules such as acid mucopolysaccharides as being related to the primitive need of unicellular organisms to regulate exchange of ionic and nonionic metabolites across cell barriers. It is at once apparent that function of the extracellular matrix is not obvious in the invertebrates. A very lucid and informative review of connective tissue phylogeny was recently presented by Mathews (1967).

Chemically the acid mucopolysaccharides are characterized as being components of large macromolecules consisting of carbohydrate moieties covalently bound to polypeptide or protein (Mathews, 1967). The carbohydrate moieties are quite variable in length and saccharide constitution. A repeating disaccharide unit of hexosamine–hexuronic acid or hexose amine–neutral sugar generally comprises the saccharide portions.

Stevenson and Murphy (1967) studied the rosette glands of the isopod *Armadillidium vulgare* histochemically. The results revealed copious carbohydrate, in which an acid mucopolysaccharide was present but not glycogen. Little protein or lipid could be demonstrated. A possible involvement as a lubricant in swallowing was suggested. Meenakshi and Scheer (1959) reported an acid mucopolysaccharide in the cuticle and hepatopancreas of the crab *Hemigrapsus nudus*. Glucose, galactose, and fucose were among the recognized components. A role in the calcification of the cuticle was suggested.

Puyear *et al.* (1965), using a radiospirometric method to investigate carbohydrate catabolism, obtained some evidence for the existence of the glucuronate pathway in the crayfish *Pacifastacus leniusculus*. In a more recent study by Puyear (1967), the enzymes UDPG dehydrogenase, UDPGA glucuronyltransferase, UDP glucuronate pyrophosphatase, alkaline phosphatase, and β-glucuronidase were demonstrated in the digestive gland of the blue crab *Callinectes sapidus*. Gilles and Schoffeniels (1969a) have further support for the existence of the glucuronic shunt in nerve cord preparations of the crayfish *Astacus fluviatilis* and the lobster *Homarus vulgaris*.

It was found that $^{14}CO_2$ production from G-1-^{14}C was approximately fivefold greater than from G-6-^{14}C in both the crayfish and the lobster. This is inconsistent with the idea that the Krebs cycle is the main oxidative pathway. Administration of veratrine and NH_4Cl enhanced $^{14}CO_2$ recovery from G-6-^{14}C while cocaine depressed $^{14}CO_2$ recovery. These results were interpreted as being consistent with operation of the glucuronate shunt and pentose pathway and inconsistent with the exclusive operation of the Krebs cycle. Assuming the glucuronic acid pathway functions primarily in acid mucopolysaccharide biosynthesis, there is presently no evidence suggesting it is unlike that found in mammals.

The physiological function of mucopolysaccharides in crustaceans, however, is very uncertain at the present time. There is virtually no evidence that supports a concrete involvement of mucopolysaccharides in any of the animals' supportive activities. Greater chemical and physiological attention is unquestionably desirable before speculating on their value to this group of arthropods.

V. Aspects of Carbohydrate Control

A succinct verbal description of the glycolytic pathway would be (1) activation, (2) interconversion, and (3) utilization. If the premise is accepted that glycogen is an important polysaccharide to crustaceans, then the above sequence is very important. Figure 1 illustrates that all catabolic routes begin with an activated product of glycogen. As such the activation process is fundamental to carbohydrate metabolism and much interest has centered on this process in crustaceans as well as mammals. Presently it is believed that glycogen is degraded by phosphorylase but synthesized through other intermediates, i.e., synthesis does not involve phosphorylase (D. H. Wang and Scheer, 1962, 1963). Phosphorylase is, therefore, central to the activation process and an ideal control point. Phosphorylase is a rather complex enzyme and its demonstrated interconversions in crustaceans are shown schematically in Fig 3.

Cowgill (1959a,b) and Sagardia (1969) have contributed most of the information available on this enzyme in crustaceans. Sagardia (1969) has also shown that phosphorylase *a* has a partial requirement for adeno-

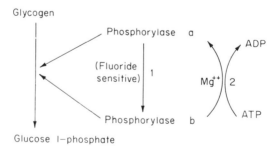

Fɪɢ. 3. The crustacean phosphorylase system. 1, Phosphorylase phosphatase; 2, phosphorylase *b* kinase.

sine 5′-monophosphate (AMP) while phosphorylase b has a total requirement for full activity. This may mean that both the a and b forms are capable of further dissociation-association reactions similar to those found in vertebrates but not yet elucidated in crustaceans. There is also indirect evidence indicating that the phosphorylase b is bound to phosphorylase kinase and that incubation with ATP and magnesium releases phosphorylase b, thus augmenting the levels of both phosphorylase a and b simultaneously (Sagardia, 1969). This is an apparent difference not common to other systems. Ramamurthi et al. (1968) report that eyestalk ablation in *Hemigrapsus nudus* results in a statistically significant decrease in both phosphorylase a and b and a decline in the ratio of a/b.

The apparent involvement of AMP in the phosphorylase system is interesting with respect to the established cellular processes affected by this nucleotide. In vertebrate systems cyclic AMP has been designated as a "second messenger" in coordinating cellular activities. According to this concept, hormones act on target cells by altering the levels of cyclic AMP. Cyclic AMP extends the hormonal control by acting on specific intracellular processes such as enzyme systems and membrane permeabilities. Steele (1969), subsequent to studies on the cockroach *Periplaneta americana* L., concluded that changes in phosphorylase activity following incubation in different concentrations of Na^+ and K^+ may reflect an ionic control on phosphorylase via phosphorylase phosphatase. Unfortunately, levels of AMP were not determined at the different ionic concentrations thus circumventing its possible participation. It would be of interest to comparative endocrinologists and biochemists to extend these observations to crustaceans.

Given the following conditions: (a) glucose is the primary blood sugar in crustaceans, (b) G 6-P is the immediate source of hemolymph glucose, and (c) blood glucose levels reflect a steady-state exchange between hemolymph and cells, it would appear that simple feedback controls would be reasonable and sufficient. This argument depends on the idea that a steady state does prevail, but (1) blood glucose and other carbohydrate is highly variable among individuals and with time, and (2) the intensity and direction of carbohydrate metabolism varies in the intermolt cycle. This may be a reflection of a more primitive system where the emphasis is placed on regulation of cellular activities rather than on strict maintenance of constant blood sugar levels. Additionally, vegetative activities of the organism would also constitute displacements away from a steady-state condition.

There is clear evidence that endocrine factors are involved in the control mechanism. These factors most probably originate in the neuroendocrine system, and attention has been focused especially on the eye-stalks, which are easily amputated and contain the well-known X-organ sinus gland complex. Injection of eyestalk extracts has long been known to result in increased blood sugar levels, due primarily to an increase in blood glucose, but the effects of eyestalk removal vary with species. It is perhaps unfortunate that the term "diabetogenic factor" has domi-nated our thinking in this field, since the site and mode of action of the endocrine factors is probably not primarily on blood sugar levels. Figure 4 indicates some possible points of endocrine control. Epidermal cells are included because, in *Panulirus japonicus* at least, the epidermal glycogen store exceeded those of muscle and hepatopancreas (Scheer *et al.*, 1952).

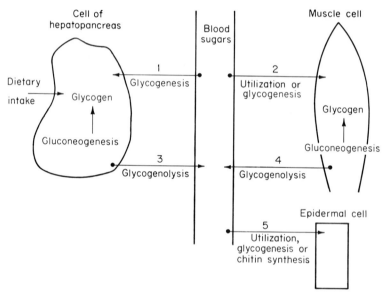

Fig. 4. Possible views of crustacean hyperglycemia.

D. H. Wang and Scheer (1962, 1963) established the presence of UDPG-glycogen transglucosylase in tissues from several species of crus-taceans (*Cancer magister, Hemigrapsus nudus, Astacus cambarus*). Ex-tracts of eyestalks inhibited the transglucosylase in muscle from these species, and also in a number of tissues from animals of other phyla, including mollusks and vertebrates. Ramamurthi *et al.* (1968) carried through a partial purification of this factor from eyestalks of *Pandalus jordani*, using muscle tissue from *Hemigrapsus nudus* and *Cancer magis-ter* for assay. Mumbach (1969) has shown that the partly purified factor inhibits a highly purified transglucosylase preparation from rat liver. Ramamurthi *et al.* (1968) also showed that eyestalk ablation is followed by increased transglucosylase activity in the muscle of *H. nudus* and *C. magister,* and increased glycogen synthesis in the hepatopancreas. Injection of the partly purified factor restores both transglucosylase activity and glycogen synthesis to near normal levels. These studies suggest control of glycogenesis in hepatopancreas and muscle (1 and 2, Fig. 4) as significant control points.

Keller (1965b) reported partial inactivation of phosphorylase after removal of eyestalks from *Cambarus affinis* Say and reversal of this effect by injection of eyestalk extract. The factor studied by Ramamurthi *et al.* (1968) has no effect on phosphorylase activity. Bauchau and Mengeot (1966a,b, 1967), Bauchau *et al.* (1968), and Keller and Bayer (1968) note an increase in blood sugar following injection of serotonin (5-hydroxytryptamine, 5-HT). Bauchau *et al.* (1968) demonstrated an increase in phosphorylase activity in the Chinese crab *Eriocheir sinensis* following injection of 5-HT and in parallel with the increase in blood sugar. The hyperglycemic response to 5-HT observed in *Orconectes limosus* by Keller and Bayer (1968) was the same in intact and eyestalkless animals, and followed a time course similar to that of the response to eyestalk extract. Reserpine and dopamine had no effect. Mumbach (1969) has demonstrated the presence of dopa and dopamine in extracts of the eyestalks of *Pandalus jordani.* Keller (see Keller and Bayer, 1968) suggests an indirect effect of 5-HT through promoting release of a hyperglycemic hormone, but if this is correct, the hormone must arise outside the eyestalks.

Kleinholz (1966) and Kleinholz *et al.* (1967) have succeeded with partial purification of a hyperglycemic factor from eyestalks of *Pandalus borealis.* The factor causes a marked increase of blood glucose within 2 hours after injection, is not dialyzable through cellophane, and is destroyed by peptidases. This factor is not identical with the transglucosylase inhibitor, or of course with 5-HT.

The available evidence suggests that factors exist in crustaceans capable of controlling both glycogenesis (1, 2, Fig. 4) and glycogenolysis (3, 4, Fig. 4). The factor that inhibits transglucosylase meets some of the classical criteria for a hormone, but is unique in being interspecific and in acting directly on a specific enzyme. The status of all the factors demonstrated thus far requires further clarification as to site of origin, normal mode of action, and target organs. The actions of these factors in the normal sequence of regulation of carbohydrate metabolism are still unclear. Crustacean hormones are discussed in more detail by Knowles and Carlisle (1956), Gorbman and Bern (1962), Barrington

(1964), Charniaux-Cotton and Kleinholz (1964), Fingerman (1965), and Sehnal (Chapter 9, Volume VI).

REFERENCES

Adiyodi, R. G. (1969). *Experientia* **25**, 43–44.
Andrews, P. (1967). Z. *Vergleich. Physiol.* **57**, 7.
Barnes, H. (1965). *J. Marine Biol. Assoc. U. K.* **45**, 321–329.
Barrington, E. J. W. (1964). *In* "The Hormones" (G. Pincus, K. V. Thimann, and E. B. Astwood, eds.), Vol. 4, p. 299. Academic Press, New York.
Bauchau, A. G., and Mengeot, J. C. (1966a). *Experientia* **22**, 238–239.
Bauchau, A. G., and Mengeot, J. C. (1966b). *Ann. Endocrinol. (Paris)* **27**, 529–530.
Bauchau, A. G., and Mengeot, J. C. (1967). *Gen. Comp. Endocrinol.* **9**, 432.
Bauchau, A. G., Mengeot, J. C., and Oliver, M. A. (1968). *Gen. Comp. Endocrinol.* **11**, 132–138.
Beenakkers, A. M. (1969). *J. Insect Physiol.* **15**, 353–362.
Boulton, A. P., Huggins, A. K., and Munday, K. A. (1967). *Life Sci.* **6**, 1293–1298.
Candy, D. J., and Kilby, B. A. (1962). *J. Exptl. Biol.* **39**, 129–140.
Carey, F. G. (1965). *Comp. Biochem. Physiol.* **716**, 155–58.
Carpenter, W. D., and Jaworski, E. G. (1962). *Biochim. Biophys. Acta* **58**, 369–371.
Charniaux-Cotton, H., and Kleinholz, L. H. (1964). *In* "The Hormones" (G. Pincus, K. V. Thimann, and E. B. Astwood, eds.), Vol. 4, p. 139. Academic Press, New York.
Clegg, J. S. (1965). *Comp. Biochem. Physiol.* **14**, 135–143.
Cowgill, R. W. (1959a). *J. Biol. Chem.* **234**, 3146–3153.
Cowgill, R. W. (1959b). *J. Biol. Chem.* **234**, 3154–3157.
Dean, J. M., and Vernberg, F. J. (1965a). *Comp. Biochem. Physiol.* **14**, 29–34.
Dean, J. M., and Vernberg, F. J. (1965b). *Biol. Bull.* **129**, 87.
Drach, P., and Lafon, M. (1942). *Arch. Zool. Exptl. Gen.* **82**, 100–118.
Eastman, R. C. (1968). *Exptl. Cell Res.* **51**, 323–329.
Fingerman, M. (1965). *Physiol. Rev.* **45**, 296–339.
Florkin, M. (1960). *In* "The Physiology of Crustacea" (T. H. Waterman, ed.), Vol. 1, p. 395. Academic Press, New York.
Florkin, M. (1966). "A Molecular Approach to Phylogeny." Elsevier, Amsterdam.
Giese, A. G. (1966). *Physiol. Rev.* **46**, 244–298.
Gilles, R., and Schoffeniels, E. (1969a). *Comp. Biochem. Physiol.* **28**, 417–423.
Gilles, R., and Schoffeniels, E. (1969b). *Comp. Biochem. Physiol.* **28**, 1145–1152.
Gilmour, D. (1965). "The Metabolism of Insects." Oliver & Boyd, Edinburgh and London.
Glaser, L., and Brown, D. H. (1957). *J. Biol. Chem.* **228**, 729–742.
Gorbman, A., and Bern, H. (1962). "A Textbook of Comparative Endocrinology." Wiley, New York.
Hackman, R. H. (1960). *Australian J. Biol. Sci.* **13**, 568–577.
Hochachka, P. W., Teal, J. M., and Telford, M. (1962). *Can. J. Biochem. Physiol.* **40**, 1143–1150.
Hu, A. S. L. (1958). *Arch. Biochem. Biophys.* **75**, 387–395.
Huggins, A. K. (1966). *Comp. Biochem. Physiol.* **18**, 283–290.
Huggins, A. K. (1969). *Comp. Biochem. Physiol.* **29**, 439–446.
Huggins, A. K., and Munday, K. A. (1968). *Advan. Comp. Physiol. Biochem.* **3**, 271–378.

Hyman, L. H. (1966). *Biol. Bull.* **130**, 94–95.

Jeuniaux, C. (1965). *Bull. Soc. Chim. Biol.* **47**, 2267–2278.

Jungreis, A. M. (1968). *Comp. Biochem. Physiol.* **24**, 1–6.

Keller, R. (1965a). *Z. Vergleich. Physiol.* **50**, 119–136.

Keller, R. (1965b). *Z. Vergleich. Physiol.* **51**, 49–59.

Keller, R., and Bayer, J. (1968). *Z. Vergleich. Physiol.* **59**, 78–85.

Kent, P. W. (1964). *Comp. Biochem.* **7**, 93–136.

Kleinholz, L. H. (1966). *Am. Zoologist* **6**, 161–167.

Kleinholz, L. H., Kimball, F., and McGarvey, M. (1967). *Gen. Comp. Endocrinol.* **8**, 75–81.

Knowles, F. G. W., and Carlisle, D. B. (1956). *Biol. Rev.* **31**, 396–473.

McWhinnie, M., and Corkill, A. J. (1964). *Comp. Biochem. Physiol.* **12**, 81–93.

McWhinnie, M., and Kirchenberg, R. J. (1962). *Comp. Biochem. Physiol.* **6**, 117–128.

McWhinnie, M., and O'Connor, J. D. (1967). *Comp. Biochem. Physiol.* **20**, 131–145.

McWhinnie, M., and Saller, P. N. (1960). *Comp. Biochem. Physiol.* **1**, 110–122.

McWhinnie, M., and Scheer, B. T. (1958). *Science* **128**, 90.

Martin, A. L. (1965). *J. Zool.* **147**, 185–200.

Mathews, M. B. (1967). *Biol. Rev.* **42**, 499–551.

Mathews, M. B., Duh, J., and Person, P. (1962). *Nature* **193**, 378.

Meenakshi, V. R., and Scheer, B. T. (1959). *Science* **130**, 1189–1190.

Meenakshi, V. R., and Scheer, B. T. (1961). *Comp. Biochem. Physiol.* **3**, 30–41.

Mumbach, M. W. (1969). Unpublished experiments.

Neiland, K. A., and Scheer, B. T. (1953). *Physiol. Comparata Oecol.* **3**, 321–326.

Philogene, B. J., and McFarlane, J. E. (1967). *Can. J. Zool.* **45**, 181–190.

Porter, C. A., and Jaworski, E. G. (1965). *J. Insect Physiol.* **11**, 1151–1160.

Puyear, R. L. (1967). *Comp. Biochem. Physiol.* **20**, 499–508.

Puyear, R. L. (1969). *Comp. Biochem. Physiol.* **28**, 159–168.

Puyear, R. L., Wang, C. H., and Pritchard, A. W. (1965). *Comp. Biochem. Physiol.* **14**, 145–153.

Ramamurthi, R., Mumbach, M. W., and Scheer, B. T. (1968). *Comp. Biochem. Physiol.* **26**, 311–319.

Renaud, L. (1949). *Ann. Inst. Oceanog.* (*Paris*) **24**, 259–357.

Riegel, J. A. (1960). *Nature* **186**, 787.

Ritter, H., and Bray, M. (1968). *J. Insect Physiol.* **14**, 361–366.

Robertson, J. D. (1961). *J. Exptl. Biol.* **38**, 707.

Sagardia, F. (1969). *Comp. Biochem. Physiol.* **28**, 1377–1385.

Scheer, B. T., and Meenakshi, V. R. (1961). *In* "Comparative Physiology of Carbohydrate Metabolism in Heterothermic Animals" (A. W. Martin, ed.), p. 65. Univ. of Washington Press, Seattle, Washington.

Scheer, B. T., and Scheer, M. A. R. (1951). *Physiol. Comparata Oecol.* **2**, 198–209.

Scheer, B. T., Schwabe, C. W., and Scheer, M. A. R. (1952). *Physiol. Comparata Oecol.* **2**, 310–320.

Skinner, D. M. (1968). *J. Exptl. Zool.* **169**, 347–356.

Steele, J. E. (1969). *Comp. Biochem. Physiol.* **29**, 755–764.

Steeves, H. R. (1963). *J. Exptl. Zool.* **154**, 21–38.

Stevenson, J. R., and Murphy, J. C. (1967). *Trans. Am. Microscop. Soc.* **86**, 50–57.

Teal, J. M., and Carey, F. G. (1967). *Physiol. Zool.* **40**, 83–91.

Telford, M. (1965). *Can. J. Zool.* **43**, 503–507.

Telford, M. (1968a). *Comp. Biochem. Physiol.* **26**, 917–926.

Telford, M. (1968b). *Can. J. Zool.* **46,** 819–826.

Telford, M. (1968c). *Biol. Bull.* **135,** 574–584.

Tracy, M. V. (1968). *Advan. Comp. Physiol. Biochem.* **3,** 233–270.

Travis, D. F. (1955). *Biol. Bull.* **108,** 88–102.

Vonk, H. J. (1960). *In* "The Physiology of Crustacea" (T. H. Waterman, ed.), Vol. 1, p. 291. Academic Press, New York.

Wang, C. M., and Patton, R. L. (1969). *J. Insect Physiol.* **15,** 861–866.

Wang, D. H., and Scheer, B. T. (1962). *Life Sci.* **5,** 209–211.

Wang, D. H., and Scheer, B. T. (1963). *Comp. Biochem. Physiol.* **9,** 263–274.

Waterman, T. H., ed. (1960). "The Physiology of Crustacea," Vol. 1. Academic Press, New York.

Zaluska, H. (1959). *Acta Biol. Exptl., Polish Acad. Sci.* **19,** 339–351.

Zandee, D. I. (1966). *Arch. Intern. Physiol. Biochim.* **74,** 45–57.

CHAPTER 6

Metabolism of Carbohydrates in Insects

Stanley Friedman[1]

I. Introduction

A number of reviews concerned with various aspects of carbohydrate metabolism have been written in the recent past, some of sufficient interest to be noted here. The most significant are those of Wyatt (1967), "The Biochemistry of Sugars and Polysaccharides in Insects," and Chefurka (1965a), "Intermediary Metabolism of Carbohydrates." Others include a second review by Chefurka (1965b) and one by Sacktor (1965).

[1] Work from the author's laboratory described in this review has been partially supported by Grant No. AI-06345 from the National Institutes of Health, USPHS, Bethesda, Maryland.

Members of the class Insecta are bound together taxonomically by the possession, in common, of a small number of structural characters. Aside from these, however, the anatomic and behavioral diversification is enormous. It is reasonable to anticipate that the ecological catholicity of the group is reflected at the molecular level, and that its various species are capable of performing most of the biochemical reactions whereby all animals support their life processes. Are there, then, any class peculiarities which serve to distinguish insects from other animals? An answer to this question might be found in an examination of the small number of substrates which remain inert or repellent to the group, but, not unexpectedly, work along these lines is lacking. In the absence of this information specific patterns are difficult to pick out, and perhaps all that can be done is to report the available data with little comment. In this context, it is important to note, and we cannot stress this too vigorously, that our total understanding of the biochemistry of insects derives, except at the most sciolistic level, from a very small number of species. Some have been chosen because they exhibit metabolic peculiarities, but most have been subjected to investigation because of the ease of culturing large numbers, or for economic reasons. In view of the general heterogeneity of the class, the question of whether they are representative is really quite meaningless.

II. "Storage" Carbohydrates

The major compounds in which hexose residues are stored in insects are presently known to be three: chitin, glycogen, and trehalose. There are indications, however, that less clearly identifiable glycoproteins may play important roles as sources of hexose [*Periplaneta americana* (Dictyoptera), Lipke *et al.*, 1965a], and that polysaccharides other than glycogen may occur [*Tribolium confusum* (Coleoptera), Villeneuve and Lemonde, 1965].

A. CHITIN

Chitin is found mainly in the endo- and exocuticle of insects, probably as a glycoprotein, since most of the attempts to isolate the polymer by methods which would disrupt any but covalent bonds have resulted in a protein residue accompanying the polysaccharide. Hackman (1960) working with cuticle from the larva of *Agrianome spinicollis* (Coleoptera), the puparium of *Lucilia cuprina* (Diptera), the squid skeletal pen, and chitins from a number of other arthropods, has claimed that the chitin–protein linkage is established through aspartyl and histidyl residues, but neither Lipke *et al.* (1965a) using *Periplaneta americana*, nor Attwood and Zola (1967), using *Calliphora* sp. (Diptera) larvae and squid skeletal pen, have been able to confirm his findings.

The classic description of chitin, i.e., a high molecular weight polydisperse compound, consisting of $\beta1 \rightarrow 4$ linked repeating units of 2-acetamido-2-deoxy-D-glucopyranose, has been the subject of disputation for a number of years. Among other evidence, an elemental analysis of α-chitin from the Norwegian lobster, *Nephrops norvegicus* (Giles *et al.*, 1958) has been interpreted to indicate the presence of a relatively high proportion of free glucosamine residues (12.5%) and bound H_2O (5%). However, Rudall (1963), has pointed out that if a "conservative" stance is taken, using physicochemical evidence such as X-ray diffraction, infrared spectrum and density measurements, a strong case can be made for the absence of any, except small amounts, of unacetylated glucosamine. In view of the relative ease with which chemical changes can be imposed upon the chitin molecule and the generally harsh methods which have been used for isolation, it would appear that there is still room for disagreement. In line with this is the recent proposal by Lipke *et al.* (1965a) that neutral sugars are either present in the chain proper or attached as substituents on carbon atoms 3 or 6 of the glucosaminyl residues.

The total quantity of chitin in an insect varies with the stage of development, but appears to average out to 1% to 4% of the fresh weight of the animal (see, for example, Fraenkel and Rudall, 1947; Lipke *et al.*, 1965a,b; Crompton and Birt, 1967). Of this amount, approximately 50% is lost in the exuvium so that at any time prior to adulthood up to 2% of its total weight may be characterized as chitin in flux, i.e., either being synthesized or degraded.

B. GLYCOGEN

It has generally been assumed when studying insect enzymes concerned with glycogen metabolism that commercially prepared oyster and rabbit glycogen are similar enough to insect glycogen to substitute as substrates, and, indeed, Stevenson and Wyatt (1964) have stated that cecropia pupal glycogen has no greater activity with phosphorylase from the same animal than does "commercial glycogen." The case for similarity between insect and other glycogens has been strengthened by an investigation of *Anthonomus grandis* (Coleoptera) larval glycogen isolated by trichloroacetic acid precipitation. An average chain length of 11 ± 1 units and an interior chain length of 3 to 3.5 glucose units have been found (Betz *et al.*, 1968). Recently, however, Childress and Sacktor (1969) have shown that glycogen isolated from *Phormia regina* (Diptera) flight muscle behaves differently as a phosphorylase substrate depending upon whether the glycogen has been extracted with cold water or KOH, again indicating the mode of isolation as an important variable in qualitative analysis. The optical rotation values of all isolated insect glycogens fall between $+184$ and $+200$ degrees (see Betz *et al.*, 1968, for references) and glucose is the major component linked $\alpha 1 \rightarrow 4$ and $1 \rightarrow 6$. Lindh (1967), working with glycogen from *Calliphora erythrocephala* (Diptera) pupae, and using various hydrogen bond breaking reagents in the isolation procedure, has found indications that it is covalently linked with proteinaceous material.

The amount of glycogen has been shown to vary considerably through development ranging from as little as 0.01% wet weight to values of more than 2% (see, for example, Kilby, 1963; Nettles and Betz, 1965). It is located in muscle and fat body, with between 60% to 90% present in the latter organ in fully developed, normally feeding adult *Phormia regina* (Hudson, 1958; Sacktor, 1965). There is practically no glycogen in the circulating hemolymph except in a few isolated cases (Wyatt, 1967).

C. TREHALOSE

This nonreducing disaccharide (α-D-glucopyranosyl-α-D-glucopyranoside) has been shown to be present in the hemolymph of almost all of the insects on which determinations have been made (Wyatt, 1967). The concentration varies from zero [larvae of various species of the family Calliphoridae (Diptera) (Crompton and Birt, 1967), larvae of *Sarcophaga bullata* (Diptera), and *Musca domestica* (Diptera) (Friedman, 1969), and the feeding larva of *Celerio euphorbiae* (Lepidoptera) (Mochnacka and Petryszyn, 1959)] to more than 7% in the female adult aphid, *Megoura viciae* (Homoptera) (Ehrhardt, 1962). The latter value is higher than that found in any other invertebrate, although the presence of trehalose has been established in almost all invertebrate phyla (Fairbairn, 1958). Analyses indicating the existence of trehalose in tissues other than blood and fat body (in which it is rapidly synthesized) are suspect due to the difficulty of separating the blood, which always contains the highest concentration of this compound, from the tissue to be examined (see Wyatt, 1967, for references). Wimer (1969) has recently shown that a small amount of a neutral compound presumed to be trehalose is present in the fat body of 3rd instar *Phormia regina* larvae at the same time that it is absent from the blood. Other tissues have been reported to have enzymes capable of low levels of trehalose synthesis (Hines and Smith, 1963), but in no cases have pure preparations been investigated, so the issue is still clouded.

As a result of the presence of a myriad of enzymes in the midgut lumen, presumably secreted by salivary gland cells, midgut epithelium, and intestinal flora (see Chapter 4), the material moving across the gut wall in even the most nutritionally specialized insects appears to consist of simple sugars, amino acids, fatty acids, and other low molecular weight compounds. The few insects which have been studied seem to have no mechanism for active uptake of these general classes of compounds but pass them across the gut wall by diffusion, in some cases facilitated by immediate turnover into higher molecular weight species. A classic example of this type of activity is found in the locust, *Schistocerca gregaria* (Orthoptera), in which glucose, upon passage across the gut wall is immediately moved out of the blood, and is either degraded or converted to glycogen in various tissues, or transformed by enzymes in the fat body into trehalose which is then liberated into the blood (Treherne, 1967).

D. OTHER COMPOUNDS

Other compounds which may contribute hexosyl residues for various functions include glycoproteins, polysaccharides which do not appear to be glycogen, and mono- and disaccharides, which, in certain instances, exceed trehalose levels in blood.

The only significant analysis of plasma glycoprotein in insects has been made by Lipke *et al.* (1965a) on *Periplaneta americana* nymphs at various developmental stages. The carbohydrate components described included not only glucose, mannose, galactose, glucosamine, and galactosamine (probably as the N-acetyl derivatives), but the pentoses xylose and arabinose. These sugars were also found bound into the cuticle, and the proportion and quantity of each compound was shown to change throughout the period of the molt.

Villeneuve and Lemonde (1965) have grown *Tribolium confusum* larvae on a synthetic diet containing no polysaccharide and extracted from the pupae a compound which electrophoretically resembles amylose rather than glycogen.

Sugars other than trehalose have been shown in large amounts in the blood of various insects. Aside from glucose and maltose, which are the major components of the hemolymph of young *Phormia regina* larvae (Wimer, 1969), fructose in high concentrations has been demonstrated in *Gasterophilus intestinalis* (Diptera) larval blood, and glucose, fructose, and sucrose, as well as trehalose have been found in the blood of the adult honeybee, *Apis mellifera* (Hymenoptera) (see Wyatt, 1967, for references). The effect of diet on the presence of these sugars has been investigated by Maurizio (1965), who fed honeybees on fructose or glucose and found that the total blood reducing sugars were fructose and glucose, respectively. It is interesting to note that when either of these sugars was fed in moderate concentration, trehalose was found in the blood in larger quantity than the monosaccharides. If, however, the concentration of sugar fed was high enough, the amount of fructose or glucose exceeded that of trehalose, the level of which appeared to be carefully controlled (F. K. Chang and Friedman, 1968). Sorbitol and glycerol have been shown in hemolymph of various insects (Somme, 1967) as has scylloinositol (Candy, 1967).

III. Synthesis of "Storage" Carbohydrates

The steps in the synthesis of chitin, glycogen, and trehalose have been examined in a few insects, and the general patterns appear to be similar to those already established in other organisms.

A. CHITIN

A crude construct of the mode of synthesis of insect chitin has been obtained through the experiments of Candy and Kilby (1962), with cell-free wing extracts of young adult locusts, and Jaworski and his colleagues (1963; Krueger and Jaworski, 1966), using *Prodenia eridania* (Lepidoptera) larval homogenates and particulate preparations. Candy and Kilby were able to demonstrate the formation of all of the intermediates noted below, but could not show incorporation of uridine diphosphate N-acetylglucosamine into chitodextrin [reaction (4)]. It remained for Jaworski to produce evidence that "chitin synthetase" is an enzyme sedimenting in a particulate fraction between 900 and 30,000 g (leaving us with the unanswered question of what the state of the chitin molecule is at the time of synthesis, and how it moves into the cuticle).

$$\text{Fructose 6-phosphate} + \text{glutamine} \rightarrow \text{glucosamine 6-P} + \text{glutamic acid} \quad (1)$$
$$\text{Glucosamine 6-P} + \text{acetyl CoA} \rightarrow N\text{-acetylglucosamine 6-P} + \text{CoA} \quad (2)$$
$$N\text{-Acetylglucosamine 6-P} + \text{UTP} \rightarrow \text{UDP } N\text{-acetylglucosamine} + \text{PPi} \quad (3)$$
$$\text{UDP } N\text{-acetylglucosamine} + (\text{chitodextrin})_n \rightarrow (\text{chitodextrin})_{n+1} + \text{UDP} \quad (4)$$

In view of the fact that purified preparations from other animals catalyze reaction (3) between N-acetylglucosamine 1-P and UTP, it is probable that a mutase capable of directing the conversion of the 6-P to the 1-P was present in the crude locust extracts. Reaction (1) also utilized glucose 6-phosphate, indicating the presence of phosphoglucose isomerase.

Recently, the first reaction in the scheme, the synthesis of glucosamine

6-P, has been examined in some detail by Benson and Friedman (1970). In contrast to locusts and cockroaches, both of which contain the amine-transferase [reaction (1)] (Benson, 1968), houseflies appear to be completely lacking in this enzyme at a time when chitin production is actively occurring. In its place is an active glucosaminephosphate isomerase [2-amino-2-deoxy-D-glucose-6-phosphate ketolisomerase (deaminating)] which catalyzes the reversible reaction:

$$\text{Fructose 6-phosphate} + \text{ammonia} \rightleftarrows \text{glucosamine 6-phosphate} + H_2O$$

Although

$$K_{eq} \frac{[\text{fructose 6-P}][\text{NH}_4^+]}{[\text{glucosamine 6-P}]} \sim 0.16$$

a number of pieces of evidence strengthen the idea that this enzyme is active in the synthesis of glucosamine 6-P. The initial rate of amination in the presence of an activator, N-acetylglucosamine 6-P, is 3.8 times that of deamination. Glucose 6-P (G-6-P), another activator, increases the rate 3.1 times in the direction of amination and has no effect on the deamination reaction. The K_m for fructose 6-P and NH_4^+ are 36 mM and 25 mM in the absence of G-6-P, in its presence (5 mM) the values are 3 mM and 3.3 mM. The K_m for glucosamine 6-P both in the presence and absence of G-6-P is 17 mM. The K_a G-6-P is 9.5 mM and that of N-acetylglucosamine 6-P is less than 0.5 mM. Other properties of the enzyme include a molecular weight of 154,000, a pH optimum for amination which is shifted from 7.2 to 8.3 in the presence of activators, and a broad optimum for deamination between 6.8–8.3, unaffected by activators.

B. GLYCOGEN

The synthesis of glycogen appears to follow the same pattern described in other animals, i.e.,

$$\text{UDP glucose} + (\text{glycogen})_n \rightarrow \text{UDP} + (\text{glycogen})_{n+1}$$

Early studies by Trivelloni (1960) using UDP glucose-^{14}C and fat body extracts from *Schistocerca cancellata* (Orthoptera) showed an incorporation of label into a glycogen pellet, but, in contrast to results obtained with mammalian liver, the preparation was not activated by glucose 6-P (G-6-P). Vardanis (1963), in studies on the fat body of the American cockroach, was also unable to obtain activation by G-6-P, but a preparation made from *Hyalophora cecropia* (Lepidoptera) larval fat body by Murphy and Wyatt (1965) showed pronounced stimulation by G-6-P, glucosamine 6-P, and galactose 6-P. Their preparation was peculiar in that activation did not include a decrease in the K_m for UDP glucose, a property of G-6-P activation of rat and rabbit skeletal muscle glycogen synthetase (Rosell-Perez and Larner, 1964), and of the rat liver enzyme (Hizukuri and Larner, 1964). The extract required addition of no primer and was, in contrast to that of Vardanis, very labile, being destroyed by freezing and thawing. The pH optimum of the synthetase was 7.7, the K_m UDP glucose in both the presence and absence of G-6-P was 1.6 mM, and the K_a G-6-P was 0.6 mM. Vardanis (1967) has recently examined the enzyme in honeybee larvae and found that it is bound to particulate glycogen and is activated (decreased K_m, increased V_{max}) by G-6-P. His preparation has not been purified to the extent that the presence of D (G-6-P dependent) and I (G-6-P independent) (see Rosell-Perez and Larner, 1964) forms of the enzyme can be substantiated. Experiments indicate that the activation by G-6-P is involved with an effect on the ability of the synthetase to handle outer branch chains of the primer. The pH optimum is 7.8, the K_m for UDP glucose in the absence of G-6-P is 2.8 mM, in its presence 0.33 mM, and the K_a G-6-P is 0.128 mM.

C. TREHALOSE

The pathway involved in the synthesis of this compound in insects was first studied by Candy and Kilby in 1961 with an extract of adult *Schistocerca gregaria* fat body. Using ^{14}C-labeled glucose, they showed that activity appeared first in glucose 6-P, then trehalose 6-P and finally trehalose. The requirement for ATP and UDP glucose, and the demonstration of the presence of ancillary enzymes indicated that the reaction proceeded through trehalosephosphate synthetase (UDP-glucose:D-glucose-6-phosphate 1-glucosyltransferase):

$$\text{Glucose 6-P} + \text{UDP glucose} \rightarrow \text{trehalose 6-phosphate} + \text{UDP},$$

and trehalose-6-phosphatase (trehalose-6-phosphate phosphohydrolase):

$$\text{Trehalose 6-phosphate} + \text{H}_2\text{0} \rightarrow \text{trehalose} + \text{inorganic phosphate}.$$

Murphy and Wyatt (1965) have examined this complex of reactions in a more purified preparation from *Hyalophora cecropia* larval fat body. They have shown that the enzymes are both soluble and have established a K_m for UDP glucose of 0.3 mM and for glucose 6-P (G-6-P) of 5 mM. The kinetic behavior of extracts containing both enzymes has led them to the belief that the synthetase is subject to allosteric regulation by both G-6-P and trehalose, the former activating the enzyme as well as functioning as a substrate, the latter occupying an inhibitory site on the enzyme. The suggestion has been made that the inhibition of the synthetase by trehalose may be important in the natural regulation of the rate of trehalose synthesis. Of interest in this regard are two recent observations made on fat body of adult *Phormia regina* by Friedman (1967, 1968). The first is that, in concurrence with the previous findings of Murphy and Wyatt on cecropia, *in vitro* trehalose synthesis or liberation by *Phormia* fat body is inhibited by low concentrations of trehalose. The second is that glucose-6-phosphatase activity in fat body extracts is enhanced in the presence of trehalose. This activity, which, by the way, appears to be inseparable from, although at another site on, the enzyme responsible for the hydrolysis of trehalose 6-phosphate (Friedman, 1969), might be implicated in the inhibition of trehalose synthesis by trehalose, since it results in an increased rate of substrate (G-6-P) degradation in the presence of relatively small amounts of trehalose.

The enzyme trehalose-6-phosphatase has been isolated and partially purified from extracts of whole adult *Phormia regina* (Friedman, 1960b). The enzyme in these extracts has a pH optimum of 7.0, and a K_m trehalose 6-P of 1.4 mM. It is inactive in the absence of a divalent metal, Mg^{++} being most effective. The location of the enzyme in *Phormia* was not determined, but some activity was shown to be present in the hemolymph. Recently, Mikolaschek and Zebe (1967), have examined various tissues of adult *Locusta migratoria* (Orthoptera) to determine whether the presence of the enzyme conforms with its presumed function. They have been able to show that it exhibits maximum activity in the cytoplasm of fat-body cells, in consonance with the fact that trehalose is synthesized in this organ. Practically no activity was found in the blood.

IV. Developmental Aspects of Polysaccharide Storage and Metabolism

This subject has been completely reviewed in the recent past (Wyatt, 1967), and there is relatively little to add at this time except for a single new observation.

The suggestion has been made by various investigators that the general disappearance of fat and increase in total carbohydrate occurring during the pupal instar in many holometabolous insects may be due to a net conversion of fat to carbohydrate at this time (see Wyatt, 1967, for references). As pointed out by Bade and Wyatt (1962), other materials, among them chitin, protein, and mucopolysaccharide, might easily provide the carbon for glycogen formation without the need to invoke a mode of synthesis that is not found in higher animals. Crompton and Birt (1967) have demonstrated that in *Lucilia cuprina* this may very likely be the case, since a closely timed study of the pupal period shows that the only increase in *total* carbohydrate comes at a time when the amount of fat is also increasing. It appears that these syntheses come about at the expense of amino acids. The major increase in glycogen, which takes place during the early pupal period (at a time when fat is decreasing), can be completely accounted for by a concomitant decrease in chitin.

V. Primary Degradative Pathways of Storage Compounds: Reaction Sequences and Controls

A. Chitin

The breakdown of chitin to N-acetylglucosamine has been studied to a very limited extent in insects. It generally occurs at the time of the molt, when the endocuticle is being resorbed and used both for the production of new cuticle and to provide energy for attendant metabolic processes. It is probable that there are at least two steps in the degradation process:

$$\text{Chitin} \rightarrow \text{chitobiose} + N\text{-acetylglucosamine}$$
$$\text{Chitobiose} \rightarrow 2 \ N\text{-acetylglucosamine}$$

but enzyme purification has not been detailed enough to permit any generalizations to be made (except, see below). Waterhouse and his co-workers (1961; Waterhouse and McKellar, 1961) have shown that chitinase activity is not restricted to immature forms where obvious function may be demonstrated, but is also present in adults of two species. In one of these, *Periplaneta americana,* the distribution of activity was studied, and the concentration of the enzyme found to be highest in the hemolymph, although total activity was greatest in the cuticle (including hypodermis and associated muscles). There was significant activity in the gut, practically none of it produced by the microflora. The gut enzyme has been purified to some extent by Powning and Irzykiewicz (1963, 1967), and separated into two fractions, chitinase I and II. Fraction I, when tested against chitobiose, -triose, -hexaose, and chitin suspensions, was found to be almost incapable of digesting the disaccharide, and split the higher oligosaccharides more rapidly than it did the triose. Powning and Irzykiewicz (1967) have examined the role of chitinases in adult cockroaches with reference to the possibility that they possess lysozyme-like activity (also a $\beta 1 \rightarrow 4$ acetylhexosaminidase), thus contributing to natural defense mechanisms, but their results indicate that the activities are entirely separate.

Metabolism of the breakdown products of chitin, i.e., glucosamine and N-acetylglucosamine, has been examined using labeled substrates, and has been shown to take place through the same general pathways as glucose (Sinohara and Asano, 1968). The deacetylation reaction has not been demonstrated, but deamination could take place by a reversal of the reaction previously described by Benson and Friedman (1970) (see Section III) as being implicated in chitin synthesis.

B. GLYCOGEN

The enzyme mainly responsible for the breakdown of glycogen, glycogen phosphorylase, has been examined with heightened interest since the discovery that its action may be changed considerably by any of a number of factors. As is well known, the enzyme in both liver and muscle of mammals assumes two forms: a (active) and b (inactive). Phosphorylase b can be changed to the a form by phosphorylation, a reaction catalyzed by an enzyme, phosphorylase b kinase, which is affected by a second enzyme, in turn activated by cyclic 3′, 5′-AMP. The production of the latter compound is, in the liver, under hormonal control. The activity of muscle phosphorylase is regulated both by a hormone and 5′-adenylic acid (AMP).

A study of phosphorylase in insects has shown it to be present in midgut, fat body, and flight muscle of various species, and to exhibit, in general, properties similar to those of the vertebrate muscle enzyme. In the fat body of the diapause pupa of Samia cynthia (Lepidoptera) it has a pH optimum of 7.0, and is activated by AMP, kinetic plots indicating multiple binding sites. In contrast to the mammalian enzyme, the silkmoth enzyme is apparently unaffected by —SH inhibitors. In pupae of both S. cynthia and Hyalophora cecropia the percentage of active enzyme (active in the absence of added AMP) is extremely low, increasing only when adult development commences and glycogen is being used (Stevenson and Wyatt, 1964). Activity has been examined further in H. cecropia by Wiens and Gilbert (1967a) who have observed that the adult fat body contains the largest amount of active enzyme at a time when glycogen has almost completely disappeared. They have also demonstrated that phosphorylase can be activated by reacting it with ATP, Mg^{++}, and extracts of any tissue, indicating the presence of phosphorylase b kinase throughout the animal.

Recently, Childress and Sacktor (1969) have purified phosphorylase a and b from adult Phormia regina flight muscle to electrophoretic and ultracentrifugal homogeneity. The molecular weight of each enzyme is about 100,000. Phosphorylase b has an absolute requirement for AMP, and is strongly inhibited by ATP. Phosphorylase a is activated 2 to 3 times by AMP and is not inhibited by ATP. Since glycogenolysis increases enormously at the inception of flight of *Phormia regina* (Sacktor and Wormser Shavit, 1966), it might be expected that phosphorylase *a* would increase with respect to total phosphorylase at this time, and this has been found to be the case. *In vivo* studies (Childress and Sacktor, 1969) show an increase of the *a* form to 72% of total phosphorylase within 15 seconds after flight begins. As an interesting aside, it has been shown that phosphorylase *b* kinase in fly flight muscle is activated by Ca^{++} at concentrations of 10^{-7} *M* (Hansford and Sacktor, 1969). The implications of this are self-evident.

Experiments done by Steele (1961) on the American cockroach have led to another possible source of control of the enzyme in certain insects. His results, confirmed by others (McCarthy and Ralph, 1962; Bowers and Friedman, 1963), indicated that a number of species of cockroaches produce a hormone which affects the rate of production of trehalose. Steele (1963) has since demonstrated that one of the effects of this hormone is to activate fat body phosphorylase in *Periplaneta americana*, and this has been corroborated by Wiens and Gilbert (1967b) using *Leucophaea maderae* (Dictyoptera), although the ratio of active to total phosphorylase in the latter experiments only increased from 0.29 without added corpora cardiaca (the glandular source of the hormone) to 0.49 in the presence of the glands. Wiens and Gilbert (1967a) have been unable to activate the phosphorylase from cecropia fat body with glands prepared either from cecropia pupae or adults or from *P. americana* adults.

C. Trehalose

The only means whereby trehalose is known to be degraded in insects is through a hydrolytic cleavage resulting in the production of two moles of glucose per mole of trehalose split.

The reaction is catalyzed by the enzyme trehalase, which has been demonstrated in a large number of species. The enzyme has been identified as a soluble protein from gut tissue [Gussin and Wyatt, 1965, *Hyalophora cecropia*; Gilby *et al.*, 1967, *Blaberus discoidalis* (Dictyoptera)], blood (Friedman, 1961, *Phormia regina*), and flight muscle (Hansen, 1966a, *Phormia regina*), and as a particulate enzyme from flight muscle (Gussin and Wyatt, 1965; Hansen, 1966a; Stevenson, 1968, *Prodenia eridania*), thoracic muscle (Zebe and McShan, 1959, *Leucophaea maderae*; Gilby *et al.*, 1967), and gut tissue (Gussin and Wyatt, 1965). The particulate enzyme appears to be localized either with the microsomes (Gussin and Wyatt, 1965; Gilby *et al.*, 1967; Stevenson, 1968) or the mitochondria (Zebe and McShan, 1959; Hansen, 1966a,b), although recent information indicates that *Phormia regina* flight muscle trehalase, which apparently cosediments with mitochondria, can be isolated from these by more sophisticated methods (Sacktor, 1969). In view of the fact that it would be difficult to envisage a function for trehalase within the mitochondrion, and that little free trehalose has ever been demonstrated in tissue, it is expected that the particulate enzyme will be found to be bound to plasma membranes. The particulate enzyme in all species studied except *Phormia regina* has a pH optimum between 6.0 and 6.5. The *Phormia* particulate enzyme has a pH optimum of 5.8, the same as that of its soluble counterpart. Soluble enzymes including those isolated from whole insects [Kalf and Rieder, 1958, *Galleria mellonella* (Lepidoptera); Saito, 1960, *Bombyx mori* (Lepidoptera); Friedman, 1960a, *Phormia regina;* Derr and Randall, 1966, *Melanoplus differentialis* (Orthoptera)], have pH optima between 5.0 and 5.7. The K_m's for trehalose range between 0.4 and 5.1 mM for all of the enzymes studied.

In view of the fact that trehalose is the major blood sugar in most insects and is used as a primary source of energy for many functions, e.g., flight (Clegg and Evans, 1961; Sacktor and Wormser-Shavit, 1966), it is interesting to note that the enzyme trehalase has been shown to be intrinsically capable of being subjected to regulatory processes.

In 1961, Friedman demonstrated the presence of a proteinaceous inhibitor in the blood of adult *Phormia regina* which served to keep blood trehalase in an inactive state. Since then, blood trehalase inhibition has been found in *Samia cynthia ricini* (Lepidoptera) larvae (C. K. Chang *et al.*, 1964), inhibition being released *in vivo* at the time of the molt, or, *in vitro,* with the same methods used by Friedman to characterize the *Phormia* inhibitor. Trehalase activity has also been shown in *Bombyx mori* larval blood at the molt, disappearing during intermolt periods (Duchâteau-Bosson *et al.*, 1963), but no attempt has been made to demonstrate any inhibitory substances.

At a different level, but indicative of other responses of which the enzyme is capable, is the discovery that particulate trehalase in species from three orders can be activated up to tenfold by repeated freezing and thawing or by treatment with substances which can modify membrane structure. None of the particulate dipteran trehalases, which are normally much more active than those from any other order, could be activated (Gussin and Wyatt, 1965; Gilby *et al.*, 1967; Stevenson, 1968).

D. OTHER COMPOUNDS

The occurrence of polysaccharides other than glycogen and chitin and of oligosaccharides, monosaccharides, and sugar alcohols other than trehalose and glucose in the blood and tissues of insects is presumptive evidence that enzymes are present to handle them, and a few scattered investigations bear this out.

An amylase with properties different from that present in the gut has been shown in the blood of *Bombyx mori* larvae (Ito *et al.*, 1962), *Drosophila melanogaster* (Diptera) larvae and adults (Doane, in Wyatt, 1967), and unfed adult female *Simulium* species (Diptera), *Culex pipiens pipiens* (Diptera), and *Aedes aegypti* (Diptera) (Yang and Davies, 1968). At present, the significance of this enzyme is unknown, although its presence and that of the amylose-like polysaccharide found by Villeneuve and Lemonde (1965) in *Tribolium* indicates the need for further investigation into the nature of polysaccharides in insects.

Enzymes capable of hydrolyzing maltose and sucrose have been shown to be present in the blood of *Apis mellifera* and in various tissues of other insects (Van Handel, 1968). This is particularly interesting in view of the number of anomalous sugars found in bee blood.

The presence of sorbitol and glycerol in the blood of certain insects appears to be involved with the ability to supercool (Somme, 1967), and the polyol dehydrogenases active in oxidizing or reducing the proper substrates have been examined by Faulkner (1956b, 1958) in blood and tissues of larval, pupal, and adult *Bombyx mori*, by Chino (1960) in *B. mori* diapausing eggs, and by Somme and Velle (1968) in diapausing pupae of *Pieris brassicae* (Lepidoptera). There is, at present, no conclusive evidence as to the singularity or multiplicity of dehydrogenase activities. The dehydrogenases were found to be NADP-specific by Faulkner and Chino and highly active with this coenzyme by Somme and Velle, but the latter investigators have also shown some activity with NAD and a minimum number of substrates. In contrast, Van Handel (1969) has found that a fat body homogenate of adult *Aedes sollicitans* (Diptera) incubated with sorbitol and NAD produces fructose, whereas NADP is inactive in the reaction.

The demonstration of scylloinositol in high concentration in locust blood has led to an investigation of its origin, and, on the basis of incorporation experiments, it has been concluded that it can arise from glucose (Candy, 1967). It is interconvertible with myoinositol in fat-body extracts through a two-step reaction with myoinosose-2 as an intermediate, and evidence indicates that the enzymes involved are a myoinositol-NAD oxidoreductase and a scylloinositol-NADP oxidoreductase. The function of this compound is still completely unknown.

VI. Further Degradation of "Storage" Compounds

The products of the above reactions, glucose 1-P from glycogen, glucose from trehalose, fructose 6-P from chitin, etc., are all immediately available to either the glycolytic or pentose phosphate pathway.

A. GLYCOLYSIS AND RELATED ACTIVITIES

It has been generally assumed that the enzymes involved in the conversion of glucose to pyruvate have no unique characteristics, so examination of many of them has been limited to simply noting their presence.

Hexokinase has been demonstrated in muscle extracts of *Triatoma infestans* (Hemiptera) (Agosin *et al.*, 1961), larval gut extracts of *Bombyx mori* (Ito and Horie, 1959), extracts of whole adult *Musca domestica* (Chefurka, 1954), and thoracic muscle extracts of *Locusta migratoria* (Kerly and Leaback, 1957). The enzymes in silkworm gut and in locust muscle have been shown to be nonspecific, phosphorylating fructose and glucose, and, in the locust, mannose as well. The affinity of the locust enzyme for fructose is lower than that for the other hexoses. It has a Mg^{++} requirement, and is completely inhibited by 5 mM glucose 6-P.

Phosphoglucomutase has been found in locust fat body (Candy and Kilby, 1961), fat body of the American cockroach (Vardanis, 1963), larval gut extracts of *B. mori,* and acetone powders of whole aphids, *Macrosiphum pisi* (Homoptera) (Newburgh and Cheldelin, 1955).

Phosphoglucose isomerase has been demonstrated in extracts of whole adult *Musca domestica* (Chefurka, 1954), albeit only by measuring fructose disappearance, in *Locusta migratoria* flight and leg muscle extracts (Delbrück *et al.*, 1959; Vogell *et al.*, 1959), in acetone powders of whole aphids (Newburgh and Cheldelin, 1955), and in larval gut extracts of *Bombyx mori* (Ito and Horie, 1959). Of interest is the relationship of this enzyme to mannose toxicity in bees and other insects. Sols *et al.* (1960), investigating this phenomenon, could show practically no phosphomannose isomerase activity in honeybee extracts, and found that mannose 6-phosphate (M-6-P) competitively inhibited bee phosphoglucose isomerase. Thus, they proposed that feeding mannose to bees leads to the production of a large amount of M-6-P which is poorly metabolized and interferes with the utilization of glucose 6-P, thereby causing a rapid decline and death. Very recently, experiments have been done (Saunders *et al.*, 1969) which show that phosphomannose isomerase is much more active in bees than was previously represented. It is lower in activity than phosphoglucose isomerase and hexokinase, but comparing it with the same enzyme in other glycolytic systems which behave normally it cannot be considered as abnormally low. The question of whether this normal imbalance, accentuated by the enormous energy requirements of honeybees, is enough to cause mannose toxicity must remain open at present.

Phosphofructokinase, found to be present in extracts of whole adult

Musca domestica (Chefurka, 1954), and locust flight and leg muscle extracts (Delbrück *et al.*, 1959; Vogell, *et al.*, 1959), has, in view of recent interest in its activity as a regulatory enzyme, been more carefully examined in the American cockroach (Grasso and Migliori-Natalizi, 1968), and the desert locust, *Schistocerca gregaria* (Walker and Bailey, 1969). The cockroach enzyme, represented by a crude extract from the coxal muscle, has a pH optimum of 7.5 and a K_m for fructose 6-P (F-6-P) of 0.069 mM, unaffected by ATP concentrations ranging from 0.5 to 2 mM. ATP is only slightly inhibitory at 2 mM. AMP, Pi, and NH_4^+ stimulate the activity of the enzyme when in combination, whereas Pi and cyclic 3',5'-AMP are both stimulatory when present alone.

Two locust enzymes have been isolated as ammonium sulfate precipitates of extracts of fat body and flight muscle. Sigmoidal F-6-P activity curves are demonstrable for both enzymes, and they resemble each other rather closely with respect to their responses to various compounds, both being activated by AMP and inhibited by high concentrations of ATP. The optimum ATP concentrations for fat body and muscle are 0.2 mM and 0.1 mM, respectively, and the K_m for F-6-P at those ATP concentrations is 0.7 mM and 1 mM. Concentrations of ATP above the optimum inhibit both enzymes by increasing the K_m for F-6-P. The muscle enzyme responds positively to cyclic 3',5'-AMP and Pi, whereas the fat body enzyme is unaffected by these compounds. An interesting anomaly is the inhibition of both enzymes by fructose diphosphate (FDP) an activator of all other animal phosphofructokinases reported to the present time.

The key glycolytic enzyme, fructosediphosphate aldolase, has been studied in a host of organisms in an effort to gain some understanding of evolution at a molecular level (Rutter, 1964), but only recently has any information been forthcoming on a purified preparation from insects. *Drosophila melanogaster* pupal aldolase has been crystallized (Brenner-Holzach and Leuthardt, 1968) and the properties of the highly purified (but precrystalline) enzyme determined (Brenner-Holzach and Leuthardt, 1967). It behaves very much like the Class I aldolase isolated from higher animals in that it has a broad pH optimum (6.8 to 8.0) and is not activated by monovalent cations such as Na^+ and NH_4^+. Similar properties have been described for purified *Phormia regina* aldolase (Rutter, 1964). Other studies on crude preparations from *Tribolium confusum* (Chaudhary *et al.*, 1966) and three mosquito species (Phifer, 1962) have been more equivocal as to the class of the enzyme, since both showed relatively sharp alkaline pH optima, although there was no apparent stimulation by metal ions. Other properties of these enzymes are also difficult to classify in view of the fact that the assay methods used for kinetic studies were different from those presently in use, and, unfortunately, methodology has a pronounced bearing on the results obtained. The enzyme from *Drosophila* shows its highest activity on the first day of the pupal instar. It has a molecular weight of 120,000 to 130,000, a K_m with respect to fructose diphosphate (FDP) of 0.027 mM, with respect to fructose 1-P (F-1-P) of 18 mM, and an FDP/F-1-P activity ratio at substrate saturation of 10 to 15. These properties resemble those of rabbit muscle aldolase, although the FDP/F-1-P ratio falls between that of the muscle (Class IA) and liver (Class IB) enzymes. In view of the fact that the enzyme was isolated from whole animals, the possibility remains that its properties are those of a mixture. Bauer and Levenbook (1969) have recently shown that in three species of flies there exist Class I aldolases of both A and B types. The A type is found in larval and adult muscle, whereas the B type is found in larval fat body. The enzyme has also been noted in muscle extracts of *Triatoma infestans* (Agosin *et al.*, 1961), extracts of whole adult *Musca domestica* (Chefurka, 1954), locust flight and leg muscle extracts (Delbrück *et al.*, 1959; Vogell *et al.*, 1959), and midgut extracts of larval *Bombyx mori* (Horie, 1967).

Triosephosphate isomerase has been demonstrated in extracts of whole adult *Musca domestica* (Chefurka, 1954), and locust flight and leg muscle extracts (Delbrück *et al.*, 1959; Vogell *et al.*, 1959), but its general properties, even in a single animal, remain completely unknown.

The presence of glyceraldehydephosphate dehydrogenase, another enzyme which has contributed to our general knowledge of molecular evolution, has been verified in a number of insects [muscle extracts of *Triatoma infestans* (Agosin *et al.*, 1961), extracts of whole adult *Musca domestica* (Chefurka, 1954), coxal muscle extracts of *Periplaneta americana* (Bettini and Boccacci, 1956), locust flight and leg muscle extracts (Delbrück *et al.*, 1959; Vogell *et al.*, 1959), and flight muscle extracts from *Hyalophora cecropia*, *Actias selene* (Lepidoptera), *Agrotis exclamationis* (Lepidoptera), *Amphimallus solstitialis* (Coleoptera), and *Pieris brassicae* (Beenakkers, 1969)], and it has recently been crystallized from honeybee (*Apis mellifera*) and bumblebee (*Bombus nevadensis*) (Hymenoptera) thoraces (Marquardt *et al.*, 1968). Gel electrophoresis has shown each of the latter enzymes to be a single molecular species, and data from the analytic ultracentrifuge have established both molecular weights at about 140,000. The native enzyme from the honeybee binds slightly more than 3 moles of NAD per mole, but it can be crystallized with less than this amount of nucleotide. The pH optimum of both enzymes is the same, about 9.1.

The first investigation of insect glyceraldehydephosphate dehydrogenase indicated that the enzyme in extracts of whole adult *Musca domestica* was resistant to 0.1 mM iodoacetic acid (IAA) (which almost completely inhibits the mammalian enzyme), and required glutathione or cysteine for activity. Other crude extracts (muscle extracts of *Triatoma infestans*, coxal muscle extracts of *Periplaneta americana*) were later prepared which showed a large response to IAA (55% inhibition at 0.066 mM; 80% inhibition at 0.5 mM, respectively) and no cysteine requirement, and still others in which an intermediate sensitivity was found. The crystalline enzyme prepared from the honeybee appears to be similar to the enzyme from mammals in its sensitivity to IAA. The same level of purification of some of the preparations discussed above might be expected to provide more meaningful data than we have heretofore obtained.

Generation of a high-energy phosphate bond in the 3-phosphoglycerate-1-kinase reaction has been shown directly by the back reaction in locust flight and leg muscle extracts (Delbrück *et al.*, 1959; Vogell *et al.*, 1959) and in midgut extracts of larval *B. mori* (Horie, 1967), and indirectly in a number of insects, but there are presently no data of value concerning the enzyme itself, nor is there any information of significance concerning the enzyme phosphoglycerate phosphomutase except for the direct determination of its presence in locust flight and leg muscle extracts (Delbrück *et al.*, 1959; Vogell *et al.*, 1959).

Enolase has been studied in locust flight and leg muscle extracts (Delbrück *et al.*, 1959; Vogell *et al.*, 1959) and in extracts of whole adult *Musca domestica* (Chefurka, 1954), the enzyme from the latter animal showing inhibition by fluoride at a concentration of 6 mM.

Pyruvate kinase has had its presence ascertained in muscle extracts from *Triatoma infestans* (Agosin *et al.*, 1961) and in locust flight and leg muscle extracts (Delbrück *et al.*, 1959; Vogell *et al.*, 1959). Recently, in view of its role in regulation, it has had a more intensive examination in another locust species (Bailey and Walker, 1969). Ammonium sulfate extracts were prepared from fat body and flight muscle of adult male *Schistocerca gregaria*, and kinase activity was examined with regard to responses to stimulatory and inhibitory compounds. The pH activity curves of the enzymes from the two sources were found to be considerably different in that the enzyme from the fat body had a single activity peak at pH 7.0, whereas the flight muscle enzyme peaked at 7.0 and remained high at least through pH 9.0. Fructose diphosphate modified the fat body enzyme so that its activity remained reasonably constant and high through pH 9.0, while the activity of the flight muscle enzyme was only positively affected by the diphosphate above pH 8.5. The enzymes were compared with respect to FDP reversal of inhibition by a number of compounds, but assays were carried out at a pH at which the fat-body enzyme was noticeably affected by FDP and the flight muscle enzyme was unaffected, so comparisons are difficult to interpret. The optimum ADP and phosphoenolpyruvate concentrations for both enzymes were 1 mM and 0.15 mM, respectively, and both enzymes were inhibited by concentrations of ADP above 10 mM. ATP inhibited both enzymes half maximally at 5 mM. It is rather interesting to note that rat liver and adipose tissue pyruvate kinases are both stimulated by FDP at neutral pH, whereas rat skeletal muscle kinase is not; these findings are completely in accord with those in locust tissues having the same general functions.

In view of the difficulty with which reduced NAD passes mitochondrial membranes (Sacktor and Dick, 1962), questions concerned with the reoxidation of cytoplasmic NAD reduced during glycolysis have come under scrutiny in many laboratories (see Chefurka, 1965a,b, for references). To all appearances, the answer as to how it is handled rests in the tissue in which the activity is taking place. Muscles which are intensely active for short time periods but have long recovery times, such as the jumping muscle, and organs in which carbohydrate utilization is at a generally low level contain relatively high concentrations of lactic dehydrogenase (LDH). On the other hand, muscle which is highly active and must remain so for long periods, such as flight muscle, contains a cytoplasmic NAD-linked α-glycerophosphate dehydrogenase (αGPD) (see Chefurka, 1965a,b, for references; Horie, 1967; Beenakkers, 1969). Bücher and his colleagues (Bücher, 1965), in a series of investigations concerned with the development of locust flight muscle, have shown that at the time the flight muscle becomes active (at the adult molt), the specific activity of αGPD increases by a factor of 20, and the αGPD/LDH ratio is 100. Brosemer (1967), has made the picture even more unmistakable by demonstrating that the specific activity of αGPD in the wing muscles of the flightless grasshopper, *Romalea microptera* (Orthoptera), does not increase at the adult molt, nor does the αGPD/LDH ratio exceed 5.

The α-glycerophosphate produced by the oxidation of NADH passes across the mitochondrial membrane where it is reoxidized to dihydroxyacetone phosphate by mitochondrial α-glycerophosphate oxidase (αGPO), a flavin-linked enzyme, and returned to the cytoplasm for further degradation. The rate of oxidation of α-glycerophosphate (αGP) by all mitochondria studied has been shown to be higher than the maximum rate of pyruvate oxidation (Sacktor, 1965; Stevenson, 1968), so there is no questioning the fact that this mode of DPN reoxidation does not limit the rate of carbohydrate utilization through pyruvate.

The enzyme, αGPD, has been isolated and crystallized from honeybee thoraces, where, probably as a result of the restriction of this animal to the utilization of carbohydrate for flight energy, it is found in higher concentrations than in either locust or moth flight muscle (Marquardt and Brosemer, 1966; Brosemer and Marquardt, 1966). It is different from the enzyme crystallized from rabbits in both its electrophoretic mobility and antigenic activity, and it is somewhat unstable in the ultracentrifuge, tending to disaggregate. Its molecular weight is about 65,400 as determined by gel filtration and amino acid analysis. The K_m for dihydroxyacetone phosphate is 0.33 mM, and the K_m for NADH is <0.01 mM. In contrast to the rabbit enzyme which has a sharp pH optimum of 7.7, the bee enzyme has a broad optimum around 6.6.

In passing, it may be noted that the discovery of the high rate of αGP oxidation by sarcosomes (flight muscle mitochondria) of the blowfly and the presence of high concentrations of αGP in resting thoracic muscle led one laboratory to suggest that the oxidation of this compound provided most of the carbohydrate derived energy used in insect flight (Sacktor, 1959). Indeed, this compound appears to be oxidized by mitochondria from a number of species at a higher rate than any other substrate tested (see above for references), but other observations have made it appear more probable that, in those cases in which carbohydrate is used for energy, the oxidation of pyruvate is, over the long run, of greatest importance. The case against αGP as the main energy source has been stated by Racker (1965) as embodying two facts: (1) the R.Q. of carbohydrate-utilizing animals in flight is close to 1, a situation which cannot be duplicated by the simple oxidation of αGP, and (2) the concentration of pyruvate must increase enormously within a relatively short time if αGP is the major substrate. The second point is of some interest since at the onset of flight of both locusts and blowflies the levels of pyruvate and other compounds arising from pyruvate rise by at least a factor of two (Sacktor and Wormser-Shavit, 1966; Childress *et al.*, 1967), indicating an increased pressure due to the utilization of some glycolytic intermediate. However, the concentration of pyruvate decreases to its normal steady-state level relatively quickly in the case of the blowfly (Sacktor and Wormser-Shavit, 1966), and more slowly in the case of the locust (Kirsten *et al.*, 1963), demonstrating that pyruvate oxidation is no longer limiting. Knowing the energy requirement for flight and the production of phosphate bond energy concomitant with the oxidation of αGP, it is reasonable to argue that some of this compound may be oxidized at the onset of flight to provide the initial burst of energy utilized before the Krebs cycle becomes maximally operative. This is borne out in the case of the locust in which the αGP level does decrease drastically in the first 20 seconds of flight, but it may not be the case with the blowfly. In the latter animal, the concentration of αGP does not change during flight, but glycogenolysis is increased 100 times during the rest to flight transition (Sacktor and Wormser-Shavit, 1966), the level of phosphorylase a increasing to 64% of the total phosphorylase present in the flight muscle within the first 5 seconds of flight (Childress and Sacktor, 1969).

The α-glycerophosphate oxidase discussed above was first examined in detail by Estabrook and Sacktor (1958) in the housefly, *Musca domestica,* and shown to have a K_m for αGP of 2 mM and a pH optimum of 6.5 to 7.0. The equilibrium of the reaction favored αGP oxidation. Inhibition of the oxidase was effected by EDTA ($K_I = 0.4$ mM), the inhibition being reversed by Mg^{++}, Ca^{++}, and a number of other divalent metals. The locus of action of the metals appeared to be at the dehydrogenase level. Recent reports indicate that Ca^{++} acts as an allosteric activator of the oxidase in insects of four separate orders at concentrations as low as 10^{-7} M (Hansford and Chappell, 1967; Donnellan and Beechey, 1969). Sr^{++} replaces Ca^{++} at 0.01 mM and Mg^{++} can replace Ca^{++} at 1 mM. The allosteric site, in confirmation of the work of Estabrook and Sacktor, appears to be located on the dehydrogenase molecule.

It might be well to interject a point here concerning the metabolism of glycerol. We have noted before that enzymes capable of producing glycerol from glyceraldehyde are present in blood and other tissues of certain insects (see Section V, D), and it has been established that free fatty acids derived from glycerides provide the energy for flight and other physiological activity in a large number of insects. The utilization of glycerol formed from either of these sources depends upon its rephosphorylation to α-glycerophosphate. The enzyme catalyzing this reaction, glycerol kinase, previously reported to be extremely low or missing in a limited number of insects, has recently been shown to be present in 28 species of 7 orders, varying greatly among species and within tissues (Newsholme and Taylor, 1969). In most cases, leg muscle activity was much lower than flight muscle, and levels of activity in flight muscle varied from as low as 0.012 μmoles/min./gm. fresh weight in *Blaberus discoidalis* to 6.78 in *Bombus hortorum* (Hymenoptera) queens (assayed at 30°). This latter value is the highest reported for any animal tissue. The activity of glycerol kinase in rat liver is 2 μmoles/min./gm., in rat diaphragm, 0.03 μmoles/min./gm. (assayed at 37°), and in sea mussel (*Mytilus edulis*) posterior adductor, 0.084 μmoles/min./gm. (assayed at 21°).

The function of the enzyme in hymenopteran and dipteran flight muscle remains rather vague since the species studied in both orders lack the ability to oxidize fatty acids at a rate which could support flight. It is thought, however, that this enzyme might play a part, in company with a phosphatase (see Wyatt, 1967), in regulating the level of α-glycerophosphate, thus regulating the rate of NADH oxidation and glycolysis.

The kinase in locust flight muscle appears to exist in two forms, particulate and soluble. The particulate enzyme is inhibited by ADP, AMP and L-α-glycerophosphate, with inhibition by the latter compound competitive with respect to glycerol ($K_I = 0.4$ mM). The K_m for glycerol is 0.37 mM.

Lactic dehydrogenase, noted in a large number of insects (see Chefurka, 1965a, for references), has been examined in detail in the supernatant fluid from *Bombyx mori* larval midgut homogenate (Horie, 1967). The pH optimum is about 7.6 and the K_m for pyruvate is 0.1 mM. The enzyme is inhibited completely by 0.1 mM p-hydroxymercuribenzoate (p-OHMB).

B. Tricarboxylic Acid Cycle

The energy obtained from the metabolism of the carbohydrates we have mentioned ultimately derives, to a great extent, from reactions coupled to the complete oxidation of C_2 units. Those reactions will be dealt with in Volume VI, Chapter 6. Consideration shall be given here only to the evidence for the occurrence of the enzymes active at the substrate level.

The movement of pyruvate into the citric acid cycle, catalyzed by pyruvic dehydrogenase, has been studied in crude preparations of solubilized honeybee mitochondria, and shown to be sensitive only to a lack of CoA, DPN, and reduced glutathione (Hoskins *et al.*, 1956). The participation of lipoic acid in the reaction is postulated from the findings that arsenite inhibits $^{14}CO_2$ evolution from glucose-6-^{14}C injected into cockroaches (Ela, in Chefurka, 1965a), and causes pyruvate accumulation in *Locusta* muscle suspensions (Rees, 1954).

The condensing enzyme has been purified 48-fold and "crystallized" from *Samia cynthia* flight muscle. The K_m for acetyl CoA is 0.2 mM and the K_m for oxalacetic acid is 0.01 mM. The latter figure is higher by a factor of 10 than that for the enzyme crystallized from pigeon breast muscle. The properties of the enzyme from *H. cecropia* are similar to those from *S. cynthia* (Srere *et al.*, 1963). The enzyme has also been demonstrated by measuring citrate production from acetate and oxalacetate in solubilized honeybee mitochondria (Hoskins *et al.*, 1956) and acetone powders of larval *Prodenia eridania* (Levenbook, 1961). Both preparations show a requirement for ATP and CoA, confirming the presence of aceto-CoA-kinase. Assays for the enzyme have been conducted in a number of other insects (Beenakkers, 1969).

Aconitase has been found in crude *Prodenia eridania* larval gut and fat body homogenates (Levenbook, 1961).

Isocitric dehydrogenase has been assayed and shown to be specific for NADP in acetone powders of *Prodenia eridania* (Levenbook, 1961), solubilized honeybee mitochondria (Hoskins *et al.*, 1956), and solubilized adult *Phormia regina* mitochondria, but a larval preparation from *Phormia* has exhibited activity with NAD as well as NADP (McGinnis *et al.*, 1956). The acetone powder from *Prodenia* and the enzyme from solubilized adult *Phormia regina* mitochondria both have a requirement for a cation, Mn^{++} being more effective than Mg^{++} in restoring activity.

The enzyme, α-ketoglutarate dehydrogenase, is present in lysed mitochondrial preparations from *Prodenia* (Levenbook, 1961) and solubilized honeybee mitochondria (Hoskins *et al.*, 1956). The requirements of the enzymes from both sources are CoA, Mg^{++}, thiamine pyrophosphate, and NAD. With reference to the participation of lipoic acid in this reaction, arsenite at a concentration of 0.05 mM inhibits *Prodenia* mitochondrial oxidation of α-ketoglutarate completely, whereas 1 mM arsenite is required to inhibit α-ketoglutarate oxidation by particles prepared from *Aedes aegypti* (Gonda *et al.*, 1957).

Nothing is presently known of succinic thiokinase in insects.

Succinic dehydrogenase has been demonstrated in many species (Chefurka, 1965a; Beenakkers, 1969), but the enzyme is not easily solubilized, so little is known of its properties. The oxidase system has been examined in some detail as part of a study of aestivation in *Hypera postica* (Coleoptera), the alfalfa weevil (Cunningham and Tombes 1966). The optimum pH has been found to be 7.1 to 7.3, and the complex is activated by both Al^{+++} and Ca^{++}.

Fumarase has been shown in acetone powders of *Prodenia eridania* (Levenbook, 1961) and particles prepared from *Aedes aegypti* (Gonda *et al.*, 1957).

Malic dehydrogenase has also been found in *Prodenia* and *Aedes*. The enzyme from *Prodenia* is specific for NAD, with an equilibrium in the direction of the reduction of oxalacetate. A more recent study has been carried out on the malate dehydrogenases of *Tribolium confusum* (Moorjani and Lemonde, 1967), utilizing mitochondrial and soluble fractions isolated from whole animals in various stages of development. The larval dehydrogenases isolated in the particulate fraction appear to be present in the soluble fraction in the pupa, based on the similarity of the K_m for L-malate of 0.275 mM in the larva and 0.3 mM in the pupa, the pH optimum 8.8 for the fractions from both, and the electrophoretic migration of NAD-specific dehydrogenases from both extracts to the same extent on agar gel. This is not surprising in view of the well-known lability of mitochondria during pupation.

C. Pentose Phosphate Cycle

Another means whereby storage carbohydrates may be metabolized and energy liberated is the so-called shunt pathway of Warburg, Lipmann, and Dickens. The major work of outlining this reaction sequence in an insect has been done by Chefurka, with crude housefly extracts (Chefurka, 1955, 1957, 1958), but others have also contributed to an understanding of the problem.

The first enzyme in the pathway, glucose-6-phosphate dehydrogenase, has been studied by a number of investigators in insects as varied as the honeybee (Hoskins *et al.*, 1956), an aphid (*Macrosiphum pisi*), (Newburgh and Cheldelin, 1955), a bug (*Triatoma*) (Agosin *et al.*, 1961), and the larva of a lepidopteran, *Bombyx mori* (Ito and Horie, 1959; Horie, 1967). The enzyme in a crude housefly extract (Chefurka, 1957), has a pH optimum in glycylglycine buffer of 9.8 to 10, a K_m for glucose 6-P of 0.5 mM, and is NADP specific. It is stimulated by Mg^{++}, Mn^{++}, and K^+ and inhibited by Hg^{++}, Zn^{++}, and low concentrations of *p*-OHMB. The activity per gram of tissue is 3.5 times as high in the abdomen as the thorax. Similar extracts from *Triatoma* have a pH optimum of 7.5. A 116-fold purified enzyme from *Bombyx* larval fat body (Horie, 1967) has a pH optimum of 7.7 in glycylglycine buffer, a K_m for glucose 6-P of 0.08 mM, and a K_mNADP of 0.031 mM. The highest specific activity of this enzyme was found in the fat body, and a comparison of the activity of the enzyme in larval intersegmental muscle with that in adult thoracic muscle showed the former to have almost 4 times that of the latter, which was lowest of all tissues tested.

Gluconolactonase has been demonstrated in crude extracts of houseflies (Chefurka, 1958), but nothing is known of its activity.

The enzyme, 6-phosphogluconate dehydrogenase, has been found in a few insects, but carefully studied in only two, the crude housefly extract (Chefurka, 1957) and an ammonium sulfate fraction of *Bombyx* larval fat body which has a specific activity ca. 3 times that of the crude extract (Horie, 1967). The pH optimum of the housefly enzyme is 7 to 7.5 in glycylglycine and 8.5 in trisglycine buffer, the silkworm, 8.3 in tris-HCl buffer. The K_m for 6-phosphogluconate (6PG) in the housefly is 0.019 mM, in the silkworm, 0.07 mM; the K_m for NADP is 0.025 mM in the housefly, 0.015 mM in the silkworm. The activity of the enzyme in the silkworm larva was shown to be higher in the fat body than in other tissues, in the housefly the activity was 2.5 times higher in the abdomen than in the thorax. The housefly enzyme is activated by Mg^{++}, Mn^{++}, Co^{++}, and K^+. In extracts of whole *Drosophila melanogaster* the enzyme has an estimated molecular weight of 79,000 (Kazazian, 1966).

The other enzymes in the shunt pathway have been directly demonstrated by showing product formation from 6PG and ribose 5-P in housefly extracts (measurements made of xylulose, ribose, ribulose, hexose, triose, and heptulose) (Chefurka, 1955, 1958), pea aphid acetone powders (measurements of pentose, heptulose, hexose) (Newburgh and Cheldelin, 1955), silkworm gut homogenates (similar measurements) (Ito and Horie, 1959), and *Triatoma* extracts (Agosin *et al.*, 1961). No tetrose has ever been shown, nor have any of the enzymes been otherwise examined in a more purified state.

Recently, Chaudhary *et al.* (1967), working with *Tribolium confusum* and attempting to relate specific enzyme concentrations to processes of growth and metamorphosis, have shown that G-6-P dehydrogenase, measured in crude extracts of various developmental stages of this insect, increases enormously in total activity at the last larval stage when a great deal of fat is being laid down, decreases during the nonfeeding pupal stage, and again increases markedly on emergence, when the animal begins to feed on a carbohydrate diet. Ribose-5-phosphate isomerase, measured in the same crude extracts, shows an increase in total activity during the prepupal and pupal stages, and a decrease at adult emergence. The authors attribute the latter activity to furnishing precursors for RNA synthesis.

VII. Utilization of Various Pathways

The contribution of the pentose phosphate pathway to the degradation of glucose has been examined in very few insects, but even from these a pattern similar to that perceived in other animals has begun to emerge. Shunt pathway utilization has been shown to occur in situations in which synthesis and breakdown of fat are predominant, or the need arises for a source of reduced NADP.

Early experiments of Wang and his colleagues (Silva *et al.*, 1958), based on yields of $^{14}CO_2$ from injected glucose-1-, -6-, and -3(4)-^{14}C, indicated that the male American cockroach metabolized glucose by the shunt pathway to the extent of only 4% to 9%. The assumptions and formulations used in these determinations were seriously criticized by Katz and Wood (1960, 1963) and Katz *et al.* (1966), and recent work has generally utilized the techniques recommended by the latter investigators. It must be said, however, that the Oregon group correctly stated that values calculated from the use of their method were minimum values, so any information available to us using their approach can be usefully viewed in that light.

Probably the most extensive piece of work bearing directly on pathway utilization has been reported by Chefurka (1965a, 1966). Using the method of Silva et al. (1958), his group found that in the male cockroach 16.7% of the total utilization of glucose took place through the shunt pathway, whereas only 2.4% moved in this direction in the female. The male and female milkweed bug, Oncopeltus fasciatus (Hemiptera), used 13.4% and 16.4%, respectively, and the grasshopper [Melanoplus bivittatus (Orthoptera)] male and female 38.7% and 39.9%. Chefurka also used an entirely different and perhaps more valid determination of shunt metabolism [measurement of ^{14}C in glucose residues of glycogen after injection with glucose-2-^{14}C (Katz and Wood, 1960)] and found that male cockroaches utilized 20% to 23% through the shunt whereas females used only 2% to 5%.

Agosin et al. (1963, 1966), using another of the methods recommended by Katz and Wood (1960) for measuring the pentose pathway have examined the relationship between the utilization of this pathway and resistance to insecticides in Triatoma infestans and Musca domestica. They (Agosin et al., 1966) have been able to show that DDT-susceptible Musca domestica utilize the shunt pathway to a small extent (less, even than the sensitivity of the method) whether or not they are under insecticide pressure, whereas resistant flies, which also normally use the pathway in a limited fashion, respond to DDT with an enormous increase in utilization. The investigators suggest that the pathway provides NADPH for detoxification mechanisms.

A recent report, utilizing the method of Wang (Horie et al., 1968), has shown that in the whole silkworm larva (5th instar) the pentose shunt may be responsible for more than 35% of the total metabolism of glucose, whereas in isolated fat body the amount may be higher than 80%. Since the method of evaluation does not take into consideration the distinct possibility that very little of the label may be used or, in fact, that little of the total substrate may be catabolized, it is difficult to comment positively on the findings.

VIII. Other Enzymic Activities

Hints at other metabolic pathways, control reactions, and synthetic processes can be obtained from a list of unrelated enzymic reactions found in various species.

A hexose-1-phosphatase, active against glucose 1-P (G-1-P), has been demonstrated in the blood of larval *B. mori* (Faulkner, 1955). The enzyme has a K_m for G-1-P of 4 mM, is competitively inhibited by fluoride ion, and is unaffected by Mg^{++}. The pH optimum of the enzyme is 4.5, but it has 40% of its maximum activity at the physiological pH of silkworm blood. At present, there is no known function for this enzyme, nor has its presence been noted in any other tissues.

Malic enzyme, a decarboxylase catalyzing the formation of pyruvate, CO_2, and NADPH from L-malate and NADP, and acting as a possible source of reduced NADP, has been found in mitochondria of *Prodenia eridania* larvae (Levenbook, 1961), larval and pupal tissue of *Tribolium confusum* (Moorjani and Lemonde, 1967), and hemolymph of a number of insects (Faulkner, 1956a). It has been more carefully examined by the last named investigator in the blood of larval *Bombyx mori*, and obtained with a 27-fold purification. It has a requirement for Mn^{++} or Mg^{++} and is inhibited by *p*-OHMB but not by iodoacetate. The pH optimum of the enzyme is 8.5 and it is NADP specific.

Cytoplasmic malic dehydrogenase, which may be considered as an alternative enzyme used in the reoxidation of cytoplasmic NADH (Sacktor, 1965), has been shown in dipteran flight muscle (Sacktor, 1953), in locust muscle (Delbrück *et al.*, 1959), and in pupal *Tribolium confusum* (Moorjani and Lemonde, 1967).

The key enzymes of the glyoxylate cycle, functioning in plants and microorganisms, have not been found in insects (Levenbook, 1961; Bade, 1962), with the exception of a report by Carpenter and Jaworski (1962) showing low isocitrate lyase activity in prepupal *Prodenia eridania* extracts.

Oxalacetic carboxylase has been shown to be extremely active in crude dialyzed extracts of *Glossina morsitans* thoraces in contrast to extracts from a number of other insects (Bursell, 1965). The enzyme appears to be activated by Ca^{++} rather than Mg^{++} (as found in vertebrates), inhibited by Fe^{++}, and has a pH optimum of 5.9. Its importance in the metabolism of the tsetse fly (ostensibly to provide pyruvate for the glutamate–alanine transamination reaction which is, in turn, fundamental to the animal's use of proline as a major energy source) is indicated by the *in vivo* toxicity of Fe^{++} at concentrations which have no effect on blowflies (*Phormia* sp.).

IX. General Remarks

A close examination of the information presented in this chapter leaves us uncertain as to the note on which it should be ended. Accepting the fact that almost all of the reactions heretofore studied in other animals have now, for all practical purposes, been demonstrated in one or another insect, we might simply state that insects generally exhibit few peculiarities with regard to the metabolism of carbohydrates and leave it at that.

The enormity, of this oversimplification becomes evident, however, when, taking a different tack, we point out that at most a dozen of what may be a million species have been examined with any care, and that even among these we find disparities in reactions leading to similar products, in transport mechanisms, in the ultimate sources from which energy is derived, and, finally, in the regulation of the enzymes involved in the reactions studied.

It seems essential, then, to emphasize, in closing, that the vast numbers of species within the class with their extraordinary ecological and biochemical variety makes it presently difficult and imminently impracticable to speak, except at the most superficial level, of carbohydrate metabolism of insects.

REFERENCES

Agosin, M., Scaramelli, N., and Neghme, A. (1961). *Comp. Biochem. Physiol.* **2**, 143.

Agosin, M., Scaramelli, N., Dinamarca, M. L., and Aravena, L. (1963). *Comp. Biochem. Physiol.* **8**, 311.

Agosin, M., Fine, B. C., Scaramelli, N., Ilivicky, J., and Aravena, L. (1966). *Comp. Biochem. Physiol.* **19**, 339.

Attwood, M. M., and Zola, H. (1967). *Comp. Biochem. Physiol.* **20**, 993.

Bade, M. L. (1962). *Biochem. J.* **83**, 478.

Bade, M. L., and Wyatt, G. R. (1962). *Biochem. J.* **83**, 470.

Bailey, E., and Walker, P. R. (1969). *Biochem. J.* **111**, 359.

Bauer, A. C., and Levenbook, L. (1969). *Comp. Biochem. Physiol.* **28**, 619.

Beenakkers, A. M. T. (1969). *J. Insect Physiol.* **15**, 353.

Benson, R. L. (1968). Unpublished observations.

Benson, R. L., and Friedman, S. (1970). *J. Biol. Chem.* **245**, 2219.

Bettini, S., and Boccacci, M. (1956). *Rend. Ist. Super. Sanita* **19**, 1086.

Betz, N. L., Nettles, W. C., Jr., and Novak, A. F. (1968). *Comp. Biochem. Physiol.* **24**, 163.

Bowers, W. S., and Friedman, S. (1963). *Nature* **198**, 685.

Brenner-Holzach, O., and Leuthardt, F. (1967). *Helv. Chim. Acta* **50**, 1336.

Brenner-Holzach, O., and Leuthardt, F. (1968). *Helv. Chim. Acta* **51**, 1130.

Brosemer, R. W. (1967). *J. Insect Physiol.* **13**, 685.

Brosemer, R. W., and Marquardt, R. R. (1966). *Biochim. Biophys. Acta* **128**, 464.

Bücher, T. (1965). *Biochem. Soc. Symp.* (*Cambridge, Engl.*) **25**, 15.

Bursell, E. (1965). *Comp. Biochem. Physiol.* **16**, 259.

Candy, D. J. (1967). *Biochem. J.* **103**, 666.

Candy, D. J., and Kilby, B. A. (1961). *Biochem. J.* **78**, 531.

Candy, D. J., and Kilby, B. A. (1962). *J. Exptl. Biol.* **39**, 129.

Carpenter, W. D., and Jaworski, E. G. (1962). *Biochim. Biophys. Acta* **58**, 369.

Chang, C. K., Liu, F., and Feng, H. (1964). *Acta Entomol. Sinica* **13**, 494.

Chang, F. K., and Friedman, S. (1968). Unpublished observations.

Chaudhary, K. D., Srivastava, U., and Lemonde, A. (1966). *Can. J. Biochem.* 44, 155.

Chaudhary, K. D., Moorjani, S., Srivastava, U., and Lemonde, A. (1967). *Biochim. Biophys. Acta* 148, 571.

Chefurka, W. (1954). *Enzymologia* 17, 73.

Chefurka, W. (1955). *Biochim. Biophys. Acta* 17, 295.

Chefurka, W. (1957). *Enzymologia* 18, 14.

Chefurka, W. (1958). *Can. J. Biochem. Physiol.* 36, 83.

Chefurka, W. (1965a). In "The Physiology of Insecta" (M. Rockstein, ed.), Vol. 2, p. 581. Academic Press, New York.

Chefurka, W. (1965b). *Ann. Rev. Entomol.* 10, 345.

Chefurka, W. (1966). *Proc. Entomol. Soc. Ontario* 96, 17.

Childress, C., and Sacktor, B. (1969). *Federation Proc.* 28, 412.

Childress, C. C., Sacktor, B., and Traynor, D. R. (1967). *J. Biol. Chem.* 242, 754.

Chino, H. (1960). *J. Insect Physiol.* 5, 1.

Clegg, J. S., and Evans, D. R. (1961). *J. Exptl. Biol.* 38, 771.

Crompton, M., and Birt, L. M. (1967). *J. Insect Physiol.* 13, 1575.

Cunningham, R. K., and Tombes, A. S. (1966). *Comp. Biochem. Physiol.* 18, 725.

Delbrück, A., Zebe, E., and Bücher, T. (1959). *Biochem. Z.* 331, 273.

Derr, R. F., and Randall, D. D. (1966). *J. Insect Physiol.* 12, 1105.

Donnellan, J. F., and Beechey, R. B. (1969). *J. Insect Physiol.* 15, 367.

Duchâteau-Bosson, G., Jeuniaux, C., and Florkin, M. (1963). *Arch. Intern. Physiol. Biochim.* 71, 566.

Ehrhardt, P. (1962). *Z. Vergleich. Physiol.* 46, 169.

Estabrook, R. W., and Sacktor, B. (1958). *J. Biol. Chem.* 233, 1014.

Fairbairn, D. (1958). *Can. J. Zool.* 36, 787.

Faulkner, P. (1955). *Biochem. J.* 60, 590.

Faulkner, P. (1956a). *Biochem. J.* 64, 430.

Faulkner, P. (1956b). *Biochem. J.* 64, 436.

Faulkner, P. (1958). *Biochem. J.* 68, 374.

Fraenkel, G., and Rudall, K. M. (1947). *Proc. Roy. Soc.* B134, 111.

Friedman, S. (1960a). *Arch. Biochem. Biophys.* 87, 252.

Friedman, S. (1960b). *Arch. Biochem. Biophys.* 88, 339.

Friedman, S. (1961). *Arch. Biochem. Biophys.* 93, 550.

Friedman, S. (1967). *J. Insect Physiol.* 13, 397.

Friedman, S. (1968). *Science* 159, 110.

Friedman, S. (1969). Unpublished data.

Gilby, A. R., Wyatt, S. S., and Wyatt, G. R. (1967). *Acta Biochim. Polon.* 14, 83.

Giles, C. H., Hassan, A. S. A., Laidlaw, M., and Subramanian, R. V. R. (1958). *J. Soc. Dyers Colourists* 74, 647.

Gonda, O., Traub, A., and Avi-Dor, Y. (1957). *Biochem. J.* 67, 487.

Grasso, A., and Migliori-Natalizi, G. (1968). *Comp. Biochem. Physiol.* 26, 979.

Gussin, A. E. S., and Wyatt, G. R. (1965). *Arch. Biochem. Biophys.* 112, 626.

Hackman, R. H. (1960). *Australian J. Biol. Sci.* 13, 568.

Hansen, K. (1966a). *Biochem. Z.* 344, 15.

Hansen, K. (1966b). *Histochemie* 6, 290.

Hansford, R. G., and Chappell, J. B. (1967). *Biochem. Biophys. Res. Commun.* 27, 686.

Hansford, R. G., and Sacktor, B. (1969). Unpublished observations.

Hines, W. J. W., and Smith, M. J. H. (1963). *J. Insect Physiol.* 9, 463.

Hizukuri, S., and Larner, J. (1964). *Biochemistry* 3, 1783.

Horie, Y. (1967). *J. Insect Physiol.* 13, 1163.

Horie, Y., Nakasone, S., and Ito, T. (1968). *J. Insect Physiol.* 14, 971.

Hoskins, D. D., Cheldelin, V. H., and Newburgh, R. W. (1956). *J. Gen. Physiol.* 39, 705.

Hudson, A. (1958). *J. Insect Physiol.* 1, 293.

Ito, T., and Horie, Y. (1959). *Arch. Biochem. Biophys.* 80, 174.

Ito, T., Mukaiyama, F., and Tanaka, M. (1962). *J. Sericult. Sci. Japan* 31, 228.

Jaworski, E., Wang, L., and Marco, G. (1963). *Nature* 198, 790.

Kalf, G. F., and Rieder, S. V. (1958). *J. Biol. Chem.* 230, 691.

Katz, J., and Wood, H. G. (1960). *J. Biol. Chem.* 235, 2165.

Katz, J., and Wood, H. G. (1963). *J. Biol. Chem.* 238, 517.

Katz, J., Landau, B. R., and Bartsch, G. E. (1966). *J. Biol. Chem.* 241, 727.

Kazazian, H. H., Jr. (1966). *Nature* 212, 197.

Kerly, M., and Leaback, D. H. (1957). *Biochem. J.* 67, 245.

Kilby, B. A. (1963). *Advan. Insect Physiol.* 1, 112.

Kirsten, E., Kirsten, R., and Arese, P. (1963). *Biochem. Z.* 337, 167.

Krueger, H. R., and Jaworski, E. G. (1966). *J. Econ. Entomol.* 59, 229.

Levenbook, L. (1961). *Arch. Biochem. Biophys.* 92, 114.

Lindh, N. O. (1967). *Comp. Biochem. Physiol.* 20, 209.

Lipke, H., Grainger, M. M., and Siakotos, A. N. (1965a). *J. Biol. Chem.* 240, 594.

Lipke, H., Graves, B., and Leto, S. (1965b). *J. Biol. Chem.* 240, 601.

McCarthy, R., and Ralph, C. L. (1962). *Am. Zoologist* 2, 429.

McGinnis, A. J., Cheldelin, V. H., and Newburgh, R. W. (1956). *Arch. Biochem. Biophys.* 63, 427.

Marquardt, R. R., and Brosemer, R. W. (1966). *Biochim. Biophys. Acta* 128, 454.

Marquardt, R. R., Carlson, C. W., and Brosemer, R. W. (1968). *J. Insect Physiol.* 14, 317.

Maurizio, A. (1965). *J. Insect Physiol.* 11, 745.

Mikolaschek, G., and Zebe, E. (1967). *J. Insect Physiol.* 13, 1483.

Mochnacka, I., and Petryszyn, C. (1959). *Acta Biochim. Polon.* 6, 307.

Moorjani, S., and Lemonde, A. (1967). *Can. J. Biochem.* 45, 1393.

Murphy, T. A., and Wyatt, G. R. (1965). *J. Biol. Chem.* 240, 1500.

Nettles, W. C., Jr., and Betz, N. L. (1965). *Ann. Entomol. Soc. Am.* 58, 721.

Newburgh, R. W., and Cheldelin, V. H. (1955). *J. Biol. Chem.* 214, 37.

Newsholme, E. A., and Taylor, K. (1969). *Biochem. J.* 112, 465.

Phifer, K. O. (1962). *J. Parasitol.* 48, 368.

Powning, R. F., and Irzykiewicz, H. (1963). *Nature* 200, 1128.

Powning, R. F., and Irzykiewicz, H. (1967). *J. Insect Physiol.* 13, 1293.

Racker, E. (1965). "Mechanisms in Bioenergetics." Academic Press, New York.

Rees, K. R. (1954). *Biochem. J.* 58, 196.

Rosell-Perez, M., and Larner, J. (1964). *Biochemistry* 3, 75, 81, and 773.

Rudall, K. M. (1963). *Advan. Insect Physiol.* 1, 257.

Rutter, W. J. (1964). *Federation Proc.* 23, 1248.

Sacktor, B. (1953). *Arch. Biochem. Biophys.* 45, 349.

Sacktor, B. (1959). *Proc. 4th Intern. Congr. Biochem., Vienna, 1958,* Vol. 12, p. 138. Pergamon Press, Oxford.

Sacktor, B. (1965). *In* "The Physiology of Insecta." (M. Rockstein, ed.), Vol. 2, p. 483. Academic Press, New York.

Sacktor, B. (1969). Personal communication.

Sacktor, B., and Dick, A. (1962). *J. Biol. Chem.* **237**, 3259.
Sacktor, B., and Wormser-Shavit, E. (1966). *J. Biol. Chem.* **241**, 624.
Saito, S. (1960). *J. Biochem.* (*Tokyo*) **48**, 101.
Saunders, S. A., Gracy, R. W., Schnackerz, K. D., and Noltmann, E. A. (1969). *Science* **164**, 858.
Silva, G. M., Doyle, W. P., and Wang, C. H. (1958). *Nature* **182**, 102.
Sinohara, H., and Asano, Y. (1968). *J. Biochem.* (*Tokyo*) **63**, 8.
Sols, A., Cadenas, E., and Alvarado, F. (1960). *Science* **131**, 297.
Somme, L. (1967). *J. Insect Physiol.* **13**, 805.
Somme, L., and Velle, W. (1968). *J. Insect Physiol.* **14**, 135.
Srere, P. A., Brazil, H., and Gonen, L. (1963). *Acta Chem. Scand.* **17**, Suppl. 1, 129.
Steele, J. E. (1961). *Nature* **192**, 680.
Steele, J. E. (1963). *Gen. Comp. Endocrinol.* **3**, 46.
Stevenson, E. (1968). *J. Insect Physiol.* **14**, 179.
Stevenson, E., and Wyatt, G. R. (1964). *Arch. Biochem. Biophys.* **108**, 420.
Treherne, J. E. (1967). *Ann. Rev. Entomol.* **12**, 43.
Trivelloni, J. C. (1960). *Arch. Biochem. Biophys.* **89**, 149.
Van Handel, E. (1968). *Comp. Biochem. Physiol.* **24**, 537.
Van Handel, E. (1969). *Comp. Biochem. Physiol.* **29**, 1023.
Vardanis, A. (1963). *Biochim. Biophys. Acta* **73**, 565.
Vardanis, A. (1967). *J. Biol. Chem.* **242**, 2306.
Villeneuve, J. L., and Lemonde, A. (1965). *Arch. Intern. Physiol. Biochim.* **73**, 681.
Vogell, W., Bishai, F. R., Bücher, T., Klingenberg, M., Pette, D., and Zebe, E. (1959). *Biochem. Z.* **332**, 81.
Walker, P. R., and Bailey, E. (1969). *Biochem. J.* **111**, 365.
Waterhouse, D. F., and McKellar, J. W. (1961). *J. Insect Physiol.* **6**, 185.
Waterhouse, D. F., Hackman, R. H., and McKellar, J. W. (1961). *J. Insect Physiol.* **6**, 96.
Wiens, A. W., and Gilbert, L. I. (1967a). *Comp. Biochem. Physiol.* **21**, 145.
Wiens, A. W., and Gilbert, L. I. (1967b). *J. Insect Physiol.* **13**, 779.
Wimer, L. T. (1969). *Comp. Biochem. Physiol.* **29**, 1055.
Wyatt, G. R. (1967). *Advan. Insect Physiol.* **5**, 287.
Yang, Y. J., and Davies, D. M. (1968). *J. Med. Entomol.* **5**, 9.
Zebe, E. C., and McShan, W. H. (1959). *J. Cellular Comp. Physiol.* **53**, 21.

CHAPTER 7

Nitrogenous Constituents and Nitrogen Metabolism in Arthropods

E. Schoffeniels and R. Gilles

I. Introduction

Amino acid and nitrogen metabolism are of the utmost importance in animals since amino acids are essential intermediates in protein synthesis, and the catabolism products of these prime constituents appear in the form of different nitrogen substances. Furthermore, amino acids and certain other nitrogenous compounds are known to play an important part in several phenomena occurring in the lifetime of Crustacea and, more specifically, during osmotic stress.

Little information is available on the biochemistry of nitrogenous compounds in Arthropoda. This is why it is rather difficult to relate this problem to the different systematic categories. In this review, we attempt to give the most recent facts on nitrogen metabolism in Arthropoda and their relationship to ecological and developmental factors.

II. Amino Acids

A. Amino Acid Patterns in Arthropoda

Generally, invertebrates have higher pools of free intracellular amino acids than vertebrates, and Arthropoda is one of the phyla in which the highest amino acid concentrations are found (Camien *et al.*, 1951;

Florkin, 1966). However, a comparative study of the amino acid pattern among the various classes of Arthropoda remains difficult to undertake at the present time. Indeed, most of the available data deal with amino acid composition of muscle in Crustacea and of hemolymph in insects. We shall therefore consider Crustacea and insects separately in the following discussion.

1. Crustacea

In Crustacean muscle, proline, glycine, and arginine appear to be more concentrated than glutamate, alanine, and aspartate. This pattern of amino

TABLE I

	Copepoda	Decapoda					
	Capanoida	Brachyura					
		Brachyrhyncha					
Amino acid	*Calanus finmarchicus*[b]	*Carcinus maenas*[c]	*Cancer pagurus*[d]	*Eriocheir sinensis*[e]	*Neptunus pelagicus*[f]	*Scylla serratus*[f]	*Paratelphusa jaquemonitii*
Alanine	9.29	20.5	10.60	53.3	17.4	22.2	18.2
Arginine	15.40	34.4	29.92	39.3	—[i]	—	—
Aspartate	0.89	3.9	2.90	9.0	1.0	1.1	1.1
Glutamate	3.20	36.0	4.21	27.2	2.5	5.8	3.1
Glycine	26.81	139.6	66.53	80.0	54.9	52.9	45.3
Histidine	1.05	0.1	1.17	—	—	—	—
Isoleucine	2.60	1.7	0.78	3.4	3.3	2.1	1.2
Leucine	3.72	2.6	1.69	4.5			
Lysine	3.90	2.1	1.62	17.3	—	—	—
Methionine	1.42	3.3	1.69	—	1.0	1.1	1.8
Phenylalanine	1.69	0.4	0.42	Tr	0.8	0.9	0.6
Proline	9.29	67.0	6.17	27.9	10.4	10.9	10.4
Serine	3.10	—	2.25	—	3.7	3.5	5.0
Taurine	19.20	—	25.50	20.6	—	—	—
Threonine	2.13	3.4	3.19	11.6	3.3	3.4	1.8
Tryptophan	—	—	—	—	1.6	1.7	1.6
Tyrosine	2.38	0.3	0.61	Tr	1.5	1.0	2.1
Valine	3.04	3.2	—	6.0	2.0	1.5	1.4

[a] Values are expressed in μmoles/gm. wet weight.
[b] Cowey and Corner (1963).
[c] Duchâteau *et al.* (1959).
[d] Gilles and Schoffeniels (1970).
[e] Bricteux-Grégoire *et al.* (1962).
[f] Gangal and Magar (1964).

acid pool seems to be a general feature in the class, since it appears in all the species studied so far (Table I). However, considerable variations among the different species have to be noted. Although the glycine concentration is always the highest, the proline concentration is sometimes higher than the arginine concentration or vice versa. Another striking feature is the variability of the glutamic acid level which is very high in *Carcinus maenas, Eriocheir sinensis, Maia squinado,* and *Homarus vulgaris* and much lower in *Calanus finmarchicus, Cancer pagurus,* and *Neptunus pelagicus* (Table I).

In addition to the considerable variations which exist in the same tissue from several different species, there is often quite a different dis-

AMINO ACID POOLS OF MUSCLES FROM VARIOUS CRUSTACEAN SPECIES[a]

	Decapoda						Unknown
Brachyura	Macrura						
Oxyrhyncha	Astacura			Encyphidea			
Maja squinado[g]	*Astacus fluviatilis*[g]	*Astacus pallipes*[h]	*Homarus vulgaris*[g]	*Leander squilla*[i]	*Leander serratus*[i]		*Etius laevimanus*[f]
22	8	8.4	23	7.8	16.8		27.1
48	8	28.6	64	24.5	24.5		—
3	8	1.1	2	0	1.8		1.0
29	35	1.6	34	0	3.2		4.3
145	52	33.0	201	80.0	112.0		52.3
0	3	1.5	1	—	—		—
2	2	0.8	2	Tr[k]	2.0		1.9
2	3	2.3	1	Tr	3.4		—
1	7	2.7	3	1.0	1.7		—
2	1	0.5	1	—	—		0.5
0	1	0.5	1	Tr	Tr		0.7
9	16	10.8	106	29.6	21.8		—
—	—	4.8	—	—	—		2.3
—	—	6.6	—	—	—		—
3	4	3.4	Tr	0	2.1		1.5
—	—	—	—	—	—		1.2
0	1	0.5	0	Tr	Tr		1.3
3	3	1.6	3	Tr	3.7		1.7

[g] Camien *et al.* (1951).
[h] Cowey (1961).
[i] Jeuniaux *et al.* (1961).
[j] —, not estimated.
[k] Tr, traces.

tribution of free amino acids in different tissues from the same species. Thus, in *Homarus vulgaris* and *Astacus fluviatilis* (Table II), proline, glycine, and arginine are highly concentrated in muscle while aspartic acid is the most important amino acid in the nerve, and alanine and glutamic acid are the major amino acids in the blood.

However, whether blood, muscle, or nerve is considered, it can be seen that the amino acid level is always higher in the marine lobster than in the freshwater crayfish. Such a difference between marine and freshwater species has already been noted when comparing the amino acid pools of various aquatic invertebrates (Table I). Thus it has been suggested that amino acids could play a prominent part in the regulation of the osmotic pressure in invertebrate tissues (Florkin, 1956; Camien *et al.*, 1951). We shall deal more fully with this particular physiological aspect of the amino acid pool variation in a later chapter (see Chapter 9).

TABLE II

FREE AMINO ACID CONTENT OF SERUM, MUSCLE, AND NERVE
FROM *Homarus vulgaris* AND *Astacus fluviatilis*[a]

Amino acid	*Homarus vulgaris*			*Astacus fluviatilis*		
	Serum[b]	Muscle[b]	Nerve[c]	Serum[d]	Muscle[d]	Nerve[c]
Alanine	0.98	23.0	11.33	1.14	6.14	2.39
Arginine	0.01	60.5	4.88	0.20	54.35	—[e]
Aspartate	0.50	2.0	32.31	0.17	7.33	5.10
Cystine	—	—	0.84	—	—	—
Glutamate	0.20	34.1	9.76	2.02	28.91	2.09
Glycine	3.2	202.0	20.55	0.80	33.73	1.45
Histidine	0.2	1.0	0.23	0.07	2.25	—
Isoleucine	—	—	0.53	0.45	1.35	0.21
Leucine	0.3	6.0	0.33	0.22	2.48	0.20
Lysine	0.15	3.2	0.36	0.20	6.98	—
Methionine	0	1.0	—	—	—	—
Phenylalanine	Traces	1.0	—	0.06	1.26	0.23
Proline	0.5	104.0	13.89	0.28	10.78	0.64
Serine	—	—	6.57	—	—	2.41
Taurine	—	—	16.13	—	—	0.47
Threonine	0	1.0	1.72	0.27	2.73	0.45
Tyrosine	0.2	0	—	0.09	1.06	0.26
Valine	0	3.0	—	0.51	2.16	0.32

[a] Values expressed in mmoles/kg. wet weight or in mmoles/liter serum.
[b] Camien *et al.* (1951).
[c] Gilles and Schoffeniels (1968).
[d] Duchâteau and Florkin (1961).
[e] Not estimated.

2. Insects

As shown in Table III, there are great variations in the amount of individual amino acids in the blood of the different insects examined; but, since the data have been obtained from insects at different developmental stages, few statements of a general character regarding the pattern of free amino acids in insect blood can be made. However, it can be noted that, as in Crustacea, glycine, proline, alanine, arginine, and glutamate are found in greater concentration than other amino acids. Large amounts of tyrosine can also be found in the blood of various species. Proline and tyrosine levels have greater variations. This fact can possibly be correlated with the important role that these two amino acids play in the formation of the cuticle at molting time.

If few comparative statements can be made from the collected results when dealing with the insect class, almost nothing can be concluded when comparing crustaceans and insects. Indeed, most of the data deal with amino acid composition of muscle in crustaceans and of hemolymph in insects. It appears, however, that generally the level of amino acids is higher in insect blood than in that of crustaceans (Tables II and III). This high concentration of free amino acids in insect hemolymph seems to be a characteristic of the class and has been tentatively used, parallel with the inorganic content of the blood, for phylogenetic considerations (Florkin, 1944, 1966; Sutcliffe, 1963; Florkin and Jeuniaux, 1964; see also Volume VI, Chapter 2). As emphasized by Sutcliffe (1962, 1963), the participation of the inorganic ions in the blood osmotic pressure tends to decrease with the phylogenetic level of the animal, this osmotic deficit being compensated by small organic molecules. Indeed, in Lepidoptera, Hymenoptera, and many Coleoptera, amino acids and other organic molecules play a large role in establishing the osmotic pressure level. If the total concentration of amino acids can be used for phylogenetic purposes, it appears from the consideration of Table III that it is difficult to consider the pattern of these amino acids from a phylogenetic point of view. The recorded data have been obtained from too few species, which moreover, were at different developmental stages.

The amino acid composition of tissues other than hemolymph is less known. However, it appears that there is also a considerable difference in the amino acid pattern of the muscles of various species and also in various tissues of the same species (Duchâteau and Florkin, 1955a).

The marked changes in the relative contribution of each amino acid to the establishment of the intracellular pool in Arthropoda is not yet clearly understood. However, the amino acid pattern obviously reflects the balance between synthesis and degradation of amino acids and also

TABLE III

Amino acid	Locusta migratoria (nymph)[b]	Schistocerca gregaria (adult)[c]	Carausius morosus (adult)[b]	Apis mellifica (larva)[d]	Hydrophilus piceus (adult)[e]	Leptinotarsa decemlineata (adult)[e]
Alanine	3.1	3.7	1.1	6.5	6.8	3.8
Arginine	1.0	—	1.0	4.3	0.4	1.1
Aspartate	1.3	—	0.5	2.4	1.4	1.6
Cystine	—	—	—	—	—	—
Glutamate	8.8	5.1	3.4	21.0	13.0	42.0
Glycine	9.3	33.2	3.1	10.0	3.5	2.2
Histidine	1.5	1.0	3.6	2.0	0.8	2.7
Isoleucine	1.9	2.6[k]	0.6	1.9	2.0	—
Leucine	1.6	0[k]	0.8	1.9	0.6	0.9
Lysine	2.7	—	2.0	7.2	1.7	2.9
Methionine	0	—	0.6	1.4	—	—
Phenylalanine	0.8	—	0.4	0.5	0.4	0.5
Proline	9.8	4.0	1.0	32.0	25.0	55.0
Serine	—	34.6	—	—	—	—
Taurine	—	—	—	—	—	—
Threonine	1.2	2.3	2.4	4.2	1.5	1.7
Tyrosine	0.3	2.5	0.3	0.2	0.5	0
Valine	2.9	5.0	1.9	5.0	1.8	2.1

[a] Values are expressed in mmoles/liter of plasma.
[b] Duchâteau et al. (1952a).
[c] Treherne (1959).
[d] Duchâteau et al. (1952b).
[e] Sarlet et al. (1952).
[f] Duchâteau and Florkin (1958).

their requirement to maintain osmotic equilibrium or as a foundation for protein synthesis. Therefore, it is clear that the amino acid pool undergoes variation when environmental or developmental changes occur. Most investigators have made use of this fact in studying variations in the amino acid pool.

Variations in the amino acid pool resulting from the adaptation of the organism to media of different salinities have been extensively studied. Chapter 9 is devoted to this problem. On the other hand, there are few investigations concerning the influence of other environmental parameters. A number of papers related to this topic may be consulted (Strong, 1964; Gilmour, 1965; Duchâteau and Florkin, 1955b; Cowey and Corner, 1963).

Literature concerning the variations of the amino acid pool during the development of Crustacea is rather scarce. There are only three brief reports dealing with free amino acids in Artemia (Bellini, 1960;

FREE AMINO ACID DISTRIBUTION IN THE HEMOLYMPH OF SEVERAL INSECTS[a]

Gasterophilus sp. (larva)[f]	Calliphora angur (larva)[g]	Cossus cossus (larva)[h]	Amathes xanthographa (larva)[b]	Imbrasia macrothysis (larva)[h]	Bombyx mori (larva)[i]
—[j]	13.0	4.2	8.9	2.7	2.0–4.8
0.5	0.1	4.9	3.6	1.2	1.2–3.2
1.1	1.1	3.8	6.3	0.7	4.4
—	—	—	—	—	—
21.3	3.3	4.8	18.0	5.7	18.0
0.8	3.9	3.1	6.4	14.0	1.7–11.0
0.08	—	5.1	7.3	2.8	9.8–18.0
0.6	1.5	2.7	2.6	0.8	0.4–1.1
0.5	1.5	4.8	1.4	0.5	0.9–1.4
0.6	0.1	10.0	4.7	4.4	5.7–7.1
0.5	0.1	1.4	0.2	0.2	0.5–1.0
0.4	1.2	1.5	1.0	0.4	0.4–0.6
2.9	8.0	11.0	14.0	0.9	0.9–2.4
—	2.4	—	—	—	1.9–4.4
—	—	—	—	—	—
2.0	0.1	2.3	3.6	0.8	2.0–3.4
1.2	7.4	6.8	0	—4.8	0.3–1.5
1.3	1.4	3.5	2.6	1.6	1.2–3.3

[g] Hackman (1956).
[h] Duchâteau and Florkin (1953).
[i] Fukuda et al. (1955).
[j] —, not determined.
[k] Given value represents leucine + isoleucine.

Dutrieu, 1960; Emerson, 1967). Modifications of the amino acid pattern in relation to developmental changes in insects have been extensively studied (Chen and Briegel, 1965; Levenbook and Dinamarca, 1966; Agrell, 1964; Mitlin et al., 1968). Since these studies have recently been reviewed by Chen (1966), we shall not deal with this subject.

The descriptive aspect of the amino acid pattern in Arthropoda having been briefly surveyed, we shall now consider some metabolic pathways implicated in the biosynthesis of these amino acids.

B. AMINO ACID BIOSYNTHESIS

1. Crustacea

Although general knowledge of the amino acid pool and of its variations in the different genera of Crustacea is available, very few investigations have been made so far dealing with the metabolism of amino acids. The only data available in this field concern the biosynthesis of amino acids from carbohydrates in some Crustacea (mainly Decapoda, *Homarus, Astacus,* and *Carcinus*).

a. Alanine, Glutamate, and Aspartate. The synthesis of the dicarboxylic amino acids from carbohydrates requires the presence of oxalacetate and 2-oxoglutarate as sources of hydrocarbon skeleton. These two keto compounds are intermediates in the Krebs cycle. One must therefore consider the Krebs cycle intermediates not only as catalytic agents implicated in the oxidation of acetate but also as substrates important in other metabolic sequences.

If large amounts of aspartate and glutamate, such as are found in the intracellular fluid of Crustacea muscle fiber (see Table I), have to be synthesized, it is clear that not only acetyl CoA has to be fed into the Krebs cycle but also another intermediate of the cycle. As classically described, the functioning of the Krebs cycle cannot lead to a net synthesis of one of its intermediates except if one of them is produced by another metabolic route. Since we are essentially dealing with the biosynthesis of amino acids, the question should be raised about the metabolic pathways which may provide the necessary substrates (anaplerotic pathways).

In a study of the synthesis of amino acids in the lobster nerve cord, Gilles and Schoffeniels (1964a) found an incorporation of ^{14}C into alanine, glycine, and glutamic and aspartic acids after incubation of the tissue with glucose-U-^{14}C, pyruvate-1-^{14}C, and pyruvate-2-^{14}C. Comparing the labeling of alanine and dicarboxylic amino acids obtained with the different substrates, they suggested the existence of at least two pathways leading to the synthesis of glutamate and aspartate. The results which prompted them to presume the existence of these pathways are shown in Table IV. The first important fact to note is that with pyruvate-1-^{14}C as substrate, labeled glutamate and aspartate can be found. Since the entrance of pyruvate in the Krebs cycle via acetyl CoA is accompanied by a decarboxylation of the C-1 of pyruvate, it can be postulated that pyruvate enters the cycle through carboxylation pathways. The existence of these pathways seems now to have been proved in Decapoda.

As a matter of fact, the existence of a malate dehydrogenase (EC 1.1.1.40) has been detected in *Astacus* (R. Keller, 1965) and also in enzymic preparations of lobster muscle (Gilles, 1969). Moreover Gilles and Schoffeniels (1966) have shown the presence of oxalacetate and aspartate decarboxylases in muscles of *Homarus vulgaris* and *Astacus fluviatilis.* The fact that dicarboxylic amino acids of *Homarus vulgaris* nerve cord can be labeled from $^{14}CO_2$ also indicates that pyruvate enters

TABLE IV

RELATIVE RADIOACTIVITY OF ALANINE, GLUTAMATE, AND ASPAR-
TATE AFTER INCUBATION OF THE LOBSTER NERVE CORD (*Homarus
vulgaris*) WITH GLUCOSE-U-^{14}C, PYRUVATE-1-^{14}C,
AND PYRUVATE-2-^{14}C[a,b]

Amino acid	Glucose-U-^{14}C	Pyruvate-1-^{14}C	Pyruvate-2-^{14}C
Alanine	1	4	8
Glutamate	1	1	2
Aspartate	1	1	2

[a] From Gilles and Schoffeniels (1964a).
[b] Numbers represent ratio of activity with glucose-U-^{14}C
taken as 1.

the Krebs cycle by carboxylation (Cheng and Mela, 1966; Gilles and Schoffeniels, 1968a; see also Table VI).

These results demonstrate the existence in Crustacea of a pathway which provides the necessary intermediates enabling the cycle to play a major role in the biosynthesis of dicarboxylic amino acids. However, on the basis of a comparison of the labeling of glutamate, aspartate, and alanine from glucose-U-^{14}C, pyruvate-1- and -2-^{14}C, Gilles and Schoffeniels (1964a) present arguments supporting the existence of another pathway, shunting the Krebs cycle and leading directly to the synthesis of glutamate from carbohydrates. The existence among Crustacea of a metabolic pathway leading to the synthesis of dicarboxylic amino acids which is different from glycolysis and the Krebs cycle has also been suggested by other authors.

Zandee (1966a) shows a labeling on C-2 of glutamate after injection of acetate-1-^{14}C in *Astacus astacus*. This study also demonstrates a concentration of radioactivity on the C-2 and C-3 of aspartate after injection of glucose-U-^{14}C (Table V). These labeling patterns cannot be explained by glycolysis and the Krebs cycle operations. Such a labeling pattern of glutamate from acetate-1-^{14}C has already been noted in other zoological groups (Sedee, 1961; van den Oord and Lafeber, 1963). Hitherto, no mechanism has been found to account for that phenomenon.

Anyway, these results are consistent with the hypothesis that the lobster or the crayfish can use a pathway different from the Krebs cycle to synthesize dicarboxylic amino acids. Such a hypothesis is also supported by the fact that the activity of the Krebs cycle appears to be very low in various Crustacea. Experiments *in vivo* have shown that 6 hours after injection of glucose-U-^{14}C into *Carcinus,* only labeled

TABLE V

LABELING PATTERN OF ASPARTIC AND GLUTAMIC ACIDS OF THE CRAYFISH *Astacus astacus* AFTER INJECTION OF ACETATE-1-^{14}C OR GLUCOSE-U-^{14}C[a]

		Activity in c.p.m.			
	Carbon atom	Acetate-1-^{14}C		Glucose-U-^{14}C	
Aspartic acid	1,4 COOH	296 ± 1.3	525.1 ± 1.6	17.4 ± 0.5	29.4 ± 0.6
	2,3 CHNH₂CH₂	Practically no activity		—[b]	—
Total activity		—	—	188.7 ± 1.1	319.5 ± 1.3
Glutamic acid	1 COOH	775.7 ± 2.0	510.8 ± 1.6	180.9 ± 1.0	
	2 CHNH₂	104.1	Probable activity	—	
	3,4 CH₂CH₂	No activity	Probable activity	—	
	3,4 CH₂CH₂ + COOH	2159.2 ± 3.3	1584.2 ± 2.8	183.7 ± 1.0	
Total activity		—	—	183.4 ± 1.0	

[a] Results taken from Zandee (1966a).
[b] —, not determined.

alanine and lactate can be recovered. A labeling of aspartate and glutamate can only be demonstrated 24 hours after the injection (Huggins, unpublished data, see Huggins and Munday, 1968). Such a finding suggests that the entry of carbohydrate carbon into the tricarboxylic acid cycle is rather slow in *Carcinus* and that the carbohydrate metabolism is directed toward anaerobiosis.

Moreover, it is worth noting in the experiments with glucose-U-^{14}C reported by Huggins and Munday (1968) that the intermediates of the Krebs cycle are very poorly labeled or not labeled at all, while the amino acids classically derived from this cycle have a high radioactivity. Similar results are obtained when using acetate-2-^{14}C as the labeled substrate (Huggins and Munday, 1968). However, as this study only gives estimations of radioactivity and not specific activity measurements, it is difficult to prejudge the part taken by the Krebs cycle in the synthesis of dicarboxylic amino acids.

These considerations may be correlated with the results obtained when studying the oxygen consumption from various substrates in Crustacea. These studies lead to the conclusion that carbohydrate metabolism in Crustacea differs considerably from the commonly accepted pattern in other organisms (Scheer and Scheer, 1951; Scheer *et al.*, 1952; Wolvekamp and Waterman, 1960). Nevertheless, it must be pointed out that the classic sequences—glycolysis, hexose monophosphate shunt, glucuronate pathway, and Krebs cycle—are operative in Crustacea (Puyear *et al.*, 1962, 1965; Puyear, 1967; MacWhinnie and Corkill, 1964; Hartenstein, 1964; Huggins and Munday, 1968; Gilles and Schoffeniels, 1964a,b, 1968a,b, 1969a). However, there is considerable evidence to suggest another metabolic pathway shunting the Krebs cycle and giving rise to glutamic and aspartic acids.

On the basis of experiments with arabinose-U-^{14}C, Gilles and Schoffeniels (1969b) have proposed such a pathway. Incubation of lobster nerve cord in the presence of arabinose-U-^{14}C induces the labeling of taurine, glutamate, and aspartate (Table VI). In the case of glutamate and aspartate, the labeling cannot be explained by a return of the ^{14}C of arabinose along the glucuronate pathway toward the classic sequence of Embden-Meyerhof and the Krebs cycle, since it has been shown that the conversion, of glucose 1-P to glucuronate is not reversible (Burns *et al.*, 1957; Eisenberg *et al.*, 1959). On the other hand, if ^{14}C were going through glycolysis, it would implicate a labeling of pyruvate and therefore of alanine, which has never been observed in the experimental conditions used by Gilles and Schoffeniels. Thus it can be considered that the labeling of glutamate from arabinose-U-^{14}C is achieved through a metabolic pathway different from glycolysis and the Krebs

TABLE VI

SPECIFIC ACTIVITY OF TAURINE, GLUTAMATE, AND ASPARTATE AFTER 2 HOURS
INCUBATION OF THE LOBSTER NERVE CORD WITH VARIOUS LABELED SUBSTRATES[a]

Amino acid	Glucose-U-^{14}C[b]		Pyruvate-1-^{14}C[b]		NaH^{14}CO$_3$[c]		Arabinose-U-^{14}C[d]	
Taurine	10680.9	10241.4	13402.9	5301.3	4011.6	3500.7	18956	17769
Glutamate	657.8	2116.1	865.7	e	2897.2	2583.6	9797	9887
Aspartate	314.1	530.4	182.9	499.2	4639.2	4305.3	3041	2953

[a] Specific activities are given in counts per micromole of amino acid.
[b] Gilles and Schoffeniels (1968b).
[c] Gilles and Schoffeniels (1968a).
[d] Gilles and Schoffeniels (1969b).
[e] Trace amounts.

cycle. This pathway could be that proposed by Weimberg and Doudoroff (1955) and Palleroni and Doudoroff (1956) which starts from an intermediate of the glucuronate pathway and leads to the formation of 2-oxoglutarate with arabinose and another substance which could be 2-oxo-3-dioxyarabonate as other intermediate.

Huggins and co-workers (1967) have detected another peculiarity in the metabolism of glutamate by *Carcinus*. In experiments using glutamic acid-U-^{14}C, they show the presence of an unidentified compound having chromatographic properties similar to malic acid. They have designated this unknown compound as "U8." It has not yet been possible to identify U8. It is ninhydrin negative and is not chromatographically identical with different products which result from glutamate metabolism. Perhaps the identification of this compound would indicate which pathway, shunting the Krebs cycle, is implicated in glutamate metabolism. The formation by *Carcinus* of high proportions of U8 is therefore interesting but until its identity is known, little comment can be made about its metabolic significance.

b. Other Amino Acids. Several authors have demonstrated by way of tracer studies that glycine, alanine, serine, proline, and hydroxyproline are steadily synthesized by Crustacea (Gilles and Schoffeniels, 1964a, 1968a,b, 1969a; Zandee, 1966a; Boulton *et al.*, 1967; Huggins and Munday, 1968). In these experiments, no radioactivity was recovered in valine, leucine, isoleucine, threonine, lysine, histidine, phenylalanine, and tyrosine, indicating their essential nature, although, as shown by Zandee (1966a), phenylalanine may replace tyrosine since, in *Astacus*, labeled tyrosine is rapidly formed from phenylalanine-3-^{14}C.

The labeling of taurine from several ^{14}C compounds has been reported only by Gilles and Schoffeniels (1968a,b, 1969b). In their experiments, the specific activity of this amine is always greater than that of other amino acids (Table VI). This should imply a rapid synthesis of the compound. Moreover, the labeling of taurine from $NaH^{14}CO_3$ (Table VI) cannot be explained by the classic formation pathways of this amine which imply serine or pyruvate as hydrocarbon skeleton donor (Chapeville and Fromageot, 1954). Thus another metabolic pathway of synthesis of taurine must be implicated.

2. Insects

While abundant information is available on amino acid occurrence in hemolymph, very little is known about its distribution and metabolism in tissues. As far as amino acid metabolism is concerned, most of the data have been obtained on larvae. After injection of glucose-U-^{14}C in larvae of the prairie grain wireworm *Ctenicera destructor*, Kasting *et al.* (1962) found a ^{14}C labeling of proline, alanine, serine, glycine, glutamic acid, and aspartic acid, thus indicating their biosynthesis by the organism. The poor labeling observed on glutamic acid is interpreted as indicating limited synthesis. Valine, lysine, phenylalanine, arginine, histidine, threonine, leucine, isoleucine, and tyrosine contain little, if any, radioactivity, indicating the essential character of these amino acids. The same kind of results was obtained with larvae of *Agrotis orthogonia* by Kasting and McGinnis (1962) and with larvae of *Neodiprion pratti* by Schaefer (1964). In the latter case, again, small amounts of radioactivity were detected on glutamic acid. These results are interpreted by Schaefer (1964) as well as by Kasting *et al.* (1962) in terms of limited biosynthesis of glutamate. However, these authors record a high level of radioactivity on proline and, in the case of *Neodiprion*, on glutamine. Classically, these two substances are directly derived from glutamate (see Fig. 1). Thus, it seems improbable that glutamic acid is little synthesized. As Kasting *et al.* (1962) work on HCl hydrolyzed tissues showed, the specific activity given for glutamic acid can result from dilution with the glutamic acid produced by the hydrolyzed compounds. However, this explanation is not applicable to the results of Schaefer (1964), who examined the labeling of the free amino acids in the hemolymph. All these experiments show that there is a possibility that insects synthesize several amino acids from glucose, thus suggesting the existence of glycolysis and the Krebs cycle. Arguments favoring the presence of the Krebs cycle, of glycolysis, and of its two shunts have already been extensively developed elsewhere (Chefurka, 1965a; Chapter 6). We shall therefore not deal further with the occurrence of these classic pathways of carbohydrate degradation.

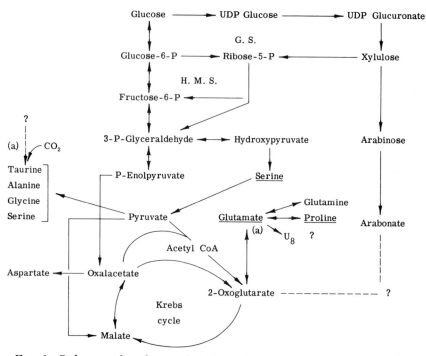

Fɪɢ. 1. Pathways of carbon carbohydrate incorporation into amino acids in Arthropoda. G.S., glucuronate shunt; H.M.S., hexose monophosphate shunt. (a) These pathways appeared to be, until now, specific to crustaceans.

The lack of labeling on tyrosine indicates that no carbon from the metabolic pool takes part in the formation of this amino acid. Tyrosine is probably formed from phenylalanine as indicated by the fact that labeled ^{14}C-phenylalanine can give rise to large amounts of radioactive tyrosine (Bricteux-Grégoire et al., 1959a; Sedee, 1961; Kasting et al., 1962). The fact that tyrosine is not essential but can only be synthesized from an essential amino acid is probably of general occurrence in Arthropoda, since it is also found in Crustacea (Zandee, 1966a).

In a study of ^{14}C incorporation from acetate-1-^{14}C into amino acids, Sedee (1961) shows a labeling of alanine, glycine, proline, serine, and glutamic and aspartic acids. Among these amino acids, alanine, aspartate, and glutamate were the most radioactive (Table VII). The labeling pattern of glutamate and aspartate can be explained by the Krebs cycle operation. However, it has already been noted in studying labeling patterns of glutamic acid from acetate-1-^{14}C in the crustacean *Astacus astacus* (see Section II,B,1,a), that a labeling in the C-2 position cannot be accounted for by the operation of the Krebs cycle. A possible mecha-

TABLE VII

LABELING PATTERN OF ALANINE, SERINE, GLYCINE, PROLINE, AND
GLUTAMIC AND ASPARTIC ACIDS FROM *Calliphora* LARVAE AFTER
GROWTH ON A MEDIUM CONTAINING ACETATE-1-^{14}C[a]

Amino acid	Carbon atom	Activity in c.p.m.[b]
Alanine	Total	169
	1 COOH	477
	2 CHNH$_2$	24
	3 CH$_3$	6
Glutamic acid	Total	312
	1 COOH	356
	2 CHNH$_2$	134
	3, 4 CH$_2$—CH$_2$	0
	5 COOH	993
Aspartic acid	Total	150
	1, 4 COOH group	287
	2, 3 CHNH$_2$—CH$_2$	12
Glycine	Total	94
	1 COOH	171
	2 CHNH$_2$	18
Serine	Total	61
	1 COOH	173
	2 CHNH$_2$	7
	3 CH$_2$OH	10
Proline	Total	23
	1 COOH	27
	2, 3, 4, 5	22

[a] Results taken from Sedee (1961).

[b] Activities are expressed as c.p.m. of fully comparable, infinitely thick BaCO$_3$ plates, 2.80 cm.^{2} in area.

nism that would explain this striking labeling pattern would be, according to Sedee (1961), a reductive carboxylation of succinic acid and a total reversal of the Krebs cycle. However, this hypothesis remains until now unproved, and more experiments have to be performed to test it and to elucidate this interesting problem.

The labeling observed on the C-1 position of alanine can be explained by the Krebs cycle operation, followed by decarboxylation of radioactive oxalacetate to pyruvate which can then be aminated to alanine. The labeling of alanine on C-2 and C-3 suggests that other pathways have

been used in the biosynthesis of pyruvate. It has to be noted here that
Bricteux-Grégoire *et al.* (1959a) also found an unexplainable labeling
on the C-2 and C-3 positions of alanine after injection of *Bombyx* larvae
with glutamate-2-^{14}C. Thus, one can postulate one or more unknown
pathways of alanine synthesis from carbohydrates in insects.

The labeling pattern obtained on glycine, serine, and proline are in
agreement with those that can be expected when following the classic
pathways of biosynthesis of these amino acids. Such a conclusion is
also supported by experiments of Bricteux-Grégoire *et al.* (1959b) and
Fukuda (1960) on *Bombyx mori*.

In conclusion, we can assume that amino acid synthesis in Arthropoda
takes place in the same way as in other animals; however a metabolic
shunt of the Krebs cycle leading to the formation of dicarboxylic amino
acids has to be postulated in Crustacea. In the same way, one can
suggest a new pathway for taurine synthesis. This pathway implies a
carboxylation reaction. As far as insects are concerned, one must also
consider pathways other than that described classically and which can
account for glutamate and alanine synthesis. These considerations are
summarized in Figs. 1 and 2. It must also be said that if some synthetic
systems for taurine, glutamate, aspartate, or alanine formation at the
present time appear peculiar to Arthropoda, it is perhaps simply because
their existence has never been investigated in other zoological groups.

The existence of most of the enzymes implicated in the pathways
of amino acid metabolism have been demonstrated in many Arthropoda
tissue preparations. The results of these enzymic studies have recently

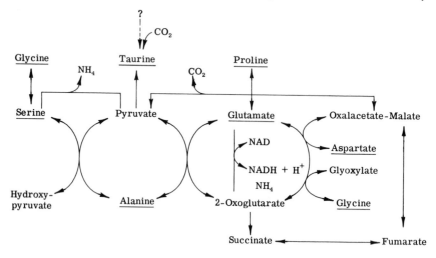

Fig. 2. Pathways of nonessential amino acid metabolism in Arthropoda.

been reviewed in Crustacea (Schoffeniels, 1967; Huggins and Munday, 1968; Florkin and Schoffeniels, 1969, see also Chapter 9) as well as in insects (Gilmour, 1965; Chefurka, 1965a,b).

C. AMINO ACID METABOLISM AND ENERGY PRODUCTION

In the previous section, the existence of glycolysis and the Krebs cycle in Arthropoda has been established. Moreover, the existence of the respiratory chain appears to be evident in Arthropoda since cytochromes are shown to be present in Crustacea (Tappel, 1960; Beechey, 1961; Burrin and Beechey, 1963, 1964, 1966) as well as in insects (Gilmour, 1965). Thus, one can expect that Arthropoda, as other animals, have the ability to derive their energy from the oxidation of carbohydrates. However, from the available data on crustacean metabolism, one can suggest that the oxidative metabolism in Crustacea can differ considerably from the commonly accepted pattern in other organisms (see Section II,B,1,a). Such data led Wolvekamp and Waterman (1960) to come to the tentative conclusion that, although carbohydrates may be the main metabolic substrate in some species, more often a mixture of proteins, carbohydrates, and lipids is needed. Thus the main substrate needed for energy production still has to be determined. Huggins (1966) showed that ^{14}C-acetate carbon is incorporated into various intermediates of the Krebs cycle. However, under the same conditions, he demonstrated little incorporation of ^{14}C-glucose carbon, although the production of labeled lactate and alanine indicates an oxidation of glucose for pyruvate. One can tentatively conclude that, at least in Decapoda, the Krebs cycle operation is slow, and therefore the energy production from glucose via this metabolic pathway plays a more minor part in Crustacea than in other animals.

In *Gecarcinus lateralis,* fat seems to be the major oxidized product as indicated by studies on respiratory quotients (Bliss, 1953). However, the small quantities of lipids found in *Astacus* and the low labeling of the fatty acids in comparison with the one obtained on amino acids led Zandee (1966b) to conclude that lipids are less important than amino acids for energy storage in this species. The large amount of free amino acids in crustacean tissues and the variability of this amount under conditions leading to an energetic adjustment may perhaps be considered as indicating the use of amino acids in the process of energy production. In fact, when studying the osmotic stress (see Chapter 9), it appears that in many euryhaline Crustacea the transfer from a concentrated medium to a more diluted one is followed by a decrease in amino acid concentration and by an increase in oxygen consumption. It thus seems probable that, in these species, the free amino acids form a readily available source of energy which may be called upon during the adaptation to a dilute medium. This hypothesis assumes the existence of a close relationship between amino acid metabolism and the respiratory chain.

Gilles and Schoffeniels (1965) have demonstrated that in the nerve cord of *Astacus*, addition of NH_4Cl induces an increase in the amino acid concentration and, at the same time, a decrease in the oxygen consumption. This can be explained by the competition for NADH between the dehydrogenation reactions implicated in amino acid synthesis and the respiratory chain (Fig. 3, see also Chapter 9). Such a relation has also been found in vertebrates (Worcel and Ericinska, 1962; Papa *et al.*, 1969a,b). The results obtained suggest that glutamate synthesis exerts a control of the respiratory chain in that the reducing equivalents available are directed toward the synthesis of glutamate or the cytochromes Fig. 3; see also Schoffeniels, 1968; Chapter 9).

Direct evidence of the utilization of an amino acid for energy production in Insecta has been given recently by Bursell (1963, 1966). During flight in *Glossina*, proline disappears from the blood. Moreover, labeled proline is converted rapidly to labeled glutamate and labeled alanine. It seems, therefore, probable that proline, after being converted to glutamic acid, loses its amino group by transamination and that its carbon skeleton is catabolized through the Krebs cycle (Fig. 3). The first step of this energy productive pathway is an oxidative conversion of proline to glutamic acid, which is known to occur in other animals and which

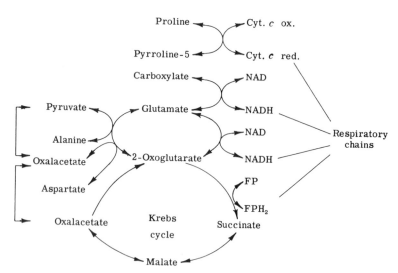

FIG. 3. Relations between amino acid metabolism and energy production.

needs cytochrome c as electron acceptor (Johnson and Strecker, 1962). Therefore, this pathway shows a direct relation between amino acid metabolism and energy production.

We do not have unequivocal evidence enabling us to decide the relative importance of amino acid oxidation in energy production. We can only propose a tentative scheme to explain the relationship between amino acids and energy metabolism. More information is needed to better understand the phenomenon (see Chapter 9).

III. End Products of Nitrogen Catabolism

Little is known about the course of nitrogen metabolism in Crustacea. The knowledge that we do have is almost entirely confined to the Decapoda.

As in many aquatic invertebrates, the main waste product of nitrogen metabolism in Crustacea, even in the terrestrial forms, is NH_3. Uric acid and urea have also been found in the excreta of some species (Parry, 1960).

In other terrestrial Arthropoda, such as most of the insects, the main end product of N_2 metabolism is uric acid. This was established in the first decades of the century (Needham, 1935; Florkin, 1945), and still prevails at the moment (Craig, 1960; Stobbart and Shaw, 1964). However, more recently, many data have been accumulated suggesting that other nitrogenous end products such as allantoin, allantoic acid, or urea may figure largely in the excreta of various insects (Bursell, 1967).

The formation of the main nitrogenous end products in animals involves mainly two metabolic pathways. The first has its origin in the degradation of nucleic acid. The second starts with protein and amino acid catabolism. The main end products of these two catabolic processes are ammonia, urea, and uric acid (Fig. 4). We shall now deal with the formation of these products in Arthropoda.

A. Ammonia Formation

A prime source of ammonia is from the deamination of amino acids. Deamination of histidine, leucine, tryptophan, arginine, and lysine can be achieved by an L-amino acid oxidase (Roche et al., 1952). Serine can be deaminated to pyruvate by an L-serine hydro-lyase (Gilles, 1969). Aspartic acid, alanine, glycine, valine, and leucine may transaminate 2-oxoglutarate to give glutamate (Chen and Bachman-Diem, 1964; Chaplin et al., 1967). The metabolism of this dicarboxylic amino acid is also controlled by the glutamic dehydrogenase activity (Schoffeniels

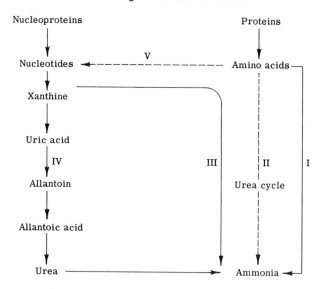

FIG. 4. Pathways of nitrogen compounds catabolism in Arthropoda.

and Gilles, 1963; Schoffeniels, 1964, 1965; Bond and Sang, 1968), and it has been emphasized that this enzyme plays an important role in nitrogen metabolism by controlling the entrance of ammonia into the metabolism and not its release from glutamate (see Section I,C).

B. Urea Cycle

The urea cycle was previously thought to be restricted to ureotelic vertebrates, but it has been shown to occur also in some terrestrial invertebrates. All urea cycle enzymes have been demonstrated in the earthworm (Bishop and Campbell, 1963), and ornithine transcarbamylase along with arginase have been found in the land planarian *Bipalium* (Campbell and Lee, 1963; Campbell, 1966). At the moment, the occurrence of the urea cycle in Crustacea is far from demonstrated but cannot be completely ruled out. Skutch *et al.* (unpublished data, see Huggins and Munday, 1968) have shown the presence of ornithine transcarbamylase, arginosuccinate lyase, and arginase in *Carcinus* hepatopancreas. Arginase activity has also been found in *Carcinus* by Baldwin (1935) and urease has been found in all the Crustacea so far studied (Florkin and Duchâteau 1943; Boulesteix, 1965).

Urea has been reported as a minor constituent of the hemolymph (Buck, 1953) and of the excreta (Powning, 1953; Razet, 1961, 1966) of many insects. Since none of the species investigated possess an allantoicase (Razet, 1966), it seems unlikely that urea could represent a purine breakdown product. Urea might thus be produced from amino acid nitrogen through the urea cycle. Arginase is present in extracts of locust tissues (Kilby and Neville, 1957) and of *Schistocerca gregaria* or *Eyprepenemia plorans* (Garcia *et al.*, 1958). However this enzyme appears to be absent from extracts of *Calliphora* fat body (Desai and Kilby, 1958). Moreover, in *Celerio euphorbiae* the urea cycle is incomplete despite the presence of its three constitutive amino acids (Porembska and Mochnacka, 1964).

Thus, before drawing any conclusion as to the existence of the urea cycle in Arthropoda, further experiments must be carried out.

C. Uricolytic System and Nucleic Acid Degradation

Another source of nitrogen end products is the degradation of puric basis to uric acid which can be converted to urea and NH_3, via allantoic acid (Fig. 4).

The existence of both adenase and guanase has been demonstrated in tissues of various Arthropoda (Duchâteau *et al.*, 1941; Roush and Betz, 1956). Moreover, adenosine deaminase is found in the hepatopancreas of *Astacus* and *Homarus* (Roush and Betz, 1956) as well as in the larva of *Calliphora erythrocephala* (Desai and Kilby, 1958). The finding of adenosine deaminase in some invertebrates indicates that the classic concept, according to which the appearance of an enzymic system for the deamination of nucleosides is a biochemical characteristic of vertebrates, must be revised. As shown in Fig. 4, the deaminated purines are oxidized to uric acid by xanthine oxidase. This enzyme appears to be widely distributed in insects (Florkin and Duchâteau, 1941; Hayashi, 1962; Ursprung and Hadorn, 1961; Cordero and Ludwig, 1963; Parzen and Fox, 1964; Munz, 1964) where it may be present in various molecular forms as has been shown in *Drosophila* (E. C. Keller *et al.*, 1963; K. D. Smith *et al.*, 1963).

Nucleic acid catabolism is not the only source of uric acid in Arthropoda. It seems now well established that the purine ring may be synthesized from amino acid residues by the same pathway as that occurring in birds (Buchanan, 1951), thus inferring the possibility of uric acid formation from protein catabolism (Fig. 4) (Heller and Jezewska, 1959; Clegg, 1965).

Uric acid derived from purine or protein catabolism may then be subjected to a series of degradative reactions in the presence of uricolytic enzymes. The distribution of these enzymes is very irregular among Arthropoda. Except for urease which is present in all Crustacea so far studied, the other enzymes of the uricolytic system have been detected all together only in *Astacus, Homarus,* and *Balanus* (Florkin and Duchâteau, 1943; Boulesteix, 1964, 1965).

Insects can be divided into three groups according to their main excretion product of nitrogen catabolism. Insects which excrete uric acid as the main product of their purine and protein catabolism can be termed uricotelic. In many species, uric acid is degraded to allantoin which is then excreted. These species would be allantoinotelic. Several species possessing an active allantoinase excrete allantoic acid and may thus be termed allantoicotelic. It appears that, except for *Attagenus piceus* and *Xenylla welchi*, the insect orders belong to one of the three groups we have described above. For instance, Thysanura, Paleoptera, and Orthoptera are mainly uricotelic while Heteroptera are generally allantoinotelic, and Mecoptera as well as Megaloptera are allantoicotelic (Razet, 1961, 1966; Bursell, 1967). However, it must be noted that in many cases, all the species of a same order cannot be restricted to a single group, since one can find Diptera representatives in the three groups (Razet, 1966).

To conclude this section, one can consider NH_3 as being the main end product of nitrogen catabolism in Crustacea. Ammonia can be obtained from amino acids or nucleotide deamination (Fig. 4, I, III). A certain amount of NH_3 could come from deamination of arginine occurring in the urea cycle since urease is present in Crustacea (Fig. 4, II). With regard to the participation of puric base in NH_3 production (Fig. 4, IV), it has been shown that the whole uricolytic system is nonexistent, some species excepted. These results invalidate the classic view according to which all Crustacea must be considered as having the uricolytic system. Since the degradation process for nucleotides and nucleosides is still unknown, the participation of this system in the production of NH_3 in Crustacea is impossible to estimate.

Except for one aquatic and two terrestrial species, insects can be divided into three groups according to the fact that they excrete mainly uric acid, allantoin, or allantoic acid. Protein catabolism appears to proceed in the same way as purine catabolism in insects, since uric acid seems to be synthesized from amino acid residues. However, protein catabolism can partly or wholly remain out of the uricolytic pathway; then urea or NH_3 excretion is involved. Ammonia secretion is peculiar to aquatic insects in which protein catabolism can be considered as independent from purine catabolism.

IV. Proteins

Data related to protein metabolism in Arthropoda are sparse. Some works are available concerning changes in protein concentration during the molting cycle in Crustacea. Generally, proteins are stored in the hepatopancreas during the intermolt period and are subsequently used for tissue growth during the molting period (Renaud, 1949; Vonk, 1960; Robertson, 1960; Kurup and Scheer, 1966; Glynn, 1968). This indicates that at least the physiological state of Crustacea has some effect on protein synthesis. However, so little information is available on protein metabolism and its control that we have to assume that it follows a sequence similar to that in other animals. It should be noted here that besides a normal DNA, several Crustacea of *Cancer* species possess a DNA rich in adenine and thymine (Sueoka, 1961; M. Smith, 1963; Pochon *et al.*, 1965). It seems unlikely that this special DNA could be related to some peculiarity of Crustacea protein metabolism since it is only found in *Cancer* species and nowhere else (M. Smith, 1964).

In insects, the fat body appears to be the major site of blood protein formation (Hill, 1965; Coles, 1965; Price, 1966). During larval development, the content of hemolymph proteins increases. Wyatt *et al.* (1956) report a rise in blood protein concentration from 1.2% in early 3rd instar to 5.3% in the late 5th instar in *Bombyx*. The same pattern of variation in the total hemolymph proteins has also been reported for *Popillia japonica* (Ludwig, 1954), *Galleria mellonella* (Denucé, 1958), *Samia cynthia* (Laufer, 1960a), and *Drosophila* (Chen, 1956). During metamorphosis, where drastic morphological changes occur, hemolymph protein concentration falls rapidly. The greatest decline occurs during the time of transformation from larva to white pupa and at adult emergence. Chen and Levenbook (1966b) report that in new emerged flies of *Phormia regina*, protein concentration amounts to about only one-sixth of the concentration in mature larva. More detailed studies indicate that these changes are correlated with important variations in the ontogenic pattern, including the appearance of new protein fractions and the disappearance of others. Such a variation has been reported for other insects (Whittaker and West, 1962; Loughton and West, 1965). Moreover, it is a well-known fact that there is a very little change in the amino acid level during metamorphosis (Levenbook, 1962; Levenbook and Dinamarca, 1966). Since, during this period, tremendous changes in protein concentration and in ontogenic pattern occur, while no variation can be observed in amino acid levels, it must be assumed that amino acids are rapidly incorporated into proteins of developing adults. Indeed, many authors show a significant incorporation of ^{14}C-amino acids into proteins (Bricteux-Grégoire *et al.*, 1957; Devi *et al.*, 1963; Skinner, 1963).

However, Chen and Levenbook (1966a) show that during metamorphosis of *Phormia regina* the rate of breakdown of injected radioactive proteins in larval hemolymph is very low, since only 5% to 15% of injected proteins are catabolized to amino acids. Moreover, they demonstrate that about three quarters of the recovered radioactivity is in tissue proteins of newly emerged adult flies. According to current genetic concepts, the synthesis of proteins is only possible from amino acid residues and not from small polypeptides. As little radioactivity is found in amino acids from labeled proteins, one must therefore conclude that there is a direct utilization of hemolymph protein by tissues. According to the results of Chen and Levenbook (1966a,b), this process would be the major mechanism of protein utilization during metamorphosis (see also Bodnaryk and Levenbook, 1968).

Following the experiments of Chen and Levenbook, it would be of interest to know if blood proteins are incorporated into tissues just as they are or if new types of proteins are formed. A direct utilization of blood proteins by tissues during metamorphosis may occur if one assumes that most of these proteins are involved in functions which are common to larvae and adults. This could well be the case since, as shown by Laufer (1960b, 1961, 1964), nearly all blood proteins in *Hyalophora cecropia* and *Samia cynthia* act as enzymes.

V. Quaternary Ammonium Derivatives

Among nitrogenous compounds occurring in Crustacea, some quaternary amine derivatives have been described (Fig. 5). Beers (1967) made a survey of the distribution of certain quaternary ammonium bases in a series of animals including Crustacea. From his results, it can be concluded that in most Crustacea studied, glycine-betaine is present in higher concentrations than other quaternary compounds. Homarine was detected in all marine Crustacea but could not be identified in the freshwater Decapoda *Orconectes* and *Trichodactylus* or the terrestrial *Gecarcinus*. The isomer of homarine, trigonelline, occurs in some marine Crustacea, but its concentration is always lower than that of homarine. Carnitine is also found in some species, but γ-butyrobetaine has never been identified in any of the species surveyed. Another quaternary ammonium derivative, trimethylamine oxide, is of general occurrence. It has been detected by Norris and Benoit (1945) in Copepoda mixture, in Cirripedia, in Amphipoda, and also in several Decapoda. The origin and function of these compounds are not well understood at the present time (Fraenkel, 1954; Kravitz et al., 1963).

Perhaps quaternary ammonium derivatives can play a role in cellular osmotic regulation. In fact, trimethylamine oxide is more concentrated in the muscle of *Eriocheir sinensis* adapted to seawater than in the muscle of animals adapted to freshwater (Bricteux et al., 1962). Further-

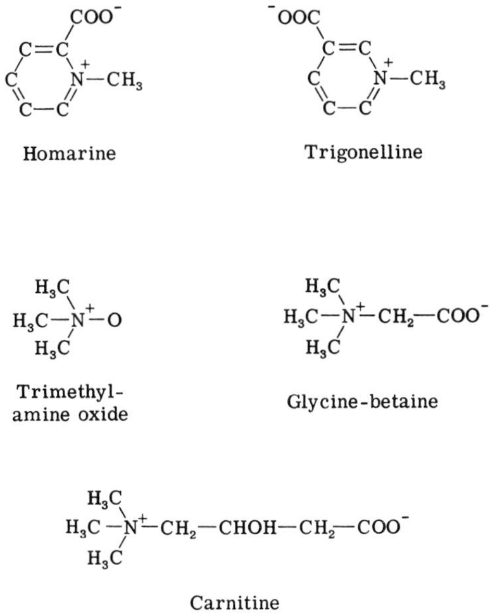

Homarine

Trigonelline

Trimethyl-amine oxide

H_3C-N^+-O (with three H_3C groups)

Glycine-betaine

$H_3C-N^+-CH_2-COO^-$ (with three H_3C groups)

Carnitine

$H_3C-N^+-CH_2-CHOH-CH_2-COO^-$ (with three H_3C groups)

FIG. 5. Quaternary ammonium derivatives occurring in Crustacea.

more, Gasteiger et al. (1960), studying the phylogenetic distribution of homarine, showed that this base occurs only in marine Crustacea. This evidence enabled them to suggest that homarine may act as an osmotic effector. However, lack of correlation between the amount of homarine in the nerve cord of Limulus polyphemus and the environmental salinity led Levy (1967) to conclude that this compound is not related to the osmoregulatory function in Limulus.

At the present time, the metabolic origin and biological role of all these bases remain obscure, and one has to await more information before being able to evaluate their metabolic importance in Crustacea.

REFERENCES

Agrell, I. (1964). In "The Physiology of Insecta" (M. Rockstein, ed.), Vol. 1, pp. 91–148. Academic Press, New York.
Baldwin, E. (1935). Biochem. J. 29, 252.
Beechey, R. B. (1961). Comp. Biochem. Physiol. 3, 161.
Beers, J. R. (1967). Comp. Biochem. Physiol. 21, 11.
Bellini, L. (1960). Ric. Sci. Suppl. 30, 816.
Bishop, S. H., and Campbell, J. W. (1963). Science 142, 1583.
Bliss, D. E. (1953). Biol. Bull. 104, 275.
Bodnaryk, R. P., and Levenbook, L. (1968). Biochem. J. 110, 771.
Bond, P. A., and Sang, J. H. (1968). J. Insect Physiol. 14, 341.
Boulesteix, R. (1964). Compt. Rend. 258, 3098.

Boulesteix, R. (1965). *Compt. Rend.* **260,** 1767.

Boulton, A. P., Huggins, A. K., and Munday, K. A. (1967). *Life Sci.* **6,** 1293.

Bricteux-Grégoire, S., Verly, W. G., and Florkin, M. (1957). *Nature* **179,** 678.

Bricteux-Grégoire, S., Verly, W. G., and Florkin, M. (1959a). *Arch. Intern. Physiol. Biochim.* **67,** 563.

Bricteux-Grégoire, S., Dewandre, A., Florkin, M., and Verly, W. G. (1959b). *Arch. Intern. Physiol. Biochim.* **67,** 687.

Bricteux-Grégoire, S., Duchâteau-Bosson, G., Jeuniaux, C., and Florkin, M. (1962). *Arch. Intern. Physiol. Biochim.* **70,** 273.

Buchanan, J. M. (1951). *J. Cellular Comp. Physiol.* **38,** Suppl. 1, 143.

Buck, J. B. (1953). *In* "Insect Physiology" (K. D. Roeder, ed.), pp. 147–190. Wiley, New York.

Burns, J. J., Dayton, P. G., and Eisenberg, F., Jr. (1957). *Biochim. Biophys. Acta* **25,** 647.

Burrin, D. H., and Beechey, R. B. (1963). *Biochem. J.* **87,** 48.

Burrin, D. H., and Beechey, R. B. (1964). *Comp. Biochem. Physiol.* **12,** 245.

Burrin, D. H., and Beechey, R. B. (1966). *Comp. Biochem. Physiol.* **19,** 745.

Bursell, E. (1963). *J. Insect Physiol.* **9,** 439.

Bursell, E. (1966). *Comp. Biochem. Physiol.* **19,** 809.

Bursell, E. (1967). *Advan. Insect Physiol.* **4,** 33–67.

Camien, M. N., Sarlet, H., Duchâteau, G., and Florkin, M. (1951). *J. Biol. Chem.* **193,** 881.

Campbell, J. W. (1966). *Nature* **208,** 1299.

Campbell, J. W., and Lee, T. W. (1963). *Comp. Biochem. Physiol.* **8,** 29.

Chapeville, F., and Fromageot, P. (1954). *Biochim. Biophys. Acta* **14,** 415.

Chaplin, A. E., Huggins, A. K., and Munday, K. A. (1967). *Comp. Biochem. Physiol.* **20,** 195.

Chefurka, W. (1965a). *In* "The Physiology of Insecta" (M. Rockstein, ed.), Vol. 2, pp. 581–667. Academic Press, New York.

Chefurka, A. (1965b). *In* "The Physiology of Insecta" (M. Rockstein, ed.), Vol. 2, pp. 669–768. Academic Press, New York.

Chen, P. S. (1956). *Rev. Suisse Zool.* **63,** 216.

Chen, P. S. (1966). *Advan. Insect Physiol.* **3,** 53–132.

Chen, P. S., and Bachmann-Diem, C. (1964). *J. Insect Physiol.* **10,** 819.

Chen, P. S., and Briegel, H. (1965). *Comp. Biochem. Physiol.* **14,** 463.

Chen, P. S., and Levenbook, L. (1966a). *J. Insect Physiol.* **12,** 1595.

Chen, P. S., and Levenbook, L. (1966b). *J. Insect Physiol.* **12,** 1611.

Cheng, S. C., and Mela, P. (1966). *J. Neurochem.* **13,** 281.

Clegg, J. S. (1965). Presented at the *132nd Meeting Am. Assoc. Advance. Sci., Berkeley, Calif., 1965.*

Coles, G. C. (1965). *J. Insect Physiol.* **11,** 1317.

Cordero, S. M., and Ludwig, D. (1963). *J. N.Y. Entomol. Soc.* **41,** 66.

Cowey, C. B. (1961). *Comp. Biochem. Physiol.* **2,** 173.

Cowey, C. B., and Corner, E. D. S. (1963). *J. Marine Biol. Assoc. U.K.* **43,** 485.

Craig, R. (1960). *Ann Rev. Entomol.* **5,** 53.

Denucé, J. M. (1958). *Z. Naturforsch.* **13b,** 215.

Desai, R. M., and Kilby, B. A. (1958). *Arch. Intern. Physiol. Biochim.* **66,** 248.

Devi, A., Lindsay, P., and Sarkar, N. K. (1963). *Experientia* **19,** 344.

Duchâteau, G., and Florkin, M. (1953). *Arch. Intern. Physiol. Biochim.* **61,** 232.

Duchâteau, G., and Florkin, M. (1955a). *Arch. Intern. Physiol. Biochim.* **63**, 35.
Duchâteau, G., and Florkin, M. (1955b). *Arch. Intern. Physiol. Biochim.* **63**, 213.
Duchâteau, G., and Florkin, M. (1958). *Arch. Intern. Physiol. Biochim.* **66**, 573.
Duchâteau, G., and Florkin, M. (1961). *Comp. Biochem. Physiol.* **3**, 245.
Duchâteau, G., Florkin, M., and Frappez, G. (1941). *Bull. Acad. Roy. Belg. Cl. Sci. [Ser. 5]* **27**, 169.
Duchâteau, G., Florkin, M., and Sarlet, H. (1952a). *Arch. Intern. Physiol. Biochim.* **60**, 539.
Duchâteau, G., Sarlet, H., and Florkin, M. (1952b). *Arch. Intern. Physiol. Biochim.* **60**, 103.
Duchâteau, G., Florkin, M., and Jeuniaux, C. (1959). *Arch. Intern. Physiol. Biochim.* **67**, 489.
Dutrieu, J. (1960). *Arch. Zool. Exptl. Gen.* **99**, 1.
Eisenberg, F., Jr., P. G., and Burns, J. J. (1959). *J. Biol. Chem.* **234**, 250.
Emerson, D. N. (1967). *Comp. Biochem. Physiol.* **20**, 245.
Florkin, M. (1944). "L'évolution biochimique." Masson, Paris.
Florkin, M. (1945). *Actualites Biochim.* **3**, 1–76.
Florkin, M. (1956). "Vergleichend biochemische Fragen, 6. Colloquium der Gesellschaft für physiologische Chemie, 1955," pp. 62–69. Springer, Berlin.
Florkin, M. (1966). "Aspects moléculaires de l'adaptation et de la phylogénie." Masson, Paris.
Florkin, M., and Duchâteau, G. (1941). *Bull. Acad. Roy. Belg. Cl. Sci. [Ser. 5]* **27**, 174.
Florkin, M., and Duchâteau, G. (1943). *Arch. Intern. Physiol.* **53**, 267.
Florkin, M., and Jeuniaux, C. (1964). *In* "The Physiology of Insecta" (M. Rockstein, ed.), Vol. 3, pp. 109–152. Academic Press, New York.
Florkin, M., and Schoffeniels, E. (1969). "Molecular Approaches to Ecology." Academic Press, New York.
Fraenkel, G. (1954). *Arch. Biochem. Biophys.* **50**, 486.
Fukuda, T. (1960). *J. Biochem. (Tokyo)* **47**, 581.
Fukuda, T., Kirimura, J., Matuda, M., and Suzumi, T. (1955). *J. Biochem. (Tokyo)* **42**, 341.
Gangal, S. V., and Magar, N. G. (1964). *Indian J. Biochem.* **1**, 59.
Garcia, I., Couerbe, J., and Roche, J. (1958). *Compt. Rend. Soc. Biol.* **152**, 1646.
Gasteiger, E. L., Haake, P. C., and Gergen, J. A. (1960). *Ann. N.Y. Acad. Sci.* **90**, 622.
Gilles, R. (1969). *Arch. Intern. Physiol. Biochim.* **77**, 441.
Gilles, R., and Schoffeniels, E. (1964a). *Biochim. Biophys. Acta* **82**, 518.
Gilles, R., and Schoffeniels, E. (1964b). *Biochim. Biophys. Acta* **82**, 525.
Gilles, R., and Schoffeniels, E. (1965). *Arch. Intern. Physiol. Biochim.* **73**, 144.
Gilles, R., and Schoffeniels, E. (1966). *Bull. Soc. Chim. Biol.* **48**, 397.
Gilles, R., and Schoffeniels, E. (1968a). *Arch. Intern. Physiol. Biochim.* **76**, 441.
Gilles, R., and Schoffeniels, E. (1968b). *Arch. Intern. Physiol. Biochim.* **76**, 452.
Gilles, R., and Schoffeniels, E. (1969a). *Comp. Biochem. Physiol.* **28**, 417.
Gilles, R., and Schoffeniels, E. (1969b). *Comp. Biochem. Physiol.* **28**, 1145.
Gilles, R., and Schoffeniels, E. (1970). Unpublished data.
Gilmour, D. (1965). "The Metabolism of Insects." Oliver & Boyd, Edinburgh and London.
Glynn, J. P. (1968). *Comp. Biochem. Physiol.* **26**, 937.
Hackman, R. H. (1956). *Australian J. Biol. Sci.* **9**, 400.

Hartenstein, R. (1964). *Enzymologia* 27, 113.

Hayashi, J. (1962). *J. Sericult. Sci. Japan* 31, 25.

Heller, J., and Jezewska, M. M. (1959). *Bull. Acad. Polon. Sci., Ser. Sci. Biol.* 7, 1.

Hill, L. (1965). *J. Insect Physiol.* 11, 1605–1615.

Huggins, A. K. (1966). *Comp. Biochem. Physiol.* 18, 283.

Huggins, A. K., and Munday, K. A. (1968). *Advan. Comp. Physiol. Biochem.* 3, 271–378.

Huggins, A. K., Rick, J. T., and Kerkut, G. A. (1967). *Comp. Biochem. Physiol.* 21, 23.

Jeuniaux, C., Bricteux-Grégoire, S., and Florkin, M. (1961). *Cahiers Biol. Marine* 2, 373.

Johnson, A. B., and Strecker, H. J. (1962). *J. Biol. Chem.* 237, 1876.

Kasting, R., and McGinnis, A. J. (1962). *J. Insect Physiol.* 8, 97.

Kasting, R., Davis, G. R. F., and McGinnis, A. J. (1962). *J. Insect Physiol.* 8, 589.

Keller, E. C., Jr., Saverance, P., and Glassman, E. (1963). *Nature* 198, 286.

Keller, R. (1965). *Z. Vergleich. Physiol.* 50, 119.

Kilby, B. A., and Neville, E. (1957). *J. Exptl. Biol.* 34, 276.

Kravitz, E. A., Kuffler, S. W., Potter, D. D., and van Gelder, N. M. (1963). *J. Neurophysiol.* 26, 729.

Kurup, N. G., and Scheer, B. T. (1966). *Comp. Biochem. Physiol.* 18, 971.

Laufer, H. (1960a). *Ann. N.Y. Acad. Sci.* 89, 490.

Laufer, H. (1960b). *Proc. 11th Intern. Congr. Entomol., Vienna, 1960* Vol. 3, p. 194.

Laufer, H. (1961). *Ann. N.Y. Acad. Sci.* 94, 825.

Laufer, H. (1964). *In* "Taxonomic Biochemistry and Serology" (C. A. Leone, ed.), pp. 171–189. Ronald Press, New York.

Levenbook, L. (1962). *J. Insect Physiol.* 8, 559.

Levenbook, L., and Dinamarca, M. L. (1966). *J. Insect Physiol.* 12, 1343.

Levy, R. A. (1967). *Comp. Biochem. Physiol.* 23, 631.

Loughton, B. G., and West, A. S. (1965). *J. Insect Physiol.* 11, 919.

Ludwig, D. (1954). *Physiol. Zool.* 27, 325.

MacWhinnie, M. A., and Corkill, A. J. (1964). *Comp. Biochem. Physiol.* 12, 81.

Mitlin, N., Wiygul, G., and Mauldin, J. K. (1968). *Comp. Biochem. Physiol.* 25, 139.

Munz, P. (1964). *Z. Verebungslehre* 95, 195.

Needham, J. (1935). *Biochem. J.* 29, 238.

Norris, E. R., and Benoit, G. J., Jr. (1945). *J. Biol. Chem.* 158, 433.

Palleroni, N. J., and Doudoroff, M. (1956). *J. Biol. Chem.* 223, 499.

Papa, S., Tager, J. M., Francavilla, A., and Quagliariello, E. (1969a). *Biochim. Biophys. Acta* 172, 20.

Papa, S., Tager, J. M., Guerrieri, F., and Quagliariello, E. (1969b). *Biochim. Biophys. Acta* 172, 184.

Parry, G. (1960). *In* "The Physiology of Crustacea" (T. H. Waterman, ed.), Vol. 1, pp. 341–366. Academic Press, New York.

Parzen, S. D., and Fox, A. S. (1964). *Biochim. Biophys. Acta* 92, 465.

Pochon, F., Nassoulié, J., and Michelson, M. (1965). *Compt. Rend.* 260, 2937.

Porembska, Z., and Mochnacka, I. (1964). *Acta Biochim. Polon.* 11, 109.

Powning, R. F. (1953). *Australian J. Biol. Sci.* 6, 109.

Price, G. M. (1966). *J. Insect Physiol.* 12, 731.

Puyear, R. L. (1967). *Comp. Biochem. Physiol.* 20, 499.

Puyear, R. L., Wang, C. H., and Pritchard, A. W. (1962). *Am. Zoologist* **2**, 439.
Puyear, R. L., Wang, C. H., and Pritchard, A. W. (1965). *Comp. Biochem. Physiol.* **14**, 145
Razet, P. (1961). Thèse, Doct. Sci. Nat., Imprimerie Bretonne, Rennes.
Razet, P. (1966). *Annee Biol.* **5**, 43.
Renaud, L. (1949). *Ann. Inst. Oceanog.* (*Paris*) **24**, 259.
Robertson, J. D. (1960). *Comp. Biochem. Physiol.* **1**, 183.
Roche, J., van Thoai, N., and Glahn, P. E. (1952). *Experientia* **8**, 428.
Roush, A. H., and Betz, R. F. (1956). *Biochim. Biophys. Acta* **19**, 579.
Sarlet, H., Duchâteau, G., Camien, M. N., and Florkin, M. (1952). *Biochim. Biophys. Acta* **8**, 571.
Schaefer, C. H. (1964). *J. Insect Physiol.* **10**, 363.
Scheer, B. T., and Scheer, M. A. R. (1951). *Physiol. Comparata Oecol.* **2**, 198.
Scheer, B. T., Schwabe, C. W., and Scheer, M. A. R. (1952). *Physiol. Comparata Oecol.* **2**, 327.
Schoffeniels, E. (1964). *Life Sci.* **3**, 845.
Schoffeniels, E. (1965). *Arch. Intern. Physiol. Biochim.* **73**, 73.
Schoffeniels, E. (1967). "Cellular Aspects of Membrane Permeability." Pergamon Press, Oxford.
Schoffeniels, E. (1968). *Arch. Intern. Physiol. Biochim.* **76**, 319.
Schoffeniels, E., and Gilles, R. (1963). *Life Sci.* **2**, 834.
Sedee, D. J. W. (1961). *Arch. Intern. Physiol. Biochim.* **69**, 295.
Skinner, D. M. (1963). *Biol. Bull.* **118**, 338.
Smith, K. D., Ursprung, H., and Wright, T. R. F. (1963). *Science* **142**, 226.
Smith, M. (1963). *Biochem. Biophys. Res. Commun.* **10**, 67.
Smith, M. (1964). *J. Mol. Biol.* **9**, 17.
Stobbart, R. H., and Shaw, J. (1964). *In* "The Physiology of Insecta" (M. Rockstein, ed.), Vol. 3, pp. 190–258. Academic Press, New York.
Strong, F. E. (1964). *J. Insect Physiol.* **10**, 519.
Sueoka, N. (1961). *J. Mol. Biol.* **3**, 31.
Sutcliffe, D. W. (1962). *J. Exptl. Biol.* **39**, 325.
Sutcliffe, D. W. (1963). *Comp. Biochem. Physiol.* **9**, 121.
Tappel, A. (1960). *J. Cellular Comp. Physiol.* **55**, 111.
Treherne, J. E. (1959). *J. Exptl. Biol.* **36**, 533.
Ursprung, H., and Hadorn, E. (1961). *Experientia* **17**, 230.
van den Tord, A. H. A., and Lafeber, A. (1963). *Arch. Intern. Physiol. Biochim.* **71**, 698.
Vonk, H. J. (1960). *In* "The Physiology of Crustacea" (T. H. Waterman, ed.), Vol. 1, pp. 291–316. Academic Press, New York.
Weimberg, R., and Doudoroff, M. (1955). *J. Biol. Chem.* **217**, 607.
Whittaker, J. R., and West, A. S. (1962). *Can. J. Zool.* **40**, 655.
Wolvekamp, H. P., and Waterman, T. H. (1960). *In* "The Physiology of Crustacea" (T. H. Waterman, ed.), Vol. 1, pp. 35–100. Academic Press, New York.
Worcel, A., and Erecinska, M. (1962). *Biochim. Biophys. Acta* **65**, 27.
Wyatt, G. R., Loughreed, I. C., and Wyatt, S. S. (1956). *J. Gen. Physiol.* **39**, 853.
Zandee, D. I. (1966a). *Arch. Intern. Physiol. Biochim.* **74**, 35.
Zandee, D. I. (1966b). *Arch. Intern. Physiol Biochim.* **74**, 45.

CHAPTER 8

Lipid Metabolism and Transport in Arthropods[1]

Lawrence I. Gilbert and John D. O'Connor

I. Introduction

Due primarily to the utilization of modern chemical and biochemical techniques, the last several years have brought us a greater understanding of the role of lipids in the Arthropoda. Lipids serve not only as vital energy stores and crucial constituents of cellular and subcellular membranes, but they also appear to play regulatory roles as chemical messengers (i.e., hormones and pheromones). As is likely true of most phenomena studied in arthropods, the great majority of data relating to lipid metabolism and transport has been gleaned from studies of insects, with the remainder derived from crustaceans. Since practically nothing on this subject is known for the other classes of Arthropoda, the present discussion will be limited to insects and crustaceans. Our efforts will be directed to the work of the last few years both because a major (142-page) review of insect lipid metabolism containing some 600 references has recently appeared (Gilbert, 1967a) and significant advances have only been recent events. Aspects of lipid metabolism such as those relating to the chemical nature or synthesis of hormones and pheromones that have been reviewed recently (Gilbert, 1969;

[1] Work of the authors and their colleagues cited in this article was supported by grant AM-02818 from the National Institutes of Health.

Regnier and Law, 1968) or covered elsewhere in this volume (cuticle, digestion, nutrition, etc.) will be omitted from this discussion. We intend to present a cohesive story rather than attempt a comprehensive review and will concentrate for the most part on the work of our laboratory which by necessity means restricting the data to only a few species of arthropods. However, we believe that much of the data can be extrapolated to many other species since the basic biochemistry is likely to be similar, and in fact little different from that of microorganisms and mammals (Gilbert, 1967b).

II. The Nature of Stored Lipid and Alterations during Development

A. GENERAL COMMENTS

The principal storage site for lipid in insects is the fat body while for crustaceans it is the hepatopancreas. In addition, both organs play important metabolic roles and may be compared to a composite analog of mammalian liver and adipose tissue. The quantity of lipid in each of these structures is thus the result of storage, synthesis, and catabolism and in general reflects the total lipid content and composition of the whole animal. During the molt cycle of crustaceans and the metamorphosis of insects, the lipids of the hepatopancreas and fat body also reflect the animal's differential utilization of lipid as an energy source and as structural components of the cell (Gilbert and Schneiderman, 1961; O'Connor and Gilbert, 1968). In some cases, lipid is sequestered at one stage while another substrate yields the energy for life processes to continue and is then utilized at a subsequent stage which is almost solely dependent on lipid as an energy source (Gilbert and Schneiderman, 1961; D'Costa and Birt, 1966; cf. Gilbert, 1967a). In the silkmoth *Hyalophora cecropia* for example, the flight muscles of the adult depend almost exclusively on lipid for oxidative energy. This lipid is stored during larval and pupal life and spared during pupal–adult development (Domroese and Gilbert, 1964).

The nature of the stored lipid in insects and crustaceans is essentially similar to that of other animals. That is, it is the neutral lipid fraction that predominates, and more than 90% of this fraction is triglyceride (Fast, 1964; O'Connor and Gilbert, 1968). The questions to be discussed here pertain almost entirely to the stored lipid. How does the quantity of stored lipid change during development? What is the qualitative nature of this lipid? What is the origin of this stored lipid; that is, what do we know of lipid biosynthesis in arthropods? How is this lipid transported from the storage site to the cells that utilize it? Do arthropods oxidize fatty acids by conventional means?

B. Changes during Development

Lipids are of vital importance to insects as substrates for embryogenesis, metamorphosis and flight (cf. Gilbert, 1967a). In *H. cecropia* for example, lipid serves as a major substrate for all three phenomena (Gilbert and Schneiderman, 1961; Domroese and Gilbert, 1964). In *Locusta migratoria* there is a 32% decrease in lipid content during the 18 days of embryogenesis, the major portion of which is due to the catabolism of glycerides (Allais *et al.*, 1964). In *Dixippus*, about two-thirds of the energy for embryogenesis comes from the oxidation of lipid (Lafon, 1950). Since the major lipid fraction in insects as in other animals is triglyceride, it is not surprising that this is the lipid class displaying the most dramatic decrease during embryonic development (Kinsella and Smyth, 1966).

As an example of changes in lipid content during development, let us look at oogenesis and embryogenesis in the ovoviviparous cockroach, *Leucophaea maderae* (Gilbert, 1967c). The data suggest that in *L. maderae,* lipid is an important substrate for embryonic development. The results indicate a rapid increase in the lipid content of the ovary (developing oocytes) during oogenesis with a maximum prior to ovulation and fertilization. We cannot state with certainty whether this sequestration of lipid is due in part to transfer of lipid from the fat body since the fat body lipid content also increases during this period (Fig. 1). The fact that the decrease in fat body lipid during the latter stages of oogenesis precedes the peak of oocyte lipid content, indirectly suggests some transfer of metabolites from the fat body to the ovary. That this transfer from fat body to ovary is physiologically possible is revealed by *in vitro* studies that demonstrated the capacity of the ovary to accept lipid from the fat body. The fact that castration prevents the decrease in fat body lipid is further evidence for this supposition. It therefore appears that the storage of lipid in the oocytes during the first 20 or so days of the reproductive cycle may be a result of transfer of substrate from the fat body, transport of digested material directly to the ovary, and synthesis of glycerides by the ovary (oocytes) from simpler molecules. The data demonstrate the capacity of the ovary to synthesize glycerides from palmitate and long-chain fatty acids from acetate. All of these processes are endergonic and it is likely that glycogen is the main substrate for providing this energy during oogenesis.

The dramatic decrease in embryonic lipid during embryogenesis is assuredly due to the use of lipid as a substrate for underwriting the synthesis of those structures needed in the development of the 1st instar nymph. The advantages of lipid for such a role include the facts that

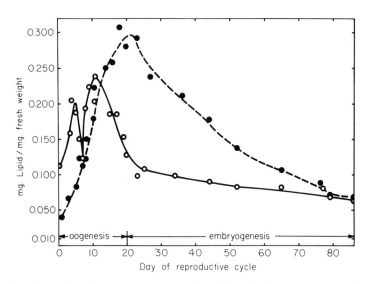

FIG. 1. Changes in lipid content of fat body and ovaries (or one egg case) during the reproductive cycle of the ovoviviparous cockroach *Leucophaea maderae*. Solid circles = ovarian (egg case) lipid; open circles = fat body lipid. (From Gilbert, 1967c.)

it contains more potential energy per unit weight and yields more metabolic water than other substrates. Both are important to *Leucophaea* since the adult female carries the embryos within her brood sac for more than 2 months and is continuously faced with the threat of desiccation. The increasing proportion of phospholipid and concomitant decrease in the proportion of glycerides during development of the embryos suggest the synthesis of phospholipid and degradation of glycerides. An increasing phospholipid content during embryogenesis has been demonstrated for *Periplaneta* (Kinsella, 1966) and *Locusta* (Allais *et al.*, 1964) as well. Phospholipid plays a variety of roles in the life of the cell and its presence in cell membranes has been unequivocally accepted. The increase in content during embryogenesis is therefore not surprising since as cell differentiation progresses, more phospholipid is needed for the construction of cellular and subcellular membranes.

C. DIGESTION

The qualitative nature of the stored lipid is a consequence of biosynthetic ability, nutrition, and environment. When lipid is ingested, lipases in the digestive tract mediate their hydrolysis into free fatty acids and partial glycerides (Vonk, 1960; Gilbert *et al.*, 1965; Kleine, 1967; cf. Gilbert, 1967a). For example, the gastric juice of the lobster causes the hydrolysis of triolein into α,β-diglycerides, β-monoglycerides, and free fatty acids (Brockerhoff *et al.*, 1967). The mechanism by which these hydrolytic products are absorbed from the alimentary canal into the hemolymph and then transported to the hepatopancreas where they become stored lipid is still obscure, although Brockerhoff and Hoyle (1967) clearly illustrated in the lobster that digested lipid was absorbed into depot lipid in the form of a β-monoglyceride. Triolein containing oleic-9,10-^{3}H acid in the β position and oleic-9-^{14}C acid in the α position was fed to lobsters, and the subsequent distribution of label in the hepatopancreatic lipid was then analyzed. The retention of the original ^{3}H/^{14}C ratio at the β position indicated a maintenance of the original β-monoglyceride structure during digestion, absorption, and subsequent storage of lipid. No information is available for insects on absorption of lipid into the hemolymph and its subsequent transport to the fat body.

D. Nature and Synthesis of Lipid

1. Fatty Acid Composition

Since the preponderance of stored lipid exists as fatty acid esters of glycerol, the total fatty acid composition of the fat body, hepatopancreas, or organism is likely a reflection of the fatty acid composition of the triglycerides. The principal fatty acid moiety in both neutral lipid and phospholipid of terrestrial and aquatic crustaceans appears to be oleic acid (O'Connor and Gilbert, 1968). In addition, most crustaceans contain a relatively high proportion of long-chain, polyunsaturated fatty acids (Ackman and Eaton, 1967) whereas the fresh water and terrestrial forms contain a relatively large quantity of C_{16} and C_{18} fatty acids. Unfortunately we know little of the adaptive significance of the structural features of the various fatty acids (Rhodes, 1964). It is of interest to note however, that the fatty acid composition of the lipid in the microsomal pellet from the hepatopancreas of *Gecarcinus lateralis* has a significantly higher percentage of long-chain polyunsaturated fatty acids than are present in the phospholipid fraction of a total lipid extract (O'Connor and Gilbert, 1967). Since phospholipids are the principal components of the microsomal lipid (O'Connor and Gilbert, 1967), the above comparison indicates that the long-chain, unsaturated fatty acids might be used as structural elements rather than as an available energy cache.

The major fatty acids of insects are oleic ($C_{18:1}$) and linoleic ($C_{18:2}$) acids (Barlow, 1964; cf. Fast, 1964; Gilbert, 1967a), but there are numerous exceptions to this generalization. For example, 80% of the total fatty acids of certain Homoptera is C_{14} (Barlow, 1964) and 50% of the triglyceride fatty acids of the mosquito is $C_{16:1}$ (Van Handel, 1967). In fact, the unique fatty acid tetradecan-1,14-dioic acid constitutes 10% of the total fatty acid composition of the mealy bug (Tamaki, 1968). Usually however, five or six common fatty acids comprise over 90% of the total fatty acid complement in arthropods.

2. Fatty Acid Biosynthesis

Recent studies reveal that arthropods have the ability to synthesize several long-chain saturated fatty acids from acetate, and can complex these to other moieties for the synthesis of phospholipids and glycerides (Lambremont et al., 1966; Keith et al., 1967; cf. Gilbert, 1967a). The mechanism of fatty acid synthesis appears to be the same as that elucidated for mammalian and microbial systems, namely, the malonyl CoA pathway. As in the mammal, no arthropod has been shown to possess the biochemical equipment for the synthesis of C_{18} polyunsaturated fatty acids. Thus, linoleate, linolenate, or both are nutritional requirements for insects (cf. Gilbert, 1967a).

In recent experiments on the nature and biosynthesis of fatty acids associated with the development of the silkmoth *H. cecropia*, Stephen and Gilbert (1969) demonstrated that the major fatty acids present throughout development are palmitic, palmitoleic, stearic, oleic, linoleic, and linolenic acids, with oleic and linolenic acids predominating. When acetate-^{14}C is administered to this insect, a significant amount of label is detected in long-chain fatty acids showing that this insect, as many other arthropods, has the capacity to synthesize fatty acids from acetate. *In vitro* studies on the locust demonstrate that the cofactor requirements are similar to those elucidated for other organisms and that insects likely synthesize fatty acids via the malonyl CoA pathway (Tietz, 1961). The data of Stephen and Gilbert (1969) clearly demonstrate that *H. cecropia* synthesizes palmitate, palmitoleate, stearate, and oleate from acetate but not linoleate or linolenate (see also Sridhara and Bhat, 1965; Nelson and Sukkestad, 1968) and the same pattern appears to be true of arthropods in general (Zandee, 1966, 1967).

Hyalophora cecropia can elongate existing fatty acids, and palmitate seems to be the primary substrate for chain elongation (Fig. 2). Upon elongation of exogenous palmitate, the major resulting unsaturated fatty acid is oleic acid and it is likely that palmitate is first elongated to stearate and then desaturated. Insects can also shorten existing fatty acids as Keith (1967) clearly showed in *Drosophila melanogaster*. He demonstrated that stearate is shortened from the carboxyl end to myristate and that linoleate is similarly shortened to C_{14} and C_{16} dienes.

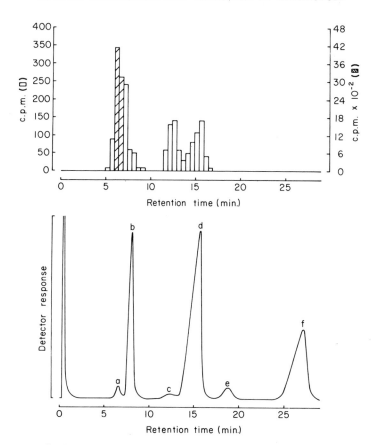

FIG. 2. Radiochromatogram of fatty acid methyl esters from a *H. cecropia* pupa which was injected with 1 μCi. palmitate-1-^{14}C and sacrificed 24 hours later. In the upper figure, the abscissa is the retention time in minutes, and the width of each bar represents the time over which each fraction was collected. The height of each open bar represents the c.p.m. per minute of collection time on the left ordinate, and the height of each hatched bar represents the c.p.m. per minute of collection time on the right ordinate. A background of 25 c.p.m. has been subtracted. The abscissa of the lower figure is also retention time in minutes. The ordinate is detector response. The analysis was performed on a 6% DEGS column with an argon flow rate of 60 ml./min. at a temperature of 175°C and a split ratio of 50:1. The compounds detected were: a, methyl palmitate; b, methyl palmitoleate; c, methyl stearate; d, methyl oleate; e, methyl linoleate; f, methyl linolenate. (From Stephen and Gilbert, 1969.)

In general, several studies indicate that insects can elongate and desaturate existing saturated fatty acids but cannot elongate or saturate existing unsaturated fatty acids. The major distinctions in fatty acid biosynthesis between insects and vertebrates are that insects cannot elongate unsaturated fatty acids or introduce a second or third double bond into any fatty acid.

3. Glyceride and Phospholipid Synthesis

Once fatty acids are synthesized, they are usually readily incorporated into the synthetic routes leading to glycerides, phospholipids, and sterol esters. Experiments in this laboratory on *H. cecropia* (Chino and Gilbert, 1965a,b; Beenakkers and Gilbert, 1968; Stephen and Gilbert, 1969) and that of several other workers on a variety of insect species (cf. Gilbert, 1967a) demonstrate that labeled fatty acids and fatty acid precursors are readily incorporated into glycerides and phospholipids. The same appears to be true of crustaceans (O'Connor and Gilbert, 1968, 1969). The available data suggest no basic differences between arthropods and other organisms in regard to biosynthetic pathways leading to phospholipids and triglycerides.

As an example of phospholipid synthesis, we will consider flight muscle development during the pupal–adult transformation of *H. cecropia* (Thomas and Gilbert, 1967a). During the adult development of *H. cecropia,* the flight muscle of this moth becomes highly differentiated and contains a high concentration of sarcosomes (giant mitochondria). The major phospholipid fractions of the flight muscle and sarcosomes are phosphatidyl choline and phosphatidyl ethanolamine. The cardiolipin fraction increases from 1.3% to 11.8% of the lipid phosphorus of the flight muscle during muscle maturation. Unsaturated fatty acids predominate in the various flight muscle phospholipids with linolenic acid comprising about 70% of the total fatty acids in the cardiolipin fraction. The phospholipid composition of the moth sarcosomes more closely approximates that of beef heart mitochondria than that of housefly flight muscle sarcosomes. Radioisotope studies indicate the synthesis of phospholipids during adult development of *H. cecropia* and these data are supported by determinations of lipid phosphorus which reveal a fivefold increase in phospholipid concentration during the development of male flight muscle (Fig. 3). This increase in phospholipid is likely due to a need for constituents of cellular and subcellular membranes as well as for ensuring optimum catalytic action by some mitochondrial enzymes.

One enzyme important in the synthesis of phospholipids is phosphatidate phosphohydrolase and it has been studied in insect tissue (Hirano

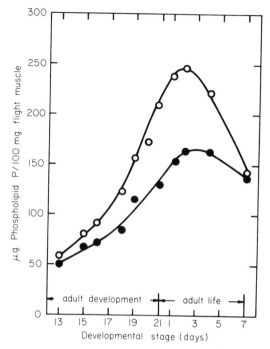

FIG. 3. The phospholipid concentration of *H. cecropia* flight muscle during adult development and adult life. Solid circles = female; open circles = male. (From Thomas and Gilbert, 1967a.)

and Gilbert, 1967). This enzyme mediates the conversion of phosphatidic acid to α,β-diglyceride and inorganic phosphate. Its importance can be seen from the fact that the diglyceride resulting from phosphatidic acid is the precursor of triglyceride, phosphatidyl ethanolamine, and phosphatidyl choline.

The data indicate that the enzyme of the *H. cecropia* fat body closely resembles the vertebrate enzyme in its association with the microsomes. Since the microsomal fraction contains for the most part pieces of endoplasmic reticulum, it is not surprising to find that the greatest activity of an enzyme involved in phospholipid biosynthesis is associated with such a membrane-rich fraction.

The optimum pH of 7.4 for the insect enzyme is almost identical to that for rabbit and rat brain phosphatidate phosphohydrolase and exhibits a similar K_m value (McCaman *et al.*, 1965). The temperature optimum and Q_{10} value for the fat body phosphatidate phosphohydrolase are similar to that of other insect enzymes. Divalent cations appear to inhibit the insect enzyme to varying degrees. Among the seven cations tested, six were inhibitory. Magnesium was not effective as an inhibitor and appeared to cause stimulation of the reaction at 5×10^{-4} *M*. Magnesium has been reported to stimulate the enzyme in the microsomal fraction of guinea pig brain and erythrocyte ghosts as well (Hokin *et al.*, 1963). The marked inhibition of the insect enzyme by *p*-hydroxymercuribenzoate and its complete reversal by reduced glutathione indicates that thiol groups are important for enzymic activity. This is in agreement with data on vertebrate microsomal preparations. The fact that a chelating agent (EDTA) did not significantly affect the activity of the fat body phosphatidate phosphohydrolase suggests the absence of a metal cofactor requirement.

The increase in activity from the beginning of adult development until adult emergence in *H. cecropia* is most likely due to the synthesis of phospholipids that contribute in large measure to cellular and subcellular membrane structures. In the pupal–adult transformation, an almost new animal must be constructed, and there is little doubt that phospholipids must be synthesized (see above on flight muscle).

Although we have emphasized the importance of phospholipids in the present discussion for the reason that phosphatidic acid is a phospholipid, we must keep in mind that it is also a most important substrate for glyceride synthesis. This is of particular importance to insects that utilize triglycerides as the major lipid storage form and most likely transport lipids in the form of glycerides. Thus, phosphatidate phosphohydrolase may play a prime role in the synthesis of substrate for a wide range of physiological activities as well as supplying membrane ingredients for the developing cell.

Past work on lipid synthesis in crustaceans dealt with alterations in the lipid content of the hepatopancreas, but recently these changes have been correlated with variations in the capacity of the hepatopancreas to synthesize lipid (O'Connor and Gilbert, 1968, 1969). Specifically, it has been demonstrated that the hepatopancreas from animals in premolt incorporates a significantly higher amount of radioactive acetate, palmitate, and glycerol into lipid than tissue from intermolt animals exposed to similar concentrations of substrate. This increase in the synthetic capacity of the hepatopancreas is seen in both naturally occurring premolt crustaceans and in those induced into premolt activity by eyestalk extirpation. Thus, destalking resulted in an increased incorporation of acetate-1-^{14}C, palmitate-1-^{14}C, and glycerol-^{14}C into the hepatopancreatic lipid of both *Gecarcinus lateralis* and *Orconectes virilis*. Furthermore, treatment of destalked *G. lateralis* with a saline extract of eyestalk partially reversed the effect of destalking. Conversely, Zandee (1966) reported that destalking decreased the incorporation of glucose-^{14}C into the hepatopancreatic lipid of *Astacus* and his data indicate a decrease in the fatty acid content of the hepatopancreas after destalking. This apparent contradiction between *Gecarcinus* and *Astacus* is resolved when one considers that the premolt activity initiated by eyestalk extirpation is not identical throughout the premolt stage. Thus, during early and mid-premolt there is a significant increase in the synthesis and storage of lipid in the hepatopancreas of crustaceans. During the later premolt stages (D_3 and D_4), the lipid content of the hepatopancreas declines simultaneously with a decrease in the rate of incorporation of labeled lipid precursors (O'Connor and Gilbert, 1969). In addition it appears that in the crayfish *Orconectes virilis*, the decrease in lipid synthesis and storage during late premolt is coupled to an increase in the rate of lipid released from the hepatopancreas into the hemolymph (O'Connor and Gilbert, 1968).

4. Substrate Interconversion

The decrease in the incorporation of glucose into hepatopancreatic lipid of *Astacus* reported by Zandee (1966) has been confirmed in our laboratory in *O. virilis*. This decrease would not be surprising if the premolt animals examined had been in the terminal phase of premolt when catabolic activity is reaching a peak. However, experiments in this laboratory have indicated that the incorporation of differentially labeled glucose into hepatopancreatic lipid is lower in early premolt than in intermolt. As in other organisms, the synthesis of lipids in crustaceans is intimately related to the catabolism of carbohydrates. Huggins (1966) has shown that the principal end products of glycolysis in the crab, *Carcinus maenas*, are lactic acid and alanine. Thus, pyruvate appears to be transaminated or reduced rather than oxidized to acetate. This helps to clarify the findings of Zandee (1966) that little glucose is incorporated into the fatty acids of *Astacus*. Thus, even with an increase in glycolytic activity which has been found to occur during premolt in the crayfish *Orconectes virilis* (McWhinnie and Corkill, 1964; McWhinnie and Chua, 1964) there would probably not be an appreciable increase in the amount of glucose carbon incorporated into fatty acids due to its incomplete oxidation to acetate via glycolysis. A number of other contingencies dictate against an increase in the incorporation of glucose into lipid during late premolt. First the pentose phosphate pathway which is very active during intermolt and early premolt and which accounts for the majority of reduced cofactors essential for fatty acid synthesis, is remarkably inactive during the late premolt stages. Without sufficient titers of NADPH, fatty acid synthesis in vertebrates, and thus presumably in invertebrates, ceases. Second, the synthesis of a new exoskeleton which began in early premolt reaches peak activity just before and after ecdysis. Since the chitinous portion of the exoskeleton is composed of polymerized N-acetylglucosamine, it is likely that glucose is converted to N-acetylglucosamine rather than utilized as a catabolic substrate (Travis, 1955; Scheer, 1957). Consequently, due to this shift in the metabolism of glucose during late premolt there would be less glucose available for conversion into lipid. These data partially explain the decrease in the conversion of glucose to lipid during the late premolt stages.

The decrease in the conversion of differentially labeled glucose to lipid during the early premolt stages is probably more apparent than real (O'Connor and Gilbert, 1969). During early premolt, a number of significant changes in metabolism are occurring simultaneously. There is an increase in the consumption of oxygen indicative of increasing catabolic activity (Scheer, 1957; McWhinnie and Kirchenberg, 1962). However, there is also an increase in the synthesis and storage of lipid and glycogen. Thus, radioactive glucose administered to crustaceans during early premolt is utilized in both the synthesis of glycogen and as a catabolic metabolite—in both cases at a higher rate than occurred in intermolt. Recently, Ramamurthi *et al.* (1968) have indicated that destalking increased the turnover rate of glycogen in the hepatopancreas of *Hemigrapsus nudus* and *Cancer magister*. Thus, with a greater turnover rate of glycogen occurring during premolt, administered glucose is diluted to a greater extent than occurs in the intermolt condition.

Finally, based on the above mentioned data, it appears that the glucose carbon is incorporated into hepatopancreatic lipid as a glycerol molecule rather than as acetate. This supposition receives additional support from the work of Hartenstein (1964) who observed that α-glycerol phosphate was the principal end product of glycolysis in the isopod *Oniscus asellus*.

The above descriptions of variations in lipid metabolism which occur during the molt cycle of some crustaceans can be summarized rather briefly. When premolt activity is initiated, either naturally or by artificial manipulation, there is an increase in oxygen consumption concomitant with an increase in the rate of lipid synthesis. A decrease in the R.Q. indicates that lipids are also serving as the source for oxidative energy at this time (Bliss, 1953). The lipid content of the hepatopancreas reaches a peak sometime during mid-premolt, declining shortly thereafter until ecdysis. During late premolt there is a dramatic decrease in the activity of the pentose phosphate pathway in the hepatopancreas with an increase in glycolytic oxidation. This results in a reduced capacity for lipid synthesis due in part to a reduction in available NADPH.

Consequently, there is the observed reduction in the amount of hepato-pancreatic lipid. Whereas there is a decrease in the lipid content of the hepatopancreas during late premolt, the amount of lipid present in the abdominal muscle of *O. virilis* continues to increase until ecdysis at which point a slight decrease is noticed (O'Connor and Gilbert, 1969). This increase is not accompanied by a simultaneous increase in the incorporation of acetate-1-^{14}C into muscle lipid. Therefore, the increase in the lipid content of the muscle during premolt may represent the sequestering of lipid from the hemolymph by this tissue.

E. STEROLS

The synthesis of sterol from acetate has not yet been demonstrated in arthropods and, indeed, arthropods require a dietary sterol for several physiological functions and in some cases for life itself (cf. Clayton, 1964; Gilbert, 1967a). Insects can synthesize terpenes however (Happ and Meinwald, 1965, 1966) and have the ability to modify dietary sterols by de-ethylation, demethylation and presumably by hydroxylation (see, for example, Dubé *et al.*, 1968). Recently a 200-fold purification of mevalonic kinase has been reported from fly larvae and this enzyme which mediates the phosphorylation of mevalonic acid is an important constituent of the scheme leading to isopentenyl pyrophosphate which itself is crucial for sterol synthesis (Barnes and Goodfellow, 1968). The unknown block in sterol synthesis in insects must therefore be subsequent to the mevalonic kinase step. Crustaceans can also modify sterols, and lobster testis has been shown to contain 17β-hydroxysteroid dehydrogenase which mediates the conversion of androstenedione to testosterone (Gilgan and Idler, 1967). The significance of this reaction is not known although the androgenic gland (presumed source of the crustacean sex hormone) showed the highest activity.

The major functional sterol in arthropods is cholesterol, although at least one insect cannot use cholesterol as its sole dietary sterol. *Drosophila pachea* which breeds only in the stems of the senita cactus utilizes schottenol (Δ^7-stigmasten-3β-ol) found in this plant as its dietary sterol and appears to require it (Heed and Kirscher, 1965). Thus, this species has come to depend on a specific ecological niche for a specific sterol. In general, cholesterol is an adequate dietary sterol for arthropods, and in plant eating insects that ingest either a minute amount or no cholesterol, the phytosterol, β-sitosterol is usually converted to cholesterol. Table I reveals that in *H. cecropia* the percentage of β-sitosterol decreases from the end of the feeding larval life to adult life while the percentage of cholesterol increases, indicating that this insect has the ability to convert β-sitosterol to cholesterol.

TABLE I

RELATIVE PERCENTAGE OF THE VARIOUS *H. cecropia* STEROLS
DURING DEVELOPMENT[a,b]

Stage	% Cholesterol	% Campesterol	% β-Sitosterol	% Unknown
Nonchorionated eggs	84.5	<1.0	13.5	–
Chorionated eggs	86.9	<1.0	12.1	–
Fifth instar larvae	44.5	9.8	42.5	3.2
Diapausing pupa	55.0	8.2	36.8	–
Chilled pupa	62.1	6.9	27.0	–
Male				
18-Day developing adult	82.5	3.0	14.5	–
Emergence	89.5	<1.0	10.5	–
Senile adult	95.2	<1.0	4.8	–
Female				
18-Day developing adult	82.2	2.0	15.6	–
Emergence	84.6	<1.0	14.4	–
Senile adult, after ovi- position	78.4	<1.0	20.6	–

[a] Derived from gas-liquid chromatography on 1% QF-1 on acid-washed, silanized Gas-Chrom S. 6 feet × 4 mm. I.D. glass column. Argon flow rate 60 ml./min., 20 p.s.i. 210°C.
[b] From Goodfellow and Gilbert (1964).

The roles of sterols in arthropods are likely manifold and include being precursors of the arthropod molting hormone(s) (cf. Gilbert, 1969) and components of subcellular membrane structures (Lasser *et al.*, 1966). Indeed, if *H. cecropia* pupae are injected with labeled cholesterol and the resulting adult tissues fractionated, most of the label is associated with "membranous" components of the cell (Table II).

III. Lipid Release and Transport

A. CRUSTACEANS

Research in the last few years has given us a greater understanding of how lipids are released from the storage organ into the hemolymph of arthropods and how lipids are transported in the hemolymph. Not only are studies of these phenomena essential to an understanding of how hormones and substrates are transported from storage and biosynthetic sites to target cells, but if complexes are formed in the hemolymph, their structure may be crucial for the penetration of these substances into cells.

The major advances in this field are a result of *in vitro* studies on the fat body of insects such as moths and locusts that primarily utilize

TABLE II

SUBCELLULAR DISTRIBUTION OF CHOLESTEROL-^{14}C AND "POLAR STEROIDS-[14]C" IN THORACIC MUSCLE OF MALE *H. cecropia* MOTHS INJECTED WITH CHOLESTEROL-4-^{14}C AS PUPAE[a]

Total steroid-[14]C (mμg./mg. wet weight)	Relative % of ^{14}C as		
	Ester	Free	"Polar"
0.230	0.3	89.8	9.9

Subcellular fraction	% Total steroid-[14]C	% Free cholesterol-[14]C	% "Polar" steroid-[14]C	% Ester cholesterol-[14]C
Nuclei and myofibrils	7	6	22	5
Sarcosomes	27	33[b]	19	4
Microsomes ("sarcoplasmic reticulum")	60	58[b]	32	11
Supernatant	6	3	27	80

[a] From Goodfellow and Gilbert (1964).

[b] Over 90% of free cholesterol-^{14}C of sarcosomes is membrane associated.

lipid as the fuel for flight, although preliminary studies with the crustacean hepatopancreas suggest that they may be ideal organisms for similar experiments.

Although the composition of the lipid in the hemolymph of several crustacean species has been elucidated (Bligh and Scott, 1966; O'Connor and Gilbert, 1967), the qualitative nature of the lipid released from the hepatopancreas has not been clearly defined. Although the relative percentages may vary somewhat between species, the large amount of phospholipid in the hemolymph seems to be characteristic of crustaceans. In many organisms the predominant plasma lipid serves a transport function, and it is reasonable to assume that phospholipids are the principal transport moiety in crustaceans since they account for 65% of the hemolymph lipid (Table III).

In addition to this correlative information, recent data obtained from *in vitro* experiments with *O. virilis* indicate a preferential release of phospholipids from the hepatopancreas into the incubation medium (O'Connor and Gilbert, 1967). Moreover, the fatty acid composition of the hemolymph lipids does not appear to differ from that of similar fractions found in the hepatopancreas of that organism. This indicates a lack of preferential release of a particular fatty acid moiety and differs from the situation in insects (see subsequent discussion).

The paucity of data concerning the transport of lipid in the crustacean

TABLE III

PERCENT LIPID COMPOSITION OF THE HEMOLYMPH OF SEVERAL
CRUSTACEAN SPECIES

Species	Fraction		
	Triglyceride	Steroid	Phospholipid
Homarus americanus[a]	15.5	15.6	65.1
Procambarus sp.[b]	14.2	16.1	68.6
Orconectes virilis[b]	15.2	9.7	63.8

[a] From Bligh and Scott (1966).
[b] From O'Connor and Gilbert (1967).

hemolymph prohibits any discussion of regulatory mechanisms, although it is assumed that the composition of hemolymph lipid is a direct reflection of the metabolism of lipid in the hepatopancreas.

B. INSECTS

1. Glycerides

On the basis of *in vitro* studies with the locust fat body in which Tietz (1962) demonstrated that glycerides are preferentially released into the medium, she suggested that these mobilized lipids are transported as lipoproteins. This work was confirmed and extended in *H. cecropia* where the major glyceride released into the hemolymph from pupal or adult fat body was identified as diglyceride (Chino and Gilbert, 1965a). Furthermore, the flight muscle of this moth preferentially hydrolyzes diglycerides (Gilbert *et al.*, 1965). The presence of diglyceride as the major lipid fraction in the hemolymph has been confirmed in several other insects as well (Cook and Eddington, 1967; Tietz, 1967). In the last several years our laboratory has further investigated the nature of the lipoproteins involved in transporting glycerides and phospholipids as well as the means by which they enter the hemolymph from the fat body.

2. Lipoprotein Characterization

Using preparative ultracentrifugal techniques (Fig. 4), Thomas and Gilbert (1968) demonstrated the presence of three lipoprotein classes in the pupal hemolymph of *H. cecropia* which resemble the LDL (low density lipoproteins), HDL (high density lipoproteins), and VHDL (very high density lipoproteins) of human serum. The three classes are clearly separated from one another by their density characteristics

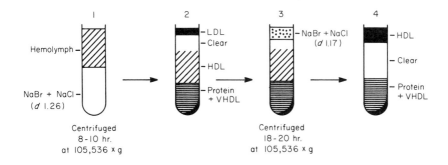

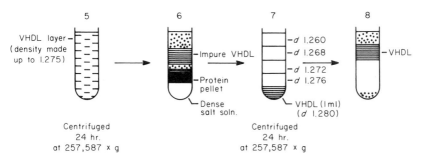

FIG. 4. Procedure for the ultracentrifugal fractionation of the hemolymph lipoproteins of *H. cecropia* pupae. (From Thomas and Gilbert, 1968.)

and are fairly homogeneous according to their flotation and sedimentation profiles (Fig. 5). In the insect hemolymph, there are appreciable quantities of HDL and VHDL and a minor amount of LDL. The HDL class of lipoprotein appears to be the most important in *H. cecropia* hemolymph since it contains 75% of the total lipoprotein lipid, and may correspond to one of the two lipoproteins isolated from the hemolymph of *P. cynthia* pupae (Chino *et al.*, 1969). This lipoprotein has many of the characteristics of the HDL of *H. cecropia* with a sedimentation coefficient of 8.7, and in addition is rich in diglycerides. In the *H. cecropia* HDL, diglycerides constitute over 69% of the total neutral lipid. Thus, the HDL of *H. cecropia* may be important in "capturing" diglyceride released from the fat body and transporting it to sites of utilization as has been postulated for the *P. cynthia* lipoprotein. The second lipoprotein described by Chino *et al.* (1969) corresponds in sedimentation properties to the minor peak observed in the sedimentation analysis of *H. cecropia* HDL ($s_{20,w} = 12.8$).

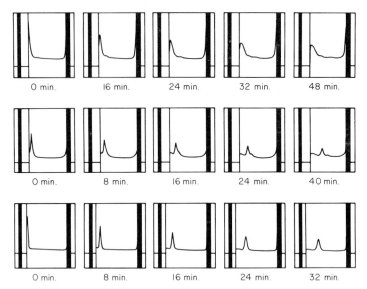

Fig. 5. Analytic ultracentrifugation sedimentation patterns of the lipoprotein classes isolated from *H. cecropia* pupal hemolymph. Upper: low density lipoproteins; middle: high density lipoproteins; lower: very high density lipoproteins. Times are those after reaching maximum speed (LDL = 52,640 r.p.m.; HDL = 42,040 r.p.m.; VHDL = 42,040 r.p.m.). Movement of boundary is from left to right. (From Thomas and Gilbert, 1968.)

The electrophoretic data indicate that each lipoprotein class is composed of several components separable on the basis of their charge. The same appears to be true of mammalian plasma lipoproteins. Although there are three classes of lipoprotein in the hemolymph of *H. cecropia*, there are at least eight individual species of lipoprotein. The molecular weight estimated for the HDL of *H. cecropia* is in the same range as the HDL_3 of human serum (Scanu and Granda, 1966).

Diglycerides are the predominant lipid moiety of the three lipoprotein classes in the hemolymph and this finding is expected since diglycerides are the major hemolymph lipid fraction in this insect. There is no comparable situation in mammalian plasma lipoproteins where the phospholipid and cholesterol ester fractions predominate in the LDL and HDL. The phospholipid content of the insect lipoprotein is significant, comprising between 11% and 28% of the total lipid and as in the vertebrate system may be a structural component of the lipoprotein complex. The high percentage of phosphatidyl choline and phosphatidyl ethanolamine is characteristic of insect phospholipids in general. Since it has been demonstrated that phospholipids are released from the insect fat body and can be taken up by developing tissues such as flight muscle (Thomas and Gilbert, 1967b), the phospholipid component of the insect hemolymph lipoprotein may have a more active role than that of stabilizing the lipoprotein complex. That is, the lipoproteins of insect hemolymph may transport phospholipid, sterol, and glycerides.

The sterols and sterol esters of the hemolymph lipoproteins comprise between 10.6% and 24.9% of the neutral lipid present. These values compare favorably with that of human serum HDL although in the latter case there is a greater concentration of ester than free sterol.

3. Phospholipid Release and Transport

Thomas and Gilbert (1967b) demonstrated that the fat body of H. cecropia is capable of phospholipid synthesis and that several substrates can be incorporated into phospholipid, including palmitate, phosphate, glycerol, and ethanolamine. A portion of these fat body phospholipids is released into the hemolymph, although this is a relatively small amount compared to the release of neutral lipid. That phospholipids exist in insect hemolymph has been demonstrated several times (Gilbert, 1967a). The means by which these compounds come to be there, however, has not been adequately explained. In H. cecropia it has been shown that the concentrations of phosphoryl choline and phosphoryl ethanolamine are higher in the hemolymph than in the fat body and that the enzymes necessary for phospholipid synthesis are absent from the hemolymph (Carey and Wyatt, 1963; Wyatt et al., 1963). These workers suggest that phospholipids are "selectively secreted" from the fat body into the hemolymph. The data of Thomas and Gilbert (1967b) indicate that this is so although the exact mechanism of transport from the fat body cell into the hemolymph is still not known. The demonstration that several stages in the life cycle of H. cecropia, as well as two species of cockroaches (P. americana and L. maderae), are capable of releasing phospholipids from the fat body into the medium suggests that this phenomenon may be common to many or all insects. The inhibition of phospholipid synthesis and release by KCN infers that both processes are endergonic and depend on oxidative phosphorylation for energy. The release phenomenon is most likely chemically mediated and may be a result of active transport. Temperature studies support this conjecture.

Since it appears that the fat body is also the site of synthesis of hemolymph proteins (Gilbert, 1967b), it is possible that the phospholipids are released as lipoproteins rather than as free phospholipids that bind to pre-existing hemolymph proteins. The cells of the fat body do contain a lipoprotein comparable in relative mobility to a hemolymph lipoprotein (Thomas and Gilbert, 1969). In fact, the lipid moiety of the fat body lipoprotein rapidly incorporates labeled substrates into phospholipid. Thus, we know that phospholipids are released by the fat body, but the exact form in which they are released is still unknown. Another crucial question regards the form in which the lipoprotein or phospholipid moiety enters other cells such as those constituting the flight muscle. Is the protein-phospholipid conjugate broken prior to entry or does the lipoprotein enter *in toto?* Again, we cannot answer this very important question. In the vertebrate, however, it may be that the entire lipoprotein enters the cell, since immunochemical studies suggest the presence within cells of substances that react strongly with antibodies prepared against plasma lipoproteins (Gurd, 1963).

Whether exogenous phospholipids are in fact needed by developing structures is conjectural. It is likely that flight muscle, for example, is capable of synthesizing much of its own phospholipid from simple precursors or by degrading triglycerides to diglycerides and then to phospholipid. The fact that diglycerides are the neutral lipid transport form of some insects suggests that these can be supplied by the fat body as substrates for phospholipid synthesis as well as potential energy. It is entirely possible that the phospholipids of the hemolymph lipoproteins are structural elements of the lipoprotein and aid in the transport of other substances (e.g., neutral lipid, sterol).

4. Two-Compartment Theory

A further question on lipid release from the insect fat body involves the nature of the diglycerides released into the hemolymph. Are they qualitatively the same as the major glyceride fraction of the fat body or must some molecular conversion take place before they can enter the hemolymph? These questions have not been completely resolved but recent studies on *H. cecropia* by Beenakkers and Gilbert (1968) have allowed them to postulate a two-compartment theory. By utilizing double-labeled glycerides in release experiments, they demonstrated a difference in the fatty acid composition of fat body glycerides and of hemolymph glycerides derived from the fat body. The differences in the constitution of diglycerides and other glycerides between fat body and hemolymph suggest that their release does not occur at random, but may be restricted to those neutral lipids with a specific fatty acid composition. On the other hand, the authors suggest that the fat body may contain two different glyceride pools, only one of which is in communication with the surrounding medium. The results demonstrating a difference between the glyceride composition of the fat body and the incubation medium support the idea of compartmentalization. Therefore, they assume that prior to being released, the glycerides that will be released undergo some metabolic rearrangement of the fatty acid moieties in both the diglycerides and remaining glycerides. A number of experiments performed with vertebrate adipose tissue indicate that the uptake of triglyceride and the release of free fatty acid is accompanied by intracellular hydrolysis and resynthesis of the glycerides. By using double-labeled triglyceride, this lipid was shown to be rearranged after entering the adipose tissue, with the original glycerol moiety being lost and the fatty acids re-esterified (Shapiro, 1964). Some authors believe that two compartments are present in vertebrate adipose tissue; an active compartment in which the glycerides are in direct interchange with the fatty acids of the medium and which exhibits a rapid turnover, and a storage compartment where the bulk of the lipids in the cell are located (Dole, 1961; Olivecrona, 1962; Stein and Stein, 1962). During lipid release from insect fat body, the following scheme may occur. The triglycerides in the storage compartment are hydrolyzed and the resulting products (free fatty acids and presumably monoglycerides) are then transported to the active compartment. In this compartment, glycerides are resynthesized (in contradistinction to vertebrate adipose tissue where only free fatty acids are released). This allows the formation of lipids with a fatty acid pattern appropriate for entering the hemolymph. The proposed re-esterification process is similar to that taking place in mammalian liver where triglycerides are released into the blood. Their experiments did not prove this hypothesis although some of their results favor it. One of the difficulties in evaluating the experimental data on the fat body is that two opposing processes take place simultaneously: esterification of free fatty acids and hydrolysis of glycerides. There is little doubt, however, that almost all of the triglycerides present in this organ is stored lipid. In the hemolymph too, this particular fraction undergoes little change. Both in chilled pupae and pharate adults, a significant difference exists in the fatty acid composition of fat body and hemolymph triglycerides, and this finding together with their *in vitro* experiments support the idea that triglycerides are specifically released. A comparison of lipid release from fat body of chilled pupae and pharate adults reveals that the more metabolically active tissue from the pharate adult releases relatively less free fatty acid and thus more labeled glycerides than the pupal fat body. This is probably a consequence of higher synthetic rate in the active compartment. Although the specific activity of the triglycerides in the fat body of the pharate adults is only about twice as high as that in the chilled pupae, its specific activity in the corresponding hemolymph differs by a factor of eight. This phenomenon is even more pronounced in regard to the monoglycerides. A comparison of the ratio palmitate-^{3}H/glycerol-^{14}C after the release of the double labeled glycerides indicates that the least difference between fat body and hemolymph exists in the monoglycerides. The difference is greater for diglycerides and still greater for triglycerides. Beenakkers' and Gilbert's hypothesis (1968) can explain these results by assuming that re-esterification in the active compartment proceeds, at least in part, by acylation of existing monoglycerides that originated in the storage compartment and were transported with the free fatty acids to the active compartment of the fat body.

5. Control

The processes of lipid release and transport are excellent candidates for control since the quality and quantity of lipid released from the fat body or hepatopancreas can drastically affect the organism. Preliminary indications are that one or both of these processes may be under endocrine control in insects (Gilbert, 1967c; Bhakthan and Gilbert, 1968). Just recently, Mayer and Candy (1969) found that extracts of adult corpora cardiaca of locusts caused an increase in hemolymph lipid when injected into locusts and the major increase was in the diglyceride fraction. They also demonstrated that corpora cardiaca extracts stimulated the release of diglyceride from the fat body *in vitro* as well. Mayer and Candy conclude that diglyceride levels in the locust hemolymph are controlled by a factor (probably polypeptide in nature) released from the corpora cardiaca.

IV. Fatty Acid Oxidation

Finally, the synthesis and transport of lipids would be of little importance to the organism if fatty acid oxidation and the concurrent capture of energy did not occur. To be sure, lipids have other physiological roles, but the energy released during the oxidation of the fatty acid moieties of glycerides cannot be overestimated.

A number of studies have been conducted on fatty acid oxidation in insect tissues, particularly the flight muscle of moths and locusts (cf. Gilbert, 1967a). In general, β-oxidation takes place in the mitochondria as it does in other organisms (Zebe, 1954, 1959; Meyer *et al.*, 1960; Beenakkers, 1963; Domroese and Gilbert, 1964). In crustaceans, most of the work has been conducted on intact organisms or isolated hepatopancreas preparations of *Carcinus maenas* by Munday and his colleagues (see for example Munday and Munn, 1965). In general, these data reveal that crustaceans utilize β-oxidation as do insects and other organisms. Graszynski (1968), in fact, has recently shown that three important enzymes of β-oxidation (crotonase, hydroxyacyl-CoA-dehydrogenase, ketoacyl-thiolase) can be fractionated from *Orconectes* tissues and that their characteristics are basically the same as those of the insect and vertebrate enzymes.

The reader is referred to Gilbert (1967a) for a comprehensive discussion of β-oxidation since any discussion here would be repetitious of the above review and many others on microbial and vertebrate fatty acid catabolism. We can conclude by stating that arthropods certainly have the ability to catabolize fatty acids to CO_2 and H_2O via β-oxidation and that the energy captured in the form of ATP can then be utilized for a variety of physiological tasks, several of which have been discussed previously.

V. Conclusion

The means by which arthropods synthesize and degrade lipids are basically similar to those utilized by other organisms. The fact that certain molecules are unique to the arthropod (molting hormone, juvenile hormone, certain fatty acids, etc.) suggests some anabolic and catabolic pathways specific to this phylum, although they have yet to be elucidated. These basic differences in lipid physiology exist between arthropods and vertebrates: arthropods cannot synthesize sterols from simple precursors and thus require them as dietary factors; the lipid composition of insect and crustacean hemolymph is quite different from that of vertebrate blood and in fact differs greatly from one class to another. We expect that work in the next few years will yield important information on the means by which arthropods synthesize and breakdown the unique molecules alluded to above and will answer questions pertaining to hormone transport and the means by which the lipid moieties of lipoproteins actually enter target cells.

REFERENCES

Ackman, R. G., and Eaton, C. A. (1967). *J. Fisheries Res. Board Can.* **24**, 467.
Allais, J. P., Bergerard, J., Etienne, J., and Polonovski, J. (1964). *J. Insect Physiol.* **10**, 753.
Barlow, J. S. (1964). *Can. J. Biochem.* **42**, 1365.
Barnes, F. J., and Goodfellow, R. D. (1968). *Am. Zoologist* **8**, 777.
Beenakkers, A. M. T. (1963). *Acta Physiol. Pharmacol. Neerl.* **12**, 332.
Beenakkers, A. M. T., and Gilbert, L. I. (1968). *J. Insect Physiol.* **14**, 481.
Bhakthan, N. M. G., and Gilbert, L. I. (1968). *Gen. Comp. Endocrinol.* **11**, 186.
Bligh, E. G., and Scott, M. A. (1966). *J. Fisheries Res. Board Can.* **23**, 1629.
Bliss, D. E. (1953). *Biol. Bull.* **104**, 275.
Brockerhoff, H., and Hoyle, R. J. (1967). *Can. J. Biochem.* **45**, 1365.
Brockerhoff, H., Stewart, J. E., and Tacreiter, W. (1967). *Can. J. Biochem.* **45**, 421.

Carey, F. G., and Wyatt, G. R. (1963). *J. Insect Physiol.* **9**, 317.

Chino, H., and Gilbert, L. I. (1965a). *Biochim. Biophys. Acta* **98**, 94.

Chino, H., and Gilbert, L. I. (1965b). *J. Insect Physiol.* **11**, 287.

Chino, H., Murakami, S., and Harashima, K. (1969). *Biochim. Biophys. Acta* **176**, 1.

Clayton, R. B. (1964). *J. Lipid Res.* **5**, 3.

Cook, B. J., and Eddington, L. C. (1967). *J. Insect Physiol.* **13**, 1361.

D'Costa, M. A., and Birt, L. M. (1966). *J. Insect Physiol.* **12**, 1377.

Dole, V. P. (1961). *J. Biol. Chem.* **236**, 3121.

Domroese, K. A., and Gilbert, L. I. (1964). *J. Exptl. Biol.* **41**, 573.

Dubé, J., Villeneuve, J., and Lemonde, A. (1968). *Arch. Intern. Physiol. Biochim.* **76**, 64.

Fast, P. G. (1964). *Mem. Entomol. Soc. Can.* **37**, 1.

Gilbert, L. I. (1967a). *Advan. Insect Physiol.* **4**, 69.

Gilbert, L. I. (1967b). *In* "Comprehensive Biochemistry" (M. Florkin and E. H. Stotz, eds.), Vol. 28, pp. 199–252. Elsevier, Amsterdam.

Gilbert, L. I. (1967c). *Comp. Biochem. Physiol.* **21**, 237.

Gilbert, L. I. (1969). *Proc. 3rd Intern. Congr. Endocrinol., Mexico City 1968,* Intern. Congr. Ser. No. 157, pp. 340–346. Excerpta Med. Found., Amsterdam.

Gilbert, L. I., and Schneiderman, H. A. (1961). *Gen. Comp. Endocrinol.* **1**, 453.

Gilbert, L. I., Chino, H., and Domroese, K. A. (1965). *J. Insect Physiol.* **11**, 1057.

Gilgan, M. W., and Idler, D. R. (1967). *Gen. Comp. Endocrinol.* **9**, 319.

Goodfellow, R. D., and Gilbert, L. I. (1964). Unpublished data.

Graszynski, K. (1968). *Z. Vergleich. Physiol.* **60**, 427.

Gurd, F. R. N. (1963). *In* "Comprehensive Biochemistry" (M. Florkin and E. H. Stotz, eds.), Vol. 8, pp. 3–16. Elsevier, Amsterdam.

Happ, G. M., and Meinwald, J. (1965). *J. Am. Chem. Soc.* **87**, 2507.

Happ, G. M., and Meinwald, J. (1966). *Advan. Chem.* **53**, 27.

Hartenstein, R. (1964). *Enzymologia* **27**, 113.

Heed, W. B., and Kirscher, H. W. (1965). *Science* **149**, 758.

Hirano, C., and Gilbert, L. I. (1967). *J. Insect Physiol.* **13**, 163.

Hokin, L. E., Hokin, M. R., and Mathison D. (1963). *Biochim. Biophys. Acta* **67**, 485.

Huggins, A. K.(1966). *Comp. Biochem. Physiol.* **18**, 283.

Keith, A. D. (1967). *Life Sci.* **6**, 213.

Keith, A. D., Gauslaa, G., and Anderson, B. S. (1967). *Lipids* **2**, 429.

Kinsella, J. E. (1966). *Comp. Biochem. Physiol.* **17**, 635.

Kinsella, J. E., and Smyth, T., Jr. (1966). *Comp. Biochem. Physiol.* **17**, 237.

Kleine, R. (1967). *Z. Vergleich. Physiol.* **55**, 333.

Lafon, M. (1950). *Arch. Intern. Physiol.* **57**, 309.

Lambremont, E. N., Bumgarner, J. E., and Bennett, A. F. (1966). *Comp. Biochem. Physiol.* **19**, 417.

Lasser, N. L., Edwards, A. M., and Clayton, R. B. (1966). *J. Lipid Res.* **7**, 403.

McCaman, R. E., Smith, M., and Cook, K. (1965). *J. Biol. Chem.* **240**, 3513.

McWhinnie, M. A., and Chua, A. S. (1964). *Gen. Comp. Endocrinol.* **4**, 624.

McWhinnie, M. A., and Corkill, A. J. (1964). *Comp. Biochem. Physiol.* **12**, 81.

McWhinnie, M. A., and Kirchenberg, R. J. (1962). *Comp. Biochem. Physiol.* **6**, 117.

Mayer, R. J., and Candy, D. J. (1969). *J. Insect Physiol.* **15**, 611.

Meyer, H., Preiss, B., and Bayer, S. (1960). *Biochem. J.* **76**, 27.

Munday, K. A., and Munn, E. A. (1965). *Biochim Biophys. Acta* **110**, 202.

Nelson, D. R., and Sukkestad, D. R. (1968). *J. Insect Physiol.* **14**, 293.

O'Connor, J. D., and Gilbert, L. I. (1967). Unpublished observations.

O'Connor, J. D., and Gilbert, L. I. (1968). *Am. Zoologist* **8**, 529.

O'Connor, J. D., and Gilbert, L. I. (1969). *Comp. Biochem. Physiol.* **29**, 889.

Olivecrona, T. (1962). *J. Lipid Res.* **3**, 439.

Ramamurthi, R., Mumbach, M. W., and Scheer, B. T. (1968). *Comp. Biochem. Physiol.* **26**, 311.

Regnier, F. E., and Law, J. H. (1968). *J. Lipid Res.* **9**, 541.

Rhodes, D. N. (1964). *In* "Metabolism and Physiological Significance of Lipids" (R. M. C. Dawson and D. N. Rhodes, eds.), pp. 622–624. Wiley, New York.

Scanu, A., and Granda, J. L. (1966). *Biochemistry* **5**, 446.

Scheer, B. T. (1957). *In* "Recent Advances in Invertebrate Physiology" (B. T. Scheer, ed.), pp. 213–227. Univ. of Oregon Press, Eugene, Oregon.

Shapiro, B. (1964). *In* "Lipid Transport" (H. C. Meng, ed.), pp. 141–154. Thomas, Springfield, Illinois.

Sridhara, S., and Bhat, J. V. (1965). *J. Insect Physiol.* **11**, 449.

Stein, Y., and Stein, O. (1962). *Biochim. Biophys. Acta* **60**, 58.

Stephen, W. F., Jr., and Gilbert, L. I. (1969). *J. Insect Physiol.* **15**, 1833.

Tamaki, Y. (1968). *Lipids* **3**, 186.

Thomas, K. K., and Gilbert, L. I. (1967a). *Comp. Biochem. Physiol.* **21**, 279.

Thomas, K. K., and Gilbert, L. I. (1967b). *J. Insect Physiol.* **13**, 963.

Thomas, K. K., and Gilbert, L. I. (1968). *Arch. Biochem. Biophys.* **127**, 512.

Thomas, K. K., and Gilbert, L. I. (1969). *Physiol. Chem. Phys.* **1**, 293.

Tietz, A. (1961). *J. Lipid Res.* **2**, 182.

Tietz, A. (1962). *J. Lipid Res.* **3**, 421.

Tietz, A. (1967). *European J. Biochem.* **2**, 236.

Travis, D. (1955). *Biol. Bull.* **108**, 88.

Van Handel, E. (1967). *J. Exptl. Biol.* **46**, 487.

Vonk, H. J. (1960). *In* "The Physiology of Crustacea" (T. H. Waterman, ed.), Vol. 1, pp. 291–316. Academic Press, New York.

Wyatt, G. R., Kropf, R. B., and Carey, F. G. (1963). *J. Insect Physiol.* **9**, 137.

Zandee, D. I. (1966). *Arch. Intern. Physiol. Biochim.* **74**, 614.

Zandee, D. I. (1967). *Comp. Biochem. Physiol.* **20**, 811.

Zebe, E. (1954). *Z. Vergleich. Physiol.* **36**, 290.

Zebe, E. (1959). *Proc. 4th Intern. Congr. Biochem., 1958*, Vol. 12, p. 197. Pergamon Press, Oxford.

CHAPTER 9

Osmoregulation in Aquatic Arthropods

E. Schoffeniels and R. Gilles

I. Definitions

One can find representatives of the phylum Arthropoda in all the salinities occurring in nature, and many of them are able to live or survive in media which are very different from their normal habitat. Organisms which can tolerate wide ranges of salinities are termed *euryhalines* whereas those restricted to narrow ranges are called *stenohalines*.

The possibility for a euryhaline arthropod to succeed in media of various salinities will undoubtedly depend for a large part on its ability to regulate the osmotic pressure of both its blood and cells. Animals which regulate the osmotic pressure of their blood and maintain a more or less constant osmotic concentration despite changed concentration in the external medium are called *homeosmotic*. Such is the case of the prawn *Palaemonetes varians*. However, few are the Arthropoda which conform to this behavior. Most of the euryhaline Arthropoda begin to regulate their blood osmotic concentration only when the external medium reaches a certain level of hypotonicity (see Lockwood, 1962). For these forms which are more or less *poikilosmotic*, the body cells can bear concentration changes of the body fluid by means of active regulatory processes. When considering the osmotic regulation in euryhaline Arthropoda, we are thus dealing with two types of mechanisms: one type which is involved in the regulation of the osmotic pressure of the blood we shall term, according to Florkin (1962), *anisosmotic regulation*, and a second one is termed *intracellular isosmotic regulation* and is involved in the regulation of the osmotic pressure of the cell. We shall thus investigate in more detail these two types of regulation.

II. Anisosmotic Extracellular Regulation

A. SURVEY

Generally, the blood of marine Arthropoda is more or less isosmotic with the surrounding medium, as first noticed by Léon Fredericq (1901). A passive equilibrium between marine environment and blood plasma cannot however account for this observation. Indeed, most of the Arthropoda so far studied show a high degree of ionic regulation (Florkin, 1960; Potts and Parry, 1964). Such an ionic regulation power is particularly important in freshwater forms.

This regulation process, which already appears in animals taken from their natural environment, becomes very important in animals which can adapt to media of different salinities. Indeed most of the euryhaline Arthropoda so far studied show a high power of anisosmotic extracellular regulation. In fact, two primary types of response to changes in salinity are known (Lockwood, 1962).

1. The blood is almost isosmotic to the medium in concentrated solutions and is hyperosmotic when the animal is in diluted saline. Animals of this category include *Carcinus maenas, Cancer pagurus* (Schlieper, 1929a), *Hemigrapsus nudus, Cancer magister* (Jones, 1941), *Marinogammarus finmarchicus* (Sutcliffe, 1968), and many freshwater forms such as *Gammarus duebeni* (Beadle and Cragg, 1940), *Potamon niloticus* (Shaw, 1959a), *Asellus aquaticus* (Lockwood, 1959), *Astacus fluviatilis* (Schwabe, 1933) and larvae of *Culex pipiens* and *Aedes aegypti* (Wigglesworth, 1938).

2. The blood is hypoosmotic to the medium in concentrated solutions and is hyperosmotic in diluted media. *Palaemonetes varians, Leander serratus* (Panikkar, 1941), *Artemia salina* (Croghan, 1958a), *Uca crenulata, Pachygrapsus crassipes* (Jones, 1941), *Macrobrachium equidens* (Denne, 1968), probably all the grapboid crabs (Lockwood, 1962; Barnes, 1967), and also the insects *Sigara lugubris* (Claus, 1937) and *Limnophilus affinis* (Sutcliffe, 1961a) belong to this second category.

All these euryhaline species, when placed in diluted medium, are able to regulate the ionic concentration of their blood to maintain an osmotic pressure higher than that of the medium. For instance, adaptation of a seawater *Eriocheir* to freshwater brings about a decrease in all the determined ions of the blood except for Ca^{++}. The concentration of Na^+, K^+, Cl^-, and Mg^{++} is however maintained at a higher level than that of the surrounding freshwater (Table I).

TABLE I

COMPOSITION OF *Eriocheir* BLOOD IN FRESHWATER (FW)
AND IN ARTIFICIAL SEAWATER (SW)[a,b]

| | Ionic concentration (meq./liter) | | | | | OP |
	Na	K	Ca	Mg	Cl	(mosmole)
Freshwater	8	0.14	—	—	—	21
Blood (FW)	300	4.9	—	—	319	615
Blood (FW)[c]	—	5.1	5	1.7	280	—
Seawater	504	9.8	—	—	546	1048
Blood (SW)	536	10.3	—	—	520	1054
Blood (SW)[c]	—	8.7	5.7	7.9	440	—

[a] The results are the means of three experiments.
[b] Dashes indicate that no values were determined.
[c] After Scholles (1933).

Anisosmotic extracellular regulation in Arthropoda is therefore a mechanism which mainly involves a regulation of the blood ionic concentration. The hyperosmotic state observed in freshwater forms or in euryhaline species adapted to dilute media implicate both passive and active mechanisms. We shall now study some of these mechanisms.

One can consider as the main passive factors the permeability of the animal to salts and water as well as a Donnan equilibrium due to the blood proteins. On the other hand, the active uptake of salts may be considered to be an active factor.

B. MECHANISMS INVOLVED

1. Donnan Equilibrium

As demonstrated mainly by Robertson (1949-1950, 1953), although a small but significant Donnan effect occurs in some Crustacea in which the blood protein concentration is particularly high, it does not account for more than a small part of the ionic regulation. The differences observed between the ionic composition of the blood and that of seawater must then be attributed to other processes.

2. Permeability to Salt and Water

a. Excretory Organ. For this purpose, one must discriminate between marine and brackish water species which produce an isosmotic urine and freshwater species which produce a hypotonic urine and in which an active reabsorption of salts may thus be expected.

Adaptation of euryhaline seawater Crustacea to diluted media induces an increase in the urine flow (Shaw, 1961a). However, as it is a well-known fact that marine and brackish euryhaline Crustacea produce an isosmotic urine (Scholles, 1933; Nagel, 1934; Panikkar, 1941; Robertson, 1949-1950, 1953) with salinities as low as 10%, one can conclude that in these species the urine production does not play any role in the anisosmotic regulation. In fact, the reverse is the case, since the loss of sodium through the urine must increase during the adaptation to diluted media. This has clearly been demonstrated by Shaw (1961a) when adapting *Carcinus maenas* to brackish water.

Freshwater animals produce a urine hypoosmotic with the blood (Ramsay, 1950; Bryan, 1960c; Lockwood, 1961; Sutcliffe, 1961a,b). This fact implies that these animals actively reabsorb salts in diluted media. In Crustacea the salt lost through urination represents a small amount when compared to the salt lost by diffusion through the body wall (see Potts and Parry, 1964); however, hypoosmotic urine cannot account completely for the hyperosmotic regulation. However, in some insect larvae such as *Sialis* in which the permeability of the body wall to salts and water is extremely low (Shaw, 1955a), this mechanism plays a great part in the hyperosmotic regulation. As a matter of fact, Shaw (1955b) is unable to detect any active uptake of sodium by *Sialis* from tap water.

It appears therefore that when dealing with the role of urine production in the anisosmotic regulation of seawater arthropods, one must consider Crustacea and Insecta separately. Indeed, in insects, the rectum appears to have an important reabsorption function producing hypoosmotic urine (Ramsay, 1950; Sutcliffe, 1960).

Nevertheless, except for a few cases, if reabsorption of salts from urine can assist regulation in diluted media, this mechanism can only compensate a small part of the salt loss both through the urine and the body wall.

b. Body Wall. It has been generally assumed that animals which are maintaining themselves hypertonic to the surrounding medium must eliminate the net influx of water as urine. Thus urine volume figures which are assumed to be equivalent to net water uptake have been used to estimate the relative permeability of various animals to water. Urine production rates for a variety of Arthropoda have been calculated for a long time by various techniques and, in a very few cases, absolute permeability data have been calculated. From the results obtained, it can be concluded that the permeability to both water and salts of most freshwater Arthropoda are remarkably low when compared to the permeability of seawater species (Gross, 1957; Shaw, 1961b; Croghan and Lockwood, 1968). A good demonstration of this fact is given by the experiments undertaken with various gammarid Crustacea by Sutcliffe and Shaw (Table II). Representatives of *Gammarid* genus can be found in seawater, in brackish water, and also in freshwater. This genus thus represents good material for examining the main features of ionic regulation in animals representing different degrees of adaptation to freshwater. The values of permeability rate constant obtained for sodium are given in Table II. One can see that it is about four times greater in marine species than in freshwater ones. K' for brackish gammarids is about the same as that obtained for freshwater species. This may be due to the fact that *G. duebeni, G. zaddachi,* and *G. tigrinus* are not true brackish gammarids and often experience very low salinities in their normal habitats.

From what has been said above, it could be tentatively concluded that permeability to salt and water is lower in freshwater than in seawater species. Such a mechanism of modification of the permeability does not seem to be at play during adaptation of a euryhaline species to various media. As a matter of fact, the rate constant for salts calculated for various euryhaline Crustacea having as habitat, marine, brackish, or freshwater, does not significantly change with adaptation to various media (Table III).

Moreover, as far as water permeability is concerned, Rudy (1967)

TABLE II
COMPARISON OF SODIUM PERMEABILITY IN A SERIES OF GAMMARIDS FROM DIFFERENT ENVIRONMENTS

Species	Rate constant[a]	Reference
Marine		
Marinogammarus finmarchicus	0.0050	Sutcliffe (1968)
Marinogammarus obturatus	0.0058	Sutcliffe (1968)
Brackish water		
Gammarus tigrinus	0.0019	Sutcliffe (1968)
	0.0021	Sutcliffe (1968)
Gammarus zaddachi	0.0014	Sutcliffe (1967a)
Gammarus duebeni	0.0009	Sutcliffe (1967a)
	0.0005	Sutcliffe (1967a)
Freshwater		
Gammarus duebeni	0.0011	Sutcliffe and Shaw (1968)
Gammarus pulex	0.0014	Sutcliffe (1967b)
Gammarus lacustris	0.0014	Sutcliffe and Shaw (1967)

[a] Rate constant is given in hr.$^{-1}$ for 200 mg. of animal.

TABLE III
SODIUM PERMEABILITY IN VARIOUS EURYHALINE CRUSTACEA
ADAPTED TO DIFFERENT SALINITIES

Species	External medium (% sea-water)[a]	Mean blood Na conc. (mmoles/ liter)	Body wall Na loss for 100 mg. of animal (μmoles/hr.)	Rate constant[b]	Reference
Carcinus maenas	100	460	2.466	0.0052	Shaw (1961b)
	50	340	1.692	0.0048	
	40	300	1.406	0.0046	
Gammarus zaddachi	—	500	0.665	0.0013	Sutcliffe (1968)
	—	300	0.457	0.0015	
	—	252	0.332	0.0013	
Marinogammarus	100	536	2.787	0.0051	Sutcliffe (1968)
finmarchicus	50	368	1.864	0.0050	
	20	324	1.520	0.0046	
Astacus pallipes[c]	—	310	0.442	0.0014	Bryan (1960a,b,c)
	—	186	0.251	0.0013	
	—	310	0.671	0.0021	
	—	180	0.371	0.0020	

[a] Dashes indicate that no data were recorded.

[b] Rate constants are expressed in hour.$^{-1}$ for 100 mg. animal.

[c] Recalculated from Potts and Parry (1964) assuming that blood volume is 35% of the body weight.

demonstrates that the H_2O influx constants (hr.$^{-1}$) for *Carcinus maenas* remains about the same whatever the external salinity (0.79 in seawater, 0.78 in 70% and 0.72 in 40% seawater). Therefore, it appears that the reduction of body wall permeability to salts and water could be a step in the course of adaptive evolution to freshwater since freshwater species have a permeability much lower than the marine one. However, such an adaptive mechanism does not seem to play any role in the osmoregulation of a euryhaline animal when passing from a concentrated medium to a more diluted one.

3. Active Uptake of Ions

The replacement of salts lost through both body wall and urine must be dealt with by absorption. This absorption, as we have seen for *Sialis*, sometimes takes place at the digestive barrier. However, even in starvation, euryhaline Arthropoda are able to maintain the hyperosmoticity of their blood in diluted media so that specialized mechanisms must be present to ensure active uptake of ions from diluted solutions.

Sodium and chloride ions account mainly for the bulk of osmotic pressure exerted by the blood (see Table I). Thus it can be assumed that the active transport for these two ions is the more effective. Many investigations therefore attempt to define the mechanisms as well as the localization of an active transport system for these two ions.

a. *Sodium Uptake.* Euryhaline Arthropoda as well as other animals are able to take up actively sodium from the surrounding medium. This active uptake is dependent on the salt concentration of both the surrounding medium and the blood.

As shown in Fig. 1, the relation between sodium influx and external sodium concentration is hyperbolic in the crayfish *Astacus pallipes.* This type of curve is reminescent of the well-known Michaelis–Menten kinetics for enzyme, where the initial velocity of the reaction is equal to the maximum velocity multiplied by the ratio substrate concentration over substrate concentration plus the so-called Michaelis constant. By direct analogy, Shaw (1959b) proposed the following relation

$$f = f_{max} \frac{[Na]}{K_s + [Na]}$$

where f is the influx, f_{max} the maximum influx, [Na] the external sodium concentration, and K_s a constant defined as the external concentration at which the influx is half the maximum value. It is directly related to the Michaelis constant and gives an idea of the affinity of the system for the ion transported.

The transport system may be described in terms of f_{max} and K_s. Table

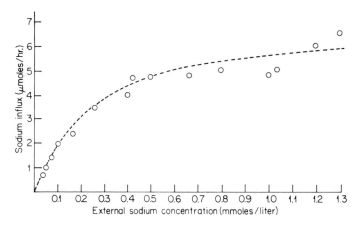

FIG. 1. The relation between the sodium influx and the external sodium concentration in the crayfish *Astacus pallipes.* From Shaw (1959b).

TABLE IV

CHARACTERISTICS OF THE UPTAKE MECHANISM OF SOME CRUSTACEA

Species	f_{max} (mmoles/ kg./hr.)	K_s (mmoles/ liter)	Reference
Marine			
Marinogammarus finmarchicus	10	2.5	Sutcliffe (1968)
Brackish			
Carcinus maenas	10	20	Shaw (1961a)
Gammarus duebeni	20	1.5	Shaw and Sutcliffe (1961)
Freshwater			
Gammarus pulex	7.5	0.15	Shaw and Sutcliffe (1961)
Potamon niloticus	2	0.1	Shaw (1959a)
Astacus fluviatilis	0.15	0.2	Shaw (1959b)

IV gives values of f_{max} and K_s for various Arthropoda. From these data, it appears that in the course of adaptive evolution to freshwater, there has been a progressive increasing ability to take up ions from low external concentrations since a decrease of the K_s value is observed in freshwater species when compared to marine or brackish water species.

As shown in Fig. 2, some euryhaline Crustacea such as *Eriocheir sinensis* (Shaw, 1961b), *Artemia salina* (Thuet *et al.*, 1968), or *Gam-*

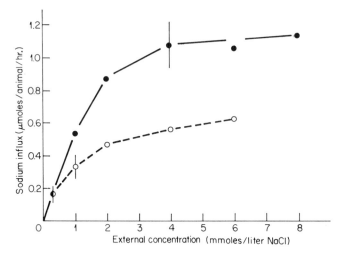

FIG. 2. The relation between the external concentration and sodium influx in *Gammarus zaddachi* adapted to media of different salinities. ○: Animal adapted to 10 mmoles/liter NaCl; ●: animals adapted to 0.3 mmoles/liter NaCl; vertical lines indicate extent of standard error of the mean. From Sutcliffe (1968).

marus zaddachi (Sutcliffe, 1968) have developed an adaptive sodium transport system by which they respond to salt depletion by an increase in f_{max} rather than by a decrease in K_s. This implies that the mechanism of adaptation must produce an increase in the concentration or the activity of the cation carrier rather than alter its affinity for sodium. This adaptive process is not however observed for all euryhaline Crustacea since Sutcliffe (1968) reports that there is no difference in f_{max} between the influxes of *Marinogammarus finmarchicus* acclimatized to 115 mmoles/liter NaCl or to 10 mmoles/liter NaCl.

The rate of sodium uptake also depends on the internal sodium concentration. The influx of sodium from a constant external concentration appears very sensitive to changes in internal sodium content. As an example, a decline from 400 mmoles/liter to 390 mmoles/liter suffices to produce, in *Carcinus,* a fourfold increase in the active uptake rate of sodium (Shaw, 1961a).

Thus, the rate of sodium uptake in a euryhaline Crustacea is a function of both the external and the blood sodium concentrations. This invalidates those theories based on a simple kinetic model such as that proposed by Shaw (1959b). The overall balance of sodium can therefore be characterized by the relation between these two variables. This has been done by Potts and Parry (1964) on the basis of the experimental data given by Shaw (1959b) when studying the fluxes of sodium in the euryhaline *Astacus.* We shall not discuss this subject further in this chapter.

b. Chloride Uptake. Although sodium uptake has been clearly demonstrated and the active nature of the process has been shown in most of the Arthropoda so far studied, the nature of chloride ion movements is far from being elucidated. The detailed investigations of Ussing and co-workers with the isolated frog skin (Ussing, 1949, 1954; Ussing and Zerahn, 1951; Koefoed-Johnsen et al., 1952) reveal that this ion is moving passively as a result of the electric field established by the transport of sodium ions. However, the chemical studies of Krogh (1938, 1939) on salt-depleted *Eriocheir* demonstrate that this animal is able to absorb chloride ions in the absence of sodium, and Krogh concludes that the mechanisms of uptake of these two ions are of an independent nature.

Evidence of an independent chloride-transporting system has also been given in *Astacus pallipes* (Shaw, 1960), in *Artemia salina* (Thuet et al., 1968), in *Callinectes* (Mantel, 1967), and also in some insect aquatic larvae (Koch, 1938; Stobbart, 1965, 1967).

If the existence of a sodium pump is known in Arthropoda (Shaw, 1959a,b; Potts and Parry, 1964; Ramsay, 1953; Treherne, 1954a,b; Stobbart, 1959, 1960) absolutely nothing is presently known about the mecha-

TABLE V

Na$_{out}$/Na$_{in}$:		1.0					0.76			
Medium (mM NaCl):		450					340			
Perfusate (mM NaCl):		450					450			

Crab gills	In^c	Out^c	PD^d	Ratio^e		In^c	Out^c	PD^d	Ratio^e	
				E	C				E	C
Maja	4.2	4.2	0	1.0	1.0	3.2	3.5	0	0.91	0.76
Eriocheir										
Anterior										
(a)	1.15	1.1	3.0	1.0	0.87	—	—	—	—	—
(b)	0.38	0.26	3.0	1.4	0.87	—	—	—	—	—
Posterior										
(a)	0.14	0.06	−15.0	2.3	1.8	—	—	—	—	—
(b)	0.68	0.02	−29.0	28.0	2.9	—	—	—	—	—

[a] After King and Schoffeniels, unpublished data (cited by Florkin and Schoffeniels, 1969), and King and Schoffeniels (1969).

[b] Perfusate was a balanced salt solution (Lockwood, 1961). Medium was composed of the balanced salt solution diluted with distilled water. Flux values are given as micromoles per minute per gill. Values represent the mean of 2 to 3 readings.

nism of chloride transport in these species. The following papers which relate to this field should be consulted: Shaw (1960), Thuet *et al.* (1968), and Stobbart (1967).

After having reviewed the ion transport systems in Arthropoda, the question to be asked is: Where are these mechanisms located?

c. Site of the Ion Transporting System. In Crustacea, evidence has been provided showing that the gills are the main site of ion absorption (Krogh, 1939; Koch, 1954; Bryan, 1960a,b,c; Habas and Prosser, 1963; Bielawski, 1964; Croghan *et al.*, 1965; Mantel, 1967). In *Artemia salina* in which the gills had been treated with KMnO$_4$, the ability to osmoregulate in diluted media is completely lost and the blood remains closely isotonic with the medium (Croghan, 1958b). In these experiments, it appears that only the first ten pairs of branchiae have been damaged by KMnO$_4$. This discrimination between the different gills is also observed in *Eriocheir sinensis*. Koch (1954) has reported that the posterior three pairs of branchiae absorb sodium more rapidly than the others. Experiments by King and Schoffeniels (1969) confirm these findings. From the results given in Table V, it is clear that sodium is absorbed by an active phenomenon in the posterior gills of *Eriocheir* since

Sodium Flux in *Eriocheir* and *Maja* Gills[a,b]

0.4 180 450					0.2 90 450					0.02 9 450				
			Ratio[e]					Ratio[e]					Ratio[e]	
In[c]	Out[c]	PD[d]	E	C	In[c]	Out[c]	PD[d]	E	C	In[c]	Out[c]	PD[d]	E	C
1.3	3.1	−0.5	0.43	0.41	0.8	2.9	−1.0	0.27	0.21	—	—	—	—	—
0.82	1.1	−5.0	0.78	0.60	0.53	0.78	−27.0	0.65	0.58	—	—	—	—	—
—	—	—	—	—	0.26	0.29	−27.0	0.88	0.58	0.15	0.37	−58.0	0.39	0.2
0.12	0.09	−15.0	1.3	0.90	0.08	0.1	−16.0	0.80	0.37	—	—	—	—	—
—	—	—	—	—	0.34	0.04	−25.0	8.8	0.50	0.13	0.06	−25.0	2.1	0.05

[c] In: appearance of ^{22}NaCl in the perfusate; Out: appearance of ^{24}NaCl in the medium.

[d] PD: potential difference between perfusate and medium. Sign is given as blood relative to medium.

[e] Ratio: E, experimental; C, calculated $(Na_{out}/Na_{in})e^{-\frac{2F}{RT}\Delta E}$. Anterior and posterior gills (a) or (b) are from animal (a) or (b). Measurements were taken at 10- to 20-min. intervals.

the observed flux ratio is always greater than the flux ratio calculated according to Ussing (1949).

It is also interesting to note that in *Maja* branchiae, the calculated flux ratio is in agreement with the observed flux ratio either in isosmotic saline or in twice diluted media. This indicates that the sodium movement through the gills of this crab is a passive phenomenon. This may probably be correlated with the fact that *Maja* is not able to regulate anisosmotically.

In Crustacea, the mechanism responsible for the active uptake of salts appears to be located mainly in the gills. From observations with the electron microscope on gill lamellae, Copeland (1964a, 1968) distinguishes an osmoregulatory tissue and a respiratory one. The typical organization of the osmoregulatory tissue has led Copeland to suggest the existence in crab gills of a mitochondrial pump which is implicated in the salt absorption. Such a mitochondrial pump seems also to be at play in the anal papillae of aquatic larvae of insects (Copeland, 1964b; Sohal and Copeland, 1966). Indeed, as we have already stated, the main sites of sodium absorption in insect larvae appears to be located in the anal papillae and rectum. The importance of the anal papillae in sodium absorption was first noticed by Martini (1923) and Wiggles-worth (1933) who demonstrated a close correlation between the size of the anal papillae in *Aedes* and *Culex* larvae and the salt content of the medium. This assumption was later clearly demonstrated (Schaller, 1949; Ramsay, 1953; Treherne, 1954a,b; Stobbart, 1959, 1960, 1965). Moreover, in mosquito larvae, the absorption of electrolytes from the medium may be regulated by varying the surface area of the plasma membrane of the epithelial cells of the papillae as demonstrated by Sohal and Copeland (1966). As to a possible role of the gut, the available data do not support the idea of a continuous drinking process, thus ruling out this organ as the main site of ionic regulation (Maluf, 1941; Bryan, 1960b).

III. Osmoregulatory Function of Amino Acids in Insect Hemolymph

In most animal phyla, the osmotic pressure of the body fluid is established by inorganic constituents. This is true with the Crustacea but it is far from being the case when dealing with insects. As Sutcliffe (1962, 1963) has pointed out, the participation of inorganic cations and anions in the osmotic pressure of the hemolymph tends to decrease with the evolutionary level of the insect; the most primitive, such as the Apterygota *Petrobius maritimus,* shows a hemolymph composition very similar to that of other arthropods, i.e., a nearly exclusive participation of inorganic ions as osmotic effectors (Lockwood and Croghan, 1959). In the exopterygotes (Ephemeroptera, Odonata, Dictyoptera, Heteroptera, and to a lesser extent, Orthoptera, Isoptera, and Dermaptera) organic molecules such as amino acids help in establishing the osmotic pressure of the hemolymph. In the endopterygotes (Megaloptera, Neuroptera, Mecoptera, Trichoptera, and Diptera) the organic ions and molecules contribute to about half the osmotic pressure. That both inorganic ions and amino acids are subjected to a control when the insect is subjected to an osmotic stress is well established in the case of dragonfly larvae and for *Dytiscus marginalis* adults (Schoffeniels, 1950, 1960a).

The mechanisms by which the aminoacidemia is controlled are not known.

To sum up, we have seen that most of the Arthropoda are able to regulate the ionic content of their blood. This ionic regulation process becomes very important for euryhaline species during adaptation to media of different salinities. The hyperosmotic state observed in these species when adapted to diluted media imply that they reach a steady state resulting in a balance between charge and discharge phenomena.

The active transport of salts by the gills in Crustacea or by the rectum and the anal papillae in insects is certainly of prime importance in this respect. However, most of the euryhaline Arthropoda begin to regulate their blood osmotic concentration only when the external medium reaches a certain level of hypotonicity. The body cell must thus bear the concentration changes of the body fluid. This regulation implies the intervention of active processes. We shall now investigate means by which the cell regulates its osmotic pressure.

IV. Isosmotic Intracellular Regulation

A. SURVEY

When considering the general problem of the penetration of marine animals into brackish or freshwater, it is clear that even in euryhaline species which have an anisosmotic regulation, such as *Eriocheir* or *Carcinus,* the cells must adapt to considerable changes in the composition of their surrounding fluid. For instance, *Eriocheir* in freshwater has a blood ionic concentration which is about half that observed in seawater (see Table I). As it is classically assumed that cells are always isosmotic with the blood (Schoffeniels, 1967; Florkin and Schoffeniels, 1969), it can be expected that a change in the blood concentration must induce a concomitant adjustment of the cell osmotic pressure to the osmotic pressure of the blood. This process of cell osmotic pressure adaptation has been termed by Florkin (1962) the intracellular isosmotic regulation. Thus, in the process of adaptation to various media, the isosmotic regulation is almost as important as the anisosmotic regulation, and in all euryhaline species having limited or no power of anisosmotic regulation, the penetration of the animal in media of different salinities must depend to a large extent on the power of the intracellular isosmotic regulation system.

Before attempting to analyze the mechanisms of the cell adaptation to changes in the blood concentration, it is necessary to know the effectors of the osmotic pressure in Arthropoda cells. In contrast to body fluids, Arthropoda muscles and nerves are rich in potassium and poor in sodium and chloride. Moreover, inorganic components account only for about half of the total osmotic pressure of the tissue. The rest of the osmotic pressure is made up of several organic compounds such as amino acids, quaternary ammonium derivatives, and organic phosphate compounds (Camien *et al.*, 1951; Robertson, 1961; Shaw, 1955c, 1958a,b, 1959a,c; Bricteux-Grégoire *et al.*, 1962, 1963, 1966). Some of these compounds, which are anionic, undoubtedly play a great part in balancing the high potassium level. The retention of potassium ions appears thus to be largely electrostatic, and if an active process is concerned in the maintenance of potassium level, it can account for only a very small part of the total potassium flux (Shaw, 1958a,b). It is certainly the mechanism by which sodium and chloride are excluded from the cell which is the most important process of ionic regulation in Arthropoda cells. Unfortunately, absolutely nothing is known about this mechanism (Shaw, 1958a,b; Potts and Parry, 1964).

Of all the organic molecules taking part in the establishment of the intracellular osmotic pressure level, amino acids occur most frequently. In *Nephrops* muscle, amino acids represent 40% to 50% of the total intracellular osmotic effectors, while trimethylamine oxide and betaine account for about 13%. A substantial amount of organic phosphate compounds is also recorded in *Nephrops* tissue (Robertson, 1961). It is interesting to note that the amount of amino acids is much higher in marine than in freshwater Crustacea. This point has been well substantiated by Florkin and co-workers (Camien *et al.*, 1951; Duchâteau and Florkin, 1955; see also Chapter 7 of this volume). This is also true when considering the amount of quaternary ammonium derivatives in marine and freshwater Crustacea (Gasteiger *et al.*, 1960; Beers, 1967). From these observations, it can be tentatively concluded that these compounds can play an important role in the isosmotic regulation process.

At present, nothing is known about the relation of metabolism of organic phosphate components to isosmotic regulation. Among other molecules, which can play a role in the cellular osmotic regulation, some quaternary ammonium derivatives have been described. These include homarine, glycinebetaine, carnitine, trigonelline, and γ-butyrobetaine. The occurrence and metabolism of these compounds have been reviewed in Chapter 7 of this volume. It is however difficult to say anything constructive about the role that quaternary ammonium derivatives play in the biology of euryhaline Arthropoda.

Most investigations have been hitherto concerned with the role of amino acids in the isosmotic regulation process. We will therefore present the different results and conclusions obtained in this field.

B. Amino Acids as Osmotic Effectors

Since the amount of free amino acids is higher in tissues of marine animals than in tissues of freshwater ones and since this observation suggests that free amino acids play an important role in the osmoregulation of the intracellular fluid, it would be of interest to compare the situation of a euryhaline marine invertebrate in a concentrated and in a diluted medium. This was first accomplished by Florkin and co-workers with the Chinese crab (Duchâteau and Florkin, 1955; Bricteux-Grégoire *et al.*, 1962). In *Eriocheir sinensis*, when adapted to freshwater, the inorganic constituents of the muscles represent about 40% of the osmotically active constituents. The rest of the osmotic pressure is due to small organic molecules, of which the determined amino acids constitute more than 50%. When animals are adapted to seawater, an increase is observed in all the osmotically active constituents. The total concentration of the free amino acids is approximately doubled. This variation of the amino acid component could only depend on an active modification since there is only a slight modification of the tissue hydration when *Eriocheir* goes from a diluted to another more concentrated medium (Scholles, 1933; Bricteux-Grégoire *et al.*, 1962). Therefore Florkin (1956, 1962) has proposed "to consider the variation of the amino acid component resulting from a change in the medium concentration, as exerting an intracellular osmotic regulation."

Many studies in recent years have dealt with the free amino acid content of euryhaline invertebrates in relation to environment. These observations show that the tissue level of free amino acids varies with the environmental salinity. This phenomenon appears to occur generally in euryhaline aquatic invertebrates since it has been recorded in all the phyla studied so far.

1. Crustacea: *Carcinus maenas* (Shaw, 1958a,b; Duchâteau *et al.*, 1959), *Leander serratus*, *Leander squilla* (Jeuniaux *et al.*, 1961a), *Eriocheir sinensis* (Bricteux-Grégoire *et al.*, 1962), and *Astacus astacus* (Duchâteau and Florkin, 1961.)

2. Arachnomorphs: *Limulus polyphemus* (Bricteux-Grégoire *et al.*, 1966).

3. Mollusca: *Mytilus edulis* (Potts, 1958; Lange, 1963; Bricteux-Grégoire *et al.*, 1964a), *Gryphea angulata* (Bricteux-Grégoire *et al.*, 1964b), *Ostrea edulis* (Bricteux-Grégoire *et al.*, 1964c), *Rangia cuneata* (Allen, 1961), *Crassostrea virginica* (Lynch and Wood, 1966), *Tegula funebralis* (Peterson and Duerr, 1969), *Glicimeris glicimeris* (Gilles and Schoffeniels, 1970), and *Mya arenaria* (Virkar and Webb, 1967).

4. Annelids: *Nereis diversicolor*, *Perinereis cultrifera* (Jeuniaux *et al.*, 1961b), and *Arenicola marina* (Duchâteau *et al.*, 1961).

5. Echinoderms: *Asterias rubens* (Jeuniaux *et al.*, 1962), *Strongylocentrotus droebachiensis* (Lange, 1964), and *Ophiactis arenosa* (Stephens and Virkar, 1966).

6. Sipuncula: *Phascolopsis gouldii* (Virkar, 1966).

It is interesting to note that the euryhalinity of several of the listed species depends only on an intracellular isosmotic regulatory mechanism. As a matter of fact, *Asterias rubens* does not show any extracellular anisosmotic regulation (Binyon, 1961), neither do *Arenicola marina*

(Schlieper, 1929b; Beadle, 1937) or *Mytilus edulis* (Potts, 1958). Thus in all the cases of euryhaline invertebrates so far studied, isosmotic regulation is found, while anisosmotic regulation is not always present. We must therefore consider the isosmotic regulation as the more primitive mechanism, to which, in several species, the anisosmotic regulation adds a new range of possibilities.

The question now arises: Which amino acids take part in the isosmotic regulation process in Arthropoda? Table VI gives values for the amino acid level in the muscle of several euryhaline species in their normal environment as well as the percentage of variations for each individual amino acid when animals are adapted to media of different salinities. From these results, it can be concluded that the adaptation to a new medium affects the level of all the amino acids determined. However, a notable part of the change in the intracellular osmotic pressure is due mainly to alanine, arginine, aspartic acid, glutamic acid, glycine, and proline. In most cases, proline which is, with glycine, the most concentrated amino acid, undergoes tremendous variations.

Thus, with the exception of arginine, the contribution of the amino acid pool to the isosmotic regulation is mainly due to the so-called nonessential amino acids. The question is therefore raised as to the origin of these amino acids. Do they originate extracellularly or are they formed within the cell?

Schoffeniels (1960b) shows that the total amino nitrogen level of isolated nerves of *Eriocheir sinensis* is higher for nerves incubated in a saline corresponding to the blood concentration of a seawater animal than for nerves placed in a saline corresponding to the blood concentration of an *Eriocheir* adapted to freshwater. Such results favor the concept of an intracellular formation of the amino acids implicated in the isosmotic regulation process in *Eriocheir*.

These results have been confirmed and extended recently by Gilles and Schoffeniels (1969) when studying the amino acid, protein, and ammonia patterns in both nerves and incubating salines after immersion of the isolated tissues in media corresponding either to the blood concentration of a seawater or freshwater *Eriocheir*. The results obtained (Table VII) suggest that the mechanism responsible for the regulation of the amino acid level during osmotic stress is not under hormonal control and involves at least two processes.

The concentration of some amino acids such as tyrosine, phenylalanine, leucine, isoleucine, or valine appears to be regulated by a mechanism involving modifications of the permeability of the nerve membrane. As a matter of fact, the intracellular modification of the concentration of these amino acids is accompanied by a reverse modifica-

TABLE VI
AMINO ACID CONCENTRATION AND VARIATION OF CONCENTRATION IN MUSCLES OF SEVERAL CRUSTACEANS ADAPTED TO MEDIA OF VARIOUS SALINITY[a]

	Eriocheir sinensis[b]			Carcinus maenas[c]			Leander serratus[d]			Leander squilla[d]			Astacus astacus[e]		
	Fresh-water	Sea-water	Variation (%)	Sea-water	50% Sea-water	Variation (%)	Sea-water	30% Sea-water	Variation (%)	Sea-water	30% Sea-water	Variation (%)	Fresh-water	50% Sea-water	Variation (%)
Alanine	1.39	3.37	144.5	2.05	0.96	−53.1	1.69	0.26	−84.6	0.79	0.63	−20.2	1.32	2.11	59.8
Arginine	2.99	4.13	38.1	3.62	3.37	−6.9	2.58	2.07	−19.7	2.58	2.47	−4.2	3.70	4.42	19.5
Aspartic acid	0.29	0.86	196.6	0.39	0.27	−30.7	0.18	0.05	−72.2	0	0.08	—	0.80	0.95	18.7
Glutamic acid	0.84	2.11	151.2	3.60	1.71	−52.4	0.32	0.11	−65.6	0	0	—	3.43	5.05	47.2
Glycine	4.64	8.00	72.4	10.07	7.13	−29.2	11.2	9.5	−15.1	8.0	5.7	−28	2.09	2.43	16.2
Histidine	f	f	f	0.01	0.004	−54.8	0	0	—	0	0	—	0.06	0.16	166.7
Isoleucine	0.08	0.24	200.0	0.17	0.03	−82.3	0.21	Tr	—	Tr	Tr	—	0.17	0.34	190.0
Leucine	0.14	0.40	185.7	0.26	0.05	−54.7	0.34	Tr	—	Tr	Tr	—	0.21	0.40	90.4
Lysine[f]	1.16	1.38	19.0	0.19	0.10	−47.3	0.16	0.05	−68.7	0.09	0.07	−22.2	0.56	0.71	26.7
Phenylalanine	0	Tr	—	0.05	0.012	−73.3	Tr	0	—	Tr	0	—	0.09	0.06	−33.3
Proline	0.77	3.50	354.5	9.84	1.83	−81.6	2.17	0.64	−70.5	2.95	2.26	−23.3	0.78	2.57	229.4
Serine	0.21	0.47	123.8	—	—	—	0.55	0.12	−78.1	0.50	0.35	−30.0	—	—	—
Taurine	1.67	2.06	23.4	—	—	—	2.56	2.32	−9.38	2.40	2.24	−6.67	—	—	—
Threonine	0.36	1.14	216.7	0.33	0	—	0.21	Tr	—	0	Tr	—	0.27	0.56	107.4
Tyrosine	0	Tr	—	0.03	0.006	−81.2	Tr	0	—	Tr	0	—	0.12	0.10	−16.6
Valine	0	0.50	—	0.33	0.046	−86.0	0.37	Tr	—	Tr	Tr	—	0.11	0.46	318.1
Total	14.54	28.16	93.7	30.9	15.5	−49.8	22.5	15.12	−73.0	17.31	13.80	−79.2	13.71	20.32	47.6

[a] Values are given in μmoles/100 mg. wet weight. Tr indicates trace; dashes indicate that values were not determined.
[b] Bricteux-Grégoire et al. (1962).
[c] Duchâteau et al. (1959).
[d] Jeuniaux et al. (1961).
[e] Duchâteau and Florkin (1961).
[f] Histidine is measured together with lysine.

TABLE VII

Amino Acid and Ammonia Content of Isolated Nerves and Incubating Media of *Eriocheir sinensis*[a]

Compounds determined	Adaptation from freshwater to seawater						Adaptation from seawater to freshwater					
	Nerves				Media		Nerves				Media	
	In freshwater (FW) saline	In seawater (SW) saline	Ratio of FW/SW saline	Ratio of FW/SW saline	Freshwater saline	Seawater saline	In seawater (SW) saline	In freshwater (FW) saline	Ratio of FW/SW saline	Ratio of FW/SW saline	Seawater saline	Freshwater saline
Taurine	1.151	1.520	0.369	0.019	0.089	0.108	1.296	0.991	−0.305	0.023	0.130	0.153
Aspartic acid	2.987	4.081	1.094	0.217	1.665	1.882	4.354	1.888	−2.466	0.012	2.046	2.058
Threonine	0.092	0.145	0.053	—	Tr	0.040	0.193	0.162	−0.031	−0.024	0.042	0.018
Serine	0.288	0.299	0.011	0.016	0.088	0.104	0.615	0.592	−0.043	−0.009	0.163	0.154
Glutamic acid	0.685	1.013	0.328	0.020	0.461	0.481	0.559	0.484	−0.260	−0.184	0.448	0.264
Proline	0.461	1.060	0.599	0.257	0.146	0.403	3.274	1.279	−1.995	2.201	3.561	1.460
Glycine	0.419	0.497	0.078	0.014	0.279	0.293	0.706	0.597	−0.109	0.010	0.202	0.212
Alanine	1.034	1.973	0.939	−0.005	0.486	0.481	2.239	1.487	−0.752	−0.068	1.116	1.048
Cystine	Tr	0.112	—	Tr	Tr	Tr	Tr	Tr	Tr	Tr	Tr	Tr
Valine	0.075	0.097	0.022	−0.029	0.049	0.020	0.107	0.096	−0.011	0.017	0.054	0.071
Methionine	0.044	0.099	0.055	Tr	Tr	Tr	0.019	Tr	—	Tr	Tr	Tr
Isoleucine	0.050	0.074	0.024	−0.015	0.080	0.065	0.093	0.056	−0.087	0.027	0.029	0.056
Leucine	0.078	0.094	0.016	−0.013	0.100	0.087	0.084	0.060	−0.024	0.029	0.038	0.067
Tyrosine	0.028	0.041	0.013	−0.018	0.041	0.023	0.056	0.040	−0.016	0.013	0.029	0.042
Phenylalanine	0.029	0.039	0.010	−0.013	0.047	0.034	0.056	0.045	−0.011	0.016	0.035	0.051
Lysine	0.085	0.095	0.010	—	—	—	0.073	0.078	0.005	—	—	—
Histidine	0.028	0.034	0.006	—	—	—	0.094	0.091	−0.003	—	—	—
Arginine	0.696	0.816	0.120	—	—	—	0.558	0.267	−0.291	—	—	—
Ammonia	2.978	0.159	−2.819	−0.679	2.228	1.549	1.841	0.404	−1.437	1.591	1.611	3.202
Proteins	22.09	21.44	−0.65	—	—	—	27.05	25.59	−1.46	—	—	—

[a] Results after Gilles and Schoffeniels (1969). Amino acids and ammonia levels are expressed in μmoles per 100 mg. wet weight of nerve incubated. Protein content is given as amino-N in μmoles of alanine per 100 mg. wet weight. Tr indicates traces; dashes indicate values not determined.

tion of about the same importance in the incubating medium. The concentration of the so-called nonessential amino acids is regulated by a mechanism involving a modification of their intracellular mechanism since the variation of the amino acid level in the nerve tissue is not followed by a concomitant variation in the medium. Moreover, the intracellular metabolic mechanism involved could result from the activity of a synthesizing process and not from a modification of the steady state between amino acids and proteins, since the content of nerve proteins does not significantly vary during adaptation. Such a conclusion is also supported by experiments on protein patterns during adaptation of *Eriocheir* (Florkin *et al.*, 1964; Schoffeniels, 1967; Florkin and Schoffeniels, 1969).

The fact that in our experiments ammonia undergoes a significant variation in nerve tissue as well as in the medium (Table VII) also agrees with this interpretation since a net synthesis of amino acids from their keto precursors would require ammonia. Concerning the control of proline concentration (Table VII), two mechanisms seem to be at play. This amino acid, although synthesized in the isolated nerve during its adaptation from a freshwater saline to a seawater medium, is nevertheless not catabolized but rather released from the nerve during the reverse adaptation.

It is probable that the mechanism described in isolated *Eriocheir* nerves is also at play in the intact animal. As a matter of fact Vincent-Marique and Gilles (1970) show that during adaptation of *Eriocheir* from seawater to freshwater, the decrease in nonessential amino acids in muscle is accompanied by a decrease in their amount in the blood, thus suggesting an intracellular degradation process. The fact that in the intact *Eriocheir* modification of the amino acid level is paralleled by concomitant modification in nitrogen excretion (Jeuniaux and Florkin, 1961; Florkin *et al.*, 1964) is in agreement with this hypothesis. As far as proline is concerned, the important decrease in muscle concentration is accompanied by an important increase in the blood (Fig. 3). This can be interpreted as the consequence of an extrusion of proline from the tissues during adaptation of *Eriocheir* from seawater to freshwater (Vincent-Marique and Gilles, 1970). Such a conclusion raises the question of the further degradation of proline. Indeed, it has been demonstrated that during adaptation of *Eriocheir* to freshwater, the modification of the ammonia level in the medium accounts for 73% to 94% of the total modification of the nitrogen excretion (Jeuniaux and Florkin, 1961). It seems therefore unlikely that proline can be excreted by *Eriocheir*. As a matter of fact, Vincent-Marique and Gilles (1970) have demonstrated the existence of "proline oxidase" activity in the

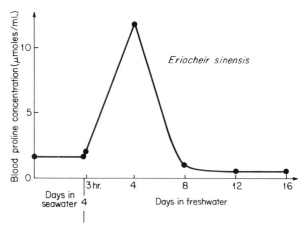

FIG. 3. Modification of the blood proline level of a single *Eriocheir sinensis* as a function of the time of adaptation from seawater to freshwater. Results taken from Vincent-Marique and Gilles (1970).

gill preparation of *Eriocheir sinensis*. It is worth noting that an appreciable enzymic activity can only be found in the gills and not in the other tissues examined (Table VIII). Moreover, one can also see that the "proline oxidase" activity is much greater in the three posterior pairs of gills than in the three anterior ones. It is only the three posterior gills which show active transport of sodium (Koch, 1954; King and Schoffeniels, 1969). Thus, the degradation of proline in these branchiae may perhaps be related to this phenomenon. It is interesting to note

TABLE VIII

PROLINE OXIDASE ACTIVITY FROM VARIOUS TISSUES
OF *Eriocheir sinensis*[a]

| | | | Gills | |
Hepatopancreas	Muscle	Nerve	Anterior	Posterior
900	—	300	500	2900
—	—	—	600	2500
100	—	300	200	2200
—	—	—	300	1900
—	—	—	800	3000
—	—	—	700	2300

[a] Activities are given as a variation of the optical density in 8 min./gm. per wet weight tissue. The modification of the optical density is due to the reduction of 2,6-dichlorophenolindophenol by proline in the presence of the enzymic preparations.

that proline can be a readily available source of energy in insects (Bursell, 1963, 1966; see also Chapter 7 of this volume). Further experiments are required to shed more light on this interesting problem.

The mechanisms leading to the modifications in the cell permeability to amino acids are far from being elucidated. The interest of research workers has been mainly centered on the ability of euryhaline invertebrates to modify their amino acid metabolism with respect to the modification of the osmotic pressure of the surroundings. We shall therefore try to investigate (1) the part taken by the different pathways leading to amino acid synthesis in the establishment of the amino acid pattern during the adaptation process, and (2) the primary cause for the modification of the activity of these different pathways during adaptation to media having different salinities.

If, in the incubating medium of isolated nerves from *Eriocheir sinensis,* an increase in osmotic pressure is achieved by addition of sucrose to the diluted medium, nerves become electrically inactive within a few hours and the intracellular amino nitrogen level considerably decreases instead of undergoing an increase, as is the case when the rise in osmotic pressure is obtained by addition of seawater (Schoffeniels, 1960b). This experiment clearly demonstrates that it is not the osmotic pressure per se which is responsible for the regulation of the amino acid level during adaptation to concentrated media.

It is also evident from the experiments performed on isolated nerves (Schoffeniels, 1960b; Gilles and Schoffeniels, 1969) that the isosmotic regulation process is not under hormonal control since the isolated tissue is able to regulate its amino acid level with respect to the osmotic pressure of the incubating medium. An argument favoring this view may also be found in the results of Duchâteau and Florkin (1962) who showed that removal of the eyestalk gland does not alter the isosmotic regulation power of *Eriocheir sinensis.*

It can therefore be suggested that it is the modification of the ionic concentration to which the cell is submitted during adaptation which controls the mechanism responsible for the modification of the amino acid level. In connection with this hypothesis, Gilles and Schoffeniels (1964, 1968b) have demonstrated that some substances, the action of which are classically explained by a modification of the intracellular ionic composition, have an effect on the synthesis of amino acids.

To explain such a type of control, two major possibilities exist. Either the ionic composition of the incubating medium acts through an intermediary substance on the amino acid metabolism or some ionic species control directly the activity of key enzymes involved in the amino acid metabolism.

In the first interpretation, one would deal with the kind of mechanism generally used to explain hormonal action, thus postulating the production of an intermediary effector such as 3',5'-AMP. So far no attempt has been made to bring experimental evidence to favor such an interpretation.

As to the second possibility, we have been looking for enzymes involved directly or indirectly in the nitrogen metabolism, the activity of which would be affected by the ionic composition of the incubating medium. Our studies were performed on the following enzyme systems.

1. Those involved directly in the amino acid metabolism such as glutamate dehydrogenase (EC 1.4.1.2), aspartate aminotransferase (EC 2.6.1.1.), alanine aminotransferase (EC 2.6.1.2.), serine hydrolyase (EC 4.2.1.13), aspartate decarboxylase (EC 4.1.1.11), or glyoxylate reductase (EC 1.1.1.26).

2. Those involved in the supply of the keto precursors required for amino acid synthesis, such as isocitrate dehydrogenase (EC 1.1.1.42), malate dehydrogenase (EC 1.1.1.37 and EC 1.1.1.40), malate hydrolyase (EC 4.2.1.2), and oxalacetate decarboxylase (EC 4.1.1.3).

3. Those involved in the fate of reducing equivalents in the intracellular medium such as lactic dehydrogenase (EC 1.1.1.27) or 3-glycerophosphate dehydrogenase (EC 1.1.1.8).

These experiments have been performed mainly in this laboratory on tissue preparations from stenohaline and euryhaline species. They have been summarized in recent monographs (Schoffeniels, 1967; Florkin and Schoffeniels, 1969) as well as in review articles (Gilles and Schoffeniels, 1966; Gilles, 1969; Schoffeniels, 1968). We shall therefore only briefly summarize the main conclusions.

Table IX reports some of the data obtained. It can be seen that at concentrations of NaCl rather close to those assumed to be found in crustacean cells, there is no difference in the effect of NaCl on the enzymic systems implicated in the metabolism of amino acids extracted from the euryhaline crayfish or from the stenohaline lobster. On the contrary, interesting differences are observed when considering the effect of NaCl on lactic dehydrogenase and 3-glycerophosphate dehydrogenase. These enzymes are generally considered to be the most important among those controlling the extramitochondrial ratio NADH/NAD (lactic dehydrogenase) as well as the transfer of reducing equivalent originating in the cytoplasm to the mitochondrial respiratory chain (3-glycerophosphate dehydrogenase) (Lehninger, 1964). It appears therefore that a biochemical difference between euryhaline and stenohaline species must be looked for in the control of the fate of the reducing equivalents.

Moreover, the results presented in Table IX show an effect of the

TABLE IX

EFFECT OF NaCl ON THE ACTIVITY OF VARIOUS ENZYMES EXTRACTED FROM MUSCLE OF *Homarus vulgaris* OR *Astacus fluviatilis*

Enzyme	Animal	NaCl concentration (mM)[a]							Reference
		0	50	100	200	300	400	600	
Glutamate dehydrogenase (EC 1.4.1.2)	Lobster	100	130	160	180	—	250	160	Gilles and Schoffeniels (1970)
	Crayfish	100	150	230	270	—	310	220	Gilles (1969)
Aspartate aminotransferase (EC 2.6.1.1)	Lobster	100	95	108	100	—	95	—	Gilles (1969)
	Crayfish	100	100	100	95	—	102	—	Gilles (1969)
Serine hydro-lyase (EC 4.2.1.13)	Lobster	100	74	36	12	—	—	—	Gilles (1969)
	Crayfish	100	63	38	3	—	—	—	
Aspartate decarboxylase (EC 4.1.1.11)	Lobster	100	—	—	99	—	104	—	Gilles and Schoffeniels (1966)
	Crayfish	100	—	—	95	—	86	—	
3-Glycerophosphate dehydrogenase (EC 1.1.1.8)	Lobster	100	—	145	117	93	50	33	Schoffeniels (1968)
	Crayfish	100	—	366	315	217	195	116	Schoffeniels (1968)
Lactic dehydrogenase (E.C 1.1.1.27) Pyruvate (5×10^{-4} M)	Crayfish	100	94	58	12	5.1	4.1	5.1	Schoffeniels (1968)
Pyruvate (10^{-2} M)	Crayfish	100	125	66	47	34	28	—	Schoffeniels (1968)
Malate dehydrogenase (E.C 1.1.1.37)	Lobster	100	100	113	105	125	125	—	Gilles (1969)
	Crayfish	100	115	112	83	78	68	—	
Malate hydro-lyase (EC 4.2.1.2)	Lobster	100	142	117	70	78	78	—	Gilles (1969)
	Crayfish	100	103	57	30	—	—	—	
Isocitrate dehydrogenase (EC 1.1.1.42)	Lobster	100	74	75	52	—	25	29	Gilles (1969)
	Crayfish	100	83	73	63	—	50	16	Gilles (1969)
Malate dehydrogenase (EC 1.1.1.40)	Lobster	100	87	69	59	—	48	31	Gilles (1969)
	Crayfish	100	80	58	51	—	43	—	
Oxalacetate decarboxylase (EC 4.1.1.3)	Lobster	100	68	95	89	—	85	80	Gilles and Schoffeniels (1966)
	Crayfish	100	98	86	72	—	65	58	
Glyoxylate reductase (EC 1.1.1.26)	Lobster	100	96	42	24	15	10	6	Schoffeniels (1968)
	Crayfish	100	—	30	15	7	6	3	

[a] Results are given as percentage of the control activity taken as 100. The activity is given:

(1) By the variation in optical density. At 340 mμ due to NADH oxidation for glutamate dehydrogenase, 3-glycerophosphate dehydrogenase, lactic dehydrogenase, malate dehydrogenase (EC 1.1.1.37), and glyoxylate reductase; at 340 mμ due to NADP reduction for malate dehydrogenase (EC 1.1.1.40); at 280 mμ due to the disappearance of oxalacetate in the case of aspartate aminotransferase; and at 240 mμ due to the decrease in fumarate concentration in the case of malate hydro-lyase.

(2) By the quantity of pyruvate appearing after a 20-min incubating period in the case of serine hydro-lyase.

(3) By the amount of CO_2 produced after a 30-min incubating period in the case of aspartate or oxalacetate decarboxylase.

See also Schoffeniels and Gilles (1963) Schoffeniels (1964, 1965) and Florkin and Schoffeniels (1969).

ionic composition on the activity of different enzymes directly involved in the synthesis and in the degradation of amino acids and particularly on glutamate dehydrogenase. It is apparent, when considering the standard oxidoreduction potentials of this system [E_0'(NADH/NAD) = −0.32 volt, E_0'(glutamate/2-oxoglutarate) = −0.108 volt], that the enzyme favors the reductive amination of 2-oxoglutarate. This fact indicates that this enzyme must play an important part in the nitrogen metabolism by controlling the entry of ammonia in the amino acid pool. The importance of glutamate dehydrogenase in controlling the synthesis of glutamate is recognized by many authors (Klingenberg and Pette, 1962; Tager and Slater, 1963; Papa *et al.*, 1969a,b; see also Chapter 7). It is of interest to note that this enzyme is activated by an increase in ionic concentration of the incubating medium. On the contrary, under the same experimental conditions, the activities of aspartate aminotransferase (Table IV) and alanine aminotransferase (Huggins and Munday, 1968) are not affected, and the activity of serine hydro-lyase is inhibited (Table IX). It can therefore be tentatively concluded that an increase in ionic concentration induces an increase in the glutamate synthesis. Under conditions of increased ionic concentration, serine hydro-lyase is inhibited thus leading to a reduced deaminating activity. In turn, the increased amount of glutamate would induce an increase in the amount of the other amino acids, the activity of the aminotransferase being unaffected (Fig. 4). This concept is in agreement with observations showing an increase in the free amino acid pool (see Table VI) and a decrease in the nitrogen excretion (Needham, 1957; Jeuniaux and Florkin, 1961; Florkin *et al.*, 1964) during adaptation of euryhaline species to concentrated media.

If the synthesis of glutamate is dependent on the availability of 2-oxoglutarate and NH_4, it is also dependent on the availability of reducing

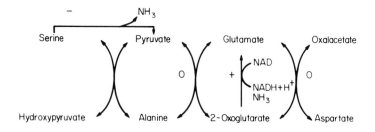

Fig. 4. Effect of NaCl on the activity of enzymes implicated in the metabolism of amino acids. +, Indicates an increase in the enzymic activity; −, indicates a decrease in the enzymic activity; ○, no effect on the enzymic activity. From Gilles (1969).

equivalents (Fig. 4). It is therefore worth noting that under conditions of ionic concentration inducing an increase in the activity of glutamate dehydrogenase, 3-glycerophosphate dehydrogenase is inhibited (Table IX). Therefore the cell metabolism is geared toward anaerobic conditions which prevent some of the reducing equivalents from entering the respiratory chain (Fig. 5). Furthermore, under the same conditions of ionic concentration lactic dehydrogenase activity is also inhibited thus making the reducing equivalents available for other purposes (e.g., glutamate synthesis). If such a scheme can be applied to crustacean amino acid metabolism, one may consider that a competition must exist between the various metabolic sequences needing reducing equivalents. As a matter of consequence, one should find some kind of interaction between the respiratory chain and the synthesis of glutamate (Fig. 5). This interpretation finds experimental support in the results obtained by Gilles and Schoffeniels (1965) on the isolated nerve chain of the crayfish. They demonstrate that addition of NH_4Cl to the incubating medium increases the intracellular pool of free amino acids (see also Gilles and Schoffeniels, 1968b) and decreases the oxygen consumption. This is at variance with the results obtained with the lobster nerve chain in which the oxygen consumption is unaffected. Such a difference between the euryhaline crayfish and the stenohaline lobster seems to indicate once more that a biochemical difference between euryhaline and stenohaline species must be looked for in the control of the fate of reducing equivalents.

Malate dehydrogenase with oxalacetate decarboxylase constitutes the main pathways of entrance of pyruvate in the Krebs cycle by carboxylation (see Chapter 6). The importance of these pathways in the supply of oxidizable material to the tricarboxylic acid cycle is demonstrated by the important rate of $^{14}CO_2$ incorporation into glutamate and aspartate which have intermediates of the cycle as keto precursors (Cheng and Mela, 1966; Gilles and Schoffeniels, 1968a).

The fact that both malate dehydrogenase and oxalacetate decar-

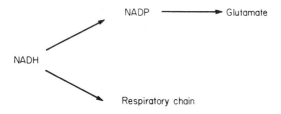

FIG. 5. Competition between glutamate synthesis and the respiratory chain. After Schoffeniels (1968).

boxylase are inhibited by an increased ionic concentration does not necessarily mean that the synthesis of malate or oxalacetate from pyruvate is inhibited. It must indeed be borne in mind that the enzyme activity is tested by measuring the formation of pyruvate from either malate or oxalacetate. If our results show an inhibitory effect of NaCl, we do not have any information as to the effect of these ions on the reverse reactions that could well be unaffected, inhibited, or even stimulated.

It is worth noting that the activity of both isocitrate dehydrogenase and malate hydro-lyase of the euryhaline crayfish is inhibited by an increased ionic concentration. It can therefore be concluded that the Krebs cycle is inhibited in the euryhaline crayfish when the ionic concentration rises in the intracellular content. This conclusion is in agreement with the inhibition of the TCA cycle observed when incubating different tissues in the presence of high NaCl concentrations or under conditions inducing a modification of the intracellular ionic content (Tustanoff and Stewart, 1965a,b; Gilles and Schoffeniels, 1968a,b; Huggins and Munday, 1968). This conclusion is also in agreement with the fact that when the euryhaline crayfish is transferred from a diluted medium to a more concentrated one, an important decrease in the oxygen consumption is recorded (Schlieper, 1929a; Schwabe, 1933; Peters, 1935).

Our results demonstrate that the biochemical events which occur when a euryhaline species such as *Astacus* or *Carcinus* is transferred from a diluted to a more concentrated medium (i.e., increase of the free amino acid pool, decrease of the nitrogen excretion and the oxygen consumption) can be explained, at least partially, by the effect the ionic concentration exerts on the activity of enzymic systems related to the amino acid metabolism. Such an explanation cannot however be generalized as such since the decrease in the oxygen consumption is not observed for all euryhaline Crustacea. As pointed out by Kinne (1964), four types of responses can be observed: (1) oxygen consumption is higher in lower salinities than in higher salinities; (2) oxygen consumption is high in both low and high salinities; (3) oxygen consumption is low in both low and high salinities; and (4) oxygen consumption is unaffected by salinity.

It must be noted here that *Astacus* and *Carcinus* belong to category (1) which includes the majority of the osmoregulating Arthropoda. However, the most efficient regulators such as *Eriocheir sinensis, Artemia salina,* or *Palaemonetes vulgaris* respire at the same rate in a wide range of salinities (McFarland and Pickens, 1965; Gilchrist, 1956; Schwabe, 1933). It is however worth noting that during osmotic adaptation of *Eriocheir,* the nitrogen excretion which, as we have seen, can be considered to be a reflection of the amino acid metabolism, shows only a transitory alteration (Florkin *et al.*, 1964). On the contrary, in a species showing an increased respiratory rate in diluted media such as *Carcinus,* it seems that a definite alteration in nitrogen excretion occurs under osmotic stress (Needham, 1957). It thus appears that the situation when dealing with osmotic regulation is far more complex than previously imagined and that for studying many aspects of this problem separate consideration of individual species will often have to be made· In the literature on Arthropoda metabolism there is little information concerning the possibility of using for glutamate synthesis the reducing equivalents implicated in the classic energy metabolism sequences. On the contrary, the important work of Slater and co-workers has brought many interesting facts concerning the utilization of the Krebs cycle in the reduction of 2-oxoglutarate and ammonia in mammals. These authors have proposed evidence demonstrating how reducing equivalents could be produced from intermediates of oxidative phosphorylation, which points to the importance, for amino acid synthesis, of energy-rich compounds that can drive the respiratory chain between succinate and NAD (Slater and Tager, 1963; Tager and Slater, 1963).

Figure 6 summarizes this interpretation. In this scheme a constant amount of energy-rich intermediate is produced. Its utilization between ATP or glutamate synthesis is well balanced so that the oxygen consumption is not affected by the pathway that is followed. In the case of

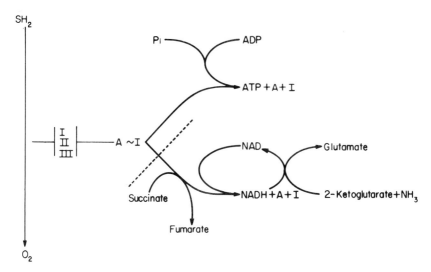

Fig. 6. Glutamate synthesis as uncoupler of oxidative phosphorylations. After Schoffeniels (1968).

a decrease in glutamate synthesis, as happens when the animal is in freshwater, more of the energy-rich intermediate could be used for ATP synthesis, that would, in turn, serve for the active transport of sodium from the dilute medium. If such correlations are correct, they would implicate direct relations between the amino acid metabolism and energy metabolism. These considerations seem to indicate that the differences between stenohaline and euryhaline species as well as those between the various categories of osmoregulators must be searched for in the way the reducing equivalents are geared toward amino acid or energy metabolism (Figs. 5 and 6).

The proposed scheme must be considered as being tentative, since more information on the intracellular localization of the enzyme involved and on the ionic composition prevailing locally is needed before a more complete picture can be produced. The relationships suggested above, if they explain satisfactorily some of the observations, are by no means considered to be exclusive of other regulatory mechanisms. For example, Schlieper (1958; see also Remane and Schlieper, 1958) has suggested that the changes in respiration rate which occur during adaptation are a consequence of changes in the hydration of the tissues which may affect the activity of some enzymic systems. A change in intracellular osmotic pressure will cause a swelling of the tissue mitochondria thus altering the activity of the mechano-enzyme complexes. Schlieper (1958) cites as an example: the close correlation between the volume of *Nereis* and its respiratory rate after transfer to diluted media. However, no direct experimental evidence has yet been given in support of this hypothesis.

Euryhalinity cannot be unequivocally defined as resulting solely from the control of enzyme systems by inorganic ions. Obviously, it results, as we have seen, from the association of a number of adaptations—some morphological, some biochemical. Euryhalinity implies the possibility of regulating adequately both the osmotic pressure of the blood and of the cells. As far as the regulation of the osmotic pressure of the blood is concerned, gills and the excretory organs are certainly of prime importance. Moreover, it appears that at least an efficient control of the amino acid and energy metabolism is necessary for the regulation of the osmotic pressure of the cell.

REFERENCES

Allen, K. (1961). *Biol. Bull.* **121**, 419.
Barnes, R. S. K. (1967). *J. Exptl. Biol.* **47**, 535.
Beadle, L. C. (1937). *J. Exptl. Biol.* **14**, 56.
Beadle, L. C., and Cragg, J. B. (1940). *Nature* **146**, 588.

Beers, J. R. (1967). *Comp. Biochem. Physiol.* 21, 11.

Bielawski, J. (1964). *Comp. Biochem. Physiol.* 13, 423.

Binyon, J. (1961). *J. Marine Biol. Assoc. U.K.* 41, 161.

Bricteux-Grégoire, S., Duchâteau-Bosson, G., Jeuniaux, C., and Florkin, M. (1962). *Arch. Intern. Physiol. Biochim.* 70, 273.

Bricteux-Grégoire, S., Duchâteau-Bosson, G., Jeuniaux, C., Schoffeniels, E., and Florkin, M. (1963). *Arch. Intern. Physiol. Biochim.* 71, 393.

Bricteux-Grégoire, S., Duchâteau-Bosson, G., Jeuniaux, C., and Florkin, M. (1964a). *Arch. Intern. Physiol. Biochim.* 72, 116.

Bricteux-Grégoire, S., Duchâteau-Bosson, G., Jeuniaux, C., and Florkin, M. (1964b). *Arch. Intern. Physiol. Biochim.* 72, 835.

Bricteux-Grégoire, S., Duchâteau-Bosson, G., Jeuniaux, C., and Florkin, M. (1964c). *Arch. Intern. Physiol. Biochim.* 72, 267.

Bricteux-Grégoire, S., Duchâteau-Bosson, G., Jeuniaux, C., and Florkin, M. (1966). *Comp. Biochem. Physiol.* 19, 729.

Bryan, G. W. (1960a). *J. Exptl. Biol.* 37, 83.

Bryan, G. W. (1960b). *J. Exptl. Biol.* 37, 100.

Bryan, G. W. (1960c). *J. Exptl. Biol.* 37, 113.

Bursell, E. (1963). *J. Insect Physiol.* 9, 439.

Bursell, E. (1966). *Comp. Biochem. Physiol.* 19, 809.

Camien, M. N., Sarlet, H., Duchâteau, G., and Florkin, M. (1951). *J. Biol. Chem.* 193, 881.

Cheng, S. C., and Mela, P. (1966). *J. Neurochem.* 13, 281.

Claus, A. (1937). *Zool. Jahrb., Abt. Allgem. Zool. Physiol. Tiere* 58, 365.

Copeland, E. (1964a). *Biol. Bull.* 127, 367.

Copeland, E. (1964b). *J. Cell. Biol.* 23, 253.

Copeland, E. (1968). *Am. Zoologist* 8, 417.

Croghan, P. C. (1958a). *J. Exptl. Biol.* 35, 219.

Croghan, P. C. (1958b). *J. Exptl. Biol.* 35, 234.

Croghan, P. C., and Lockwood, A. P. M. (1968). *J. Exptl. Biol.* 48, 141.

Croghan, P. C., Curra, R. A., and Lockwood, A. P. M. (1965). *J. Exptl. Biol.* 42, 463.

Denne, L. B. (1968). *Comp. Biochem. Physiol.* 26, 17.

Duchâteau, G., and Florkin, M. (1955). *Arch. Intern. Physiol. Biochim.* 63, 249.

Duchâteau, G., Florkin, M., and Jeuniaux, C. (1959). *Arch. Intern. Physiol. Biochim.* 67, 489.

Duchâteau-Bosson, G., and Florkin, M. (1961). *Comp. Biochem. Physiol.* 3, 245.

Duchâteau-Bosson, G., and Florkin, M. (1962). *Arch. Intern. Physiol. Biochim.* 70, 393.

Duchâteau-Bosson, G., Jeuniaux, C., and Florkin, M. (1961). *Arch. Intern. Physiol. Biochim.* 69, 30.

Florkin, M. (1956). *Colloq. Ges. Physiol. Chem.* 6, 62–99.

Florkin, M. (1960). In "The Physiology of Crustacea" (T. H. Waterman, ed.), Vol. 1, pp. 141–159. Academic Press, New York.

Florkin, M. (1962). *Bull. Acad. Roy. Med. Belg., Cl. Sci.* 48, 687.

Florkin, M., and Schoffeniels, E. (1969). "Molecular Approaches to Ecology." Academic Press, New York.

Florkin, M., Duchâteau-Bosson, G., Jeuniaux, C., and Schoffeniels, E. (1964). *Arch. Intern. Physiol. Biochim.* 72, 892.

Fredericq, L. (1901). *Bull. Acad. Roy. Med. Belg., Cl. Sci.* 428.

Gasteiger, E. L., Haake, P. C., and Gergen, J. A. (1960). *Ann. N.Y. Acad. Sci.* **90**, 622.

Gilchrist, B. M. (1956). *Hydrobiologica* **8**, 54.

Gilles, R. (1969). *Arch. Intern. Physiol. Biochim.* **77**, 441.

Gilles, R., and Schoffeniels, E. (1964). *Biochim. Biophys. Acta* **82**, 525.

Gilles, R., and Schoffeniels, E. (1965). *Arch. Intern. Physiol. Biochim.* **73**, 144.

Gilles, R., and Schoffeniels, E. (1966). *Bull. Soc. Chim. Biol.* **48**, 397.

Gilles, R., and Schoffeniels, E. (1968a). *Arch. Intern. Physiol. Biochim.* **76**, 441.

Gilles, R., and Schoffeniels, E. (1968b). *Arch. Intern. Physiol. Biochim.* **76**, 452.

Gilles, R., and Schoffeniels, E. (1969). *Comp. Biochem. Physiol.* **31**, 927.

Gilles, R., and Schoffeniels, E. (1970). Unpublished studies.

Gross, W. J. (1957). *Biol. Bull.* **112**, 43.

Habas, L. B., and Prosser, C. L. (1963). *Biol. Bull.* **125**, 379.

Huggins, A. K., and Munday, K. A. (1968). *Advan. Comp. Biochem. Physiol.* **3**, 271–378.

Jeuniaux, C., and Florkin, M. (1961). *Arch. Intern. Physiol. Biochim.* **69**, 385.

Jeuniaux, C., Bricteux-Grégoire, S., and Florkin, M. (1961a). *Cahiers Biol. Marine* **2**, 373.

Jeuniaux, C., Duchâteau-Bosson, G., and Florkin, M. (1961b). *J. Biochem.* (*Tokyo*) **49**, 527.

Jeuniaux, C., Bricteux-Grégoire, S., and Florkin, M. (1962). *Cahiers Biol. Marine* **3**, 107.

Jones, L. L. (1941). *J. Cellular Comp. Physiol.* **18**, 79.

King, E., and Schoffeniels, E. (1969). *Arch. Intern. Physiol. Biochim.* **77**, 105.

Kinne, O. (1964). *Oceanograph. Marine Biol. Ann. Rev.* **2**, 281.

Klingenberg, M., and Pette, D. (1962). *Biochem. Biophys. Res. Commun.* **7**, 430.

Koch, H. J. (1938). *J. Exptl. Biol.* **15**, 152.

Koch, H. J. (1954). *In* "Recent Developments in Cell Physiology," Proc. Symp. Colston Res. Soc., Vol. 7, p. 5. Butterworth, London and New York.

Koefoed-Johnsen, V., Levi, H., and Ussing, H. H. (1952). *Acta Physiol. Scand.* **25**, 150.

Krogh, A. (1938). *Z. Vergleich. Physiol.* **25**, 335.

Krogh, A. (1939). "Osmotic Regulation in Aquatic Animals." Cambridge Univ. Press, London and New York.

Lange, R. (1963). *Comp. Biochem. Physiol.* **10**, 173.

Lange, R. (1964). *Comp. Biochem. Physiol.* **13**, 205.

Lehninger, A. (1964). "The Mitochondrion." Benjamin, New York.

Lockwood, A. P. M. (1959). *J. Exptl. Biol.* **36**, 546.

Lockwood, A. P. M. (1961). *J. Exptl. Biol.* **38**, 647.

Lockwood, A. P. M. (1962). *Biol. Rev.* **37**, 257.

Lockwood, A. P. M., and Croghan, P. C. (1959). *Nature* **184**, 370.

Lynch, M. P., and Wood, L. (1966). *Comp. Biochem. Physiol.* **19**, 783.

McFarland, W. N., and Pickens, P. E. (1965). *Can. J. Zool.* **43**, 571.

Maluf, N. S. R. (1941). *J. Gen. Physiol.* **24**, 151.

Mantel, L. H. (1967). *Comp. Biochem. Physiol.* **20**, 743.

Martini, E. (1923). *Verhandl. Intern. Ver. Limnol.* **1**, 235.

Nagel, H. (1934). *Z. Vergleich. Physiol.* **21**, 468.

Needham, A. E. (1957.). *Physiol. Comparata Oecol.* **4**, 209.

Panikkar, N. K. (1941). *J. Marine Biol. Assoc. U.K.* **25**, 317.

Papa, S., Tager, J. M., Francavilla, A., and Quagliariello, E. (1969a). *Biochim. Biophys. Acta* **172**, 20.
Papa, S., Tager, J. M., Guerrieri, F., and Quagliariello, E. (1969b). *Biochim. Biophys. Acta* **172**, 184.
Peters, H. (1935). *Z. Morphol. Oekol. Tiere* **30**, 355.
Peterson, M. B., and Duerr, F. G. (1969). *Comp. Biochem. Physiol.* **28**, 633.
Potts, W. T. W. (1958). *J. Exptl. Biol.* **35**, 749.
Potts, W. T. W., and Parry, G. (1964). "Osmotic and Ionic Regulation in Animals." Pergamon Press, Oxford.
Ramsay, J. A. (1950). *J. Exptl. Biol.* **27**, 145.
Ramsay, J. A. (1953). *J. Exptl. Biol.* **30**, 79.
Remane, A., and Schlieper, C. (1958). *In* "Die Binnengewässer" A. Thienemann, 1 ed., Vol. XXII, p. 348. Schweizerbartsche Verlags Buchhandlung, Stuttgart.
Robertson, J. D. (1949–1950). *J. Exptl. Biol.* **26**, 182.
Robertson, J. D. (1953). *J. Exptl. Biol.* **30**, 277.
Robertson, J. D. (1961). *J. Exptl. Biol.* **38**, 707.
Rudy, P. P. (1967). *Comp. Biochem. Physiol.* **22**, 581.
Schaller, F. (1949). *Z. Vergleich. Physiol.* **31**, 684.
Schlieper, C. (1929a). *X. Vergleich. Physiol.* **9**, 478.
Schlieper, C. (1929b). *Verhandl. Deut. Zool. Ges.* **33**, 214.
Schlieper, C. (1958). *Vie et Milieu* **9**, 139.
Schoffeniels, E. (1950). *Arch. Intern. Physiol.* **58**, 1.
Schoffeniels, E. (1960a). *Arch. Intern. Physiol. Biochim.* **68**, 507.
Schoffeniels, E. (1960b). *Arch. Intern. Physiol. Biochim.* **68**, 696.
Schoffeniels, E. (1964). *Life. Sci.* **3**, 845.
Schoffeniels, E. (1965). *Arch. Intern. Physiol. Biochim.* **73**, 73.
Schoffeniels, E. (1967). "Cellular Aspects of Membrane Permeability." Pergamon Press, Oxford.
Schoffeniels, E. (1968). *Arch. Intern. Physiol. Biochim.* **76**, 319.
Schoffeniels, E., and Gilles, R. (1963). *Life Sci.* **2**, 834.
Scholles, W. (1933). *Z. Vergleich. Physiol.* **19**, 522.
Schwabe, E. (1933). *Z. Vergleich. Physiol.* **19**, 183.
Shaw, J. (1955a). *J. Exptl. Biol.* **32**, 353.
Shaw, J. (1955b). *J. Exptl. Biol.* **32**, 330.
Shaw, J. (1955c). *J. Exptl. Biol.* **32**, 383.
Shaw, J. (1958a). *J. Exptl. Biol.* **35**, 920.
Shaw, J. (1958b). *J. Exptl. Biol.* **35**, 902.
Shaw, J. (1959a). *J. Exptl. Biol.* **36**, 157.
Shaw, J. (1959b). *J. Exptl. Biol.* **36**, 126.
Shaw, J. (1959c). *J. Exptl. Biol.* **36**, 145.
Shaw, J. (1960). *J. Exptl. Biol.* **37**, 557.
Shaw, J. (1961a). *J. Exptl. Biol.* **38**, 135.
Shaw, J. (1961b). *J. Exptl. Biol.* **38**, 153.
Shaw, J., and Sutcliffe, D. W. (1961). *J. Exptl. Biol.* **38**, 1.
Slater, E. C., and Tager, J. M. (1963). *Biochim. Biophys. Acta* **77**, 276.
Sohal, R. S., and Copeland, E. (1966). *J. Insect Physiol.* **12**, 429.
Stephens, G. C., and Virkar, R. A. (1966). *Biol. Bull.* **131**, 172.
Stobbart, R. H. (1959). *J. Exptl. Biol.* **36**, 641.
Stobbart, R. H. (1960). *J. Exptl. Biol.* **37**, 594.
Stobbart, R. H. (1965). *J. Exptl. Biol.* **42**, 29.

Stobbart, R. H. (1967). *J. Exptl. Biol.* **47**, 35.
Sutcliffe, D. W. (1960). *Nature* **187**, 331.
Sutcliffe, D. W. (1961a). *J. Exptl. Biol.* **38**, 501.
Sutcliffe, D. W. (1961b). *J. Exptl. Biol.* **38**, 521.
Sutcliffe, D. W. (1962). *J. Exptl. Biol.* **39**, 325.
Sutcliffe, D. W. (1963). *Comp. Biochem. Physiol.* **9**, 121.
Sutcliffe, D. W. (1967a). *J. Exptl. Biol.* **46**, 529.
Sutcliffe, D. W. (1967b). *J. Exptl. Biol.* **46**, 499.
Sutcliffe, D. W. (1968). *J. Exptl. Biol.* **48**, 359.
Sutcliffe, D. W., and Shaw, J. (1967). *J. Exptl. Biol.* **46**, 519.
Sutcliffe, D. W., and Shaw, J. (1968). *J. Exptl. Biol.* **48**, 399.
Tager, J. M., and Slater, E. C. (1963). *Biochim. Biophys. Acta* **77**, 227.
Thuet, P., Motais, R., and Maetz, J. (1968). *Comp. Biochem. Physiol.* **26**, 793.
Treherne, J. E. (1954a). *Trans. Roy. Entomol. Soc. London* **105**, 117.
Treherne, J. E. (1954b). *J. Exptl. Biol.* **31**, 386.
Tustanoff, E. R., and Stewart, H. B. (1965a). *Can. J. Biochem.* **43**, 341.
Tustanoff, E. R., and Stewart, H. B. (1965b). *Can. J. Biochem.* **43**, 359.
Ussing, H. H. (1949). *Acta Physiol. Scand.* **17**, 1.
Ussing, H. H. (1954). *Symp. Soc. Exptl. Biol.* **8**, 407.
Ussing, H. H., and Zerahn, K. (1951). *Acta Physiol. Scand.* **23**, 110.
Vincent-Marique, H. C., and Gilles, R. (1970). *Life Sciences,* **9**, Part I, 509.
Virkar, R. A. (1966). *Comp. Biochem. Physiol.* **18**, 617.
Virkar, R. A., and Webb, K. L. (1967). *Am. Zoologist* **7**, 735.
Wigglesworth, V. B. (1933). *J. Exptl. Biol.* **10**, 1.
Wigglesworth, V. B. (1938). *J. Exptl. Biol.* **15**, 235.

CHAPTER 10

Osmoregulation in Terrestrial Arthropods[1]

Michael J. Berridge

I. Introduction

Osmotic homeostasis is achieved by striking a delicate balance between uptake and loss of solutes and water. Terrestrial arthropods are particularly susceptible to desiccation because they have a large surface to volume ratio; therefore, their osmoregulatory mechanisms are mainly concerned with minimizing water losses through transpiration and excretion. Despite the efficiency of these mechanisms, some water is always lost and must be replaced by uptake through the gut or general body surface or both.

Terrestrial arthropods display varying degrees of terrestrialness; on an ecological basis they may be divided into two main groups. The first comprises the crustaceans and myriapods which are very susceptible to water loss through the integument and are essentially cryptozoic. The second group consists of the arachnids and insects which can exploit a wider range of terrestrial habitats because they possess surface layers of lipid, which severely restrict transpiration. An important difference between the two groups is the nature of their nitrogenous end products.

[1] This work was supported by NIH grant AM-09975-03.

Crustacea and myriapods excrete nitrogen mainly as ammonia (Dresel and Moyle, 1950; Bennett and Manton, 1962; Hartenstein, 1968; Horne, 1968), whereas arachnids and insects excrete the insoluble purines guanine and uric acid, respectively (Anderson, 1966; Bursell, 1967). Excretion of waste nitrogen in an insoluble form greatly reduces water loss via the excretory system. The degree of terrestrialness achieved by any given species depends on its ability to conserve water and thus remain in osmotic equilibrium.

II. Osmoregulatory Capacity of Terrestrial Arthropods

To assess osmoregulatory ability it is necessary to measure the variation of blood osmotic pressure of animals subjected to the range of conditions found in their natural environment. Unfortunately little is known about the characteristics of the microclimates occupied by terrestrial arthropods, and an objective appraisal of osmoregulatory capacity is very difficult.

An indirect assessment of osmoregulatory capacity can be obtained from the range of blood osmotic pressures recorded in a natural population. In nature the brachyuran crabs, *Gecarcinus lateralis* and *Cardiosoma carnifex,* and the anomuran crabs, *Birgus latro, Coenobita brevimanus,* and *Coenobita cavipes,* achieve some degree of osmotic homeostasis (Gross, 1963, 1964; Gross *et al.,* 1966). Osmoregulation is achieved by behavioral (Section III,A) rather than by physiological mechanisms because blood osmotic pressure increases rapidly in the absence of water. The terrestrial hermit crab *Coenobita perlatus* is not confined to habitats where evaporation is reduced. However, its freedom of movement is at the expense of greater water loss, and uniform blood concentrations are not maintained (Gross, 1964). Terrestrial isopods likewise show a wide range of blood osmotic pressure which may reflect limited osmoregulatory capacity (Parry, 1953). *Oniscus* and *Porcellio,* which are less terrestrial, have much wider ranges than *Armadillidium.* Comparable information on arachnids and insects is not available. Determinations made on laboratory populations of insects indicate that osmotic pressure may show very little variation (Berridge, 1965a; Djajakusumah and Miles, 1966; Edney, 1968a). Such attempts to assess the osmoregulatory capacity of arthropods are complicated because osmotic pressure can vary according to sex and age. For example, the blood osmotic pressure of *Galleria mellonella* varies appreciably during the larval to adult transformation (Laviolette and Mestres, 1967).

Another method of determining osmoregulatory capacity of a terrestrial animal is to observe the effect of osmotic stress such as dehydration

(Fig. 1). *Oniscus* displays no osmoregulatory capacity because blood osmotic pressure rises in proportion to the amount of water lost from the animal (Bursell, 1955). Insects can regulate their osmotic pressure despite large decreases in wet weight (Fig. 1). For example, *Arenivaga* can lose 26.3% of their wet weight while blood osmotic pressure increases by 4.4% only; in the absence of regulation the osmotic pressure would have increased by 42.5% (Fig. 1).

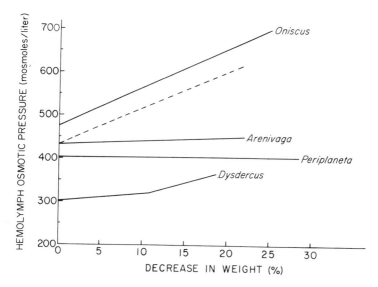

FIG. 1. The effect of a decrease in wet weight on the hemolymph osmotic pressure of an isopod *Oniscus* (Berridge, 1968a), the cockroaches *Arenivaga* (Edney, 1966) and *Periplaneta* (Wall, 1968), and the cotton stainer *Dysdercus* (Berridge, 1965a). The broken line represents the calculated increase of osmotic pressure in *Arenivaga* in the absence of regulation (Edney, 1966).

Osmoregulation in insects can occur despite a large reduction in blood volume, indicating that osmotically active substances are removed from the hemolymph (Djajakusumah and Miles, 1966; Edney, 1966). The fate of these molecules is unknown; although some solute may be excreted, a large proportion is probably dispersed within the tissues. Wall (1968) has suggested that ions may be stored in the lumen of the midgut and rectum. Further evidence for storage of ions comes from studies where hydrated animals are subsequently allowed to take up water in the absence of dietary solutes. Hemolymph osmotic pressure remains constant when dehydrated insects restore their original blood volume either by drinking or by uptake of water from the atmosphere (Djajakusumah and Miles, 1966; Edney, 1966). The osmotically active substances removed during dehydration are presumably returned to the hemolymph. Amino acids are partially responsible for keeping the osmotic pressure constant during rehydration of the locust (Djajakusumah and Miles, 1966). Amino acids are also involved in osmoregulation during the normal molt cycle of *Dysdercus fasciatus* (Berridge, 1965b). Little is known about the role of other solutes during dehydration and rehydration in arthropods. Consequently, further discussion will be restricted to water metabolism.

An important adaptation of arthropods to terrestrial life is a remarkable tolerance of wide variations of blood osmotic pressure. Despite changes in blood composition induced by adverse conditions, arthropods remain mobile and can thus respond to the behavioral mechanisms designed to direct them to more favorable conditions. Indeed, the behavioral responses of many arthropods to humidity may be regulated by their blood osmotic pressure (see Section III).

III. Mechanisms for Reducing Water Loss

A. Behavioral Mechanisms

Complex behavioral mechanisms have enabled crustaceans and myriapods to survive on land by restricting them to cool humid microenvironments. The efficiency of these mechanisms can be judged from the fact that woodlice and centipedes, which are very prone to desiccation, live in deserts (Cloudsley-Thompson, 1956a).

The burrowing habit of crabs reduces transpiration and also brings the animals into contact with damp sand from which they can absorb water (Section V,A). *Gecarcinus* and hermit crabs also osmoregulate by selecting fluid of the correct salinity. This selection mechanism is particularly important for hermit crabs because the fluid they place in their adopted shells equilibrates with the blood very rapidly (Gross, 1964).

Much more attention has been paid to the behavioral mechanisms which restrict isopods and myriapods to moist environments (Perttunen, 1953; Edney, 1954, 1968b; Warburg, 1968). Cryptozoic arthropods aggregate in damp dark places by means of hygrokinetic and phototactic mechanisms. The intensity of the response of isopods to humidity and light is inversely related to their recognized degree of terrestrialness: *Philoscia* > *Oniscus* > *Porcellio* > *Armadillidium* (Waloff, 1941; Cloudsley-Thompson, 1956b). The situation in certain millipedes is complicated because a weak hygrokinetic mechanism operates against a positive phototactic mechanism. If the humidity is high enough the latter mechanism predominates and *Oxydesmus* and *Habrodesmus* are often found in the open during the day. Dry conditions are avoided by their "overriding" hygrokinetic mechanism (Toye, 1966b).

The orientation mechanisms of arthropods display considerable plasticity, allowing them to broaden their range of habitat. A waxing and waning of orientation mechanisms forms the basis of rhythmic activity in cryptozoic animals. The mechanisms which cause aggregation under logs and stones during the day are altered to allow dispersion at night when the humidity is higher. The diurnal rhythm of woodlice and millipedes is primarily a response to light and darkness (Cloudsley-Thompson, 1951, 1952) although fluctuating temperatures may be a cue for some animals. Some millepedes and centipedes have an endogenous rhythm which may persist for days in complete darkness at constant temperature and humidity (Cloudsley-Thompson, 1951, 1956a). Orientation mechanisms may also be affected by blood osmolality. For example, the negative phototaxis of most woodlice may be reversed if the animals are dehydrated (Waloff, 1941; Cloudsley-Thompson, 1952).

While insects have efficient osmoregulatory systems, they still have humidity preferences. For example, *Agriotes* (Lees, 1943) which lives in damp soil and *Cosmopolitus* which lives in banana roots (Roth and Willis, 1963) show strong preferences for high humidities (wet reaction). Other insects prefer intermediate humidities and in some cases, such as *Schistocerca*, the preferred humidity can be correlated with the optimal humidity for development (Bursell, 1964). Many insects display very strong dry reactions, and it has been suggested that avoiding wet conditions will reduce the risk of infection with pathogens and the chance of overhydration. To guard against dehydration, such insects usually show a reversal of the dry reaction to a strong wet reaction when desiccated (Perttunen, 1953; Pulliainen and Nederström, 1965). Migration into humid regions reduces transpiration and may enable certain species to absorb water from moist air (Section V,A) and others to find free water to drink (Section V,B). A correlation exists between the rate at which species lose water and the speed with which reversal occurs (Bursell, 1964). Reversal of the humidity reaction depends on a change in the water content of the animal because a dry reaction is rapidly reinstated if desiccated insects are allowed to drink water (Bentley, 1943; Willis and Roth, 1950). This ability of arthropods to alter their behavioral responses according to their water content constitutes an important regulatory mechanism. More detailed discussion on behavioral responses and their ecological significance is provided by Barton Browne (1964a), Bursell (1964), Bliss (1968), and Edney (1968b).

The speed with which arthropods respond to humidity gradients indicates a sophisticated sensory apparatus capable of detecting small variations in atmospheric humidity. Hygroreceptors have been located in woodlice (Jans and Ross, 1963), spiders (Blumenthal, 1935), and insects (Barton Browne, 1964a; Amos, 1967). The mode of action of the receptors is open to speculation; they may function as hygrometers, evaporimeters, or chemoreceptors. Hygroreceptors are important not only in behavioral responses to humidity but also in the mechanisms which regulate water loss by respiration (Section III,B).

B. Control of Water Loss by Transpiration

The two main avenues of transpirational water loss are through the body surface and respiratory surfaces. Such losses are reduced by the presence of an impermeable cuticle and by withdrawing the moist respiratory surfaces into the body. These mechanisms for reducing water loss through transpiration can be carefully regulated.

1. Transpiration through the Integument

The exoskeleton of arthropods is composed of a chitin–protein complex laid down by a single layer of epidermal cells (Fig. 2a). In crustaceans and myriapods the cuticle is relatively permeable to water, resulting in high rates of water loss (Edney, 1968b). In arachnids and insects the cuticular surface is waterproofed by a thin layer of orientated lipid attached to the epicuticle. The nature of this lipid layer has been described in a number of papers (Lees, 1947; Beament, 1964, 1965, 1968) and will not be considered further. Of importance with regard to osmoregulation are the ways in which transpiration is regulated.

When arthropods are exposed to low humidities, rate of transpiration decreases with time. Further, rate of water loss shows a curvilinear relationship to saturation deficiency, indicating that water loss under dry conditions is relatively less than that under moist conditions (Bursell, 1955; Loveridge, 1968a). To discuss these control mechanisms it is useful to describe the permeability barriers involved and the various compartments through which water must move during its passage from the animal into the surrounding air. The compartments are the blood (the major water reservoir in most terrestrial arthropods), the epidermal cell, the cuticle, and the surrounding air (Fig. 2a). The nature of water movement from one compartment to the other will depend on the gradient of water activity between compartments and on the permeability of the barriers between the compartments. Thus there are several possible schemes for regulation of integumental permeability, depending on the location of the major permeability barrier. In Fig. 2b the barrier is

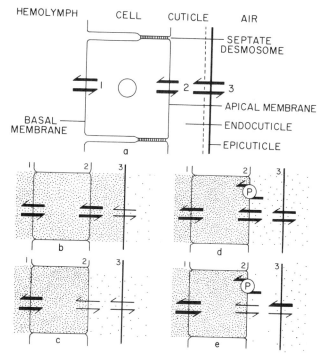

FIG. 2. Schematic representation of the mechanisms responsible for regulating water loss from the integument of arthropods. a, The major permeability barriers restricting water movement from hemolymph to air are the basal membrane (1), apical membrane (2), and cuticle (3). b–e Represent how the activity of water in the cuticular compartment can be altered by varying the permeability of barriers (2) and (3), or by imposition of a water pump (P). Water will move from a region of high water activity (heavy stippling) to regions with lower activity (light stippling). See text for further details.

within the cuticle. Removal of water from the cuticle of *Oniscus* may result in shrinkage and a closer packing of the glycoprotein and lipoidal components resulting in an overall decrease in permeability (Bursell, 1955). A similar change may occur in insect and arachnid cuticle, perhaps involving changes in the lipid monolayer brought on by conformational changes within the underlying epicuticle. If the epidermal cell membranes are permeable to water, the cuticular compartment will be in equilibrium with the cell and blood (Fig. 2b).

A second possibility, shown in Fig. 2c, is that the apical plasma membrane (barrier 2) may also be an important permeability barrier to water. If the water permeability of barrier 2 is less than that of barrier 3, the cuticular compartment will approach equilibrium with the surrounding air rather than with the cell and blood. The initial rapid rate of water loss observed in woodlice and locusts (Bursell, 1955; Loveridge, 1968a) could represent water leaving the cuticular compartment, whereas subsequent water loss would depend on the rate at which water passes through the apical membrane. Regulation in this system could be accomplished by adjustment of the permeability of the apical membrane. However, a permeability change is not an essential feature of the model, since the apical membrane could act as a secondary barrier of fixed permeability that only becomes the primary barrier when the outer compartment is depleted of water. If there is cellular control of a permeability barrier it is easier to envisage the apical plasma membrane as the site of control rather than cuticular barriers that are a distance from the cell.

Another possible mechanism of regulating water loss from the integument involves inward secretion of water by the epidermal cells (Lees, 1946a; Davies and Edney, 1952; Winston and Nelson, 1965). Presumably the pump is located on the apical membrane and functions by transporting water from the cuticle into the cell, and reduces water loss by decreasing the gradient between cuticle and air (Fig. 2d). Winston (1967) considers that the lower water activity recorded in the cuticle of *Periplaneta* and *Locusta* relative to blood is evidence for a "cuticular water pump." However, consideration of Fig. 2c clearly indicates that a low water activity in the cuticle is not *prima facie* evidence for a water pump. The mechanism in Fig. 2c could also provide an alternative explanation for water absorption from drops of salt solutions placed on the surface of cockroaches (Beament, 1964). If the cuticular compartment is in equilibrium with air at a relative humidity of less than 80% (equivalent to a saturated sodium chloride solution), it is conceivable that water could leave drops of salt solution by simply evaporating into this compartment and thus may not be evidence of active water transport as Beament (1964) has suggested. Moreover, if a water pump exists in the integument of *Periplaneta*, *Locusta*, and the mite *Bryobia praetiose*, it is difficult to understand why these species cannot take up water from air (Winston and Nelson, 1965; Edney, 1966; Loveridge, 1968a). If the pump is capable of lowering the water activity in the cuticular compartment below that of the surrounding air, water will move into the cuticle resulting in water uptake from air (Fig. 2e). Such water uptake mechanisms have been demonstrated in some insects and arachnids and will be described in greater detail in Section V,A.

Previous studies on transpiration from arthropods have stressed the importance of the cuticle as the major permeability barrier to water. However, on the basis of the theoretical considerations outlined above we can assume that the apical plasma membrane of the underlying epidermal cells may play an equally important role in restricting water loss to the environment. The models outlined in Fig. 2 should provide a useful framework for future studies on water movement across the integument of arthropods.

2. Transpiration through the Respiratory System

In terrestrial arthropods water loss through respiration has been reduced to varying degrees by involution of the moist respiratory surfaces and by protecting the external openings with special closing devices such as the spiracles found in myriapods, arachnids, and insects.

Much of the transpiration from terrestrial isopods occurs through the moist abdominal pleopods. The principal structural adaptation of the respiratory organs to aerial respiration is the development of pseudotracheae in the pleopods. Pseudotracheae are saclike invaginations through which most of the respiratory exchange takes place. The openings of pseudotracheae lack the controlling sphincters which are present in other arthropods (Cloudsley-Thompson, 1956a). Respiratory water loss in certain terrestrial crabs is reduced because the gills are enclosed within a branchial chamber with few external openings (Bliss, 1968). An overall reduction in the surface area of the gills also helps to reduce water loss.

Myriapods have a well-developed tracheal system with spiracles which may regulate rate of water loss during desiccation (Lewis, 1963). The habit of rolling into a ball and thus covering the spiracles may reduce water loss in certain millipedes (Toye, 1966a).

Complex tracheal systems with openings guarded by spiracles exist in various arachnid orders (Solifuga, Pseudoscorpionidae, Phalangidae, Acarina, and Araneidae). Water loss from the tracheal system of Acarina is regulated by spiracles (Lees, 1946a; Winston and Nelson, 1965). The function of tracheae in Araneidae is augmented by lung books. Terrestrial scorpions respire solely by means of lung books which consist of parallel leaflets sunk into pits with a confined opening guarded with a spiracle. In spiders, this spiracle has a closing mechanism which regulates water loss from the lung books (Davies and Edney, 1952). Lung books can be ventilated, but there is no information on whether or not water loss from these organs can be regulated by varying pumping rate.

Much more information is available on the respiratory system of insects (Schneiderman, 1960; Miller, 1964a,b; Loveridge, 1968b). The tracheal system is made up of a complex network of interconnected tubes whose openings are protected by spiracles. Gases move through the tracheae by diffusion or by ventilation brought on by abdominal or thoracic pumping movements. Since the air in tracheae is saturated with water (Beament, 1964), ventilation will greatly accelerate loss of water. Loveridge (1968b) has demonstrated that a close correlation exists between rate of ventilation and rate of water loss. Regulation of tracheal water loss involves control over both spiracular opening and rate of ventilation. Proportionately less water is lost through the spiracles at low humidities than in conditions where water loss is less critical (Bursell, 1964; Loveridge, 1968b). Water loss is also much less from partially desiccated insects than from normal insects.

The opening and closing of spiracles is achieved by a spiracular muscle which is controlled by motor neurons from abdominal or thoracic ganglia. Desiccation of adult dragonflies results in an increased frequency of motor impulses to the spiracular muscle whereas hydration has the opposite effect (Miller, 1964a). Similar changes in motor frequency can be induced by perfusing the insect with different strength salt solutions indicating that it is the hemolymph solute concentration that regulates spiracular opening and closing.

Regulation of water loss in locusts is achieved by controlling abdominal respiratory movements (Loveridge, 1968b). Locusts respond to dry air almost immediately by reducing rate of ventilation indicating that control may be exercised through sensory input from hygroreceptors. These may be located on the antennae (Loveridge, 1968b). Information from the receptors may alter the setting of the "respiratory centers" which are thought to drive and coordinate pumping movements (Miller, 1964b).

C. Water Conservation by the Excretory System

1. Excretory Mechanisms

During adaptation of arthropods to terrestrial life, Malpighian tubules have replaced the primitive segmental excretory organs. The antennal or maxillary glands of crustaceans and the coxal glands of arachnids are examples of segmental organs which have retained an excretory function.

The antennal glands of terrestrial crabs play little or no direct role in osmoregulation because the urine they secrete remains isosmotic with the blood even when the osmotic pressure of the latter is elevated (Gross, 1963; Gross *et al.*, 1966). They may play an indirect role in osmoregulation, however, by conserving water through a reduction in rate of fluid secretion (Gross, 1964; Gifford, 1968). Water loss from these glands is further reduced since the urine drains into the branchial cavity (Gifford, 1968) where water may be recovered by an uptake mechanism located on the gills (Copeland, 1968).

There is little information on the role of antennal glands in the osmoregulation of terrestrial isopods. Dye injection experiments suggest that they may have no excretory function. When phenol red is injected into *Oniscus,* the dye is rapidly cleared from the blood by the hepatopancreas (Berridge, 1968a). The gut may thus play a major role in excretion and, possibly, also in osmoregulation as already noted in some other Crustacea (Mantel, 1968). Isopods have well-developed rectal glands (M. Gupta, 1961) which may be involved in extracting water from the rectal contents since the feces can be drier than the food initially consumed (Kuenen, 1959).

Myriapods have Malpighian tubules resembling those of insects (Füller, 1966). The role of the excretory system in water conservation is unknown. There is no evidence that the segmental organs in centipede heads are excretory (Bennett and Manton, 1962).

Most terrestrial arachnids possess both coxal glands and Malpighian tubules. The homology between coxal glands and the antennal glands of Crustacea is reflected in an overall structural similarity. The distal saccule of the coxal gland is designed for filtration since the basement membrane is the only barrier separating blood and urine (Rasmont, 1960). The urinary side of the basement membrane is covered with fine cytoplasmic extensions resembling the podocytes found in the vertebrate glomerulus and coelomosac of crustacean antennal glands (Schmidt-Nielsen et al., 1968; Tyson, 1968). The tubular region of the gland has two discrete segments. Cells in the first region have an elaborate brush border and resemble kidney proximal tubule cells; the brush border of the cells in the second region is much reduced (Rasmont, 1960). The osmoregulatory role of coxal glands in argasid ticks is described later (Section IV,A). The significance of coxal glands and Malpighian tubules in the osmoregulation of other arachnid orders is largely unknown. Since arachnids have successfully invaded the terrestrial environment, it would be of interest to know if they can produce a hypertonic urine.

Excretion in insects is achieved by a urinointestinal system. Malpighian tubules which lie free in the body cavity are attached to the gut at the junction of the midgut and hindgut. Since insect blood is not under pressure, urine formation by Malpighian tubules must be achieved by a process of cell secretion rather than by ultrafiltration. The Malpighian tubules of most insects play no role in osmoregulation because the urine they secrete is isosmotic to the hemolymph (Ramsay, 1954; Berridge, 1966, 1968). Osmoregulation occurs in the rectum which modifies the primary tubular fluid and digestive residues by a selective absorption of useful substances. Of special importance is the ability of the rectum to reduce water loss via the urine and feces by absorbing water against very large osmotic gradients (Berridge and Gupta, 1967).

Phillips (1965) has established that the rectum of insects can actively absorb sodium, potassium, chloride, and water against very large concentration gradients. Detailed discussion on the role of the rectum in ionic regulation is presented elsewhere (Shaw and Stobbart, 1963; Chapter 7 in Volume VI). Under normal conditions, much of the water absorbed by the rectum is linked to the uptake of solute. On the other hand, water uptake by the rectum can occur against an osmotic gradient and in the complete absence of a net uptake of solute. Since the rectal cuticle is very permeable to ions and water (Phillips and Dockrill, 1968), the activity gradient responsible for moving water cannot be developed within the cuticular compartment and must therefore occur within the epithelium.

Ultrastructural studies on the rectum of the blowfly suggested that the osmotic gradient responsible for water uptake from the lumen was developed within the intercellular spaces of the rectal gland (B. L. Gupta and Berridge, 1966; Berridge and Gupta, 1967). Rectal glands are a characteristic feature of insect rectum and may take the form of papillae as in Diptera (B. L. Gupta and Berridge, 1966; Hopkins, 1966) or pads as in Orthoptera (Sekhon, 1962; Oschman and Wall, 1969) and Hemiptera (Swartzendruber, 1962; Bahadur, 1963; Goodchild, 1966). The epithelia of these glands are characterized by extensive intercellular spaces opening to the blood only at a few points. The lateral plasma membranes lining the intercellular spaces have complex infoldings associated with mitochondria (Hopkins, 1966; Wessing, 1966; Berridge and Gupta, 1967, 1968; Oschman and Wall, 1969). The basal surface of the rectal gland is usually separated from the blood by a sheath to form a distinct sinus. The general arrangement is represented diagrammatically in Fig. 3. Solute transport into the intercellular space (IS) creates the osmotic gradient for a passive influx of water first from the cell and then from the lumen. A build up of hydrostatic pressure forces fluid out of the intercellular spaces into the sinus (S) and finally into the blood through openings in the surface sheath.

The amount of water which can be absorbed from the lumen is limited by the availability of solutes to create a high osmotic pressure in the intercellular space. Water movement against an osmotic gradient and in the absence of solutes in the lumen can be explained if the pumps on the lateral membrane can obtain solutes from alternative sources (Berridge and Gupta, 1967). Oschman and Wall (1969) have further

developed this idea in terms of solute recycling within the rectal glands
or recruitment of solute from the hemolymph (Fig. 3). As fluid leaves
the intercellular spaces, solutes, but not water, could be returned to
the cell and re-used to carry water from the cell and lumen into the
intercellular space. Re-entry of solute could occur either across the lateral
membrane (a), or across the basal membrane (b). In *Blaberus*, re-entry
of solute across the basal surface might be mediated by special cells
lying within indentations of the rectal pad cells (Oschman, 1968).
Solute recruitment from the blood could occur across the cell surfaces

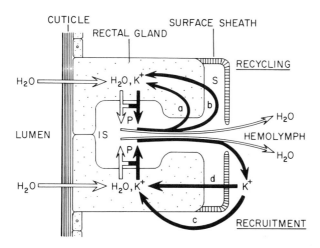

FIG. 3. Diagram illustrating the possible role of solute recycling (a and b) and
recruitment (c and d) in water uptake from the lumen of insect rectal glands.
Solutes (mainly potassium) and water are pumped (P) into the intercellular space
(IS) and move towards the hemolymph via the sinus (S) and openings in the
surface sheath. For further explanation, see text.

exposed to the blood (c), or across the surface sheath (d). In certain
insects a layer of secondary cells lying in the surface sheath may facilitate solute recruitment from the blood. Secondary cells have been described in *Schistocerca* (Irvine, 1966) and in various Hymenoptera
(Bahadur and Reddy, 1967). In *Schistocerca*, the surface of the secondary cells is extensively infolded and associated with mitochondria suggesting an active participation in solute transport (Irvine, 1966). In
all these cases it is necessary to assume that the membranes across
which solute is recycled or recruited are impermeable to water.

The rectal papillae of *Calliphora* have a structural organization which
could allow for both recycling and recruitment. Solutes might be re-

turned to the cells across the basal membranes because fluid leaving the intercellular space at the tip of the papilla must travel over the entire basal surface before escaping into the hemolymph. Solutes could also be recruited across the surface which directly faces the blood (B. L. Gupta and Berridge, 1966). In *Periplaneta*, however, the entire epithelium is enclosed by the surface sheath, composed of muscles and connective tissue, ruling out solute recruitment (Oschman and Wall, 1969) except by mechanism (d). The geometry of the lateral plasma membrane, however, clearly suggests the possibility of solute recycling. Some evidence for recycling has been obtained by analyzing the fluid in the sinus beneath the surface sheath. When animals are dehydrated, the osmotic pressure and concentration of sodium and potassium in sinus fluid is much less than that in the lumen (Wall and Oschman, 1970). Not only does this suggest solute movement by routes (a) or (b) but it also indicates that the sinus may be a separate compartment from the blood.

In the cryptonephric system of Coleoptera and larval Lepidoptera (Saini, 1964; Meyer, 1966; Dürr, 1967), the secretory activity of Malpighian tubules is added to the absorptive capacity of the rectal epithelium to produce a very efficient concentrating mechanism (Ramsay, 1964; Grimstone *et al.*, 1968). The rectum of *Tenebrio* can produce fecal pellets in equilibrium with 90% relative humidity which corresponds to an osmotic pressure in excess of 6000 mosmoles. The distal ends of the six Malpighian tubules are closely applied to and lie within a perinephric membrane which completely surrounds the rectal epithelium and is analogous to the surface sheath found in other rectal glands (Fig. 4). The enclosed perinephric space forms a separate compartment from the blood because the perinephric membrane is impermeable to ions and water. Dispersed throughout the perinephric space (stippled area) is a proteinaceous material which is more concentrated in the posterior region. The only gaps in the perinephric membrane are the tiny circular windows at the leptophragmata. These are special Malpighian tubule cells that stretch across the windows and are structurally different from their neighbors. Proximally the Malpighian tubules lie free in the body cavity and connect to the gut at the junction between midgut and hindgut (Fig. 4).

Absorption by the rectal epithelium is potentiated by maintaining a highly concentrated fluid within the perinephric space. Fluid in the posterior region of the perinephric space is twice as concentrated as that in the anterior region. Malpighian tubule fluid is isosmotic with the perinephric fluid and thus is also more concentrated in the posterior region of the complex. This gradient of osmotic pressure within the rectal complex is correlated with increased concentrating ability down

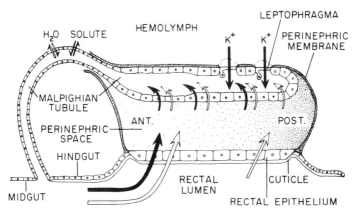

FIG. 4. The crytonephric system of *Tenebrio* (After Ramsay, 1964; Grimstone *et al.*, 1968). Solutes (solid arrows) and water (open arrows) enter the perinephric space across the rectal epithelium and leave the rectal complex mainly in the Malpighian tubules. Water absorption from the lumen is facilitated by recruiting potassium from the hemolymph across the leptophragma.

the length of the rectal lumen. Intestinal fluid, isosmotic with blood, enters the anterior part of the rectal lumen where most of the solutes and water are rapidly absorbed and fecal material is compacted into pellets. In the posterior region of the rectum these fecal pellets are surrounded with air, and water removal must occur by absorption of water vapor. The initial uptake of water in the anterior region depends both on the high osmotic pressure maintained within the perinephric space and on the simultaneous uptake of solute (Fig. 4). However, the very high osmolarity found within the perinephric space and tubular lumen cannot be accounted for solely by solute absorption from the rectal lumen. Extra solute is obtained by the leptophragmata (Fig. 4) which can recruit potassium from the hemolymph while remaining impermeable to water (Grimstone *et al.*, 1968). This additional solute input into the posterior region of the complex creates the very high osmotic pressures necessary to facilitate water uptake from the dry fecal pellets. The solutes and water which leave the rectal complex via the Malpighian tubules probably equilibrate with the blood in the free proximal portions (Fig. 4).

The concentrating mechanism found in *Tenebrio* has some interesting parallels with that found in the vertebrate kidney. First, nonelectrolytes make up a major part of the osmotically active components of the perinephric fluid (Ramsay, 1964), reminiscent of the role of urea in the concentrating mechanism of certain mammalian kidneys. Since the osmotic contribution of nonelectrolyte is so high, it is probably not the proteinaceous material viewed in electron micrographs but is more likely to be smaller molecules such as amino acids. Second, Kirschner (1967) has pointed out that the cryptonephric system contains some of the components of a countercurrent multiplier system. Finally, the concentrating ability of the rectum is regulated according to the water balance of the animal. When water is plentiful, the animals excrete moist fecal pellets and the fluid in the anterior and posterior perinephric space is isosmotic with the blood. When animals are dehydrated, however, the rectal complex is activated and the osmotic pressure of the perinephric fluid increases, especially in the posterior region. These changes in concentration may be induced by varying the permeability of the perinephric membrane (Grimstone *et al.*, 1968).

2. Hormonal Control of Excretion

Hormonal control of excretion has been studied mainly in insects where evidence is accumulating for both diuretic and antidiuretic hormones. Rate of fluid secretion by Malpighian tubules is regulated by a diuretic hormone originating from the nervous system (Maddrell, 1963; Berridge, 1966; Mills, 1967). Control of diuresis in *Rhodnius* is described in detail later (Section IV,A). The osmotic pressure of urine secreted by Malpighian tubules is not altered after addition of diuretic hormone even though rate of secretion is greatly accelerated (Berridge, 1966). Thus the main function of the diuretic hormone in insects is to regulate the fluid load presented to the rectum. Water loss from the excretory system will therefore depend on the extent to which water is subsequently absorbed by the rectum.

Rate of fluid absorption by the rectum can vary according to the availability of water (Bursell, 1960; Phillips, 1965; Berridge, 1965a; Wall and Oschman, 1970) and may be regulated by an antidiuretic hormone originating in the nervous system (Vietinghoff, 1966; Wall, 1967). The same hormone may simultaneously reduce fluid input into the rectum by inhibiting the Malpighian tubules (Wall and Ralph, 1964; Mills and Nielsen, 1967; Wall, 1967). Antidiuretic hormone apparently arises in neurosecretory cells in the ventral nerve cord, particularly the last abdominal ganglion (Delphin, 1963; Wall, 1967). Ultrastructural studies of rectal glands have revealed the presence of axons containing dense granules within the sheath covering the absorptive cells (B. L. Gupta and Berridge, 1966; Oschman and Wall, 1969). Since these axons probably originate in the last abdominal ganglion, the dense-cored granules may contain the antidiuretic hormone. Release of hormone adjacent to the absorptive cells may be necessitated because these cells are insulated from the surrounding blood by a surface sheath.

D. WATER STORES

When desiccated, some terrestrial arthropods can counteract an increase in hemolymph osmotic pressure by withdrawing water from special reservoirs within the body. The pericardial sacs of *Gecarcinus* are an example of such a water reservoir (Bliss, 1968). During desiccation, the blood sodium of *Gecarcinus* does not elevate to the same extent as observed in *Pachygrapsus* which lacks a water store (Gross, 1963).

In insects, various parts of the intestine and associated structures may function as water reservoirs. The enlarged crop of certain insects may function in this way. Blowflies remain in water balance only so long as water remains in the crop. Water may also be retained in the rectum and absorbed as needed (Goodchild, 1963b; Berridge, 1965a). When faced with evaporative water loss, the cotton stainer, *Dysdercus fasciatus*, regulates its blood osmotic pressure by drawing upon hypotonic urine stored in the rectum (Berridge, 1965a). This species is potentially capable of replacing 43% of its blood volume by water from the rectum. The salivary glands of some insects have large saclike reservoirs containing a dilute fluid that is thought to be stored water (Wigglesworth, 1965; Sutherland and Chillseyzn, 1968).

IV. Mechanisms for Rapid Elimination of Water

Terrestrial arthropods with liquid diets have the problem of water elimination. Excess water may be a temporary problem, as occurs immediately following a meal in bloodsucking arthropods, or a continuous problem as faced by sapsucking arthropods. In the former case, animals osmoregulate by conserving water in the long periods between meals and by rapidly excreting excess water and solutes immediately following a blood meal. Such temporary diuretic mechanisms may involve either the Malpighian tubules as in insects or the coxal glands and salivary glands of ticks. Sapsucking arthropods continuously imbibe dilute fluid from which they must extract nutrients before eliminating the excess water. Both arachnids and insects have developed special structural adaptations of the gut which rapidly shunt water into the rectum, thus preventing dilution of the blood.

A. BLOODSUCKING ARTHROPODS

1. Insects

Osmoregulation in bloodsucking insects has been studied extensively in *Rhodnius prolixus* (Wigglesworth, 1931a,b; Ramsay, 1952, 1953;

Swartzendruber, 1962; Maddrell, 1963, 1964a,b, 1966). An adult *Rhodnius* weighing 50 to 80 mg. will take in 140 to 180 mg. of blood at a single meal (Wigglesworth, 1931a). Two hours after feeding, 76.5% of the total fluid ingested is excreted as a dilute urine. This rapid diuresis involves both water elimination and excretion of excess solutes (mainly sodium, potassium, and chloride). After this short diuretic period urine is secreted very infrequently, since animals must conserve water during the 5 to 6 weeks required to digest the blood meal. Even though there is no further intake of fluid, the osmotic pressure of hemolymph soon after feeding is no different from that at the end of the digestion period (Ramsay, 1952). The hypotonic urine secreted during diuresis (Ramsay, 1952; Maddrell, 1964a) becomes considerably hypertonic during the period of water conservation (Wigglesworth, 1931a).

The structure of the excretory system of *Rhodnius* (Fig. 5) will provide a basis for understanding how water elimination and conservation are achieved by the same organ. There are four Malpighian tubules, each composed of two distinct segments. Cells of the upper segment have basal infoldings associated with mitochondria and an apical surface covered with closely packed microvilli, many of which contain mitochondria (Fig. 5). In general, mitochondria are more numerous in this apical region than in the basal zone. This mitochondrial distribution is reversed in cells of the lower segment where mitochondria tend to be associated more with the basal surface. The density of microvilli on the apical surface of these cells (Fig. 5) is also much less than that found in the upper segment. Each tubule enters the rectum through a small bulbous ampulla whose cells have long processes which may extend into the rectum. The basal plasma membrane of these ampullae cells is infolded and closely associated with mitochondria (Fig. 5). The elongated apical region is composed of filaments which may be compacted microvilli.

Rectal glands are confined to an area around the opening of the ampullae into the ovoid rectal sac. The structural organization of the rectal gland resembles that found in other insects (Section III,C) in that there are tracheolar elements ramifying among the rectal gland cells (Wigglesworth, 1931b). In the light of recent ultrastructural studies on insect rectal glands, we can assume that the tracheae and tracheoles are probably distributed along the intercellular spaces. The basal plasma membrane of the epithelial cells of *Rhodnius*, unlike that of most other rectal glands investigated so far, has basal infoldings associated with mitochondria (Swartzendruber, 1962). The remainder of the rectal sac is composed of thin rectal epithelial cells.

The exact mechanism for producing hypotonic urine during diuresis

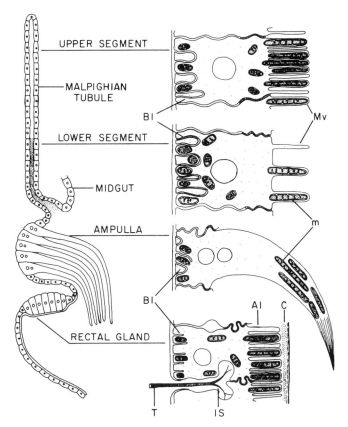

FIG. 5. The excretory system of *Rhodnius* with inserts indicating the ultrastructural features of the various regions. AI, apical infolds; BI, basal infolds; C, cuticle; IS, intercellular space; m, mitochondria; Mv, microvilli; T, tracheae. (After Wigglesworth, 1931b; Swartzendruber,1962; Wigglesworth and Salpeter, 1962.)

is unclear. Maddrell (1963) considers that the rectum plays a minor role because rate of excretion from the whole animal is about the same as that obtained from the four Malpighian tubules when set up *in vitro*. During diuresis, the initial urine secreted by the upper segment is hypertonic to the blood (Ramsay, 1952). If the rectum does not reabsorb solutes, the hypotonicity of the final urine must arise by solute absorption in the lower segment and/or by the ampullae cells (Fig. 5). At the end of diuresis fluid secretion by the Malpighian tubules declines, and water is retained by absorption in the rectum against large osmotic gradients (Wigglesworth, 1931a). The rectal glands may absorb water by a mechanism similar to that found in other insects (Section III,C).

Osmoregulation in *Rhodnius* depends upon precise control of these excretory mechanisms. The secretory activity of the Malpighian tubules is regulated by the diuretic hormone already mentioned above (Section III,C). Release of hormone is signaled by nervous information from the abdominal stretch receptors associated with the tergosternal muscles that are stimulated by distension of the abdomen during feeding (Maddrell, 1964b). Since the abdominal stretch receptors adapt very slowly (Van der Kloot, 1961), release of hormone continues until a large part of the blood meal has been eliminated. Urine flow ceases soon after the hormone is withheld because the hormone is unstable and is also destroyed by the Malpighian tubules.

In the tsetse fly, *Glossina*, the amount of water lost during diuresis is regulated according to the water content of the fly prior to feeding (Bursell, 1960). Bursell has also demonstrated that flies can regulate excretory water loss in the long period between meals. Water loss is highest in a moist environment but declines appreciably if flies are kept at 0% relative humidity. Absorption of water from the excreta under dry conditions represents a saving of more than 30% of the animal's water reserves.

2. Arachnids

Various acarines display rapid diuresis immediately after a blood meal, followed by water conservation in the period between feeding. The diuretic mechanisms of ticks do not involve the Malpighian tubules. Both argasid and ixodid ticks have well-developed Malpighian tubules but they function only to secrete guanine which gradually accumulates in the tubule lumen and rectal sac in the long interval between blood meals (Balashov, 1958). Both families rely upon alternative mechanisms to eliminate excess water and solutes obtained in the blood meal. Argasid ticks use coxal glands (Lees, 1946b), whereas ixodid ticks which lack such organs use their salivary glands (Tatchell, 1967).

Argasid ticks feed quickly and can engorge fully in 15 to 30 minutes. An average female *Ornithodorus moubata* weighing 29 mg. can ingest approximately 100 mg. of blood. Within an hour, 45% of the water and 61% of the chloride in this meal is eliminated through the coxal glands. During this diuretic period, the chloride concentration of the hemolymph is unchanged.

In *Ornithodorus* the two coxal glands are small bulbous structures which lie near the ventral body wall and open behind the coxae via a short duct. Morphologically the glands are composed of three distinct systems, a filtration chamber, tubule, and accessory gland (Fig. 6). Small coxal gland muscles inserted on the adjacent body wall and internal

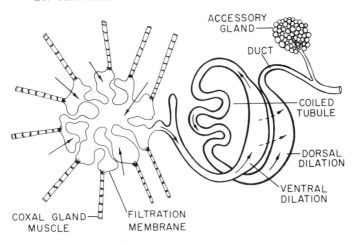

FIG. 6. The coxal glands of the tick *Ornithodorus moubata*. (After Lees, 1946b.) *In situ* the fenestrated filtration membrane envelopes the tightly coiled tubular region. Arrows indicate the direction of fluid movement.

organs are attached to the filtration chamber at numerous points. The membrane which comprises the filtration chamber is exceedingly thin (1–2 μ) and apparently well adapted for filtration. The lumen of the filtration chamber connects with the tubule at a single point. The first part of the tubule empties into a ventral dilation followed by a coiled length which leads into a dorsal dilation which finally leads into the coxal gland duct. The tubule is made up of large columnar cells richly supplied with tracheae. The function of the racemose accessory gland is unknown.

The origin of coxal fluid is still debated since the presence of hemocytes in this fluid suggests that it may arise by reflex bleeding (Sidorov, 1960) rather than by filtration (Lees, 1946b). However, Lees (1946b) has studied the "hemocytes" in coxal fluid and finds that they are refractile granules without a nucleus and may originate from within the coxal gland itself. Perhaps these concentric structures are similar to the "formed bodies" described by Riegel (1966). Furthermore, if coxal fluid originated by reflex bleeding, it is hard to explain how its chloride concentration (137 mmoles/liter) can be so different from that of hemolymph (164 mmoles/liter) (Lees, 1946b). Therefore, the description which follows will deal with Lees's hypothesis of a filtration/reabsorption mechanism which is certainly consistent with the ultrastructure of coxal glands as described earlier (Section III,C).

Filtration is achieved by creating a negative pressure within the lumen of the filtration chamber by contracting the coxal gland muscles (Lees,

1946b). When these muscles relax, the filtration chamber collapses and fluid passes into the tubules. The permeability of the filtration membrane resembles that of the vertebrate glomerulus in that it will permit the passage of hemoglobin but not larger proteins such as casein and albumin. Fluid passing down the tubule can either pass through the complete tubular system or it may bypass the thin coiled loop by moving across from the ventral dilation into the dorsal dilation (Fig. 6, dashed arrows). Chloride, together with other substances are reabsorbed by these tubules.

Ixodid ticks, which lack coxal glands, feed much more slowly than argasid ticks, and Lees (1946b) originally suggested that the blood meal was concentrated by cuticular water loss while chloride was slowly eliminated by the Malpighian tubules. However, transpiration or excretion by Malpighian tubules cannot account for concentration of the blood meal in the cattle tick *Boophilus microplus* (Tatchell, 1967). The salivary glands of ixodid ticks function in osmoregulation by periodically secreting ions and water back into the host (Tatchell, 1967). A similar adaptation is found in littoral centipedes which osmoregulate by secreting excess salts through their salivary glands (Binyon and Lewis, 1963).

The salivary glands of ixodid ticks consist of a pair of racemose organs lying on either side of the gut. The tubular component consists of a main salivary duct which divides into two subsidiary ducts and then into a larger number of smaller ducts finally terminating in bulbous acini. The acini are not uniform but show distinct morphological and histochemical differences (Balashov, 1965; Chinery, 1965; Dzhafarov, 1965; Balashov and Dzhafarov, 1966). As yet, the origin of the watery saliva has not been correlated with any particular region of the salivary gland. The sodium and chloride concentration of saliva collected from recently fed ticks is higher than that of the blood, whereas other components (potassium, calcium, magnesium, amino acids, and urea) were present at lower concentrations (Tatchell, 1968).

B. Sapsucking Arthropods

Special structural devices have been developed by sapsucking Hemiptera to excrete the excess water obtained in their diet (Goodchild, 1963a,b, 1966). The filter chamber of Homoptera involves a complex association between different parts of the gut and Malpighian tubules.

In the Cicadoidea, the main feature of the filter chamber is close apposition of the anterior and posterior regions of the gut (Fig. 7a). The whole complex is surrounded by a peritoneal membrane. Excess water is thought to pass directly from the anterior region of the gut into the posterior regions and hence into the rectum. The concentrated

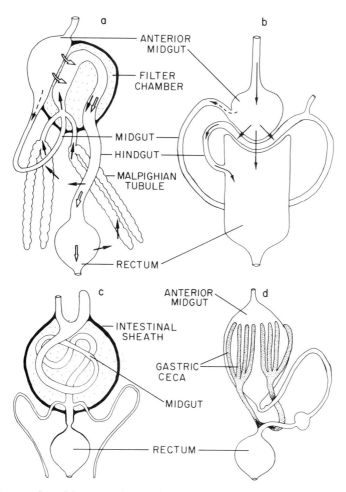

FIG. 7. Intestinal modifications of sapsucking Hemiptera. a, Solute (closed arrows) and water (open arrows) movement in the filter chamber of Cicadoidea. b, Filter chamber of Coccoidea, arrows represent some possible routes for water movement. Nutrients concentrated in the anterior midgut of Cicadoidea and Coccoidea pass into the main digestive segment of the midgut (a and b, dashed arrows). c. Arrangement of the intestinal sheath in Fulgoroidea. d, Modification of the gastric ceca in a heteropteran (After Pesson, 1951; Goodchild, 1963a,b).

nutrients left behind then pass into the middle part of the gut where absorption occurs. Goodchild (1963a) has considered the forces involved in moving water through the filter chamber and has ruled out hydrostatic pressure and active secretion. Water probably moves out of the anterior regions by osmosis down the gradient created by solutes entering the filter chamber via the Malpighian tubules (Fig. 7a). The epithelia (Malpighian tubule and intestine) which lie within the filter chamber have structural features which would permit rapid water movement. Not only are the cells very thin (1μ), but they also have an enormous surface area achieved through microvilli on the apical surface and membrane infoldings on the basal side (Gouranton, 1968). Fluid discharging from the Malpighian tubules will be diluted with water entering from the anterior midgut so that a hypotonic fluid will flow into the hindgut. In many respects the filter chamber and cryptonephric system (Fig. 4) utilize the same functional design in that there is a special arrangement between the Malpighian tubules and gut so that tubular secretion provides the osmotic gradients that extract water from the intestinal lumen (from anterior midgut in filter chamber and from the rectal lumen in the cryptonephric system). In order to complete the cycle, solutes must be returned to the hemolymph either by the hindgut or the rectum (Fig. 7a) without a concomitant movement of water. This mechanism would resemble that found in the rectum of mosquito larvae which can elaborate a hypotonic urine by absorbing solutes but not water (Ramsay, 1950). Absorption of solutes may be achieved by rectal glands. In some species the distal portions of the Malpighian tubules lie within grooves in the rectal epithelium (Goodchild, 1966) forming a relationship similar to the cryptonephric system described earlier (Section III, C).

The filter chamber of Coccoidea is further complicated by the inclusion of the rectum in the liaison between the anterior and posterior regions of the gut (Fig. 7b). As before, the two extremities of the gut are closely apposed (often forming a complex spiral arrangement) and lie within a deep invagination of the rectum (Pesson, 1951; Goodchild, 1966). In this arrangement, water movement from anterior to posterior regions of the gut may occur by hydrostatic pressure rather than by osmosis (Goodchild, 1966).

The Fulgoroidae differ from most large sapsucking Homoptera because they lack a filter chamber. However, in members of this superfamily most of the midgut is enclosed in an "intestinal sheath" usually composed of a double layer of cells (Fig. 7c). The sheath may function as a barrier to water, preventing dilution of the hemolymph (Goodchild, 1963a).

There are many other arrangements of the filter chamber in Homoptera and also in some Heteroptera (Goodchild, 1963a). However, in the absence of physiological data on the different systems, further discussion is unwarranted. There is an obvious need for information on the osmotic and solute gradients within the different regions of the filter chamber.

Many sapsucking Heteroptera lacking filter chambers may use gastric ceca to eliminate excess water obtained from the diet (Goodchild, 1963b). Gastric ceca are thin-walled pouches originating from the posterior region of the intestine. In some species the ceca are long tubular structures which closely invest the dilated anterior region of the midgut (Fig. 7d); perhaps such an arrangement facilitates water uptake from the dilute ingesta.

Certain phytophagous arachnids such as the two-spotted spider mite also imbibe excess water with their food. As in Hemiptera, water is rapidly shunted into the hindgut leaving the food particles behind to be digested in the midgut (McEnroe, 1963). Contraction of the dorsoventral muscles during feeding brings the esophageal valve into close juxtaposition with the opening of the hindgut. Fluid passes from the esophagus into the hindgut while particulate material is funneled into the midgut because the opening of the hindgut has a mechanical filter.

V. Mechanisms for Uptake of Water

Osmotic equilibrium is maintained if obligatory water loss is balanced by water uptake from the environment. Terrestrial arthropods can take up water either through the general body surface or through the gut. These uptake mechanisms must be carefully regulated to prevent excessive hydration.

A. Water Uptake through the Body Surface

Terrestrial hermit crabs can take up water from fluid which they carry in their adopted shells. Since the fluid they place in their shells reaches rapid equilibrium with the blood (Gross, 1964), these animals osmoregulate by a behavioral mechanism which enables them to select fluid of the correct salinity (Section III,A). Certain terrestrial crabs have become independent of free water because they can obtain water from damp sand (Gross et al., 1966; Bliss, 1968). Water is conveyed from the sand into the branchial chamber by means of setae and grooves in the arthrodial membrane. Water may enter the animal via special cells located mainly on the posterior gills (Copeland, 1968). *Gecarcinus* can take up water only when the sand is moistened with hypotonic fluids, suggesting that water entry is passive. On the other hand, *Cardiosoma* can reduce its blood osmotic pressure by absorbing water from a hypertonic solution (Gross et al., 1966). Either they can absorb water against an osmotic gradient or they must have an extrarenal mechanism for eliminating excess solute taken in during solute-linked isotonic water movement across the gills (Copeland, 1968).

Certain arthropods have the remarkable ability to absorb water from unsaturated air (Table I). A characteristic feature of this uptake mechanism is that it fails below a particular species-specific "equilibrium humidity." At the equilibrium humidity water loss by transpiration is balanced by water uptake; if the humidity is lowered, a net loss accrues, whereas at higher humidities water is absorbed. Studies with tritiated water have shown that water movement across the integument is a dynamic phenomenon because the total water flux is much larger than

TABLE I

THE EQUILIBRIUM HUMIDITIES OF ARTHROPODS THAT CAN ABSORB ATMOSPHERIC WATER

	RH (%)	Osmotic pressure (osmoles)	References
Arachnids			
Acarini			
Ixodes ricinus	92.0	4.8	Lees (1946a)
Ixodes canisuga	94.0	3.6	Lees (1946a)
Ixodes hexagonus	94.0	3.6	Lees (1946a)
Ornithodorus moubata	85.5	9.6	Lees (1946a)
Rhipicephalus sanguineus	84.0–90.0	10.8–6.2	Lees (1946a)
Dermacentor andersoni			
Larvae	80.0–85.0	13.9–10.0	Knülle (1965)
Adult	85.0	10.0	Lees (1946a)
Dermacentor variabilis	80.0–85.0	13.9–10.0	Knülle (1965)
Dermacentor reticulatus	86.0–88.0	9.2–7.8	Lees (1946a)
Amblyomma cajennense			
Larvae	80.0–85.0	13.9–10.0	Knülle (1965)
Adult	91.0	5.5	Lees (1946a)
Amblyomma maculatum	88.0–90.0	7.8–6.2	Lees (1946a)
Acarus siro	71.0	22.6	Knülle and Wharton (1964)
Echinolaelaps echidninus	90.0	6.2	Wharton and Kanungo (1962)
Insecta			
Thysanura			
Thermobia domestica	45.0	67.0	Beament *et al.* (1964)
Siphonaptera			
Xenopsylla brasiliensis	50.0	55.5	Edney (1947)
Xenopsylla cheopsis	65.0	30.0	Knülle (1967a)
Ceratophyllus gallinae	82.0	12.2	Humphries (1967)
Coleoptera			
Tenebrio molitor	88.0	7.8	Mellanby (1932)
Orthoptera			
Chortophaga viridifasciata	82.0	12.2	Ludwig (1937)
Arenivaga sp.	82.5	11.8	Edney (1966)

the total net movement. The half-life for water exchange in the mite, *Laelaps echidnina* is 18.6 hours (Wharton and Devine, 1968). The equilibrium humidities listed in Table I indicate that water can be absorbed against enormous activity gradients. In order to appreciate the magnitude of such gradients, the activity of water in the air has been expressed both as relative humidity and as an equivalent osmotic pressure. In most arthropods, the blood osmotic pressure is 0.3 to 0.5 osmoles (Fig. 1).

Water uptake occurs through the general body surface and not through the respiratory system. For example, some acarines, lacking a respiratory system, can absorb water vapor (Knülle, 1965). Further, water absorption by ticks is not affected by blocking the spiracles (Lees, 1946a). If the external cuticle is abraded, water uptake ceases but resumes when the cuticle is repaired (Lees, 1947; Edney, 1966). However, Lees (1947) and Locke (1968) have demonstrated that water absorption can resume long before the cuticle regains its normal degree of impermeability to water. Further, *Xenopsylla cheopsis* can absorb water from humidities above 65% relative humidity even though it is very susceptible to water loss below this humidity (Knülle, 1967a). Arthropods can thus absorb water from moist air even though they may be very prone to water loss in dry air.

Two theories have been proposed for water uptake (Beament, 1964, 1965; Locke, 1964). Beament's theory involves discontinuous uptake of water whereas the mechanism suggested by Locke could result in continuous uptake. Both theories attempt to explain how epidermal cells can create a region within the cuticle where the activity of water is less than that in the surrounding air (Fig. 2e). In order for the cuticle to have such a low water activity, the apical membrane (barrier 2) must be relatively impermeable to water, otherwise the gradient for water uptake from air would be swamped by water entering from the cell and blood.

Beament has proposed that the epidermal cell can alter the degree of cuticular hydration by varying the charge of the chitin-protein complex of the endocuticle. Least water is bound to a protein at its isoelectric point; however, on either side of the point, unmasked polar groups strongly attract water. If the hydration state of the cuticle could be varied cyclically, water could be taken up from the air in one phase and given up to the cell in the alternate phase. In order to avoid oscillation, it is necessary to introduce a rectifier or valve to maintain unidirectional flow. Beament (1965) considers that this valve involves the surface monolayer of lipid, working in conjunction with minute water-filled pores in the epicuticle. During one phase of the cycle, when the hydration of the cuticle is reduced, water will be drawn down the pores causing the formation of menisci. Since the vapor pressure over a meniscus in a capillary is lower than ambient, condensation of atmospheric water will occur. In the second phase of the cycle, cuticular hydration increases and the water level in the capillaries rises. Evaporation back into the air is prevented because a mobile lipid layer rapidly reforms over the surface so that water released in the endocuticle will move unidirectionally into the cell. Beament (1965) suggests that the species-specific equilibrium humidities (Table I) may depend on the size of the pores, since this would determine the curvature of the meniscus and hence the degree to which vapor pressure can be lowered. There is no suggestion as to how epidermal cells can achieve cyclic changes of cuticular hydration. Perhaps discontinuous respiration could induce cyclic changes in the pH of cuticle and hence the cuticle's ability to bind water.

Locke (1964) considers that water uptake may occur by a mechanism similar to that involved in cuticular resorption during molting or starvation. Indeed, starved animals have always been used to demonstrate water vapor uptake. During starvation lytic enzymes may be released by epidermal cells to depolymerize glycoproteins within the endocuticle. Since the products of digestion (mostly amino acids and glucosamine units) will be released in a small volume of water, a very high osmotic pressure could be developed to trap water from the air (Locke, 1964). Extensive septate desmosomes and tight junctions between epidermal cells may help to maintain a large osmotic pressure difference between the cuticular compartment and blood. Consequently, water uptake into the cell must occur across the impermeable apical membrane and against a very large osmotic gradient. The mechanism may involve pinocytosis, a characteristic feature of the apical membrane of epidermal cells. If small vesicles of the concentrated solution are taken into the cell, the water could become available to the animal if the amino acid and glucosamine subunits are subsequently metabolized or repolymerized. A possible objection to this hypothesis is that the osmotic activity of saturated solutions of these organic molecules may not be high enough to account for water uptake in insects with low equilibrium humidities. Clearly much more experimental information is required before this intriguing phenomenon is understood. As yet, there is no ultrastructural information on epidermal cells which can absorb water vapor. A structural comparison of the epidermal cells of *Arenivaga* males, which cannot absorb water, with those of nymphs and females, which can, may be particularly instructive (Edney, 1966).

Despite the uncertainty concerning the mechanism of water uptake, there is no doubt that it plays an important role in osmoregulation. The hemolymph osmotic pressure of *Arenivaga* is initially elevated during desiccation but returns to normal levels by uptake of water vapor (Edney, 1966). Water absorption by arthropods is usually observed only after desiccation, and ends abruptly when the animal restores its normal water balance. This suggests a very precise control mechanism (Lees, 1946a; Edney, 1966; Knülle, 1967a). Lees (1946a) considers that cessation of water uptake when the animal is fully hydrated is due to a decrease in the inward secretion of water.

B. WATER UPTAKE THROUGH THE GUT

The water requirements of many arthropods are satisfied by water taken in with the food. Some arthropods, however, are known to supplement their diet by drinking free water (Mellanby and French, 1958; Edwards, 1962; Barton Browne, 1964a; Bursell, 1964; Knülle, 1967b). The behavioral response of arthropods to water is regulated according to need.

When *Oniscus* is dehydrated, its blood osmotic pressure increases markedly (Fig. 1) and the animals become very responsive to water. If given distilled water, the dehydrated animals drink avidly and soon regain their original weight, and drinking ceases. However, if the animals are given salt solution they continue to imbibe fluid far in excess of their original weight (Berridge, 1968a). Thus the drinking response of *Oniscus* is apparently regulated by internal receptors sensitive to hemolymph solute composition.

The drinking response of *Lucilia cuprina* is also correlated with blood composition (Barton Browne, 1964b, 1968; Barton Browne and Dudziński, 1968). The level of responsiveness of the fly increases markedly when the chloride concentration in the blood rises, either during dehydration or following injection of concentrated salt solutions. On the other hand, the drinking response of another dipteran *Phormia regina* is set by blood volume (Dethier and Evans, 1961). Responsiveness to water can be abolished by allowing flies to ingest concentrated sugar solution or by injecting concentrated sugar or salt solutions into the hemocoel. Since the effect is independent of chemical composition or concentration of the injected solution, the response must be related to volume, and may be mediated by mechanoreceptors. Sensory information from these receptors probably travels down the recurrent nerve, because flies become polydypsic if this nerve is sectioned (Dethier and Bodenstein, 1958). After a while polydypsic flies stop drinking because the water stimulus is not strong enough to produce effective sucking against the back-pressure of ingested water. However, vigorous sucking is renewed and the flies burst if provided with sugar solutions, suggesting that water and sugar may act on separate receptors. Indeed, a specific water receptor distinct from receptors for salt and sugar has been identified in the blowfly (Evans and Mellon, 1962).

VI. Conclusion

The degree of terrestrialness achieved by arthropods depends on the efficiency of their osmoregulatory mechanisms. Crustacea and myriapods lack efficient physiological mechanisms and rely almost completely on behavioral mechanisms to restrict them to a cryptozoic environment. The key to attaining a full degree of terrestrialness by arachnids and insects was the development of surface wax to restrict transpiration. Further independence of the environment has been obtained through the development of systems that regulate osmotic pressure and reduce respiratory and excretory water loss.

The osmoregulatory mechanisms of terrestrial arthropods are finely adjusted by means of sensory information received from hygroreceptors, mechanoreceptors, and receptor organs sensitive to variations in blood composition. The nature of these receptors and the connection between receptors and effectors remains to be explored.

Terrestrial arthropods are very tolerant of wide variations of blood osmotic pressure. Mobility of the animals remains enabling the behavioral mechanisms to achieve movement to more favorable surroundings where a return to normal blood concentrations can occur.

REFERENCES

Amos, T. G. (1967). *Entomol. Exptl. Appl.* **10**, 1.
Anderson, J. F. (1966). *Comp. Biochem. Physiol.* **17**, 973.
Bahadur, J. (1963). *Proc. Roy. Entomol. Soc. London* **A38**, 59.
Bahadur, J., and Reddy, K. K. (1967). *Zool. Anz.* **178**, 262.
Balashov, Y. S. (1958). *Parazitol. Sb., Akad. Nauk SSSR, Zool. Inst.* **18**, 120.
Balashov, Y. S .(1965). *Entomol. Obozrenie* **44**, 462.
Balashov, Y. S., and Dzhafarov, T. E. (1966). *Zool. Zh.* **45**, 1134.
Barton Browne, L. (1964a). *Ann. Rev. Entomol.* **9**, 63.
Barton Browne, L. (1964b). *Nature* **202**, 1137.
Barton Browne, L. (1968). *J. Insect. Physiol.* **14**, 1603.
Barton Browne, L., and Dudziński, A. (1968). *J. Insect Physiol.* **14**, 1423.
Beament, J. W. L. (1964). *Advan. Insect. Physiol.* **2**, 67.
Beament, J. W. L. (1965). *Symp. Soc. Exptl. Biol.* **19**, 273.
Beament, J. W. L. (1968). *Brit. Med. Bull.* **24**, 130.
Beament, J. W. L., Noble-Nesbitt, J., and Watson, J. A. L. (1964). *J. Exptl. Biol.* **41**, 323.
Bennett, D. S., and Manton, S. M. (1962). *Ann. Mag. Nat. Hist.* **5**, 545.
Bentley, E. W. (1943). *J. Exptl. Biol.* **20**, 152.
Berridge, M. J. (1965a). *J. Exptl. Biol.* **43**, 511.
Berridge, M. J. (1965b). *J. Exptl. Biol.* **43**, 523.

Berridge, M. J. (1966). *J. Exptl. Biol.* **44**, 553.
Berridge, M. J. (1968). *J. Exptl. Biol.* **48**, 159.
Berridge, M. J. (1968a). Unpublished experiments.
Berridge, M. J., and Gupta, B. L. (1967). *J. Cell. Sci.* **2**, 89.
Berridge, M. J., and Gupta, B. L. (1968). *J. Cell Sci.* **3**, 17.
Binyon, J., and Lewis, J. G. E. (1963). *J. Marine Biol. Assoc. U.K.* **43**, 49.
Bliss, D. E. (1968). *Am. Zoologist* **8**, 355.
Blumenthal, H. (1935). *Z. Morphol. Oekol. Tiere* **29**, 667.
Bursell, E. (1955). *J. Exptl. Biol.* **32**, 238.
Bursell, E. (1960). *J. Exptl. Biol.* **37**, 689.
Bursell, E. (1964). *In* "The Physiology of Insecta" (M. Rockstein, ed.), Vol. 1, p. 323. Academic Press, New York.
Bursell, E. (1967). *Advan. Insect Physiol.* **4**, 33.
Chinery, W. A. (1965). *Acta Trop.* **22**, 321.
Cloudsley-Thompson, J. L. (1951). *J. Exptl. Biol.* **28**, 165.
Cloudsley-Thompson, J. L. (1952). *J. Exptl. Biol.* **29**, 295.
Cloudsley-Thompson, J. L. (1956a). *Ann. Mag. Nat. Hist.* **9**, 305.
Cloudsley-Thompson, J. L. (1956b). *J. Exptl. Biol.* **33**, 576.
Copeland, E. (1968). *Am. Zoologist* **8**, 417.
Davies, M. E., and Edney, E. B. (1952). *J. Exptl. Biol.* **29**, 571.
Delphin, F. (1963). *Nature* **200**, 913.
Dethier , V. G., and Bodenstein, D. (1958). *Z. Tierpsychol.* **15**, 129.
Dethier, V. G., and Evans, D. R. (1961). *Biol. Bull.* **121**, 108.
Djajakusumah, T., and Miles, P. W. (1966). *Australian J. Biol. Sci.* **19**, 1081.
Dresel, E. I. B., and Moyle, V. (1950). *J. Exptl. Biol.* **27**, 210.
Dürr, H. J. R. (1967). *S. African J. Agr. Sci.* **10**, 723.
Dzhafarov, T. E. (1965). *Tsitologiya* **7**, 233.
Edney, E. B. (1947). *Bull. Entomol. Res.* **38**, 263.
Edney, E. B. (1954). *Biol. Rev.* **29**, 185.
Edney, E. B. (1966). *Comp. Biochem. Physiol.* **19**, 387.
Edney, E. B. (1968a). *Comp. Biochem. Physiol.* **25**, 149.
Edney, E. B. (1968b). *Am. Zoologist* **8**, 309.
Edwards, J. S. (1962). *J. Insect Physiol.* **8**, 113.
Evans, D. R., and Mellon, DeF. (1962). *J. Gen. Physiol.* **45**, 487.
Füller, H. (1966). *Z. Wiss. Zool.* **173**, 191.
Gifford, C. A. (1968). *Am. Zoologist* **8**, 521.
Goodchild, A. J. P. (1963a). *Trans. Roy. Entomol. Soc. London* **A115**, 217.
Goodchild, A. J. P. (1963b). *Proc. Roy. Soc.* **B141**, 851.
Goodchild, A. J. P. (1966). *Biol. Rev. Cambridge Phil. Soc.* **41**, 97.
Gouranton, J. (1968). *J. Microscopie* **7**, 559.
Grimstone, A. V., Mullinger, A. M., and Ramsay, J. A. (1968). *Phil. Trans. Roy. Soc. London* **B253**, 343.
Gross, W. J. (1963). *Physiol. Zool.* **36**, 312.
Gross, W. J. (1964). *Biol. Bull.* **126**, 54.
Gross, W. J., Lasiewski, R. C., Dennis, M., and Rudy, P. (1966). *Comp. Biochem. Physiol.* **17**, 641.
Gupta, B. L., and Berridge, M. J. (1966). *J. Morphol.* **120**, 23.
Gupta, M. (1961). *Nature* **191**, 406.
Hartenstein, R. (1968). *Am. Zoologist* **8**, 507.
Hopkins, C. R. (1966). *J. Roy. Microscop. Soc.* [3] **86**, 235.

318   *Michael J. Berridge*

Horne, F. R. (1968). *Comp. Biochem. Physiol.* **26,** 687.

Humphries, D. A. (1967). *Nature* **214,** 426.

Irvine, H. B. (1966). M.Sc. Thesis, University of British Columbia.

Jans, D. E., and Ross, K. F. A. (1963). *Quart. J. Microscop. Sci.* **104,** 337.

Kirschner, L. B. (1967). *Ann. Rev. Physiol.* **29,** 169.

Knülle, W. (1965). *J. Med. Entomol.* **2,** 335.

Knülle, W. (1967a). *J. Insect Physiol.* **13,** 333.

Knülle, W. (1967b). *J. Med. Entomol.* **4,** 322.

Knülle, W., and Wharton, G. W. (1964). *Acarologia* **6,** 299.

Kuenen, D. J. (1959). *Entomol. Exptl. Appl.* **2,** 287.

Laviolette, P., and Mestres, G. (1967). *Compt. Rend.* **265,** 979.

Lees, A. D. (1943). *J. Exptl. Biol.* **20,** 43.

Lees, A. D. (1946a). *Parasitology* **37,** 1.

Lees, A. D. (1946b). *Parasitology* **37,** 172.

Lees, A. D. (1947). *J. Exptl. Biol.* **23,** 379.

Lewis, J. G. E. (1963). *Entomol. Exptl. Appl.* **6,** 89.

Locke, M. (1964). *In* "The Physiology of Insecta" (M. Rockstein, ed.), Vol. 3, p. 379. Academic Press, New York.

Locke, M. (1968). Personal communication.

Loveridge, J. P. (1968a). *J. Exptl. Biol.* **49,** 1.

Loveridge, J. P. (1968b). *J. Exptl. Biol.* **49,** 15.

Ludwig, D. (1937). *Physiol. Zool.* **10,** 342.

McEnroe, W. D. (1963). *Advan. Acarol.* **1,** 225.

Maddrell, S. H. P. (1963). *J. Exptl. Biol.* **40,** 247.

Maddrell, S. H. P. (1964a). *J. Exptl. Biol.* **41,** 163.

Maddrell, S. H. P. (1964b). *J. Exptl. Biol.* **41,** 459.

Maddrell, S. H. P. (1966). *J. Exptl. Biol.* **45,** 499.

Mantel, L. H. (1968). *Am. Zoologist* **8,** 433.

Mellanby, K. (1932). *Proc. Roy. Soc.* **B111,** 376.

Mellanby, K., and French, R. A. (1958). *Entomol. Exptl. Appl.* **1,** 116.

Meyer, A. J. (1966). *Ann. Univ. Stellenbosch* **41,** 271.

Miller, P. L. (1964a). *J. Exptl. Biol.* **41,** 331.

Miller, P. L. (1964b). *In* "The Physiology of Insecta" (M. Rockstein, ed.), Vol. 3, p. 557. Academic Press, New York.

Mills, R. R. (1967). *J. Exptl. Biol.* **46,** 35.

Mills, R. R., and Nielsen, D. J. (1967). *Gen. Comp. Endocrinol.* **9,** 380.

Oschman, J. L. (1968). Personal communication.

Oschman, J. L., and Wall, B. J. (1969). *J. Morphol.* **127,** 475.

Parry, G. (1953). *J. Exptl. Biol.* **30,** 567.

Perttunen, V. (1953). *Ann. Zool. Soc. Zool.-Botan. Fennicae Vanamo* **16,** 1.

Pesson, P. (1951). *In* "Traité de Zoologie" (P. P. Grassé, ed.), Vol. 10, p. 1390. Masson, Paris.

Phillips, J. E. (1965). *Trans. Roy. Soc. Can., Sect. V* [4] **3,** 237.

Phillips, J. E., and Dockrill, A. A. (1968). *J. Exptl. Biol.* **48,** 521.

Pulliainen, E., and Nederström, A. (1965). *Ann. Entomol. Fennici* **31,** 132.

Ramsay, J. A. (1950). *J. Exptl. Biol.* **27,** 145.

Ramsay, J. A. (1952). *J. Exptl. Biol.* **29,** 110.

Ramsay, J. A. (1953). *J. Exptl. Biol.* **30,** 358.

Ramsay, J. A. (1954). *J. Exptl. Biol.* **31,** 104.

Ramsay, J. A. (1964). *Phil. Trans. Roy. Soc. London* **B248,** 279.

Rasmont, R. (1960). *Ann. Soc. Zool. Belg.* **89**, 239.

Riegel, J. A. (1966). *J. Exptl. Biol.* **44**, 379.

Roth, L. M., and Willis, E. R. (1963). *Ann. Entomol. Soc. Am.* **56**, 41.

Saini, R. S. (1964). *Trans. Roy. Entomol. Soc. London* **A116**, 347.

Schmidt-Nielsen, B., Gertz, K. H., and Davis, L. E. (1968). *J. Morphol.* **125**, 473.

Schneiderman, H. A. (1960). *Biol. Bull.* **119**, 494.

Sekhon, S. S. (1962). Ph.D. Thesis, University of Iowa.

Shaw, J., and Stobbart, R. H. (1963). *Advan. Insect. Physiol.* **1**, 315.

Sidorov, V. E. (1960). *Dokl.—Biol. Sci. Sect.* (*English Transl.*) **130**, 176.

Sutherland, D. J., and Chillseyzn, J. M. (1968). *J. Insect Physiol.* **14**, 21.

Swartzendruber, D. C. (1962). Ph.D. Thesis, University of Iowa.

Tatchell, R. J. (1967). *Nature* **213**, 940.

Tatchell, R. J. (1968). Personal communication.

Toye, S. A. (1966a). *Entomol. Exptl. Appl.* **9**, 378.

Toye, S. A. (1966b). *Entomol. Exptl. Appl.* **9**, 468.

Tyson, G. E. (1968). *Z. Zellforsch. Mikroskop. Anat.* **86**, 129.

Van der Kloot, W. G. (1961). *Am. Zoologist* **1**, 3.

Vietinghoff, U. (1966). *Naturwissenschaften* **53**, 162.

Wall, B. J. (1967). *J. Insect Physiol.* **13**, 565.

Wall, B. J. (1968). Personal communication.

Wall, B. J., and Oschman, J. L. (1970). *Am. J. Physiol.* **218**, 1208.

Wall, B. J., and Ralph, C. L. (1964). *Gen. Comp. Endocrinol.* **4**, 452.

Waloff, N. (1941). *J. Exptl. Biol.* **18**, 115.

Warburg, M. R. (1968). *Am. Zoologist* **8**, 545.

Wessing, A. (1966). *Naturw. Rundschau* **19**, 139.

Wharton, G. W., and Devine, T. L. (1968). *J. Insect Physiol.* **14**, 1303.

Wharton, G. W., and Kanungo, K. (1962). *Ann. Entomol. Soc. Am.* **55**, 483.

Wigglesworth, V. B. (1931a). *J. Exptl. Biol.* **8**, 411.

Wigglesworth, V. B. (1931b). *J. Exptl. Biol.* **8**, 428.

Wigglesworth, V. B. (1965). "The Principles of Insect Physiology." Methuen, London.

Wigglesworth, V. B., and Salpeter, M. M. (1962). *J. Insect Physiol.* **8**, 299.

Willis, E. R., and Roth, L. M. (1950). *J. Exptl. Zool.* **115**, 561.

Winston, P. W. (1967). *Nature* **214**, 383.

Winston, P. W., and Nelson, V. E. (1965). *J. Exptl. Biol.* **43**, 257.

CHAPTER 11

Chemistry of Growth and Development in Crustaceans

Larry H. Yamaoka and Bradley T. Scheer[1]

I. Introduction

There is a paucity of information available on the chemistry of growth and development of the Crustacea. Most of the work has been done on only a few species of decapod crustaceans. What is presented here is a discussion of some of the metabolic changes the animal undergoes as related to tissue growth and an increase in body size; we will not discuss the development of gametes or the reproductive system.

II. The Intermolt Cycle

When one discusses growth and development of the Crustacea, one must, as a consequence, discuss the molt cycle. The life cycle of a typical decapod crustacean alternates between a relatively long intermolt period during which it feeds and is active and a relatively short molt period during which it sheds its old exoskeleton (ecdysis) and increases in

[1] Supported in part by a grant GB 7219 from the National Science Foundation.

size. The cycle is closely connected to the processes of growth, as ecdysis is the only means by which án animal with a rigid exoskeleton can grow.

Since the molt cycle is of primary consideration in most studies of crustacean physiology, it was necessary to establish a coherent and consistent scheme of describing the various stages of the molt sequence. The modern scheme was proposed by Drach on work done on *Cancer* and *Maia* (Drach, 1939) and modified for natantians (Drach, 1944). Changes have been made by other workers for other species, i.e., by Hiatt (1948) for a grapsoid brachyuran, by Scheer (1960) for natantians, by Kurup (1964) for an anomuran, by Stevenson (1968) for a macruran.

The primary divisions of the molt cycle and its characteristic morphological changes are presented in Table I. The principal physiological characteristics of the typical decapod molt cycle are (1) an accumulation of reserves; (2) formation of the new exoskeleton accompanied by a resorption of organic and inorganic material from the old exoskeleton during premolt; (3) shedding of the old exoskeleton at ecdysis accompanied by a large intake of water; (4) building-up and hardening the new exoskeleton from reserve stores and from ions in the medium; (5) tissue growth. Each of the major tissues undergoes changes which can be correlated with the molt cycle.

III. Physiology of the Adult Molt Cycle

A. HEPATOPANCREAS

The accumulation of reserves is an important part of intermolt cycle physiology. The reserves are important not only as a source of material for the new exoskeleton but also for energy during molting. Accumulation of organic reserves characterizes the intermolt (stage C_4). The animal continues to accumulate reserves into early premolt (stages D_0 and D_1) until it ceases to feed (stage D_2). Since the animal does not feed during the period of ecdysis (stages D_2 through C_1) the reserves are of extreme importance.

The hepatopancreas is the primary organ for the storage of reserves. The blood may play a secondary role and some glycogen accumulation occurs in the epithelium and subepithelial tissue. The somatic muscle tissue does not seem to play an important role in storage although there are important molt-associated changes occurring. It has been estimated that at least half of the total dry weight increase of the hepatopancreas is due to the accumulation of organic reserves; the other half due to tissue growth (Drach, 1939).

TABLE I

DECAPOD INTERMOLT CYCLE

Period	Stage	General	Characteristics			Duration[b]
			Dorsal carapace[a]	Branchiostegites	Appendage bristles	
Postmolt	A_1	Continued water absorption and initial mineralization	Soft	Membranous	Soft	3–6 hr
	A_2	Exocuticle mineralized	Parchmentlike	Soft	Soft	20–40 hr
	B_1	Endocuticle secretion begins	Protogastric area hard; rest thin	Thin	Supple	3–6 days
	B_2	Active endocuticle formation; tissue growth begins	As above and pressure-yielding	Flexible	Fairly hard	—
Intermolt	C_1	Main tissue growth	Gastric areas hard	Flexible	Increased hardness	4–8 days
	C_2	Tissue growth continues	Hard except cardiac area	Rigid	Hard and break on being bent	7–15 days
	C_3	Completion of exoskeleton; membranous layer formed	Uniformly hard	Entirely rigid	As above	2–6 weeks
	C_4	"Intermolt"; major accumulation of organic reserves	Very rigid	Very hard	Very hard	Many months
	$C_4 T^c$	Terminal stage in certain species; no further growth				Permanent
Premolt	D_1	Epidermal and hepatopancreas activation; epicuticle formation	Hard but gradually thinned	Rigid	Bristle formation	5–12 days
	D_2	Exocuticle formation	Pigmented layer clearly noticeable	Rigid but gradual thinning	Bristle growth	6–12 days
	D_3	Major portion of skeletal resorption	Splits through epimeral suture if pressed	Rigid but gradual thinning	Bristles invaginate in epidermis	2–5 days
	D_4	Ecdysial sutures open	About to separate off	As above	Old bristles about to fall off	15–30 hr
Molt	E	Exuviation[d]				2–8 hr

[a] As observed especially in brachyurans; the extent of hardening and calcification varies with species.

[b] The duration of stages may vary considerably from species to species and is subject to temperature, season, and size or age of the animal. Values are taken from Drach (1939) for *Cancer pagurus* and from Scheer (1960) for *Leander xiphias* in winter.

[c] Defined from *Pachygrapsus* (Hiatt, 1948), but applies to any forms in terminal anecdysis (Passano, 1960).

[d] Rapid water uptake and active withdrawal from exuvium.

1. Lipids

The major portion of the organic reserves of the hepatopancreas is lipid. Lipids constitute about 8% of the fresh weight but almost 30% of the dry weight of the hepatopancreas of *Cancer pagurus* (Renaud, 1949). Lipid stores undergo a cyclic variation related to the molt cycle. In *Cancer*, most of the accumulation occurs between stages C_4 and D_1, with maximum lipid concentration at the latter stage. Concentration then decreases during the nonfeeding pre- and postmolt stages, reaching a minimum value at stage C_1 (Renaud, 1949). Histochemical data from *Panulirus argus* suggest a similar stage-dependent variation (Travis, 1955a). In *Gecarcinus lateralis* and in *Orconectes virilis*, the initiation of premolt by destalking increases the lipid content of the hepatopancreas (O'Connor and Gilbert, 1968). By late premolt (stage D_3), lipid content begins to decrease. The increase in lipid content during premolt was measured by the incorporation of ^{14}C-acetate and ^{14}C-palmitate into both the neutral lipid and phospholipid of the hepatopancreas (O'Connor and Gilbert, 1969). With the induction of premolt activity, the ratio of neutral lipid to phospholipid decreased while the composition of fatty acids remained relatively the same (O'Connor and Gilbert, 1969). In late premolt, corresponding to the synthesis of the new exoskeleton, there was an increase in the release of lipid from the hepatopancreas.

2. Protein

There is next to nothing known about protein and nitrogen metabolism in the crustaceans. Changes in the nitrogen content of the hepatopancreas suggests that proteins may be an important reserve material. However, the concept of "protein storage" should be regarded skeptically, and the observed changes may represent necessary synthesis and breakdown of specific enzymes and other functional cell components. Protein makes up almost 24% of the dry weight of the hepatopancreas of *Cancer* (Renaud, 1949). The total nitrogen content of the hepatopancreas increases from a minimum value immediately after molt to a maximal value at intermolt (stage C_4) and decreases during premolt. Kurup and Scheer (1966) found a slightly different pattern in *Petrolisthes cinctipes*, an anomuran crustacean, in that there was an increase in total nitrogen from stage A to C_1 followed by a decrease during C_2. It then increased during premolt (D_2) and decreased at late premolt (D_4). It has been estimated that 70% of the protein nitrogen of the hepatopancreas of *Cancer* is utilized during ecdysis (Renaud, 1949).

Skinner (1965) found that the rate of incorporation of leucine-1-^{14}C

and valine-1-^{14}C into trichloroacetic acid-precipitable proteins of the hepatopancreas of *G. lateralis* was highest during premolt. Changes in the ribonucleic acid content of the hepatopancreas paralleled the incorporation changes (Skinner, 1966b). The ribonucleic acid content and the rate of protein synthesis returned to intermolt levels prior to ecdysis. These observations are consistent with the possible role of the hepatopancreas in synthesizing the enzymes necessary for the resorption of the old exoskeleton and synthesis of the new.

3. Carbohydrates

The role of glycogen in the hepatopancreas is twofold. It serves as a precursor of chitin synthesis and as the energy source in intermediary metabolism. Carbohydrate metabolism is discussed more fully by Hohnke and Scheer in this volume so it will be only briefly discussed here.

There is very little accumulation of glycogen in the hepatopancreas as it forms only 2.3% of the dry weight of the hepatopancreas (Renaud, 1949). The content of glycogen reaches a maximum at stage D_2 and decreases during stage D_3 to a minimum value at C_1.

Although the primary entry of carbohydrates into oxidative pathways in the decapod crustaceans is by glycolysis, there is significant oxidation through the hexose monophosphate pathway (McWhinnie and Chua, 1964) and the glucuronic acid pathway (Puyear, 1967) during the intermolt (stage C). With the onset of premolt, there is a significant shift to glycolysis (McWhinnie and Corkill, 1964). The possible significance of the hexose monophosphate pathway may be the production of reduced nicotinamide dinucleotide phosphate (NADP) for the large amount of lipid and protein accumulation occurring during intermolt.

B. INTEGUMENT

More than any other tissue, the integument reflects the periodic, regulated growth that is characteristic of the crustaceans. Much of what is known about changes in the integument has come from histochemical work on the spiny lobster *Panulirus argus* (Travis, 1955a, 1957) and on the crayfish *Orconectes virilis* (Travis, 1960, 1963, 1965).

During intermolt (stage C_4), the integument consists of five layers. Beginning with the most external, (1) the epicuticle is the thinnest of all the layers. It is deposited during premolt (D_2–D_3) and is completed after ecdysis. It is lipoprotein in nature and is hardened by sclerotization and by calcification. (2) The exocuticle is also deposited during premolt (D_2–D_3) and completed after molting. It is composed of chitin, protein, and lipid and is hardened by sclerotization and in many species calcification as well. These two outer layers are deposited during premolt and have been designated the pre-exuvial layers (Drach, 1939). (3) The endocuticle is the thickest of all the layers. It is deposited in early postmolt (stage B) and is completed by intermolt (stage C_4). It is composed of chitin and protein and is hardened by calcification only. (4) The membranous layer is the last major zone of the exoskeleton. It is deposited during postmolt (stage C_1) and is completed by intermolt (stage C_4). It is uncalcified. (5) The epidermis is the only living tissue and is responsible for the deposition of the four outer layers.

With the initiation of premolt, three processes are begun. They are (1) the growth activity of the epidermis; (2) breakdown and resorption of the old exoskeleton; (3) construction of the new exoskeleton under the old.

With the initiation of premolt (stage D_0), there is no immediate histological activity evident. Most insects show immediate mitotic activity in the epidermis with the initiation of premolt. This activity appears to be absent in the crustaceans. There was no evidence of mitotic activity in either stage D_0 in *Gecarcinus lateralis* (Skinner, 1958) or in any other premolt stage (Drach, 1939). However, the cells and their nuclei enlarge reaching a maximum size at D_2 (Skinner, 1958). The cells decrease in size prior to ecdysis (stage D_4). Since the postmolt epithelium encloses an animal larger than at premolt, the cells apparently divide during late premolt (Skinner, 1962).

The first step in the synthesis of the new exoskeleton is the breakdown and resorption of the membranous layer, causing the epidermis to separate from the old exoskeleton. This is followed by an enlargement of the epidermal cells as discussed above. The epidermal cells then secrete the new epicuticle and new exocuticle under the old exoskeleton (Travis, 1960). Both of these pre-exuvial layers are hardened by sclerotization soon after formation and are complete except for calcification by stage D_4.

At this time, protein synthesis and ribonucleic acid content are at a maximum. The incorporation of radioactive amino acid into epithelial proteins reaches a maximal rate in later premolt corresponding to the period of maximum epidermal cell size and of the laying down of the protein-rich, pre-exuvial layers (Skinner, 1965, 1966b). Ribosomal ribonucleic acid content is three to four times intermolt levels. However, most of this synthesis precedes the increase in protein synthesis as the rate of ^{3}H-uridine incorporation into ribonucleic acid is greatest during intermolt (stage C_4) (Skinner, 1966b).

Also during stages D_2 to D_3, much of the inorganic and organic content of the endocuticle is resorbed (Drach, 1939; Travis, 1955a, 1960). Most of the resorbed minerals are stored either in the hepatopancreas, or in a special gastric structure called a gastrolith, or are excreted.

Corresponding to the synthesis of the pre-exuvial layers during pre-molt, glycogen and acid mucopolysaccharides increase in the epidermal tissue (Travis, 1955a, 1960, 1965). Glycogen is found in the matrix of the new exoskeleton, which also gives positive tests for acid mucopoly-saccharide at this time. Alkaline phosphatase activity increases in the epidermis and becomes localized in the apices of the epidermis. Lipids decrease, but after the new pre-exuvial layers are completed (stage D_4) lipid content increases (Renaud, 1949).

Early postmolt is marked by the beginning of the deposition of the new endocuticle. Glycogen content remains high and increased alkaline phosphatase activity is evident at the junction of the epi- and exocuticle, in the epidermis and in the reserve cells. This body of histochemical changes indicates that glycogen and alkaline phosphatase are involved in the synthesis of the glycoprotein and lipoprotein matrix and its subse-quent calcification.

Little calcium is observed in the epidermis immediately after molt. However, calcium begins to accumulate as calcification of the endo-cuticle as well as the pre-exuvial layers begin (Travis, 1957, 1960, 1963). However, in most decapods, much of the calcium is obtained from the medium (Passano, 1960; Digby, 1968; Sather, 1967). The structural fea-tures of calcification of the matrix will not be discussed here and the reader is referred to papers by Dennell (1960), Travis (1963), and Digby (1968).

Since little is known about the glycoprotein and lipoprotein compo-nents of the exoskeletal matrix, it will not be discussed. There seems to be a relationship between the protein/chitin ratio of the exoskeleton and the degree of calcification (Drach and Lafon, 1942; Lafon, 1943, 1948). In heavily calcified integuments, the ratio is small while it in-creases in less calcified integuments.

In addition to calcification, the protein component of the integument is hardened by sclerotization. Cuticle hardening or sclerotization has been well documented in insects (Hackman, 1959; Pryor, 1962; Karlson and Sekeris, 1964). A similar mechanism is believed to occur in crustaceans although it is not as well documented.

In insects, N-acetyl dopamine is believed to be the immediate pre-cursor of an o-quinone which interacts with the cuticular proteins to effect sclerotization. The enzymically catalyzed formation of N-acetyl dopamine from tyrosine via dopa (3,4-dihydroxy-L-phenylalanine) and dopamine (3,4-dihydroxyphenylethylamine) has been shown in insects.

The conversion of tyrosine to dopa is catalyzed by a phenol oxidase. Dopa is then decarboxylated to form dopamine which is in turn N-acetylated with acetyl CoA as the acetyl donor.

The presence of a phenol oxidase has been shown in the cuticle of several crustaceans (Dennell, 1947; Krishnan, 1951; Stevenson, 1963; Stevenson and Adomako, 1967; Martin, 1965). Positive histochemical tests associated with sclerotization in insects is evidence for the occurrence of sclerotization in crustaceans. The presence of phenol oxidase in soft cuticles and its absence in hard cuticles is additional evidence (Stevenson, 1963).

In addition, phenol oxidase activity has been demonstrated in the hemolymph of several crustaceans and correlated to the molt cycle. Phenol oxidase activity drops in the hemolymph in stage D in *Cancer* (Decleir and Vercauteren, 1965), during early D in *Uca pugilator* (Summers, 1967), and in late D in *Carcinus* (Krishnan, 1954). Decrease in enzyme activity may be due to transport of enzymes to the cuticle, but transport of enzymes in body fluids is not usual. Most recently, Summers (1968) showed that an *in vitro* epidermal tissue preparation of *Uca pugilator* can convert tyrosine to N-acetyl dopamine via dopa and dopamine.

C. Blood

In insects, the hemolymph shows significant changes in free amino acids and in hemolymph proteins during molting and development (Agrell, 1964; Chen, 1962; Chen and Levenbook, 1966; Fox and Mills, 1969). Crustaceans, on the other hand, do not seem to show many changes in the hemolymph during the molt cycle. Woods *et al.* (1958), after examining several species, concluded that "within a given species, differences in sex, size, or stages of the molt cycle produced no significant differences in electrophoretic patterns." Manwell and Baker (1963) showed a quantitative variability but tentatively agreed with Woods *et al.* (1958) that "the existing variation is never so extreme as to obscure species specificity of the patterns." Recent work, however, seems to cast doubt on this concept, particularly as related to sex (Adiyodi, 1968; E. C. Horn and Kerr, 1963, 1969; Kerr, 1969).

The resorption of cuticular protein is accompanied by a rise in blood serum protein in early premolt stage D and has been reported for *Astacus* (Damboviceanu, 1932), *Maia* (Drilhon, 1935), *Panulirus argus* (Travis, 1955b), and *Homarus vulgaris* (Glynn, 1968). The level then falls rapidly just prior to molt due to a rapid intake of water. After molting, serum protein levels reach a minimum value during stage B as the protein is re-utilized for exoskeleton synthesis.

Maia apparently uses hemocyanin for respiration only during pre-ecdysis and breaks it down during the postecdysial fast (Zuckerkandl, 1956). As the hemocyanin disappears from the hemolymph, the copper moiety is stored in the hepatopancreas (Zuckerkandl, 1957, 1960).

Skinner (1965) found very little incorporation of leucine-1-^{14}C and valine-1-^{14}C into the trichloroacetic acid-precipitable proteins of the blood throughout the molt cycle of *G. lateralis*. There was a slight increase in incorporation during premolt above intermolt levels. Due to the small amount of turnover, however, she concluded that the increase was due to either "an increase in turnover *per se* or was the transport of newly synthesized protein from one tissue to another."

D. MUSCLE

Although the tissues most concerned during ecdysis are the blood, hepatopancreas, and integument, there are also changes occurring in muscle tissue.

In *Gecarcinus lateralis,* an extensive histolysis of the large chela muscle occurs during premolt (Skinner, 1966a). Although the deoxyribonucleic acid content remained relatively constant, there was a loss of almost 40% of the muscle protein. Skinner suggested that this degradation of muscle tissue was necessary to aid in removing the large mass of tissue through the narrow basal joint during the act of ecdysis.

This extensive degradation of muscle tissue occurred at the time when the rate of protein synthesis as measured by the incorporation of radioactive amino acids was the greatest (Skinner, 1965, 1966a). This increased synthesis may be the synthesis of the enzymes responsible for the degradation of the muscle tissue.

Several weeks after ecdysis, there was a second burst of incorporation of isotope into muscle tissue probably corresponding to the laying down of new tissue. Drach (1939) had shown that an increase in tissue mass usually begins in B_2 or early C stage and continues through C_2 and C_3. The tissues grow up to the volume established by tissue hydration at ecdysis.

The content of ribonucleic acid paralleled that of the tissue incorporation of radioactive amino acids. Muscle ribosomes appeared to be very stable and were conserved for the second period of protein synthesis which was observed (Skinner, 1966b).

The lipid content of the muscle increased during premolt. However, while the content decreased in the hepatopancreas during premolt stage D_2, the lipid content of the abdominal muscle of *Orconectes virilis* continued to increase (O'Connor and Gilbert, 1969). It was suggested that if a similar tissue histolysis occurs in *Orconectes,* the lipids would serve as a reserve store of material used in the regeneration and synthesis of muscle tissue.

E. Macromolecular Metabolism

There has been a small amount of work done on the nucleic acids of crustaceans and changes associated with molting. Most of the information is from studies of the land crab *Gecarcinus lateralis*.

1. Ribonucleic Acid

Skinner (1966b, 1968) found that the ribonucleic acid content of muscle, hepatopancreas, and integument of *G. lateralis* was highest during premolt, corresponding to the period of maximum protein synthesis as measured by the incorporation of radioactive amino acids into trichloroacetic acid-precipitable proteins.

Epidermal ribosomal RNA increased five times between intermolt and late premolt stage D_2 (Skinner, 1968). The increase corresponded to the maximum protein synthesis (Skinner, 1965) and maximum epithelial cell size (Skinner, 1962). All three parameters decreased prior to the molt. Hepatopancreas RNA doubled during premolt. As in epidermal tissue, the levels decreased after ecdysis. Similarly, the increase in ribosomal RNA correlated closely with the increase in protein synthesis.

In muscle tissue, ribosomal RNA increased four- to fivefold during late premolt. In contrast to the content of the hepatopancreas and epidermis, the levels remained high through ecdysis and for at least two weeks after (Skinner, 1966b, 1968). The maintenance of high levels was related with the fact that protein synthesis resumes after ecdysis to synthesize new tissue as well as resynthesize that which was degraded.

The ribosomal ribonucleic acid from *G. lateralis* has been partially characterized. It has sedimentation values in cesium chloride of 28 S and 18 S. The base composition of the 28 S component was (in mole %) U = 21.2; A = 19.6; G = 32.0; C = 26.9; while that of the 18 S fraction was U = 23.6; A = 22.0; G = 28.6; C = 25.8 (Skinner, 1968).

2. Deoxyribonucleic Acid

Sueoka (1961) found that the crab *Cancer borealis* contained a significant amount of deoxyribonucleic acid (DNA) which was very different from the primary fraction. Since then, several other species have been found to contain these "satellite DNA's" comprising 10% to 30% of the total DNA. However, DNA from *Maia squinado* appears to occur only as a single fraction (Skinner, 1967).

The DNA isolated from the tissues of *Gecarcinus lateralis* contains three components (Skinner, 1967). The main band has a density of

1.701 gm./cm.³ in cesium chloride and makes up 78% of the total DNA. A satellite rich in guanylate and cytidylate residues makes up 4% of the DNA and has a density of 1.721 gm./cm.³. A second satellite rich in adenylate and thymidylate residues makes up 18% of the total and has a density of 1.677 gm./cm.³.

DNA isolated from the testis of *Cancer pagurus* has similar densities but is composed of different fractions; the primary component makes up 72%, the G + C rich fraction 4%, the A + T rich residue 24% (Pochon *et al.*, 1966). Astell *et al.* (1969) have isolated DNA of density 1.701 and 1.677 gm./cm.³ from the nuclei of spermatogonia and spermatocytes of *Cancer productus*. The composition of the two satellites has been partially determined. About 57% of the heavy satellite is guanidine and cytidine residues while the light satellite is over 90% adenine and thymidine residues in an alternating sequence (Schwartz *et al.*, 1962; Pochon *et al.*, 1966). The biological significance of these satellites is as yet unknown.

F. ENDOCRINE REGULATION

Since the rediscovery by Abramowitz and Abramowitz (1940) of the phenomenon that eyestalk removal results in an increase in the frequency of molting, crustacean endocrinology has progressed a long way. Present knowledge suggests that the molt-inhibiting hormone is formed in the X-organ—a discrete group of neurosecretory cell bodies located in the eyestalk, transported in their axons to the sinus gland, stored there, and released by the sinus gland into the blood. Its primary effect is the inhibition of the Y-organ, an endocrine gland which secretes the molting hormone (Passano, 1960).

Removal of this inhibition of the Y-organ results in the release of molting hormone and a series of morphological and biochemical changes are begun which culminate in ecdysis. There are a variety of premolt events occurring which have been discussed previously. The diversity of changes which occur gives rise to numerous questions. Does a single hormone control all the changes by acting sequentially on the different tissues? Does a single hormone initiate an inevitable series of events? Or, are there several hormones acting under some master control?

There has been much progress made in understanding some of the chemical changes occurring during the molt cycle, especially regarding carbohydrate metabolism and its regulation, and, more recently, lipid metabolism. However, information on the regulation of tissue growth and protein turnover is very sketchy.

After ecdysis, there is a distinct increase in size (Baumberger and Olmsted, 1928). This increase in size is primarily a physical process due to the uptake of water through the digestive tract (Baumberger and Olmsted, 1928; Drach, 1939; Passano, 1960). Eyestalk removal increases the frequency of molting as well as accentuating the size increase beyond that found in normal animals (Abramowitz and Abramowitz, 1940; Scudamore, 1947). This is due to an abnormal increase in water uptake since there is no increase in total nitrogen (Bauchau and Hontoy, 1968; Koch, 1952).

Tissue growth appears to occur during distinct periods of the molt cycle. Drach (1939) showed that synthesis of new tissue in *Maia squinado* and *Cancer pagurus* does not begin until stage C, although the volume increase is complete within a few hours. The tissues then grow up to the volume established by hydration. In the epidermis, cuticle secretion and epidermal cell growth occur during premolt (stage D) (Travis, 1955a, 1963; Skinner, 1966b). Renaud (1949) found that in *C. pagurus*, the total nitrogen of the hepatopancreas increased during postmolt reaching a maximum content during D_1. Although most of this was reserve material, part of it was due to tissue growth.

Scheer and his co-workers have suggested the existence of a factor influencing protein metabolism. Neiland and Scheer (1953) found that the removal of sinus gland superimposed on fasting resulted in a decrease in the nitrogen and lipid content of the hepatopancreas of *Hemigrapsus nudus*. Kincaid and Scheer (1952) found evidence of an increase in the organic content of fed crabs following extirpation of the sinus gland. Although this work was done before knowledge of the role of the X-organ, Neiland and Scheer (1953) suggested that there was an eyestalk principle which directed tissue metabolism toward tissue growth and away from processes concerned with ecdysis. This is no longer tenable as ecdysis and growth are closely related. However, Kurup and Scheer (1966) found that the incorporation of radioactive amino acids into the muscle and hypodermis increased while incorporation into the hepatopancreas decreased in eyestalkless anomurans (*Petrolisthes cinctipes*). They suggested that there may be a factor in the eyestalk neuroendocrine system which restrains protein metabolism during intermolt.

Skinner (1965, 1966b), on the other hand, observed an increase in the incorporation of radioactive amino acids during premolt in hepatopancreas, epidermis, and muscle.

Fingerman and his co-workers (1967) found that eyestalk removal resulted in a decrease in RNA and amylase in the hepatopancreas of the crayfish *Procambarus clarkii*. They suggested that an eyestalk factor stimulates ribonucleic acid synthesis which in turn is responsible for the synthesis of amylase. Thornborough (1968), however, suggested that rather than a direct effect upon ribonucleic acid synthesis, eyestalk extract influenced ribonuclease activity of the hepatopancreas. He found that eyestalk extract repressed ribonuclease activity of the hepatopancreas of the prawn *Palaemonetes vulgaris.*

There is some evidence as to the chemical nature of crustacean hormones. Molt-inhibiting hormone may be a peptide (Ranga Rao, 1965). Crustacean molting hormone has been identified as 20-hydroxyecdysterone, a molecule similar to insect ecdysone except it has an —OH group at the 20 position (Adelung, 1967). It has been isolated from tissues of the marine crayfish, *Jasus lalandii* (D. H. S. Horn et al., 1968). Low concentrations of crustecdysone (0.0125 to 0.05 μg./gm.) reduced the molting time in crayfish (*Procambarus simulans*) only after eyestalk removal (Lowe et al., 1968). In higher concentrations (3 to 200 μg./gm.) ecdysterone stimulated molting in several arthropods, including *Limulus polyphemus,* the horseshoe crab; *Araneus cornutus,* the spider; and *Procambarus* sp., a crayfish (Krishnakumaran and Schneiderman, 1968). Most recently, Stewart and Green (1969) have related changes in protein synthesis and ribonucleic acid content to ecdysone levels in *Uca pugilator.*

The titer of molting hormone in *Carcinus maenas* appears to be low during much of the premolt period, rising just prior to ecdysis (Adelung, 1967). Skinner (1966b) had observed in *Gecarcinus lateralis* that although ribonucleic acid content is 3 to 4 times intermolt levels by stage D_1 the synthesis of ribosome ribonucleic acid (measured by the incorporation of ^{3}H-uridine) is highest during intermolt and decreases with the onset of premolt. This could lead to a suggestion that another hormone influences RNA synthesis from either the eyestalk X-organ or the Y-organ.

IV. Chemistry of Larval Growth and Development

Though little is known about adult growth, even less is known about the chemistry of the growth and development of crustacean larvae. Much of the work on larval development has been limited to an elucidation of the number of stages, their duration, and their morphology. However, with the development of better techniques, brachyuran larvae have been successfully reared from egg to the first crab stage in the laboratory. With the availability of well-defined stages there has been an increase in the information available about the physiology of the growth and development of crustacean larvae.

Green (1965) recently reviewed the chemical aspects of crustacean development and Costlow (1968) has discussed crustacean metamorphosis.

A. Carbohydrate Metabolism

Hoshi (1951, 1953, 1954) studied the variation in glycogen content of the developing eggs of *Simocephalus vetulus*. Glycogen content of the gastrula is 0.7% of the wet weight. This rises to 0.91% then falls to 0.71% of the wet weight when the young are released from the brood pouch. The embryos appear to synthesize glycogen in the early stages and use small amounts during the later stages.

The eggs of *Balanus balanus* and *Balanus balanoides* show a net loss of glucose and soluble and insoluble glycogen during development. Small increases of glucose are found at certain stages (Barnes, 1965). *Balanus balanoides* loses 74.6% of the total carbohydrate while the figure for *Balanus balanus* is 79.8%.

In the developing eggs of the barnacle *Pollicipes polymerus*, there is some indication that the pentose shunt may play a major role in glucose degradation during embryogenesis (Eastman, 1968). The rates of activity of glucose-6-phosphate dehydrogenase, 6-phosphogluconate dehydrogenase and fructose diphosphate aldolase showed major activity between the blastula stage and the naupliar rudiment stage. The ratio of fructose diphosphate aldolase to glucose-6-phosphate dehydrogenase was lowest in the early stages and highest at hatching.

Trehalose is the major carbohydrate reserve of *Artemia salina* and appears to play a major role in the encystment of *Artemia*. After 10 hours of development, the presumptive dormant embryo contains eight times as much trehalose as the presumptive nondormant embryo (Clegg, 1965). When the blastula enters dormancy, the trehalose constitutes 15% of the dry weight while nondormant embryos have essentially no trehalose. The glycogen content decreases in the presumptive dormant embryo but remains high in the nondormant embryo. The trehalose is synthesized by the dormant embryo only. Glucose is the major blood sugar of the female adult.

Upon rehydration, the dormant cysts proceed through two stages (Whitaker, 1940). In the first step the hard outer cyst wall splits and the embryo emerges within a hatching membrane (emergence). In the second stage (hatching) the nauplius swims free of the membrane. The hatching enzyme which helps break the hatching membrane has been partially characterized by Sato (1967). The inactive form of the enzyme is found associated with Fe^{++}. It is activated when the metal ion is removed by chelating agents. Ca^{++} reinforces the activity of the enzyme while Fe^{+++} and Cu^{++} inhibit it.

In the development after rehydration, trehalose content decreases from

15.3% to 0.6% of the dry weight. Glycogen at the same time increases from 1.5% to 5% (Dutrieu, 1960; Clegg, 1964). The external osmotic pressure appears to play a significant role in the hatching of the *Artemia* cysts. Normal desiccated cysts contain 36 μg. glycerol/mg. dry weight. When cysts are placed in 0.25 *M* sodium chloride, glycerol content increases to 56 μg./mg. dry weight and in 0.75 *M* sodium chloride to 80 μg./mg. (Clegg, 1965). The source of the glycerol and glycogen appears to be trehalose, as its decrease corresponds to an increase in the former.

Glycerol is located in two distinct regions: in the embryo and between the embryo and the shell (Clegg, 1964). When the shell breaks and the embryo emerges, the external glycerol is lost to the medium. It is proposed that glycerol in the cyst aids in the retention of water in the desiccated stage and also aids in emergence by imbibing water which increases the internal osmotic pressure which in turn helps break the shell.

B. LIPID METABOLISM

Direct observation of centrifuged eggs of *Simocephalus vetulus* indicates that the lipid content decreases during development. A large oil droplet decreases in size and eventually disperses during development (Hoshi, 1950a,b).

Dutrieu (1960) found that the total lipid content of *Artemia salina* increased during development from egg to nauplius from 20% to 24% of the dry weight. The unsaponifiable fraction also increased from 4.8% to 12% of the total lipid content. Urbani (1962), however, found the total lipid content decreasing in *Artemia salina*. Bellini and Lavizzari (1958) measured total lipase activity and found it highest prior to hatching. The increase was three- or fourfold between immersion and emergence.

In *Ligia oceanica*, 32% of the initial lipid content is lost by the time the neonate emerges, while in *Homarus vulgaris* 60% is used (Saudray, 1954). In *Balanus balanoides*, the figure is 11.5% and in *B. balanus* 17.3% is lost (Barnes, 1965). Triglyceride is lost during development. After an initial loss, lecithin and phosphatidyl ethanolamine accumulate in the later stages. Cardiolipin shows a marked increase from 0.5% to between 3.6% and 4.1% of the phospholipids (Dawson and Barnes, 1966). Dawson and Barnes (1966) carried out a fairly complete study on the lipids of *Balanus balanus* and *B. balanoides*. Triglyceride and phospholipid were the main lipid fractions. Lecithin and phosphatidyl ethanolamine were the primary fractions of phospholipid. Only small amounts of free fatty acids and sterols were present. The fatty acid spectrum was rich in unsaturated fatty acids with eicosapentaenoic (20:5) and docosahexaenoic (22:6) fatty acids the major fractions.

C. AMINO ACIDS AND PROTEINS

In the eggs of *Balanus balanus* and *B. balanoides,* protein accounts for 70% to 80% of the dry weight (Barnes and Evans, 1967). The amino acid composition is similar to that of *Calanus finmarchicus* (Cowey and Corner, 1963). During development, *Balanus balanus* loses 35.2% of the total nitrogen while *B. balanoides* loses 25.6% (Barnes, 1965). All the amino acids decrease but the relative amounts of alanine and glycine increase during the late stages. In *B. balanoides,* there is a distinct decrease in the rate of loss of amino acids in the final stages of development (H-stage defined by Barnes, 1965, after Groom, 1894), coincident with a slowdown in the loss of other metabolites and in development (Barnes and Evans, 1967).

Dutrieu (1960) found some changes in the relative proportions of some free amino acids during the development of *Artemia salina.* The six most abundant acids in the eggs were aspartic acid, cysteine, serine, glycine, alanine, and glutamic acid. In the hatched nauplius, alanine, serine, glycine, proline, tyrosine, and glutamic acid were the most abundant. Arginine and threonine increased from a trace to higher concentrations between egg and nauplius.

Emerson (1967) found that the amino acid content depended upon the embryonic development as well as on external salinity. If *Artemia* was incubated in distilled water, total amino acid concentration declined during development. In either 0.5 M or 1.0 M sodium chloride, total amino acid content increased. During development, alanine, glycine, threonine, histidine, and lysine increased while aspartic acid, serine, and arginine decreased. The activity of glutamate-pyruvate transaminase appeared to parallel the change in alanine concentration, increasing until emergence followed by a slight decrease following emergence.

In *Artemia,* during the period between rehydration and emergence, there is no cell division (Emerson, 1963; Nakanishi *et al.,* 1959). Total nitrogen increases very little (Urbani, 1959) and there is no increase in DNA or RNA content (Bellini, 1960). This is probably a period of cellular differentiation and reorganization. Protein synthesis is, however, occurring at this time. Although labeled amino acids were not incorporated, possibly due to the impermeability of the shell, $^{14}CO_2$ was incorporated into glutamate and aspartate residues (Clegg, 1966). Ribosomes have been isolated from the embryos of *Artemia* (Hultin and Morris, 1968; Golub and Clegg, 1968; Clegg and Golub, 1969).

The formation of small polyribosomes was detected 5 minutes after the dormant embryos were allowed to resume development. The ribosomes were shown to be functional by their ability to incorporate leucine-^{14}C into hot TCA-insoluble material *in vitro.*

In *Callinectes sapidus* and *Rhithropanopeus harrisii,* the relative concentration of free amino acids was highest in the eggs and decreased in the first two zoeal stages (Costlow and Sastry, 1966). In *Callinectes,* the relative concentration increased during the first crab stage. The amino acid composition did not vary under different conditions of temperature and salinity. In *Rhithropanopeus,* the composition and relative concentration varied with temperature and salinity.

D. ENVIRONMENTAL EFFECTS ON GROWTH AND DEVELOPMENT

In *Balanus improvisus,* carbonic anhydrase has been identified in the shell-forming tissue (Costlow, 1959). Larvae maintained in solutions containing carbonic anhydrase inhibitors failed to develop the typical six plate shell of the adult. However, metamorphosis was not affected. If the larvae were removed from the inhibitor 3 to 6 days after metamorphosis, normal shell development occurred. If this was delayed to 8 days after metamorphosis, normal shell development did not occur.

There has been a large number of studies on the effects of salinity and temperature on crustacean metamorphosis and survival. Some of the species studied are *Callinectes sapidus* (Costlow, 1967), *Cardisoma guanhumi* (Costlow and Bookhout, 1968), *Sesarma reticulatum* (Costlow *et al.,* 1960), and *Rhithropanopeus harrisii* (Costlow *et al.,* 1966). As most of these results deal with the effects of salinity and temperature on physical parameters of metamorphosis and molting they will not be discussed.

E. ENDOCRINE REGULATION

The effect of eyestalk removal on crustacean larvae has been studied in only a few species. An excellent discussion is presented by Costlow (1968) so this topic will only be briefly mentioned.

In *Callinectes sapidus,* metamorphosis to the first crab stage is accelerated only if the eyestalks are removed within the final 12 hours after the final zoeal molt (Costlow, 1963). In *Sesarma reticulatum,* acceleration is caused if removal occurs prior to day 4 of megalops life. Depending upon when extirpation occurs, an extra zoeal and extra megalops stage is seen (Costlow, 1966a). In *Rhithropanopeus harrisii,* eyestalk removal caused 2 extra zoeal stages but acceleration of metamorphosis did not occur (Costlow, 1966b). Hubschman (1963) found that eyestalk removal in the shrimp *Palaemonetes* had no effect upon either molting or metamorphosis of the larvae.

The results indicate that there are differences in development of a functional neuroendocrine system among different species.

V. Summary and Conclusion

The periodic growth of crustaceans offers some unique opportunities for study of a controlled sequence of metabolic changes in which growth processes are uncomplicated by developmental changes. Accumulation of reserves of lipid and carbohydrate characterizes the late intermolt period of the intermolt cycle. Considerable turnover of protein, as one pattern of enzyme activity follows another, is evident, and the possibility of protein storage has been suggested. A complex sequence of events is involved in formation of the rudiments of a new cuticle underneath the old in the premolt period, and the completion of this structure in the postmolt and early intermolt: secretion of successive layers, synthesis of protein, sclerotization by quinone tanning, synthesis of chitin and mucopolysaccharide, calcification, and associated changes in blood composition all deserve more study. Changes in protein and nucleic acid content of muscle and other tissues occur in the normal growth processes, but study of these has only begun. Many of the events in this complex sequence are under neuroendocrine control, but knowledge of the hormones and mechanisms of action remains meagre.

The recent development of techniques for rearing crustacean larvae has opened the possibility of extending these studies to the developmental stages and of comparing the chemical aspects of crustacean development to the well-known features of insect development. Only a beginning has been made here, and most of the studies have been confined to the relatively specialized barnacles and the brine shrimp *Artemia salina*. The largest group of living animals, after the insects, offers to comparative biochemistry a host of fascinating problems.

REFERENCES

Abramowitz, R. K., and Abramowitz, A. A. (1940). *Biol. Bull.* **78**, 179–188.
Adelung, D. (1967). *Zool. Anz.* **30**, 264–272.
Adiyodi, R. G. (1968). *Indian J. Exptl. Biol.* **6**, 144–147.
Agrell, I. (1964). *In* "The Physiology of Insecta" (M. Rockstein, ed.), Vol. 1, pp. 91–148. Academic Press, New York.
Astell, C. R., Suzuki, D. T., Klett, R. P., Smith, M., and Goldberg, I. H. (1969). *Exptl. Cell Res.* **54**, 3–10.
Barnes, H. (1965). *J. Marine Biol. Assoc. U.K.* **45**, 321–339.
Barnes, H., and Evans, R. (1967). *J. Marine Biol. Assoc. U.K.* **47**, 171–180.
Bauchau, A. G., and Hontoy, J. (1968). *Crustaceana* **14**, 67–75.

Baumberger, J. P., and Olmsted, J. M. D. (1928). *Physiol. Zool.* **1**, 531–544.
Bellini, L. (1960). *Atti Accad. Nazl. Lincei, Ric.* **30**, 816–833.
Bellini, L., and Lavizzari, G. S. (1958). *Atti Accad. Nazl. Lincei, Ric.* **24**, 92–95.
Chen, P. S. (1962). *In* "Amino Acid Pools" (J. T. Holden, ed.), pp. 115–135. Elsevier, Amsterdam.
Chen, P. S., and Levenbook, L. (1966). *J. Insect Physiol.* **12**, 1595–1609.
Clegg, J. S. (1964). *J. Exptl. Biol.* **41**, 879–892.
Clegg, J. S. (1965). *Comp. Biochem. Physiol.* **14**, 132–143.
Clegg, J. S. (1966). *Nature* **212**, 517–519.
Clegg, J. S., and Golub, A. L. (1969). *Develop. Biol.* **19**, 178–200.
Costlow, J. D. (1959). *Physiol. Zool.* **32**, 177–184.
Costlow, J. D. (1963). *Gen. Comp. Endocrinol.* **3**, 120–130.
Costlow, J. D. (1966a). *In* "Some Contemporary Studies in Marine Science" (H. Barnes, ed.), pp. 209–224. Allen & Unwin, London.
Costlow, J. D. (1966b). *Gen. Comp. Endocrinol.* **7**, 255–274.
Costlow, J. D. (1967). *Helgolaender Wiss. Meeresuntersuch.* **15**, 84–97.
Costlow, J. D. (1968). *In* "Metamorphosis" (W. Etkin and L. I. Gilbert, eds.), pp. 3–41. Appleton, New York.
Costlow, J. D., and Bookhout, C. G. (1968). *Am. Zoologist* **8**, 399–410.
Costlow, J. D., and Sastry, A. N. (1966). *Acta Embryol. Morphol. Exptl.* **9**, 44–55.
Costlow, J. D., Bookhout, C. G., and Monroe, R. J. (1960). *Biol. Bull.* **118**, 183–202.
Costlow, J. D., Bookhout, C. G., and Monroe, R. J. (1966). *Physiol. Zool.* **39**, 81–100.
Cowey, C. B., and Corner, E. D. S. (1963). *J. Marine Biol. Assoc. U.K.* **43**, 485–493.
Damboviceanu, A. (1932). *Arch. Roumaines Pathol. Exptl. Microbiol.* **5**, 239–309.
Dawson, R. M. C., and Barnes, H. (1966). *J. Marine Biol. Assoc. U.K.* **46**, 249–261.
Decleir, W., and Vercauteren, R. (1965). *Cahiers Biol. Marine* **6**, 163–172.
Dennell, R. (1947). *Proc. Roy. Soc.* **B134**, 485–503.
Dennell, R. (1960). *In* "The Physiology of Crustacea" (T. H. Waterman, ed.), Vol. 1, pp. 449–472. Academic Press, New York.
Digby, P. S. B. (1968). *J. Zool.* **154**, 273–286.
Drach, P. (1939). *Ann. Inst. Oceanog. (Paris)* **19**, 103–391.
Drach, P. (1944). *Bull. Biol. France Belg.* **78**, 40–62.
Drach, P., and Lafon, M. (1942). *Arch. Zool. Exptl. Gen.* **82**, 100–118.
Drilhon, A. (1935). *Ann. Physiol. Physicochim. Biol.* **11**, 301–326.
Dutrieu, J. (1960). *Arch. Zool. Exptl. Gen.* **99**, 1–134.
Eastman, R. C. (1968). *Exptl. Cell Res.* **51**, 323–329.
Emerson, D. N. (1963). *Proc. S. Dakota Acad. Sci.* **42**, 131–135.
Emerson, D. N. (1967). *Comp. Biochem. Physiol.* **20**, 245–261.
Fingerman, M., Dominiczak, T., Miyawaki, M., Oguro, C., and Yamamoto, Y. (1967). *Physiol. Zool.* **40**, 23–30.
Fox, F. R., and Mills, R. R. (1969). *Comp. Biochem. Physiol.* **29**, 1187–1195.
Glynn, J. P. (1968). *Comp. Biochem. Physiol.* **26**, 937–946.
Golub, A. L., and Clegg, J. S. (1968). *Develop. Biol.* **17**, 644–656.
Green, J. (1965). *Biol. Rev. Cambridge Phil. Soc.* **40**, 580–600.
Groom, T. T. (1894). *Phil. Trans. Roy. Soc. London* **B185**, 119–232.
Hackman, R. H. (1959). *Proc. 4th Intern. Congr. Biochem., Vienna, 1958*, Vol. 12, pp. 48–52. Pergamon Press, Oxford.
Hiatt, R. W. (1948). *Pacific Sci.* **2**, 135–213.

Horn, D. H. S., Fabbri, S., Hampshire, F., and Lowe, M. E. (1968). *Biochem. J.* **109,** 399–406.

Horn, E. C., and Kerr, M. S. (1963). *Biol. Bull.* **125,** 499–507.

Horn, E. C., and Kerr, M. S. (1969). *Comp. Biochem. Physiol.* **29,** 493–503.

Hoshi, T. (1950a). *Sci. Rept. Tohoku Univ., Fourth Ser.* **18,** 316–323.

Hoshi, T. (1950b). *Sci. Rept. Tohoku Univ., Fourth Ser.* **18,** 464–466.

Hoshi, T. (1951). *Sci. Rept. Tohoku Univ., Fourth Ser.* **19,** 123–132.

Hoshi, T. (1953). *Sci. Rept. Tohoku Univ., Fourth Ser.* **20,** 6–10.

Hoshi, T. (1954). *Sci. Rept. Tohoku Univ., Fourth Ser.* **20,** 260–264.

Hubschman, J. H. (1963). *Biol. Bull.* **125,** 96–113.

Hultin, T., and Morris, J. E. (1968). *Develop. Biol.* **17,** 143–164.

Karlson, P., and Sekeris, C. E. (1964). *Comp. Biochem.* **6,** 221–243.

Kerr, M. S. (1969). *Develop. Biol.* **20,** 1–17.

Kincaid, F. D., and Scheer, B. T. (1952). *Physiol. Zool.* **25,** 372–380.

Koch, H. J. A. (1952). *Mededel. Koninkl. Vlaam. Acad. Wetenschap. Belg., Kl. Wetenschap.* **14,** 3–11.

Krishnakumaran, A., and Schneiderman, H. A. (1968). *Nature* **220,** 601–603.

Krishnan, G. (1951). *Quart. J. Microscop. Sci.* **92,** 333–342.

Krishnan, G. (1954). *Proc. Natl. Inst. Sci. India* **B20,** 157–169.

Kurup, N. G. (1964). *Biol. Bull.* **127,** 97–107.

Kurup, N. G., and Scheer, B. T. (1966). *Comp. Biochem. Physiol.* **18,** 971–973.

Lafon, M. (1943). *Ann. Sci. Nat. Zool. Biol. Animale* [11] **5,** 113–146.

Lafon, M. (1948). *Bull. Inst. Oceanog.* **45,** 1–28.

Lowe, M. E., Horn, D. H. S., and Galbraith, M. N. (1968). *Experientia* **24,** 518–519.

McWhinnie, M. A., and Chua, A. S. (1964). *Gen. Comp. Endocrinol.* **4,** 624–633.

McWhinnie, M. A., and Corkill, A. J. (1964). *Comp. Biochem. Physiol.* **12,** 81–93.

Manwell, C., and Baker, C. M. A. (1963). *Comp. Biochem. Physiol.* **8,** 193–208.

Martin, A. L. (1965). *J. Zool.* **147,** 185–200.

Nakanishi, Y. H., Iwasaki, T., Okigaki, T., and Kata, H. (1959). *Annotationes Zool. Japon.* **35,** 223–228.

Neiland, K. A., and Scheer, B. T. (1953). *Physiol. Comparata Oecol.* **3,** 321–326.

O'Connor, J. D., and Gilbert, L. I. (1968). *Am. Zoologist* **8,** 529–539.

O'Connor, J. D., and Gilbert, L. I. (1969). *Comp. Biochem. Physiol.* **29,** 889–904.

Passano, L. M. (1960). *In* "The Physiology of Crustacea" (T. H. Waterman, ed.), Vol. 1, pp. 473–536. Academic Press, New York.

Pochon, F., Massoulie, J., and Michelson, A. M. (1966). *Biochim. Biophys. Acta* **119,** 249–257.

Pryor, M. G. M. (1962). *Comp. Biochem.* **4,** 371–396.

Puyear, R. L. (1967). *Comp. Biochem. Physiol.* **20,** 499–508.

Ranga Rao, K. (1965). *Experientia* **21,** 593–594.

Renaud, L. (1949). *Ann. Inst. Oceanog.* (*Paris*) **24,** 259–357.

Sather, B. T. (1967). *Pacific Sci.* **21,** 193–209.

Sato, N. L. (1967). *Sci. Rept. Tohoku Univ., Fourth Ser.* **33,** 319–327.

Saudray, Y. (1954). *Compt. Rend. Soc. Biol.* **148,** 814–816.

Scheer, B. T. (1960). *Comp. Biochem. Physiol.* **1,** 3–18.

Schwartz, M. N., Trautner, T. A., and Kornberg, A. (1962). *J. Biol. Chem.* **237,** 1961–1967.

Scudamore, H. H. (1947). *Physiol. Zool.* **20,** 187–208.

Skinner, D. M. (1958). *Anat. Record* **132,** 507.

Skinner, D. M. (1962). *Biol. Bull.* **123,** 635–647.

Skinner, D. M. (1965). *J. Exptl. Zool.* 160, 225–234.
Skinner, D. M. (1966a). *J. Exptl. Zool.* 163, 115–124.
Skinner, D. M. (1966b). *Am. Zoologist* 6, 235–242.
Skinner, D. M. (1967). *Proc. Natl. Acad. Sci. U.S.* 58, 103–110.
Skinner, D. M. (1968). *J. Exptl. Zool.* 169, 347–356.
Stevenson, J. R. (1963). *Biol. Bull.* 125, 92–393.
Stevenson, J. R. (1968). *Biol. Bull.* 134, 160–175.
Stevenson, J. R., and Adomako, T. Y. (1967). *J. Insect Physiol.* 13, 1803–1811.
Stewart, J. R., and Green, J. P. (1969). *Am. Zoologist* 9, 579.
Sueoka, N. (1961). *J. Mol. Biol.* 3, 31–40.
Summers, N. M., Jr. (1967). *Comp. Biochem. Physiol.* 23, 129–138.
Summers, N. M., Jr. (1968). *Comp. Biochem. Physiol.* 26, 259–269.
Thornborough, J. R. (1968). *Comp. Biochem. Physiol.* 24, 625–628.
Travis, D. F. (1955a). *Biol. Bull.* 108, 88–112.
Travis, D. F. (1955b). *Biol. Bull.* 109, 484–503.
Travis, D. F. (1957). *Biol. Bull.* 113, 451–479.
Travis, D. F. (1960). *In* "Calcification in Biological Systems," Publ. No. 64, pp. 57–116. Am. Assoc. Advance Sci., Washington, D.C.
Travis, D. F. (1963). *Ann. N.Y. Acad. Sci.* 109, 177–245.
Travis, D. F. (1965). *Acta Histochem.* 20, 193–222.
Urbani, E. (1959). *Acta Embryol. Morphol. Exptl.* 2, 171–194.
Urbani, E. (1962). *Advan. Morphogenesis* 2, 61–108.
Whitaker, D. M. (1940). *J. Exptl. Zool.* 38, 391–399.
Woods, K., Paulsen, E. C., Engle, R. L., and Pert, J. H. (1958). *Science* 127, 519–520.
Zuckerkandl, E. (1956). *Compt. Rend. Soc. Biol.* 150, 39–41.
Zuckerkandl, E. (1957). *Compt. Rend. Soc. Biol.* 151, 850–853.
Zuckerkandl, E. (1960). *Ann. Inst. Oceanog.* (*Paris*) 38, 1–122.

CHAPTER 12

Chemical Aspects of
Growth and Development in Insects

Colette L'Hélias

I. Introduction

In the last 20 years, knowledge of the biochemistry of insects has expanded considerably, becoming as important as the chemistry of vertebrates and microorganisms. Although it is impossible to investigate all published works, numerous authors have written complete reviews which consider different aspects of the biochemistry of insects. Alfert (1954), Wigglesworth (1964), Gilbert (1964, 1966), Schneiderman and Gilbert (1964), Harvey and Haskell (1966), Kilby and Neville (1957), and Wyatt (1961, 1963, 1967), in particular, have studied insect metabolism during development from different viewpoints. A survey of energy metabolism, structural metabolism, and finally mechanisms of genetic and hormonal control of development are given here.

II. Energy Metabolism

A. CARBOHYDRATES

1. Action of Growth Hormones on Carbohydrate Metabolism

During the development of *Carausius morosus,* the corpora allata and corpora cardiaca control metabolism up to the penultimate stage. At the last stage preceding adult metamorphosis, the allata secretion diminishes greatly. Removal of the corpora allata and cardiaca results in a considerable decrease in blood sugar and in an accumulation of glycogen in the tissues, but removal of the allata alone leads to a decrease in protein synthesis (L'Hélias, 1953b). Hyperglycemia induced by the corpora cardiaca was noticed by Steele (1961) and McCarthy and Ralph (1962) who also observed a hyperglycemic activity of the allata, which was confirmed by Steele (1969). The synthesis of trehalose, the main sugar in insect blood, occurs in the fat body which might thus have a function analogous to the glycogenic function of the liver in mammals (Candy and Kilby, 1961).

Trehalose synthesis from glycogen depends upon activation of the fat body phosphorylase by the cardiaca, as previously noted (Steele, 1963). Stanley (1967) found that an extract of cardiaca has hyperglycemic activity in *Phormia* only if it has been submitted to a previous 24-hour fasting period; the sugar content of the insect crop seems to be a limiting factor (Gelperin, 1966). Trehalose, even in low concentrations, produces a feedback inhibition of trehalose synthesis. Murphy and Wyatt (1965) also observed this effect in *Hyalophora* where glucose-1-^{14}C is incorporated into glycogen in the presence of high concentrations of trehalose. In the adult *Calliphora erythrocephala* and *Aedes aegypti* (Van Handel and Lea, 1965), hyperglycemic activity occurs in the pars intercerebralis cells (Thomsen, 1952). Removal of these cells results in an accumulation of glycogen in the fat body and in inhibition of vitellogenesis. Carbohydrates normally metabolized and producing the energy required for protein synthesis are stored since brain hormone is necessary for glycogen consumption.

Yamashita and Hasegawa (1964) have demonstrated that *Bombyx* females which are laying diapausing eggs have 50% more glycogen in their ovaries than females in which the subesophageal ganglion is at rest. This phenomenon can already be observed in the ovaries of female pupae. Removal of the subesophageal ganglion produces a decrease of the total glycogen and re-establishes the normal glycogen level in the ovaries. The diapausing hormone present in the eggs promotes the transfer of sugars of the blood to the ovary and stimulates glycogen synthetase in the tissues. Male pupae in which an ovary has been implanted react in the same manner as females in which the subesophageal ganglion has been removed, but do not react at all if they do not receive the ovarian transfer during their larval life.

In all species studied, the hyperglycemic factor is localized in a part of the retrocerebral complex, either in the neurosecretory cells or in the cardiaca or allata. Depending upon the level of evolution of the organ, the factor is stored sooner or later in the neuroendocrine path; it can even be secreted, because the cells involved in the formation of the factor can migrate more or less deeply into the corpora cardiaca.

The case of the subesophageal ganglion needs to be considered separately because the diapause hormone of the egg has an action which differs from that of brain hormone and juvenile hormone. The hormone is involved in accumulation of foodstuffs for hibernation of the eggs and not in promoting growth.

Ecdysone activates the transformation of glucose-^{14}C injected into decerebrated pupae (Kobayashi and Kirimura, 1967). Glucose-^{14}C is incorporated into trehalose in pupae treated with ecdysone and into glycogen in untreated pupae.

Trehalose

2. Glycogenolysis and Glycogen Synthesis

Though trehalose represents a very important source of energy for insects which utilize carbohydrates, glycogen also plays an important role. It can be retransformed into glucose for new synthesis of blood trehalose. Glycogen synthetase also acts on UDPG:

$$UDPG + glycogen_n \rightarrow UDP + glycogen_{n+1}$$

Changes in the glycogen supply occur during the reproductive cycle in Leucophaea (Wiens and Gilbert, 1967b). In ovaries and embryos in development, glycogen increases slowly except for a short period in the last half of embryogenesis in which it disappears quickly just before parturition. This sudden disappearance of glycogen at the end of embryogenesis can be correlated with the synthesis of the cuticle. Lipke *et al.* (1965) made the same observation in *Periplaneta* undergoing metamorphosis, suggesting again that glycogen breakdown is hormonally controlled.

Glycogen synthetase is inhibited by glucose 6-phosphate and activated by glucose 1-phosphate. Glycogen phosphorylase, catalyzing the reaction:

$$\text{Glycogen}_n + \text{phosphate} \rightarrow \text{glycogen}_{n-1} + \text{glucose 1-phosphate}$$

occurs in insects. Shigematsu (1956a) and Ito and Horie (1959) have demonstrated the presence of this enzyme in *Bombyx* embryos and in pupae of *Samia cynthia* in which the activity is enhanced by AMP and not by cysteine (Stevenson and Wyatt, 1964). There is an important increase in the enzyme concentration during development of the *Hyalophora* adult until the first days of the adult stage (Wiens and Gilbert, 1968). This phosphorylase (α-1,4-glucose-5-phosphate glucosyltransferase) is activated by the phosphorylase kinase (ATP phosphoryltransferase).

There is a progressive increase in glycogen during the larval stage with very definite drops at each molt. Glycogen stored at pupation is consumed during metamorphosis. Lipids can be transformed into glycogen and increase the supply; chitin decreases suddenly in the *Bombyx* prepupa, and may undergo an analogous transformation (Bade and Wyatt, 1962).

There is little accumulation of trehalose during diapause. The concentration of trehalose in diapausing eggs of *Bombyx* is slightly higher (4 mg./gm.) than in nondiapausing ones (Yamashita, 1965). Some diapausing pupae which have to survive freezing periods have a high concentration of trehalose; others which are not submitted to severe climatic conditions do not show this adaptation; others react by transforming their supply into glycerol and sorbitol.

3. Sugar Catabolism

a. Sugar Supply. Glycogen and trehalose are the main sources used for energy production. Sugar concentration can be extremely high, especially in hibernating insects. *Trichiocampus populi* larvae, ready to begin the pupal instar, are able to survive at $-30°C$ in liquid nitrogen for 2 hours. Their sugar content, 97% of which is trehalose, is 5% to 9% of the fresh weight (Asahina and Tanno, 1964). Solitary bees, *Ceratina flavipes japonica*, contain 15% of their weight as sugars, mainly fructose, 45 to 77 mg./gm., and glucose, 30 to 48 mg./gm., but only 4 mg./gm. of trehalose (Tanno, 1964). This last concentration is equivalent to that found in nonhibernating insects. In general, the concentration seems to be higher in the hemolymph than in the tissues. Mochnachka and Petryszyn, 1959 find 10 mg./ml. of trehalose in the blood of *Celerio* pupae and none at all in the tissues during diapause. Trehalose appears in the tissue and decreases again during metamorphosis. In *Hyalophora,* Wyatt detected 15 mmoles/ml. in the fat body and 50 mmoles/ml. in the blood. Clegg and Evans (1961) found 10 to 30 mg./ml. of trehalose and 4 mg./ml. of glucose in the hemolymph and only 0.3 mg./ml. in flight muscles.

The glucoside reserves vary according to the different stages of development: they increase during resting periods and decrease during growth crisis (i.e., metamorphosis and gonad maturation stages). Changes in the glycogen supply are discussed in Section II, A, 2.

The end product of glycolysis in insects is α-glycerophosphate, in vertebrates lactic acid, and in plants pyruvic acid. Though insects possess all required enzymes, the most active is α-glycerophosphate dehydrogenase (Chefurka, 1958; Delbrück *et al.*, 1959).

b. Phosphatases and Kinases. The presence of the Embden–Meyerhof pathway enzymes has been demonstrated. The enzymic activities vary during development under the influence of specific hormones. Glucose-6-phosphatase can be detected only at the end of larval life and in the pupa; therefore, another enzyme is involved in the formation of glucose from glycogen. Trehalose-6-phosphatase shows some activity on glucose 6-phosphate (Faulkner, 1955; Murphy and Wyatt, 1965).

Hexokinases are present in insects; after the splitting of trehalose into glucose by trehalase, a kinase is involved for phosphorylation to glucose 6-phosphate (Chefurka, 1954). Other kinases exist, acting specifically on phosphorylation of sugars present in the diet (mannose, fructose, etc.).

c. Transphosphorylation. In young allatectomized larvae there is a decrease in the ratio of protein nitrogen to total nitrogen and a decrease in organic phosphate, while phosphatases intensify inorganic phosphate elimination (L'Hélias, 1954a,b). This strong phosphatase activity seems to be directly related to the absence of juvenile hormone and results in blocking the sugar reserves and in the accumulation of mineral phosphorus. Formation of phosphorylated esters and the Embden–Meyerhof cycle are blocked (Chefurka, 1958); therefore, it is the first step of glycolysis which is inhibited. Transphosphorylations by means of ATP do not occur. The considerable amounts of energy required for the synthesis of the proteins of large molecules are not released.

Carey and Wyatt (1963) have found an ATP/ADP ratio of 12 in dormant pupae of *Platysamia cecropia* and a ratio of 17 in metamorphosing pupae. The chrysalis, therefore, retains its ability to synthesize ATP during diapause. Inorganic phosphate accumulates in the gut and the Malpighian tubules. The level of inorganic phosphate in blood drops simultaneously; this supports Heller's suggestion that inorganic phosphorus works as a regulator of oxidations in dormant chrysalids. ADP may play a regulatory role, controlling respiration. Endergonic processes may enhance this control by liberating ADP.

In the hemolymph of *P. cecropia* larvae, many uridine diphosphate sugars can be found, as well as a phosphorylated base which might be phosphoarginine, a source of high energy for insects equivalent to phosphocreatine in vertebrates. Their concentration is very high at the beginning of adult development, and this could be related to chitin synthesis because uridine diphosphoglucose and uridine-N-acetylglucosamide are the precursors of chitin and other polysaccharides.

The corpora allata activate formation of compounds able to transfer energy to other parts of the cell not only in the anaerobic phase (oxidation of triose phosphate, dehydration of 2-phosphoglycerate) but also in the aerobic phase (oxidation of α-ketoglutarate into succinyl coenzyme A).

Horie *et al.* (1968) have demonstrated by use of glucose-^{14}C that glucose catabolism occurs not only through the Embden–Meyerhof cycle but also more than 35% through the pentose phosphate pathway. The final products are CO_2 and C_2 sugars. These sugars are then transformed into fatty acids and incorporated into lipids. α-Glucose phosphate and 6-phosphogluconate dehydrogenases control glycolysis through the pentose phosphate pathway; they are very active in larval tissues, particularly in the fat body (Horie, 1967).

B. Respiratory Metabolism

1. Changes in Metabolism during Development

The most evident manifestations of metabolism during molting and metamorphosis are respiratory exchanges. In *Rhodnius* there is a respiratory crisis at each molt with intensive oxygen consumption, followed by a quiet phase during the intermolt period. When the prothoracic glands start secreting and the insect forms a new cuticle, respiration increases and reaches a maximum at ecdysis. Fourche (1968) has observed that during metamorphosis oxygen consumption follows a U-shaped curve. During puparium formation, the larval nymph molt, and increase of respiration in imaginal ecdysis reaches its maximum rate.

In *Galleria*, the penultimate and last larval stages are both characterized by cycles of oxygen consumption which show a maximum in the
middle of the intermolt period; increases in oxygen consumption parallels
the increase in weight of the insect. The pupal intermolt period, on
the contrary, shows the typical U-curve of metamorphosis: decrease
in basal metabolism immediately after pupation, a level period at the
time of ecdysone secretion and development of adult organs (Slama,
1965), and then a sudden increase.

Changes of the same order appear during the growth of Lepidoptera
(Williams, 1968). *Platysamia cecropia* shows short moments of respiratory rest during intermolt periods; during the long diapause, respiration
falls to one-fiftieth of its normal intensity; respiration is insensitive to
inhibitors (Kurland and Schneiderman, 1959; Shappirio, 1960). The
tissues contain much more cytochrome oxidase than cytochrome c. It
appears that the differences in the energy-producing systems are simply
due to different concentrations of respiratory enzymes. Ecdysone, then,
produces a shift in the ratio of concentration of enzymes rather than a
change in their nature. However, if cytochrome oxidase is still present in
the diapausing pupa and if it is inhibited by carbon monoxide only when
it is saturated with electrons, there is no active NADH oxidase. NAD
and NADH (oxidized and reduced nicotinamide adenine dinucleotide),
electron donors able to diminish the enzyme activity, undergo a significant decrease. In the diapausing pupa, only cytochromes a, a_3 and b_5,
are spectroscopically detectable; b and c reappear only at the beginning
of adult life, and their concentrations increase during the whole period
of adult development.

2. Action of the Corpora Allata on Respiratory Metabolism

Removal of the corpora allata of *Carausius morosus* at the 3rd or
4th instar results in a significant decrease in oxygen consumption (Pflugfelder, 1940; L'Hélias, 1954c; Neugebauer, 1961) except for a short
period immediately following the surgical procedure when there is a
strong increase of oxygen consumption due to surgical shock and at
the last instar before imaginal molting when juvenile hormone is no
longer active. This decrease in respiration confirms that metabolism considerably reduced as already shown by the accumulation of reserves
in the tissues.

However, Williams (1959) and Gilbert and Schneiderman (1961) have
wondered if this action was direct or if the allata were not promoting
a secretion of ecdysone which would finally be responsible for activation
of metabolism; extracts of juvenile hormone, compared with injections
of peanut oil, enhance respiration and, at the same time, accelerate

the appearance of an early molt. It is also possible to reverse the reasoning and to say that allata activity increases metabolism in such a way that ecdysone secretion is accelerated. DeWilde and Stegwee's results (1958) support this last idea. They have shown that injection of extracts of male *P. cecropia* abdomens containing juvenile hormone into allatectomized potato beetles stimulates respiration. Succinate oxidation is stimulated, and the authors have suggested that the site of stimulation is between succinate and cytochrome *c*. On the other hand, Keeley and Friedman (1967) have found that the corpora cardiaca and allata have an influence on the respiratory metabolism of *Blaberus discoidalis* males and on the respiration of the fat body *in vitro;* in this instance there is no variation in dry weight. The respiration of the fat body in the males, then, depends upon a "cardiacal" factor different from the corpora allata factor. But allatectomy also affects the mitochondrial function in disrupting the synthesis or release of factors from the brain or corpora cardiaca (Keeley and Friedman, 1969).

When brain–cardiaca allata complexes are injected during the last larval instar, two to five supernumerary larval molts occur, giving rise to giant pupae and reproducing the observed larval and nymphal respiratory cycles. This confirms that the allata are responsible for the increase of oxygen consumption during larval growth. In holometabolic insects, the allata lose their activity during nymphosis, metabolism follows a U-shaped curve, and the sequence of metabolic activity corresponds to the action of ecdysone. In the Exopterygota, allata activity stops at the antepenultimate larval instar (L'Hélias, 1953a); the last stage can be called nymphosis. Allata activity reappears in adults, at least in females, for the process of vitellogenesis (Thomsen, 1952; Thomsen and Hamburger, 1955). In *Pyrrhocoris* adult females, Slama and Hrubesova (1963) and Slama and Janda (1965) have distinguished three respiratory cycles: (1) a respiratory metabolism of digestion depending upon nutritional activity, (2) a cellular basal metabolism independent of hormones, and (3) a respiratory metabolism characteristic of reproduction, depending upon allata activity and directly related to ovarian growth. In allatectomized *Pyrrhocoris* females, the follicular ovarian cells remain inactive indefinitely, allata re-implantation re-establishes follicular activity, vitellogenesis, and respiratory metabolism.

Farnesol derivatives, applied to the cuticle, produce a juvenilizing action on the activity of the follicular cells and on the corresponding respiratory cycle; however, they give negative results on allatectomized organisms, and it seems that they cannot replace the juvenile hormone. The metathetelic effects of these terpenes and steroids on the larval cuticle must be dissociated from the true effects of the juvenile hormone.

C. Lipids

Lipid constitution of insects resembles that of other animals. The lipid content can vary from 1% to 50% of the fresh weight (Niemierko, 1959), depending on the species and on whether or not the adults feed and hence have to carry a smaller or larger reserve for egg production. Generally, the lipid reserve is much higher in females than in males except in certain Lepidoptera (Niemierko, 1959; Demyanovsky and Zubova, 1959; Gilbert and Schneiderman, 1959, 1961).

1. Lipid Composition

a. Changes during Development. During development, lipid composition can change (Rothstein, 1952). In *Papilio japonica,* lipids are the most important source of energy during embryogenesis. Lipid metabolism can undergo variations due to growth and also modifications due to differentiation of sexes or castes.

Sexual dimorphism can be observed in the Lepidoptera; it appears at the larval stage and is accentuated when gonads differentiate. During the nymph–adult transformation, the female uses more of its supplies than the male (Gilbert and Schneiderman, 1961). Probably the male uses another substrate for its development.

In the ant (Schmidt, 1966), total lipids and free lipids diminish greatly in the pupa. Bound lipids change also, but the decrease is different in females and in workers. Lipid phosphorous varies periodically. During metamorphosis, free fatty acids increase and esterified lipids decrease.

Lipid degradation begins with the transformation of triglycerides into diglycerides. Following hydrolysis, glycerides are incorporated into phospholipids (Kinsella, 1966). In the silkworm *Bombyx,* degradation of glucose occurs mainly through the pentose phosphate pathway rather than through normal glycolysis, accounting for 35% of glucose degradation in the intact larva and an even greater percentage in the isolated fat body (Horie *et al.,* 1968). Pyruvate decarboxylation gives rise to C_2 units which are then incorporated into lipids. This phenomenon is detected when labeled pyruvate is used. Fatty acid synthesis occurs from glucose via pyruvate. Starting from glucose completely labeled with ^{14}C, palmitic, oleic, stearic, and palmitoleic, but no linoleic or linolenic acids, can be obtained. Constitution in saturated and unsaturated acids varies greatly during larval life. Females use more fatty acids during their pupa–adult transformation than males (Nakasone and Ito, 1967).

b. Action of the Corpora Allata on Lipids. The different experiments previously described show that the corpora allata also act on lipid metabolism. Allatectomized animals synthesize lipids, but do not use them as an energy source. This observation and particularly the fact that re-implantation of the corpora allata re-established respiratory metabolism supports the previous results (Thomsen, 1952; L'Hélias, 1954c).

Where lipids were labeled with acetate-^{14}C in *Periplaneta*, allatectomized animals produced 66% more lipids than the controls: 68% of these lipids are triglycerides and 28% phospholipids, as opposed to 52% and 32%, respectively, in the controls (Vroman *et al.*, 1965).

It is possible that the juvenile hormone is involved in the transfer of lipids from storage tissues to growing tissues. Larsen and Bodenstein (1959) have reported that unpurified extracts have a gonadotropic effect on the ovaries of mosquitoes. Lipid mobilization by the juvenile hormone corroborates the observed facts in the study of the different phases of metabolism. The corpora allata hormone mobilizes all stored substances and utilizes them to produce energy necessary for protein and large molecule synthesis, allowing growth of larval tissues (L'Hélias, 1953b).

2. *Phospholipids: Their Role in Lipid Formation and Transfer*

Phosphatides, mainly phosphatidylethanolamine and phosphatidylcholine are abundant in insects. They are synthesized in the fat body, and their importance in exchanges at the cell membrane level is well established (Gilbert, 1966). Phosphatidylethanolamine is formed from phosphatidylserine (Crone, 1967). *In vitro*, the fat body incorporates L-serine-3-^{14}C quickly. Labeled ethanolamine is formed rapidly. Progressively, the phosphatidylserine formed loses its radioactivity, which passes to phosphatidylethanolamine. Many compounds related to ethanolamine or choline can replace them in phospholipids. *Musca domestica* larvae raised axenically on a medium containing amino alcohols incorporate these alcohols in their phospholipids; 2-aminobutane-1-ol and 2-amino-2-methylpropane-1-ol are relatively toxic and induce belated growth or larval death. Addition of choline to the diet reestablishes normal growth; the percentage of artificial phospholipids is much lower in adults than in larvae raised on these media because the larvae synthesize their normal phospholipids from the given amino alcohols (Crone, 1967). The incorporation seems to follow Kennedy's scheme via the cytidine coenzyme. A cytidyl transferase allows formation of a complex cytidine-diphosphoryl base from cytidine diphosphonate and a phosphoryl base. Diptera accumulate lipids during their development (Levinson and Silverman, 1954; Pearincott, 1960; Wimer, 1962; Sridhara and Bhat, 1965; Wlodawer and Baranska, 1965).

Wimer and Lamb (1967) have extracted the lipids from *Phormia regina* in the 3rd larval instar; the lipids have been fractionated by silica column chromatography and analyzed by gas chromatography. In *Phormia*, lipid concentration increases from 21.8% to 52.5% between the beginning and the end of the 3rd larval instar. Triglycerides are predominant (90%) but the analysis of the different fractions (triglycerides, glycerides, fatty acids, and phospholipids) shows a high proportion of unsaturated fatty acids and palmitoleic acid particularly at the end of the larval life. First, there is a storage of lipids (triglycerides) before the formation of structural lipids (phospholipids) for metamorphosis; at the beginning there are only 21.8% triglycerides, and their progressive storage allows the phospholipids of the cellular membranes to participate in the constitution of larval structures. Distribution of palmitoleic, oleic, and palmitic acids changes greatly in the prepupa phospholipids. These changes may result from a turnover of the fatty acids of specific phospholipids, particularly important at metamorphosis because they are involved in protein synthesis. In the *Galleria* larva, direct release of free fatty acids into the hemolymph seems to be an adaptive exception (Niemierko *et al.*, 1956; Wlodawer, 1956).

Protein synthesis occurs also in the fat body, and phospholipids are released as lipoproteins in hemolymph. Like glycerides, sterols are also found bound to lipoproteins (Goodfellow and Gilbert, 1964) and, probably, lipid transfer occurs in this form. Do they penetrate as such into the cells, as in vertebrates, or are they broken down *de novo* into lipids?

3. External Factors

Lipid metabolism can be modified under the influence of external factors to lead to a fat body adapted to climatic environment which will allow the survival of hibernating species. *Culex tarsalis* females spend the winter in the adult instar. Harwood and Halfill (1964) have shown that short photoperiod and low temperature induce an increase of the fat body. When the photoperiod is long and the temperature moderate (Takata and Harwood, 1964), there is a great predominance of triglycerides. Fatty acids with 16 carbon atoms are predominant in the larva; there is a slight decrease in the nymph, and again an increase in the young adult, mainly in palmitic, palmitoleic, and oleic acids. After emergence, females lose the major part of their linoleic acid. The high concentration of C_{16} fatty acids is characteristic of the Culicinae, and accumulation of palmitoleic and oleic acids seems to be necessary for hibernation. Respective values of 43% and 26% have been registered in females raised at low temperature and in short photoperiod as opposed to 31% and 20% in females raised at moderate temperature and in long photoperiod.

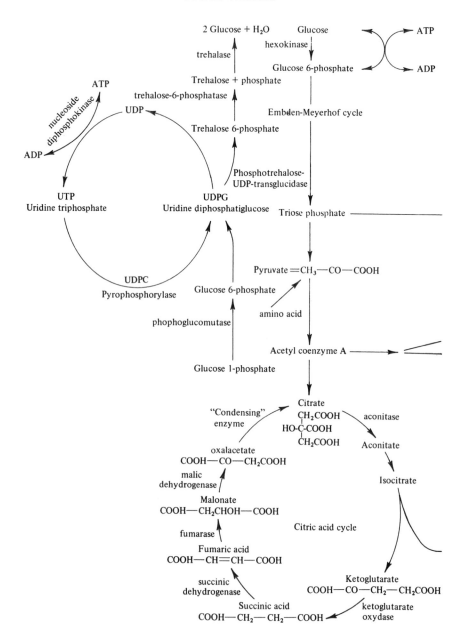

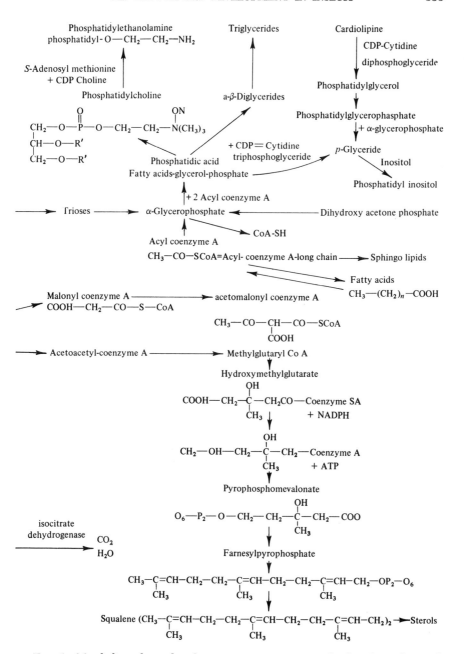

Fig. 1. Metabolic relationship between proteins, sugars, lipids, glycerides, and phospholipids.

4. Sterols

Apparently, insects cannot synthesize squalene, the acyclic percursor of sterols, or build derivative compounds, and probably have to obtain them from their food sources. Kinsella (1966) has found 2.7 mg.% sterols, mainly cholesterol, in *Periplaneta* adult females. Sterol level in the embryo remains constant during its development though the proportion of esterified sterols increases. Twenty-five different fatty acids are esterified and metabolized actively in this way. The embryo, like the adult, does not have the ability to synthesize sterols. Allais *et al.* (1964) have also found a constant sterol concentration during the embryogenesis of *Locusta migratoria*. If larvae are fed ^{14}C-sterols, they are found stored and esterified in the oocytes of the adults (Monroe *et al.*, 1967). On the other hand, acetate-^{14}C labeled fatty acids are esterified with glycerol and sterols, but these sterols were never radioactive (Lambremont *et al.*, 1966).

Bergmann and Levinson (1966) have injected fifteen different cholesterol isomers into *Musca vicina* and *Dermestes maculatus* larvae to investigate the mechanism of cholesterol utilization. They also checked the proportion of pupation after treatment. Metamorphosis is normal only with cholesterol and cholesteryldihydrogen phosphate. The other derivatives induce a longer survival without pupation. Consequently, stereochemical factors are very important. Epimerization can destroy cholesterol activity. Some injected esters, such as cholesteryl phosphate, must be hydrolyzed by a lipase and act as free cholesterol (Clement and Frisch, 1946), since they show a certain activity and are more toxic when ingested. The dependance of the toxicity on the mode of application appears to reflect the different availability of lipases.

5. Coenzymes q

Coenzymes *q* play a very important role in electron transfer during synthesis which leads to the sterol nucleus. They are made of a quinone and a more or less long isoprenic chain, the precursor of which is mevalonate. Like sterols, coenzymes *q* are important constituents of mitochondria. Laidman and Morton (1962) have noticed the presence of Co q_8, q_9, and q_{10} in *Calliphora* larvae and suggested that they probably come from the diet.

6. Role of Sterol or Terpene Precursors in the Mimetism of Hormones Controlling Insect Octogeny

a. Action of Farnesol. Assimilation and transformation of sterols are very important in insects because these compounds are part of the structure of hormones controlling insect development. The discovery of the presence of cholesterol (Kobayashi and Kirimura, 1967), farnesol, and farnesylaldehyde was a stimulus for research on the action of these compounds. Farnesol is a terpenic alcohol:

$$CH_3 \diagdown \atop CH_3 \diagup C{=}CH{-}CH_2{-}CH_2{-}\underset{\underset{CH_3}{|}}{C}{=}CH{-}CH_2{-}CH_2{-}\underset{\underset{CH_3}{|}}{C}{=}CH{-}CH_2OH$$

Wigglesworth (1963) has experimented with farnesol and farnesol aldehyde and also *Rhodnius* extract on decapitated females and obtained results which are similar to those following corpora allata implantation. There is a metathetelic effect: formation of larval cuticle on nymphs in which the cuticle has been eroded and the denudated zone rubbed with farnesol. At the same time, the treated nymphs develop normal eggs and vitellogenesis occurs. Consequently, farnesol shows the juvenilizing as well as the gonadotropic activity of the corpora allata. However, Slama (1965) showed later that an identical farnesol treatment did not have any action on *Pyrrhocoris apterus*. Vitellogenesis does not occur in allatectomized females treated with farnesol, though the alar lobes exhibit a regressive metathetelic reaction (simple prevention of imaginal differentiation without formation of the larval hypoderm). Metathetely is also induced by fatty acids, fatty alcohols, colchicine, and synthetic derivatives of benzoic acid (*p*-1, 5-dimethylphenylbenzoic acid) (Slama and Hrdy, 1967). Therefore, the metathetelic effect is not specific for farnesol. Farnesol and cholesterol can be compared: both compounds are terpene derivatives and have a juvenilizing or metamorphosing activity in growth. This could be considered as a pharmacodynamic activity. The other hypothesis suggested by Gilbert (1966), considering their isoprenoid structure and their formation from mevalonate, is that these substances are precursors of juvenile hormone or ecdysone.

Krishnakumaran and Schneiderman (1965) demonstrated that farnesol and its derivatives can activate the prothoracic gland of diapausing pupae of *Antheraea polymorpha* and induce molting. Farnesol acts not only like juvenile hormone but also like brain hormone; this fits with the previous hypothesis: pharmacodynamic activity or structure similar to isoprenoid substances which are all derived from mevalonate and used in ecdysone synthesis.

Juvenile hormone is absent in extracts of allatectomized male abdomens (Williams, 1959; Gilbert and Schneiderman, 1959), but farnesol and its derivatives are present in allatectomized as well as in normal males. Farnesol is perhaps a natural synergistic activator of the hormone because its presence in the fat extract enhances hormonal activity; but it seems difficult to identify farnesol and its derivatives with the juvenile hormone because the latter reaches, after purification, a degree of activity very much higher than the former. Purification of the hormone has been carried out by different teams in recent years, and the hormone has been definitely separated from farnesol.

a. Juvenile Hormone. Williams *et al.* (1966) have shown that the abdomens of male *Platysamia cecropia* contain a high concentration of hormone. Röller *et al.* (1967) and Meyer *et al.* (1968) separated two compounds identified as methyl 10,11-epoxy-3, 7-dimethyl- and 3,7, 11-trimethyl-2,6-tridecanoate; they thought that sesquiterpene epoxy groups exhibited juvenile hormone activity. Finally, however, Röller *et al.* (1969) proved that juvenile hormone is not identical with any epoxy compound previously reported to have juvenile hormone activity. By a five-step purification procedure they obtained a 1.25×10^{-5}-fold purified juvenile hormone. The first compounds found in 1967 and 1968 are pyrolytic breakdown products of purified juvenile hormone which do not carry epoxy groups and show stronger prothoracotropic activity in *Hyalophora cecropia* and gonadotropic activity and occurrence of supernumerary molt in *Galleria* larvae and *Tenebrio molitor* pupae.

Methyl epoxydimethyl tridecanoate

It is possible that insects use both brain and juvenile hormone to control the prothoracic gland during larval life. The gland would secrete continuously a small amount of hormone to maintain imaginal disc metabolism; juvenile hormone would act as an inhibitor of high secretion. Periodically, brain hormone would act alone, during resting periods of the corpora allata, and then the prothoracic gland would function at full yield to secrete ecdysone and promote molting. This possible relationship could also be supported by the fact that in *Leucophaea* the cells of the corpora allata and of the prothoracic gland have the same type of endoplasmic reticulum as mammalian cells involved in sterol metabolism (Scharrer, 1964).

b. Ecdysone Activity. Actually, two forms α and β of ecdysone are known; β is more soluble (450 μg./ml.) than α (250 μg./ml.). These two compounds are present in insects and crustaceans. α-Ecdysone-23,

24-³H injected in various stages of the molting cycle is metabolized to β-ecdysone in tissue. α-Ecdysone synthesized in molting gland would indeed be a precursor of β-ecdysone, and this conversion occurs peripherally. In extracts, only β-ecdysone is recovered. Thus, the function of the glands is not to secrete β-ecdysone, but to supply the blood with the necessary precursors or the enzymes or both involved in the production of the molting hormone β (King, 1969). In addition, ecdysone is rapidly inactivated *in vivo* (Karlson and Bode, 1969) by the fat body enzymic system localized in "cytosol," and can be extracted in 100,000 g supernatant. Ecdysone induces the DNA-dependent synthesis of messenger RNA and of certain enzyme proteins and provokes mitosis of hypoderm or imaginal discs by regulating the synthetic activity of genes. Substances related to ecdysone, pterosterone, and inokosterone induce an abnormal development of the pupae, suggesting that there is an interference with the genetic information of the pupae (Williams, 1968).

α-Ecdysone   β-Ecdysone

III. Structural Metabolism

A. AMINO ACIDS AND PROTEINS

1. Amino Acid Metabolism

a. Amino Acid Pool Composition during Development. Cellular differentiation involves a large accumulation of proteins. Therefore, protein metabolism is of prime importance during insect development and is under hormonal control.

The concentration of free amino acids, which reaches a high level during development, is very low in the egg just after fertilization. In *Bombyx,* the number of free amino acids at this time is only four—glutamic acid, serine, alanine, valine—and reaches twelve at the end of embryogenesis; besides the four amino acids cited above, tyrosine, leucine, glycine, tryptophan, proline, hydroxyproline, cystine, and histidine can be found (Drilhon and Busnel, 1950). Crone-Gloor (1959) found 16 amino acids in *Drosophila melanogaster* embryos, but β-alanine and γ-aminobutyric acid appeared only at hatching. In general, most of the amino acids can be detected progressively during embryogenesis in correlation with their utilization by the vitellus and with morphogenesis. Idris (1960), Oelhafen (1961), and Chen and Briegel (1965) have demonstrated that there is a large increase in the concentration of total amino acids at the beginning of embryogenesis resulting from the release of vitellin storage products for the initiation of protein synthesis in the embryo; this release corresponds with blastoderm formation and later with gastrulation and elongation of the germinative zone. Amino acid concentration is maintained at a high value during mesenteron growth and during formation of the dorsal groove. Later there is a slight decrease; the amino acid pool is similar to that of the adult which transmits amino acids to the oocyte through the hemolymph and incorporates them directly into the vitellus [Telfer working with *Hyalophora* (1960) and Hill working with *Schistocerca* (1962)]. In the tissues, concentration of free amino acids is very high; it may be 30 times higher than in other groups of animals. Florkin (1937) has indicated that the average blood concentration is 293 to 300 mg./100 ml. and can reach 2340 mg./100 ml. in certain cases.

It is possible to identify in the different proteins all the amino acids known, in addition to those commonly occurring in other organisms; β-alanine, ornithine, γ-aminobutyric acid, phenylglutamic acid, taurine, cystathionine, methyl histidine, 8-methyl cysteine, 3-hydroxykynurenine, and D-α-alanine have been found (Wyatt, 1961; Irreverre and Levenbook 1960; Villeneuve, 1962; Rodriguez and Hampton, 1966). Some of them have a special utilization in *Bombyx*. Florkin has demonstrated a continuous increase of histidine during the 5th larval instar and pupal life; this amino acid is not utilized by the serigenous glands and remains at high concentration in the blood. On the other hand, decrease of aspartic and glutamic acids at the beginning of the spinning period corresponds to their incorporation into silk. Methionine as well as alanine, glutamic acid, and glycine increase in the blood and then decrease. At the end of the transformation of pupa to adult, a new increase in glutamic acid, histidine, methionine, and lysine can be registered. During the adult instar there is a decrease of glycine, histidine, and lysine. Glutamic acid and methionine are the main components. The only understandable fluctuations are those which correspond to incorporation into fibroin. Tyrosine and proline continue to increase during development. The larval cuticle thickens considerably before pupation and contains a high percentage of proline and tyrosine; this last amino acid is a precursor of polyphenols and o-quinones necessary for the puparium to harden and darken (Dennell, 1947; Hackman, 1953; Fraenkel and Rudall, 1940).

Body and blood extracts of *Drosophila* contain, at the end of the larval instar, an excess of tyrosine, proline, and glutamic acid which diminish afterwards during metamorphosis. In the salivary glands (Chen and Baumann, 1966), glutamate concentration is 10 times higher than in the blood. The distribution in the tissues varies greatly. Total quantity of peptides accounts for 29% of free ninhydrin-positive compounds in the hemolymph; the corresponding value in the salivary glands is only 5%. The *in vitro* incorporation of glucose labeled with ^{14}C and of acetate and succinate into amino acids and other intermediary metabolites by muscle, fat body, and head homogenates of *Schistocerca* is highly variable and certainly expresses specific metabolic activities that differ in tissues (W. J. W. Hines and Smith, 1963). The fat body synthesizes proteins which are released into the incubation medium and which can be separated by electrophoresis on acrylamide gel. Price and Bosman (1966) and Stevenson and Wyatt (1962) have succeeded in incorporating leucine-^{14}C into the fat body of *Hyalophora cecropia* larvae; more leucine is incorporated when the concentration of magnesium chloride is increased. An increase in sodium and potassium diminishes incorporation. After 60 minutes of incubation, aspartate, valine, and glutamate disappear from the medium and glutamine and tyrosine appear. In the larva, phenylalanine and tyrosine accumulate in the fat body. Phenylalanine-^{14}C is transformed into tyrosine-^{14}C. The high quantity of tyrosine suggests that it is produced and stored in the fat body until metamorphosis. Mitlin and co-workers (1968) report large diurnal variations in the amino acid concentration in *Anthonomus guardis* adults, especially of tyrosine, the concentration of which also varies with sex and age.

The amino acid requirements vary in different insects. However, the ten amino acids normally required by mammals are also required by insects (Lipke and Fraenkel, 1956; House, 1962) (arginine, histidine, lysine, tryptophan, phenylalanine, methionine, threonine, leucine, isoleucine, and valine). For *Myzus persicae*, tyrosine must also be present in the diet (Strong and Sakamoto, 1963). Egg and pupa can be considered closed systems but the larva, with its external nutritional sources, renews the amino acid pool continually; composition and concentrations of amino acids as well as metabolic relationships vary according to the diet. The same is true for the adult (Bodnaryk and Morrison, 1966).

b. Transaminations among Intermediary Pathways. Transamination occurs in insects as in bacteria and mammals (Leuthardt, 1963; Chen and Bachman-Diem, 1965); it takes place mainly in the fat body which has the metabolic functions of the vertebrate liver and of the mollusk and crustacean hepatopancreas (Urich, 1961; Kilby, 1963; Nair and George, 1964). Wang and Dixon (1960) noticed a decrease of trans-aminases in the muscles of allatectomized *Periplaneta*. The activity of these enzymes in enhanced during larval development and adult differen-tiation and there is a parallel increase in protein synthesis.

2. Peptides

Paper chromatography reveals unknown ninhydrin-positive spots which after hydrolysis liberate amino acids. At least half of the amino acids found in the tissues are in the form of polypeptides. Mitchell and Simmons (1962) have detected by column chromatography about 600 peptides in *Drosophila* larvae. Some of these peptides are conjugated to lipids (Wren and Mitchell, 1959).

Chen and Hanimann (1965) have followed by chromatography (auto-matic analyzer) the changes in these amino acids during *Drosophila* development. Variations are quantitative rather than qualitative: aspartic acid undergoes the largest variations—it disappears nearly completely at the end of larval life and increases again afterwards. Injected amino acids are incorporated first into polypeptides rather than into proteins (Simmons and Mitchell, 1962).

A certain number of complex peptides conjugated to lipids and carbo-hydrates have been identified in *Bombyx* hemolymph (Sissakian, 1959) and in *Ephestia* (Chen and Kühn, 1956). Peptides are more abundant in the blood than in the tissues. Chen and Hanimann (1965) and Levenbook *et al.* (1965) have identified peptides in certain peaks of chromatograms of *Drosophila* larvae and of *Phormia regina*, as well as the following compounds (in order of occurrence on the chromatogram): phos-phoserine, tyrosine phosphate, glycerophosphoethanolamine, phosphoe-thanolamine, taurine, γ-aminobutyric acid, ornithine, and ethanolamine.

In the blood of *Phormia* larvae, Levenbook and co-workers (1965) found at least 19 polypeptides. These are acid peptides and basic di- and tripeptides containing lysine or histidine; their concentrations change considerably during larval growth, being maximal at the beginning of the third stage and nearly nonexistent at the end, before pupation. Howells and Birt (1964) have followed the incorporation of pyrophos-phate labeled with ^{32}P into ATP and analyzed the level of activation of amino acids during the development of *Lucilia cuprina*. The highest activation occurs during larval life; it falls in the middle of pupation and increases again until emergence. These variations seem to reflect protein synthesis during larval life and adult differentiation.

Dinamarca and Levenbook (1966) have shown that alanine is oxidized more completely and rapidly than lysine. Its turnover is maximal at the nonpigmented pupa stage; it decreases at the end of metamorphosis and increases again in adult *Phormia*.

3. Proteins

a. Protein Turnover. Wyatt (1961) believes that during larval life blood proteins increase in parallel with the increase of insect size. The increase continues until the last larval stage, at which point the larva reaches its maximal growth. The protein level then stays constant at the beginning of pupation. Finally, the transformation of nymph into adult is accompanied by a sudden decrease of blood proteins as they are utilized for the differentiation of adult structures. Agrell and Lindh (1966) noted a marked increase in the synthesis of basic proteins during histogenesis and differentiation of adult tissues in *Calliphora*. But the rise in total concentration is not due to a general increase in all proteins—there are variations of relative contents of individual compounds during ontogenesis.

Telfer and Williams (1953) utilized the agar diffusion immunological technique and found nine antigens in the blood of the silkworm cecropia. They studied the concentration of seven of these antigens during metamorphosis. Five are present in all stages. The sixth protein appears only at the 5th intermolt period and persists during the pupal period. It disappears during adult development, but the concentrations of all the antigens fluctuate, suggesting that each of them plays a definite role. Antigen 7 is a " ♀ antigen" because female blood contains 1000 times more of it than male blood (Telfer, 1954). It appears only at the prepupal stage during oocyte development it concentrates in the oocyte and disappears from the blood.

Absorption tests reveal that five of these antigens are present during metamorphosis. There is an increase of the number of zones and bands during larval life, a decrease in the pupa and again in the adult. The sudden fall between pupa and adult could correspond to a diminution of activity of the genes responsible for larval proteins and then to an increase of activity of the genes regulating the synthesis of adult specific proteins.

Steinhauer and Stephen (1959) separated three fractions in the blood of *Periplaneta;* one of them, probably involved in molting processes, appears only at molting times and then disappears. Chen (1959, 1962) finds an increase at the end of the larval instar of *Culex* and *Drosophila*. Separation by starch gel electrophoresis yields seven fractions in *Drosophila* and four in *Culex*. The variation in concentration of these different fractions indicates that they have different functions. Duke and

Pantelouris (1963) have been able to separate nineteen fractions in the *Drosophila* hemolymph, but there are never more than eleven at each instar. Some seem to have an enzymic activity, others may participate in lipid transfer, protein storage, and immunological responses.

In saturniids, Telfer and Williams (1960) have recorded the incorporation of labeled amino acids into hemolymph proteins; it is very high at the beginning of nymphal development and progressively lower during diapause. Is it then a true turnover, since a wound can also induce protein formation and incorporation into hemolymph? Five main bands can be detected; at least three of them are composite. The relative proportions vary enormously during larval life. Turnover is studied by disc electrophoresis. When labeled homologous proteins of the hemolymph are injected into nonlabeled animals, the amino acids of the donor are redistributed among other proteins of the receiver's hemolymph. Turnover has been demonstrated in larvae and pupae. Parallel experiments with heterologous proteins have shown that turnover is specific for homologous proteins. After puparium formation, a group of proteins is quickly re-formed within a half-period of 13 hours. Another group is relatively inert in the pupa. In general, the body proteins may be in constant turnover. In insects, the occurrence of a massive turnover of the tissues should permit detection of protein turnover. A number of high molecular weight proteins increase during the development, decline at the beginning of the pharate pupal stage, and continue to decline after larval pupal ecdysis. They are mainly glycolipoproteins—some are larva-specific, others pupa-specific—enzymes, esterases, aminopeptidases, and phosphatases (Boyd and Mitchell, 1966; Mitlin *et al.*, 1967; Van der Geest and Borgsteede, 1969). In contrast, in short photoperiod-reared diapausing larvae, proteins are stored in significant amounts. Two of these diapause proteins decrease significantly at the beginning of the pupal stage (Claret, 1970). In *Lymantria dispar*, a sexual difference can be noted at spinning time; however, the hemolymph proteins are not used by the sericigenous glands but by the gonads for vitellogenesis (Lamy, 1967). During the second part of the pupal instar, there is a difference of behavior between male and female bands during all stages of development which have been studied (in *Formica polytena*, Schmidt, 1966). After a progressive increase in total protein up to the end of larval life, turnover begins at the end of the larval instar and is maximal at the time of formation of the white pupa (Chen and Levenbook, 1966a). Labeled hemolymph proteins injected at the end of the larval stage are incorporated in the proteins of adult tissues (Chippendale and Beck, 1966; Chippendale and Kilby, 1969; Ludwig, 1954; Locke and Collins, 1968; Tobe and Loughton, 1969). First stored in fat body they are transferred to all tissues. Protein hemolymph deposits are sequestered by protein granules of fat body in multivescular bodies, which contain lytic enzymes, and in storage protein granules. Numerous mitochondria and ribosomes disappear in the last larval instar. Fat body and albuminoids contain soluble proteins (calliphorin I and II in *Calliphora*, Munn *et al.*, 1969) which are released in blood for the formation of adult tissues, and are probably synthesized in the fat body.

b. Hormone Action on Proteins. During larval development, the juvenile hormone plays a very important role in tissue formation because it stimulates the general metabolism of the animal.

Removal of corpora allata in *Carausius morosus* (L'Hélias, 1953b) inhibits the synthesis of new nitrogenous compounds. Total nitrogen remains constant, but there is a distinct decrease of protein synthesis and a storage of free amino acids in the tissues. In the allatectomized animal, there is no mobilization in the blood. The absence of corpora allata inhibits the synthesis of new proteins, particularly of the large molecules necessary for the growth of tissue. The juvenile hormone allows growth of larval tissues by endoploidy by promoting the formation of high energy bonds by increasing glycolysis and activating phosphate bonds. Removal of corpora cardiaca and allata results in an accumulation of the glycogen stored in the tissues (L'Hélias, 1953a). Accumulation of inorganic phosphate suggests that phosphorylases are also affected.

Alkaline phosphates, when very active in the tissues, deprive the insect of its sources of high energy carbohydrates; as a result there is a decrease in protein and RNA synthesis. The latter is probably partially compensated for by the action of ecdysone when *Carausius* reaches the adult stage (L'Hélias, 1953b). Although the corpora allata play an important role in the control of protein synthesis and the corpora cardiaca play a more specialized role in glycolysis (L'Hélias, 1957c), they are not the only organs influencing these processes. Thomsen's work (1952) on adult female *Calliphora* proves that the neurosecretory cells of the brain permit perfect development of the ovaries, the corpora allata, oenocytes, and accessory glands and have an effect on proteinase synthesis by the gut. These cells might play a role in protein synthesis, but it is not known if the same processes are involved. Wigglesworth (1964) has also observed that digestion of gut content is very active in *Rhodnius* females during the development of eggs, which is controlled by the corpora allata. Gut proteins were perhaps activated by juvenile hormone as they are in *Calliphora* by the pars intercerebralis cells. Vitellogenesis in many insects depends on the secretion of juvenile hormone, which stimulates blood protein synthesis and the appearance of vitellogenic proteins in particular (Telfer, 1965; Engelmann, 1968). Weed-Pfeiffer

(1939, 1945) has also found that the corpora allata control egg production by the action of a hormone which mobilizes stored substances for oocyte growth; its absence leads to lipid storage and to an increase of blood volume and vitellogenesis arrest. Thomas and Nation (1966) have noted the gradual decrease of one [Fraction 5 (electrophoresis on cellulose acetate)] of the main proteins of allatectomized *Periplaneta* females. Fraction 5 increases in the ovariectomized female while it remains constant in the male at all stages; it is therefore sex-linked. After allatectomy, proteins and RNA diminish and uric acid remains constant while its concentration doubles in the control. Amino acids labeled with tritium are incorporated to a slight degree by the fat body and the ovaries, to a greater degree by the midgut.

Slama and Hrubesova (1963) and Slama and Janda (1964) have demonstrated that ovarian follicular cells of *Pyrrhocoris* are inactive for long periods. Their growth and functional activity are directly related to juvenile hormone.

On the basis of experiments with the desert locust, Highnam (1964) proposed that yolk deposition requires the action of two hormones, with protein uptake by the oocytes being controlled directly by juvenile hormone, while neuroscretory material from the cardiacum serves to stimulate secretion of vitellogenic proteins. Allatectomy prevents the appearance of vitellogenin, while normal levels are found following the implantation of corpora allata; corpora cardiaca and brain are ineffective. Vitellogenin injections fail to stimulate yolk deposition in allatectomized females of *Periplaneta* (Bell, 1969). In *Leucophaea*, a single specific "female protein" is synthesized in the presence of juvenile hormone. The synthesis of five out of six blood proteins during oocyte maturation depends on neuroendocrine factors. Thus, it is clear that different hormones have specific effects upon different protein synthesis processes and that investigations of the influence of hormones on total protein synthesis can be of limited value only (Scheurer, 1969). Castrated females of *Leptinotarsa* produce a vitellogenic protein under the influence of cardiaca allata and neurosecretory material; allatectomy is followed by an accumulation of specific diapause proteins in short-day photoperiods. Implantation of corpora allata represses these diapause proteins after exposure to long-day photoperiods (DeLoof, 1970).

Ecdysone is also involved, through a different pathway, as will be seen in Section IV. In the case of juvenile hormone, formation of high energy bonds is initiated by stimulation of certain genes which give the necessary information. Ecdysone controls different genes and is not involved in endoploid cellular growth. When acting alone, it activates cell division and acts mainly on larval and nymphal cells which have remained embryonic. As we will see later, it induces increased synthesis of specialized DNA and messenger RNA which carry the transcribed information specific for adult differentiation. Consequently, synthesis of specific proteins will occur, the first of which will be respiratory enzymes and cytochromes and their blood and tissue proteins; they increase suddenly at the beginning of adult development (Laufer, 1961; Telfer and Williams, 1953). By correlated histochemical and agar immunodiffusion studies of the blood proteins Laufer has been able to identify specific enzymes: esterases, phosphatase, carbohydrase, sulfatase, tyrosinase, dehydrogenase, and chymotrypsin.

Ecdysone plays the role of an organizer. New structures are formed from the nuclei of embryonic islets which are "derepressed." Brain hormone induces a transfer of messenger RNA which stimulates the corpora allata and the prothoracic gland. Juvenile hormone and ecdysone, respectively, derepress specific genes which synthesize specific DNA. Messenger RNA and soluble RNA, which conglomerate on polysomes and synthesize enzymes, will transcribe its information. K. Clark and Gillott (1967a,b) have demonstrated in *Locusta migratoria* that nervous ganglia have a mechanical effect on the filling of the foregut and direct the release of neurosecretion from the pars intercerebralis and its transfer by the cardiacal nerves; this, secondarily, affects nucleic acid and protein metabolism. The uptake of food in the gut controls synthesis or the release of neurosecretion which might influence growth and protein synthesis in *Locusta*.

The frontal ganglion may act on the modification or the release of hormonal secretion by the corpora cardiaca. Daily injections of corpora cardiaca extracts re-establish normal metabolism, and the locusts resume growth. In the absence of the frontal ganglion, synthetic activity of the nuclei is diminished, RNA is less abundant, nucleoli are very small, the cytoplasm is depleted, and consequently protein synthesis is affected though DNA is still intact.

c. Functions. By electrophoresis it was demonstrated that bands of specific proteins appear at different stages of development. That each protein appears at a definite stage and has specific behavior suggests that the synthesis mechanism is under control. Duke and Pantelouris (1963) have shown that in *Drosophila* the formation of each protein fraction of the hemolymph is controlled by a different gene.

The physiological activity of some of these proteins has been established; some of them act as enzymes. Laufer (1961) has confirmed the work of Telfer and Williams by starch gel electrophoresis. He has shown that in the silkworm *Platysamia cecropia* and *S. cynthia ricini* the proteins separated by electrophoresis and identified by histochemical staining as well as immunodiffusion on agar are enzymes, mainly esterases, phosphatases, sulfatases, dehydrogenases, carbohydrase, tyrosinase, and chymotrypsin. Other studies previously reviewed by Chen (1962) reported the presence of some of these enzymes and also of a hexose-1-phosphatase, a TPN-L-malic enzyme, and a polyol dehydrogenase bound to TPN (Faulkner, 1956, 1958).

The fat body seems to be the site of blood protein synthesis. Shigematsu (1960) incubated *Bombyx* fat body with labeled amino acids and demonstrated the synthesis of labeled proteins in the incubation medium—proteins identified with blood proteins by paper electrophoresis. This very important anabolic role of the fat body has been noted by many other authors.

The adult ovaries, larval ovaries, and developing embryos of *Leucophaea* contain 1-glycerophosphate dehydrogenase, 2-malate dehydrogenase, and the 1-, 2-, 3-, and 5-lactate dehydrogenases. Lactate dehydrogenase may play a role in energy production for vitellogenesis and embryo development (Gilbert and Goldberg, 1966).

The larval gut, hemolymph, cuticle, adult body, and flight muscles of *Pieris brassicae* contain numerous esterases (Clements, 1967). There are thirteen esterases which have been incubated with inhibitors for further identification. These esterases, completely inhibited by organophosphates, are carboxylesterases which hydrolyze esters of low molecular weight acids. No lipase activity (hydrolysis of glyceryl tripalmitate-1-^{14}C) has been observed.

Using precipitin tests, Terando and Feir (1967a,b) detected, in the hemiptera *Oncopeltus*, 5 to 10 antigens at the 1st, 2nd, and 3rd intermolting periods and 11 antigens at the 4th and 5th intermolting periods and in the adult. Some of the antigens give a positive reaction with the 1-naphthyl acetate. Two of the arcs, incubated with dihydroxyphenylalanine, react like tyrosinase; one also gives a lipoprotein reaction and acts like a glycoprotein. Though protein concentration changes during development, there is no qualitative change.

d. Changes in Enzymic Activity during Metamorphosis. If constitutive enzymes keep a constant ratio of activity, repressible enzymes (Jacob and Monod's classification), the concentration of which is controlled by small molecules, undergo variations at pupation time after a regular increase during larval growth.

The first category of constitutive enzymes include the phosphotriose glycerophosphate group—triosephosphate isomerase, glyceraldehyde phosphate dehydrogenase, phosphoglycerate kinase, phosphoglycerate mutase, and enolase—and mitochondrial enzymes—malate, glutamate, isocitrate dehydrogenases, glutamate oxalotransaminase, and pyridine nucleotides. Respiratory enzymes and enzymes specifically bound to metamorphosis processes—proteases, tyrosinase, cholinesterase, etc.—belong to the second category.

i. Oxidative enzymes. During nymphal development, oxygen consumption and respiratory enzymes follow a U-shaped curve. Activity diminishes until the middle of pupal life and resumes progressively until hatching. These variations are related to disintegration of larval tissues and formation of imaginal structures. The most recent reviews by Gilbert and Schneiderman (1961), Harvey (1962), and Wigglesworth (1964) give a complete account of the work on this topic. In diapausing chrysalids, there is a large excess of cytochrome oxidase compared to cytochromes *b* and *c* which cannot be detected spectroscopically. This explains the insensitivity of chrysalids to carbon monoxide and cyanides when they are not subjected to conditions such as wounding, low oxygen tension, or dinitrophenol injection. Carey and Wyatt (1963) suggested that the limiting factor in the metabolism of diapausing nymphs might be the mineral phosphate supply which increases in the digestive tract and diminishes in the blood. This problem should be investigated; all that is known is that at the beginning of adult development, enzyme synthesis accelerates and the cytochrome system is reconstituted in its entirety. Wigglesworth (1964) and Shappirio and Williams (1957a,b) have also noticed that following ecdysone action mitochondria became very active.

In the mosquito *Aedes*, Lang (1959, 1961) observed that DPN, TPN, and succinocytochrome *c* reductase activity decreases in the nymph and increases quickly at the time of adult hatching; only TPN-cytochrome *c* reductase stays at a low level.

ii. Proteases. Proteases are very active during histolysis. According to Agrell (1948), lower pH activates protein activity in the descending phase of the U-shaped curve and favors destruction of larval tissues. Raising the pH again reverses the process and thus protects adult tissue formation. The activity of an acid proteinase pH 4.7 to 4.9 remains high and constant during metamorphosis while the alkaline proteinase pH 8.6 disappears. The dipeptidase which hydrolyzes alanylglycine increases greatly, then disappears at hatching time (Russo-Caia, 1960).

iii. Phosphatases. In *Drosophila*, Yao (1950) reported a considerable increase in alkaline phosphatase activity at the beginning of pupation. Sridhara and Bhat (1963) found that acid phosphatase participates in the destruction of larval tissues in *Bombyx*, and this might be related to glycogen catabolism by dephosphorylation in acid medium.

iv. Tyrosinases. Puparium formation occurs by incorporation of quinone into the cuticle through the intermediary N-acetyldopamine, which is oxidized. The quinones formed react with cuticular proteins in a tanning reaction of the quinones. Ecdysone is responsible for the decrease of the three necessary enzymes: tyrosinase, dopa decarboxylase, and phenoloxidase (Karlson and Schweiger, 1961; Karlson and Sekeris, 1962). In the presence of ecdysone, activation of these enzymes occurs through gene intermediaries. Ecdysone stimulates inorganic phosphate incorporation into the RNA of the epidermis. Extracted messenger RNA promotes amino acid incorporation into proteins *in vitro* (Sekeris and Lang, 1964). The genetic code is universal and the language of base combinations is the same for all animals. Incubation of this insect messenger RNA with ribosomes of rat liver and amino acids produces dopa decarboxylase. The different proteins comprising phenoloxidases are synthesized at maximum level in the larvae and are stored until their utilization 3 or 4 days later for melanin production (Mitchell, 1966).

   v. Cholinesterase. Shappirio *et al.* (1967) studied cholinesterase activity in *Hyalophora cecropia*, *Samia cynthia*, and *Antheraea*. In giant butterflies, pupal diapause results from the failure of brain neurosecretory elements and corpora cardiaca to produce the hormonal stimulus necessary to initiate development. Development resumes many months later when the pupae have been exposed to proper temperature and photoperiod. To solve the problem of development and diapause control, it was first necessary to discover the physiological processes which permit endocrine activity of the brain and later inhibit it. The behavior of the cholinesterase of the brain is then of great interest. Van der Kloot (1955) had already established the disappearance of cholinesterase and of spontaneous electrical activity from the brain at the beginning of diapause and its reactivation with the synchronous reappearance of electrical and endocrine brain activity. It is important to consider that variations in cholinesterase activity occur only in the brain, whereas in the thorax and abdominal ganglia activity remains constant. However, Schoonhoven (1963) and Tyschtchenko and Mandelstam (1965) observed in diapausing pupae of Lepidopterae (*Bupalis piniarius*) electrical activity as well as hydrolytic enzyme activity. This observation was confirmed by Shappirio *et al.* in 1967. Continuation of cholinesterase activity during metamorphosis and diapause shows that disappearance or reappearance of this activity cannot be responsible for the control of the neurosecretory mechanism. Mansingh and Smallman (1967) obtained similar results, but it has been proved that insect brain contains different esterases (Gilmour, 1960). One of them, detected by Van der Kloot, could be involved in endocrine brain activity.

   e. Protein Metabolism Deficiencies due to Lethal Genes. Part of the synthesized enzymes are required only at certain critical periods of development; all synthesized proteins are under genetic control so that a deficiency of these genes results in the death of homozygous individuals. According to the importance of the genetic disorder, death will not occur during the entire sequence of development but rather at certain periods in which ontogenetic processes are particularly critical: hatching of the embryo, at the beginning of the last larval stage, at the beginning of puparium formation, and during nymph development. In some cases, correlation among genetic, biochemical, and physiological deficiencies has been established by biochemical studies. Hadorn (1961) described the mechanisms of genetic development and lethal factors. In these lethals, protein synthesis can be inhibited (Gloor, 1949; Chen and Hadorn, 1965), free tyrosine decreased, and tyrosine-o-phosphate greatly increased (lethal mutant *translucida*) (Mitchell and Simmons, 1962) Homozygote larvae of *lethal meander* (*Drosophila melanogaster*) synthesize per DNA unit 3 or 4 times less RNA than normal (Chen and Hadorn, 1965) and have a very low amino acid pool, except for glycine which is present in high concentration. Other mutants carry isoenzymes controlled by deficient genes (Hadorn and Mitchell, 1951; Hadorn and Stumzollinger, 1953).

B. PIGMENTS

1. Pigment Metabolism

Many pigments have been isolated and identified in insects (see recent review by Cromartie, 1959). Most of them will not be discussed here because insects do not synthesize them. They are provided by the diet and are excreted or stored in the fat body, the hypodermis, or the cuticle. This is true for carotenes, anthocyans, and biliverdin or bilirubin, which arise from hemoglobin or chlorophyll breakdown. On the other hand, pterines, melanins, and ommochromes are synthesized by insects and play a physiological role either in metabolism or in growth.

a. Ommochromes and Melanins. These pigments can be found in the cuticle or the hypodermis and in the eyes. Pigment formation can be deficient when one of the enzymes required for the synthesis of the intermediary products is absent. A beautiful series of combined microchemical and genetic studies on mutants has given the first indication that genes express themselves phenotypically in the control of enzyme synthesis (Ziegler made a complete review of these studies in 1961).

i. Ommochrome synthesis. Tryptophan is oxidized to hydroxykynurenine; two molecules of this compound combine to form xanthommatin after elimination of one molecule of NH_3 and loss of 8 hydrogens by oxidation. Dopaquinone is the hydrogen acceptor at this stage and is reduced to dopa which can be reoxidized to dopaquinone in the presence of tyrosine and oxygen (Fig. 2).

Kynurenine accumulates in the fat body of *Drosophila* at the end of pupation and can be detected with a U.V. microscope as blue

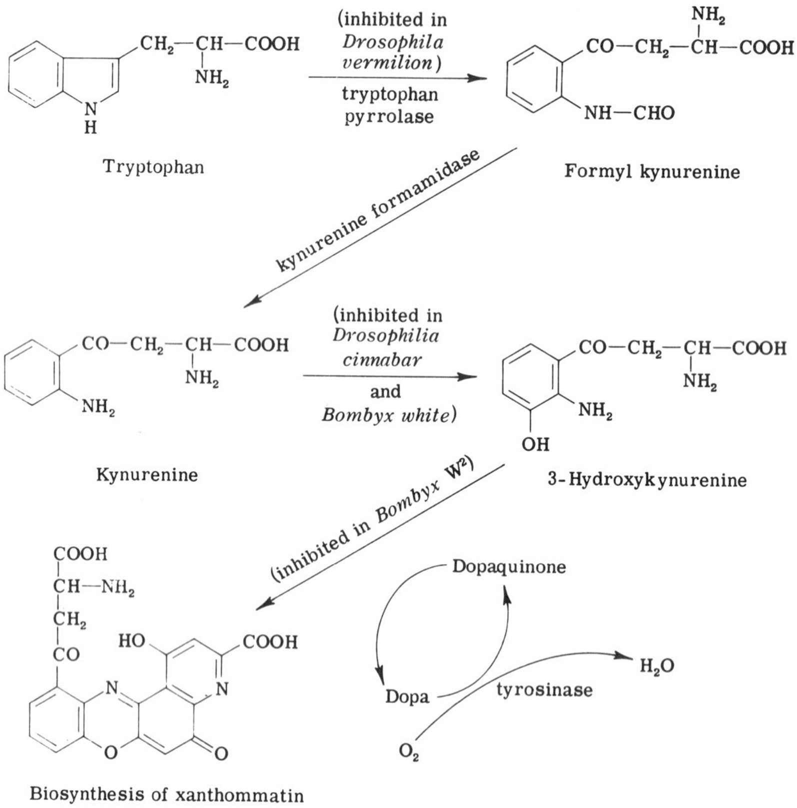

Biosynthesis of xanthommatin

FIG. 2. Ommochrome synthesis.

fluorescing globules (Rizki, 1961); it appears at the end of the larval life (96 hours) in the cells of the anterior fat body near the nucleus. This fluorescence does not appear in the mutant *vermilion* which lacks tryptophan pyrrolase and cannot, therefore, perform the first reaction of the chain tryptophan → formylkynurenine.

A red ommochrome pigment appears in the epidermis and fat body cells of *Cerura vinula* larvae 5 days before nymphal molt; this is the first sign of thoracic gland activity (Buckmann, 1965).

Umebachi and Katayama (1966) have shown that tryptophan pyrrolase is very active at the end of nymphosis. At emergence time, there is very little tryptophan and much kynurenine, part of which is excreted and part binds to a phenolic substance (dopa) to form the yellow pigment of *Papilio xuthus* wings. Tryptophan-^{14}C and dopa-^{14}C injected into the prepupa can be detected in the yellow pigment. This pigment, though derived from tryptophan, is not an ommochrome and does not have redox properties. This accumulation and localization of kynurenine seem to exist only in the Papilionidae; the other Lepidoptera excrete it completely in the meconium (Harmsen, 1966b).

ii. Melanin synthesis. Melanin pigments are formed in the exocuticle from tyrosine which oxidizes and does not undergo deamination into quinones. A parallel oxidation pathway of the tyrosine gives rise to diphenols: protocatechuic, veratric, and phenyl lactic acids, which might produce tanning quinones (Fig. 3).

iii. Chromatotropic action of ecdysone. A change in color is the first visible response to ecdysone action in certain insects. The caterpillars of *Cerura vinula* are red on the back and green on the sides. Eight days before pupation, the lateral pigmentation turns to brownish red by incorporation of xanthommatin, which undergoes redox changes under the influence of internal metabolism. If the larva lacks oxygen, reduction to dihydroxanthommatin occurs. The critical period, before which ligature behind the prothorax prevents color changes, appears 8 days earlier than that for pupation. Injection of small doses of ecdysone into isolated abdomens produces these color changes. Injection of high doses causes immediate nymphosis (Buckmann, 1965). In *Calliphora* there is sclerotization, browning, and hardening of the larval cuticle which becomes the puparium. Hackman (1953) and Dennell (1958) have shown that phenolic compounds are responsible for this process of protein tanning. After injection of tyrosine-^{14}C, 80% of the radioactivity is found in the cuticle. This is really due to ecdysone action because there is almost no incorporation in ligatured larvae. Dopa is better incorporated than N-acetyltyramine or N-acetyldopamine. Tyrosine at the beginning of the last larval stage is catabolized by transamination into *p*-hydroxyphenylpyruvic acid and *p*-hydroxyphenylacetic acid. First there is hydroxylation of tyrosine (dopa), then decarboxylation which gives dopamine, which in turn is acetylated by the successive actions of dopa decarboxylase, acetyl CoA transacetylase, and phenoloxidase (Sekeris and Karlson, 1961). Acetyldopamine is also a sclerotizable compound

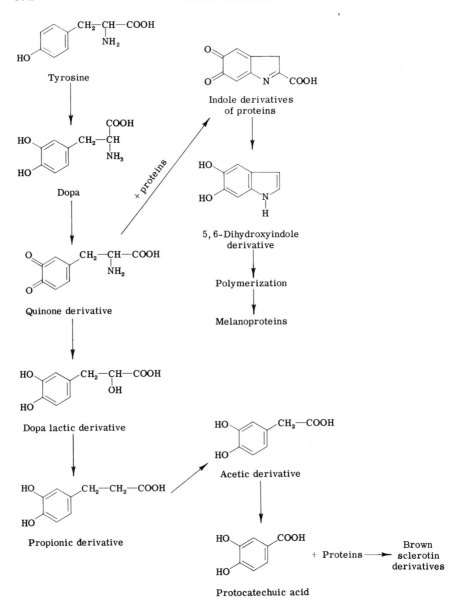

Fig. 3. Oxidation of tyrosine.

since it is incorporated into the cuticle. It is oxidized by a phenoloxidase which seems to be the sclerotizing factor, and is specific for diphenols since it does not act on tyrosine, tyramine, or N-acetyltyramine. Dihydroxyphenols diffuse through the cuticle and accumulate in the epithelium where they are converted by phenoloxidase into o-quinones. The quinones diffuse into the epicuticle and tan the proteins by a peptidation between amines and quinones, when quinones are in excess, giving rise to N-catechol proteins and quinonoid proteins. These quinones react with the terminal amino groups of other proteins and with the lysine ε-amino groups which appear along the chains. Finally, there is formation of a cross-linked structure. Only dopa derivatives are oxidized; other diphenols such as protocatechuic acid are not utilized. There are many phenoloxidases. They arise from proenzymes which are activated by proteins. In Diptera (Fraenkel, 1935) an activating hormone prevents the control of inhibitors which repress proenzyme activation (Horowitz and Fling, 1955; Mitchell, 1966; Evans, 1968). Cauterization of the Weissmann ring produces a decrease in activator concentration in pupa, which is restored by ecdysone injection (Karlson and Schweiger, 1961).

However, sclerotization and melanization depend upon ecdysone in pupation and upon Fraenkel's activating hormone in adult emergence when the second peak of activity of dopa decarboxylase occurs. Fraenkel and Hsiao (1962) have demonstrated that the pars intercerebralis secretes a melanogenic hormone of peptide nature, bursicon, which in Diptera governs cuticle melanization in the adult fly immediately after imaginal molt. Bursicon has an approximate molecular weight of 40,000 (Mills and Nielsen, 1967). It induces melanization of exocuticle by mobilization of blood tyrosine, but it does not induce uridine-^{3}H incorporation in RNA epidermis for the deposition of endocuticle requiring the synthesis of proteins and chitin. Leucine-^{3}H is incorporated in epidermis if fat body is juxtaposed: bursicon could mobilize fat body-synthesized proteins by contact with epidermis (Fogal and Fraenkel, 1969). The tanning process does not use tyrosine phosphate as intermediate but as a proteinaceous precursor of tyrosine which is degraded during the first 5 hours of adult life (Seligman *et al.*, 1969).

iv. Chromatotropic action of other endocrine glands. The cuticle is not subject to the action of ecdysone alone during metamorphosis and larval life. Other glands can produce color changes. The corpora allata are responsible for the green color of *Locusta* larvae (Joly, 1960) and *Melanoplus* blood (Weed-Pfeiffer, 1942). Hidaka and Ohtaki (1963) have induced the appearance of a green spot by implanting corpora allata into brown nymphs. This action has been associated with the environment. Tetsuya and Ohnishi (1967) have noticed that the green color (resulting from the presence of a carotene in the cuticle and a blue biliverdin in the hypodermis) turns to brown, depending on the color of the substrate, by formation of melanins in the cuticle and ommochromes in the hypodermis.

Following removal of the corpora allata, the phasmids acquire a copper-colored tint; following corpora cardiaca removal the color turns to silver gray (black and white pigments in the hypodermis) (L'Hélias, 1957c). Fraenkel (1963) and Girardie and Cazal (1965) detected a melanogenic activity of the pars intercerebralis in *Calliphora* and *Locusta*. Raabe (1959, 1966) noticed the same thing as well as physiological and morphological adaptations.

b. Pteridines. i. Physiological role. Pterins are well represented in insects where their most evident function is to serve as white, yellow, or red pigments in the scales, the wings, the hypodermis, or the eyes where they may play a role analogous to that of carotene in vertebrates (Albert, 1957). In fact, their physiological properties are much more important. The visible pigments deposited in the tissues are only products of excretion and elimination substances that have played an important role in the metabolic exchanges necessary for growth. They are end products of folic acid hydrogenated compounds decomposition and are formed during the synthesis of amino acids (glycine, serine), purines, and pyrimidines (incorporation of a methyl group in uracil to form thymine). These di- or tetrahydrogenated formyl folic derivatives (FH_2 and FH_4) permit the transfer of formyl, methenyl, or methylene radicals. Grzelakowska-Stabert and Zielinska (1967) noted that in insects the N^{10}-formyl-tetrahydrofolate synthetase (N^{10}-fFH_4) is much more active than serine FH_4 hydroxymethyltransferase. The utilization of formates as a source of carbon units is greater than that of serine for the transfer of carbon units through the intermediary of N^5,N^{10}-formyl FH_4 and N^{10}-formyl FH_4. A tetrahydrogenated pteridine similar to sepiapterin and biopterin is the cofactor catalyzing the hydrolyzation of phenylalanine to tyrosine (Kaufman, 1964).

The discovery of nonfluorescent di- or tetrahydropterin derivatives in insect tissue, always in the eyes, leads to the supposition that they play a role in hydrogen, carbon, or electron transfer. These compounds are very unstable, and in the presence of light give rise immediately to the fluorescent pterins (Ziegler and Nathan, 1961; Ziegler, 1963). Photolability is a very interesting property of these compounds; they react to external factors and their influence on metabolism varies with seasonal variations of light.

Di- or tetrahydrogenated biopterin and sepiapterin depend on sepiapterin reductase (Tsujita, 1961; Tsujita and Sakurai, 1963a,b) in the *lemon* mutant of *Bombyx*. This enzyme is not identical to tetrahydrofolic reductase. Akino and Matsubara (1963) have demonstrated that both enzymes exist in the silkworm, but folate reductase disappears at the end of the larval life. Sepiapterin reductase, after a decrease at the same period, resumes strong activity during nymphosis. Unfortunately, studies on the characterization and evolution of pteridines during development are not conclusive regarding their physiological role in this period.

ii. Pterin synthesis. Complex derivatives of folic acid are not only necessary coenzymes for purine and pyrimidine synthesis, but are also necessary for pterin synthesis of which insects are capable. The 2,4,5-triamino-6-hydroxypyrimidine-^{14}C ingested by caterpillars gives rise to radioactive xanthopterin in the wing of *Pieris brassicae* (Weygand and Waldschmidt, 1955).

Albert (1957) proved that the imidazole nucleus of purines opens in position 8 to give an amino pyrimidine. This in turn combines with glyoxal to form hydroxypteridine. It has been suggested that the initial step of the transformation is cleavage of the imidazole ring of a purine nucleotide to form 5-amino-4-ribosyl aminopyrimidine. Aminoimidazol-carboxamide-4-^{14}C + glycine-2-^{14}C injected in *Pieris brassicae* pupae gives labeled leucopterine, adenine, and guanine. Simon *et al.* (1964) conclude that the conversion purine → pteridine proceeds via a minimum of structural changes.

Glassman and Mitchell (1959) have shown that the purified xanthine oxidase of *Drosophila* oxidizes xanthopterin to leucopterin and 2-amino-4-hydroxypteridine to isoxanthopterin; it also oxidizes purines. It is mainly localized in the fat body and also, in smaller quantities, in the larval Malpighian tubules (Ursprung and Hadorn, 1961). The lack of this enzyme in certain mutants inhibits development of normal eye coloration. *Drosophila ry* and *Ma-l* do not have xanthine oxidase; they have an excess of hypoxanthine and pterines not oxidized. Hadorn and Schwink (1956) demonstrated that wild-type larvae into which mutant eye imaginal discs have been transplanted have normal eye development and that eye pigment formation is inhibited when wild-type discs are transplanted into *ry* mutant hosts. If these mutants receive an implant of wild-type fat body, they form normal pigments. Xanthine oxidase is responsible for the development of these pigments.

C. Ion Exchange, Cellular Permeability, and Excretion

The variations in the ionic environment of the tissues are partially regulated by the insect excretory system and the variations in water elimination. During larval life, the insect has a high content of water, and a large amount of liquid is eliminated at nymphosis. Water content falls from 90% to 60%. These changes depend in large part upon hormonal secretions. Ionic regulation sites are the epithelial membranes such as the midgut, rectum, sericigenous glands, labial glands, membranes separating the cells, plasma, cell organelles, and nuclear envelope. According to physiological observations, there are two antagonistic principles. Water elimination is subjected to hormonal control. In insects the presence of antagonistic factors has been demonstrated in the endocrine complex; they act on the two mechanisms involved in water discharge: excretion by the Malpighian tubules and resorption of liquid in the hindgut and the rectum. Depending on the insect, factor localization can be different or inverted. An antidiuretic factor has been localized in the brain (pars intercerebralis) (Stutinsky, 1953). A diuretic factor has been found in the brain by Nuñez (1956), Highnam et al. (1965), and Berridge (1966); both a diuretic factor and an antidiuretic one by Raabe (1959) and Gersch et al. (1964). Corpora allata can also contain an osmoregulatory hormone (antidiuretic) (Altmann, 1956).

Ionic concentration of the cellular medium is very important for molecular activity. In bacteria, protein synthesis requires an optimal potassium ion concentration, ribosomal structure and activity, and an exact magnesium concentration. The formation of the DNA–histone complex depends upon the ionic strength. *Hyalophora* midgut is the ideal material in which to study the changes in ionic transport during development.

Oxidative metabolism, nucleic acid and protein "timing," and active transport of potassium have been studied in connection with hormonal control.

Harvey et al. (1968) isolated midguts of *Platysamia cecropia* larvae and found that they are able to transport large quantities of potassium from the blood to the lumen of the gut.

Electrical potential of the isolated gut has been observed during the 4th intermolt period while feeding, at molting time from the 4th to the 5th instar, at the 5th intermolting period while feeding, when the intestinal content is discharged, and when the cocoon is spun. Average registered potentials are, respectively, 68, 89, 90, 124, and 2 mV. in a solution containing K, Mg, and Ca but no Na.

In vivo this transport permits elimination of the excess of potassium from the blood. Perfused with a solution containing 30 mM KCl, 5 mM MgCl$_2$, 4.5 mM CaCl$_2$, 2 mM HKCO$_3$, and 65 mM sucrose, the guts of larvae at the 5th intermolt period develop a positive potential difference of 84 mV. in the direction lumen–blood; the diffusion potential does not modify this transepithelial potential. In all stages which have been studied, except the last, reduction of potassium concentration from 32 to 2 mmoles/liter on the "blood" side of the gut decreases the potential, the potential on the "lumen" side increases, and, in between, the value of the potential is intermediate. Diminishing magnesium concentration or adding sodium does not have any effect. A decrease in calcium changes the direction of the potential (this can be predicted by the Nernst equation). The pH of the midgut content increases between the 4th and 5th instar; hydrogen ion concentration in blood is 1000 times higher than in the intestinal lumen. Ecdysone and juvenile hormone have no action even if the measurement of the values is prolonged for 30 minutes. This electric potential increases just before cocoon spinning and then diminishes gradually. Prepupa and pupa intestine do not exhibit any potential difference. Flux measurements with radioisotopes have shown that this current is due to active transport of potassium in the direction blood–lumen of the intestine. It is not affected by ouabain, inhibitors of cholinesterase, adrenaline, hypophyseal hormones, or pH changes, but it is inhibited by anoxia, 2,4-dinitrophenol, iodoacetate, 25% CO_2, and by inhibitors of carbonic anhydrase. This system might utilize a mechanism associated with H^+–K^+ ions rather than K^+–Na^+.

IV. Nucleic Acid Metabolism and Control Mechanisms of Growth and Development

A. NUCLEIC ACIDS

Hormones act on tissues whose type of growth is determined by genetic constitution; many probably act by inducing or inhibiting the expression of genetic potentialities. Certainly, the juvenile hormone controls metamorphosis in this way. Ecdysone controls the processes leading to molt. Juvenile hormone activates the genes which govern the larval structures, since its partial and progressive decrease gives rise to intermediate forms with characters intermediate between larval and adult; finally its complete disappearance allows adult metamorphosis. Juvenile hormone is the metabolizing hormone which liberates large quantities of energy and supports formation of high polymers. The cells acquire a complex and differentiated structure and greatly increase in volume. Often, larval cells develop by endoploidy; the brain and the prothoracic gland act primarily on nucleic acid synthesis and on the response of the cells of imaginal discs which have remained in the embryonic stage and divide faster. Observation of chromosomes reveals that the loci reacting to these hormones are different.

Six hours after ecdysone injection into *Rhodnius,* Wigglesworth (1957) noticed a swelling of the nucleoli of the epidermal cells; then nucleolar RNA increased greatly and accumulated afterwards in the cytoplasm around the nucleus; this seems to prove a mobilization of messenger RNA. Simultaneously, the filamentous mitochondria change their shape and give rise to oval vesicles which may correspond to a renewal of protein synthesis.

1. Nucleic Acid Synthesis

Nucleic acids are synthesized from storage products of the egg. Nucleotides or nucleosides are stored in the egg and are progressively transformed.

Forrest and co-workers (1967) noticed that at the beginning of their development *Oncopeltus* eggs have a significant quantity of nucleosides (inosine and guanosine), which disappear progressively during development. Uric acid concentration does not vary; these purines are not broken down but are used after transformation into inosinic acid for the synthesis of DNA and RNA, which increase in parallel. There is no pyrimidine storage, but a derivative of imidazole might be a more distant precursor. Inosine is perhaps not completely incorporated into RNA as a purine base; part of it may be transformed into the deoxyribose series and enter the DNA.

A series of experiments effected during recent years has permitted comparison of nucleic acid metabolism in vertebrates and invertebrates. (1) Blaustein and Schneiderman (1960) studied the effects of purine and pyrimidine analogs. 6-Hydroxyuracil or barbituric acid induce analogous development of the wing scales, but have no effect on the insect organism. Contrary to what happens in vertebrates and bacteria, barbituric acid-^{14}C is not incorporated into RNA, but partially inhibits the formation of epidermal RNA in the same way as a ribonuclease injection. (2) Blaustein and Schneiderman (1960) have shown that besides the four usual bases, traces of methyladenine are also utilized. (3) Wyatt (1959) has followed ^{32}P incorporation in the wings of *Bombyx* chrysalids during development and diapause. At the beginning of adult development (period at which ecdysone is active) there is a strong increase in the RNA/DNA ratio. Therefore, RNA is synthesized before DNA. At all stages of development, the period following the injection (0 to 4 hours) corresponds to a phase of slow incorporation, a period during which RNA precursors are synthesized until a maximal specific activity is reached. The following linear phase (4 to 24 hours) corresponds to a period during which incorporation is limited by the quantity of RNA synthesized. Wyatt and Raghupathi Rami Reddy (1967) investigated uridine-^{14}C incorporation *in vitro* in the wing epidermis of *Hyalophora* and noticed the increase of *de novo* RNA synthesis under ecdysone influence.

2. Ecdysone Action

Ecdysone is probably responsible for the earliest changes, but it should be mentioned that wounding also induces RNA and DNA synthesis (Wyatt, 1961; Davis and Schneiderman, 1960). Wigglesworth (1957) had already observed in *Rhodnius* a strong basophilia of the epidermis after wounding, without any following metamorphosis; nucleic acid synthesis as a reaction to trauma is not accompanied by derepression of the genes regulating development as normally occurs under hormonal influence.

Krishnakumaran *et al.* (1965) noted that adult tissues resemble those of diapausing pupae. There is no DNA formation; the RNA synthesis level is low, but a single ecdysone injection is sufficient to stimulate the capacity for cell synthesis, and the adults undergo a supernumerary molt.

Recent work indicates that DNA synthesis can also be related to a primary action of ecdysone. This is necessary for activation of epidermal cells and intersegmentary muscle cells, but it is not necessary for the other cells of *Rhodnius* (Wigglesworth, 1963). The same thing happens in *Hyalophora cecropia* but only for DNA synthesis in the hypodermis and the intersegmentary muscular cells (Bowers and Williams, 1964). Krishnakumaran *et al.* (1967) suggested that ecdysone might be required for the formation of a key-enzyme such as DNA polymerase or thymidylate kinase. In response to ecdysone, the epidermal cells, the cells of the fat body, of the tracheae of larvae, and pupae of several Saturniidae synthesize DNA of each stage. During each larval intermolting period, there is definite temporary activity of DNA synthesis in each tissue. The chitinogenic epithelium, the Malpighian tubules, and the nervous system synthesize their DNA right after ecdysone secretion. Continuous synthesis occurs in the prothoracic gland, the mesenteron, and the hemocytes during the whole cycle but increases at the time of ecdysone secretion.

In other tissues, such as imaginal discs and muscles, DNA synthesis during larval life does not seem to be affected by ecdysone secretion. In most tissues of diapausing species, DNA synthesis stops immediately after pupation when ecdysone is absent and cannot be detected in diapausing chrysalids. Only hemocytes, gonads, fat body, and the regenerating mesenteron cells remain somewhat active. The "repose" of DNA is not due to a decrease of metabolism because a wound in the pupa induces resumption of general metabolism (increase of respiration, and of RNA and protein synthesis) without stimulation of DNA synthesis. This lack of synthesis is therefore a fundamental characteristic of the diapause state.

Some tissues (Malpighian tubules, prothoracic gland) which synthesize DNA during larval and larva-pupa molts, do not exhibit any activity during the pupa-adult molt. Nondiapausing species exhibit some syntheses characteristic of adult development early in the transformation of larva-pupa (*Samia cynthia ricini*) while diapausing species exhibit this activity only at the time of adult metamorphosis.

Insects which have a short adult life cease DNA synthesis 3 days after ecdysis. Insects which have a long adult life exhibit active synthesis during their whole adult life in some tissues such as midgut and muscles. Where repeated mitomycin C injections are given to chilled pupae which would normally resume their development, DNA synthesis is inhibited and diapause is maintained for 6 weeks. Mitomycin C injected into developing pupae stops DNA synthesis and the division of the cells necessary for scale formation, but does not inhibit cuticle formation.

The fact that DNA is not renewed during diapause suggests that the enzymes involved in the synthesis are inhibited or absent. Brookes and Williams (1965) tested thymidine kinase and thymidylate kinase activity in the wing epithelia of diapausing pupae, wounded pupae, and pupae at the beginning of adult development, and found that diapausing pupae possess both enzymes and do not incorporate thymidine-^{3}H. Ecdysone secretion induces incorporation and cell division again; simultaneously both kinases increase twenty times, but they increase also in wounded pupae without simultaneous DNA formation, and therefore enzyme deficiency cannot explain lack of formation. It is possible that DNA polymerase is absent or that feedback inhibition of thymidine kinase by d-thymidine triphosphate and by d-cytosine triphosphate or nondialyzing inhibitor occurs. In fact, considering bacteria, small molecules can have an effect on the gene synthetic activity in metazoan cells. DNA fibers are associated with many proteins, particularly histones which may exert a certain control by inhibiting messenger RNA formation and repressing gene transcription. If information comes from chromosomal DNA, the cytoplasma may contain, besides messenger RNA, DNA able to direct the synthesis of cytoplasmic messenger RNA.

3. Action of Other Hormones on RNA Synthesis

Juvenile hormone injected into Saturniidae (Oberlander and Schneiderman, 1965) induces a second pupal molt and RNA synthesis in the fat body, the hemocytes, and the tracheal epithelium at a level higher than normal. But the juvenile hormone has no effect on RNA synthesis in isolated pupal abdomens which lack the thoracic gland. The metabolic effect might not be directly on the tissues but, on the other hand, juvenile hormones may stimulate RNA synthesis in the prothoracic gland. This is a primary effect, specific to the glandular tissue. Only certain tissues respond to each hormone.

According to K. Clark and Gillott (1967b), who partially inhibited nucleolar RNA synthesis by removing the frontal ganglion and stopping the transport of the neurosecretory material, the brain hormone seems to affect messenger RNA mobilization.

L'Hélias (1954a) observed a decrease in nucleic acids after removal of the corpora cardiaca and allata; this decrease is reversed at the beginning of adult life, probably after ecdysone action at the last larval stage. Berreur (1965) has also shown that in the imaginal discs RNA synthesis occurs *before* DNA synthesis in cells which are ready to divide. Before mitosis and during activation of the genes which control metabolism, "puffs" of messenger RNA can be observed.

Antibiotic inhibitors specifically inhibit nucleic acid synthesis and it is possible, by this means, to follow the successive effects of ecdysone. Berry et al. (1967) have shown that RNA synthesis varies in the different tissues and phases of larval life in the Saturniidae. Some tissues exhibit RNA synthesis directly associated with the molt process. RNA is synthesized in the epidermal cells as soon as ecdysone is secreted, then DNA synthesis occurs, and finally RNA synthesis decreases 2 days before ecdysis, though ecdysone concentration is higher and cuticle synthesis is still incomplete. Ecdysone may stimulate a sudden formation of messenger RNA, necessary for DNA synthesis, cell division, and the subsequent cuticle secretion; after induction of the reaction, RNA would cease activity until the cells have completed their program.

Madhavan and Schneiderman (1968) have demonstrated that mitomycin C, a DNA inhibitor, blocks the pupa-adult transformation of *Polyphemus* pupae which have been reactivated by cold treatment. If the injection is given during DNA synthesis, the secretion of a new cuticle is not inhibited, and this shows that intermediary DNA is necessary for the transmission of the ecdysone program; at the same time, edysone secretion is not prevented by mitomycin. Crystallized ecdysone cannot overcome DNA inhibition, it can only produce apolysis (retraction of the epidermis of the old cuticle).

Juvenile hormone acts on certain genes specific for larval growth and activates only certain tissues: ovaries, fat body, intestine, epidermis, etc. Ecdysone activates other genes, releases the transcription of messenger RNA and the formation of specific proteins in cells which remain embryonic during larval life and can resume growth only when ecdysone acts alone.

4. Evidence for Soluble DNA

In the larva of the mosquito *Aedes aegypti,* Lang and Meins (1966) found 32% to 41% of the DNA in the supernatant (soluble DNA) after differential centrifugation. This DNA disappears nearly completely in the pupae and the adults (only 3% can be found). It has the normal double helix configuration but its molecular weight is low (470,000). Its solubility in salt solution suggests that it is bound to histones in the cell. While total DNA remains constant, physiological release of soluble DNA follows periods of active growth of the larva, reaching a maximum on the third and fourth day before pupation and diminishing after the sixth and seventh day. In the mixture of adult high molecular weight plus larval soluble DNA, the quantity of soluble DNA from the larva decreases in the presence of the residual DNA fraction of the adult. Consequently, the soluble DNA of the larva is not an artifact due to the presence of nucleases. There are, in the adult, fractions which can precipitate it. This soluble DNA cannot be associated with mitochondria because it does not precipitate after many hours of centrifugation at 124,000 g. It has been detected histologically in the cytoplasm and may more likely be of nuclear origin.

5. Supernumerary DNA of the Genome

Rudkin and Corlette (1957) have also detected this metabolic and unstable DNA with low molecular weight. Even in the nucleus, a mass of supernumerary chromosomal DNA can appear, develop in the germ cells, and transmit particular genetic information for gamete growth and development. This occurs in the Cecidomyidae in which Geyer-Duszynska (1966) has noted that somatic cells carry six to eight chromosomes while the germ cells have more than forty. The clumps disappear once the gonia have started to divide into somatic cells, at the beginning of the embryonic life, and remain in the germ line only. They are indispensable for the normal sequence of oo- and spermatogenesis. If the supernumerary DNA is eliminated by centrifugation of the embryos at the binucleate stage, the surviving embryos develop normally until pupation, but in the adult females obtained, eggs abort at the oocyte stage and the males do not form any sperm cells. Do these clumps carry the necessary genetic information for normal development of the gonia or only storage DNA necessary for the final development of the embryo?

6. Specific DNA of the Nucleolar Organizers

Synthesis of ribosomal RNA 16 S and 23 S occurs in bacteria at precise and localized positions which do not involve more than 0.3% of the genome. In insects, drosophilids constitute the material of choice to obtain information about this organizer zone at the level at which a DNA-RNA hybrid and ribosomal RNA are synthesized because some mutants carry a different number of nucleolar organizers (NO) on the X and Y chromosomes (Ritossa and Spiegelman, 1965). A labeled RNA is prepared and hybridized *in vitro* with each of the DNA's extracted from the different mutants. These hybrids are treated with ribonuclease to eliminate the unpaired RNA. According to the quantity of hybrids synthesized and collected, it is possible to say that this quantity is proportional to the number of NO carried by the different mutants and expected according to their genetic constitution. This confirms that the DNA complementary for the ribosomal RNA is found in the loci of the NO. Identifying the segment of the nucleolar organizer with the site of the DNA template, the results show that the nucleolus is really the site of ribosomal RNA synthesis in insects.

7. Evidence of the Activation of Amino Acids for the Elaboration of New Proteins by Soluble or Transfer RNA in Insects

The genome assembles sets of separated information depending upon sets of specialized genes. The transcription of genome information into messenger RNA is normally inhibited by repressors, according to the scheme of Jacob and Monod. Inducers are required to nullify the effect of the repressors and unblock the cell genome; then each messenger RNA (mRNA or codon) collects on the 30 S ribosomes and each soluble or transfer RNA (anticodon) on the 50 S. These ribosomes in turn lump together to form polysomes (mRNA-30 S + 50 S-aminoacyl RNA) (S = 1 Svedberg unit, molecular sedimentation coefficient in density gradient). Each codon-anticodon unit is particular for each amino acid. Codons are homo- or polynucleotides and collect on the nonhelicoïdal band of soluble RNA. They are composed of triplets of nucleotides (uridine-uridine-uridine available for phenylalanine for example) and corresponding zones of anticodons (sRNA) are composed of complementary triplets. These polysomes, carrying codons-aminoacyl-soluble RNA, are the sites of nuclear and cytoplasmic proteins synthesis.

According to their complement of inhibitors and derepressors, the cells of the different tissues respond differently, but the code of the messenger RNA base triplets and its correspondence to each amino acid is rigorously specific and universal (Gros, 1965). This code has now been deciphered in microorganisms.

Howells *et al.* (1967) carried out the first investigation of aminoacyl-soluble RNA-synthetase in insects, and of the activation of amino acids incubated with an extract centrifuged at 105,000 *g* containing soluble RNA and amino acid-activating enzymes during the development of *Lucilia cuprina*. At the end of larval life, sRNA incorporates less serine and glutamic acid and more alanine, aspartic acid, and tyrosine. Incorporation changes occur for leucine, proline, and threonine. ATP is required and ribonuclease annuls the activation.

Sekeri *et al.* (1968) have been able to induce labeled amino acid incorporation by a preparation of ribosomes extracted from *Calliphora* at different stages. The maximal activity of these polysomes appears at the time of larva-pupa transformation and again 7 days after the puparium formation, two periods at which ecdysone is abundantly secreted. These polysomes also undergo changes during development, and their sedimentation coefficient is higher at the end of larval life.

B. Visible Expression of Synthetic Activity of Chromosomes

1. Synthetic Activity of the Cell

It has been possible to establish aspects of the control of metabolism by observation at the chromosome level. Reactions of certain genes and resumption or inhibition of activity have been followed. The material of choice for these observations is of course the giant chromosomes of Diptera. These polytene chromosomes have a characteristic type of transverse bands identical for all homologous chromosomes of tissues of the same species. The number of bands is related to gene loci of the species. These bands exhibit individual variations in their fine structure corresponding to synthesis of DNA and histones. Each of these bands can vary in shape, from a very thin disc with a high concentration of DNA to intermediary swollen stages (puffings) and finally to a swollen ring which stains diffusely. These rings were discovered by Balbiani (1881) and, according to Breuer and Pavan (1955) and Beermann (1963), it is possible to conclude that they correspond to gene activity at the chromosome level.

Puffing is caused by the elongation of a fiber of DNA-histone to give a coiled filament. The intensity of the Feulgen reaction decreases in proportion to the increase of puffing of the bands. Thymidine-^{3}H incorporation shows that radioactivity concentrates first in the areas which correspond to bands stained blue-violet by metachromatic coloration with toluidine blue. On the other hand, uridine-^{3}H is incorporated in

high quantities in the puffs of *Chironomus tentans,* and this shows intensive RNA synthesis at the level of the coils (staining pink with toluidine
blue, Pelling, 1959; Woods *et al.,* 1961). RNA is synthesized *in situ*
(Pelling, 1964). Uridine-^{3}H specifically labels bands which stain with
toluidine blue. The labeling is sensitive to ribonuclease. Changes in the
degree of puffing are accompanied by differences in incorporation. A
general relationship exists between the rate of synthesis and the size of
a puff. RNA synthesized by the large chromosomes of *Chironomus* is
produced by the two Balbiani rings in full activity or even one of the
two nucleolar organizers. The nucleolar incorporation starts from a zone
adhering to the centromeres and spreads progressively toward the
periphery; it is therefore a zone rich in DNA, the nucleolar organizer
(NO), which is concerned in RNA synthesis.

Animals treated by short pulses of isotopes exhibit labeled puffs and
nucleoli in the salivary glands indicating that these regions are the sites
of high RNA synthesis (Beermann, 1963). Rudkin and Woods (1959)
obtained identical results with *Drosophila* and Sirlin (1960) with
Smittia.

Edström and Beermann (1962) have determined, by microelectro-
phoresis, the RNA base composition in samples of giant chromosomes,
isolated segments of puffed chromosomes, nucleoli, and cytoplasm of
Chironomus tentans. The ratios adenine/guanine and adenine/uracil
differ in different samples and in chromosomal RNA. None of the soluble
chromosomal RNA possesses base symmetry, and the ratio guanine/cyto-
sine is different from that of DNA. The chromosomal RNA, then, may
not be a complete copy of the two helices of chromosomal RNA, but
in spite of the difference in guanine/cytosine ratio between the two
nucleic acids, the RNA can still be partially or completely the copy
of a single helix.

Puffing is reversible in polytene chromosomes of *Rhynchosciara
angelae* (Breuer and Pavan, 1955; Rudkin and Corlette, 1957). In some
loci, puffing is accompanied by a massive accumulation of DNA. Proteins
may be associated with the puffed regions in strong accumulation but
synthesis of new proteins may not always be localized in the puffs
(Sirlin, 1960; Clever and Beermann, 1965a,b).

2. *Control of Gene Activation by Growth Hormones*

Bodenstein's (1943) and Becker's (1959) studies demonstrated that
chromosomal changes and puffs depending upon hormone action were
more numerous at the time of the last larval molt and of the pupal
molt. Clever (1962, 1964) distinguishes two kinds of puffs in the salivary
glands of *Chironomus tentans:* one group of loci is independent of larval

development and corresponds to genes governing basal metabolism; the second group is active only at certain phases of the molting process and is consequently related to it.

However, the puffs at the loci which are independent of development show a decrease during the intermolt period preceding pupal molt; this is the sign of a decrease of metabolism. At the beginning of this last molt, there is an increase in some of the puffs which are not specific for development; this may indicate an increase of part of the functional metabolism.

Clever and Karlson (1960) have observed in *Chironomus tentans* that shortly after ecdysone injection (15 to 30 minutes) the gene loci *I 18C* and *IV 2B* show puffs. The swelling and its duration are proportional to the quantity of ecdysone injected. During normal development, puffs appear during the molt from the 3rd to the 4th larval stage and disappear at the end of this stage. They reappear as soon as the process of pupal molt is started; this indicates their relation to the presence of ecdysone. However, the two loci exhibit independent behavior. *I 18C* develops 1 or 2 days before *IV 2B* and disappears more slowly at the end of larval molt; it does not disappear after pupal molt while *IV 2B* disappears (Clever and Beermann, 1965a). Both puffs depend upon ecdysone concentration. The authors have been able to determine from the disappearance of *IV 2B*, in spite of the presence of a large quantity of ecdysone during pupal molt, that a mechanism antagonistic to ecdysone was involved. Puffs *I 18C* and *IV 2B* produce a series of new puffs specific for pupation. Some changes in puffs are visible before pupation of *Drosophila hydei* (Berendes, 1967) and *Calliphora* (Ribbert, 1967; Mattingly and Parker, 1968). Ecdysone effects are really specific for metamorphosis and not for molt in general. Metamorphosis of salivary glands consists of autolysis of larval glands and differentiation of new glands; juvenile hormone may inhibit the catabolic effects of ecdysone during larval life. Clever (1962) has noticed that when pupae are in diapause, there is a reduction in puff frequency. However, a few puffs which are active during the last period of growth of the larvae keep their activity in diapausing pupae. The frequency of some others does not change; these are involved in processes of cellular metabolism. When there is a deficiency of ecdysone in the hemolymph, the pupae which do not undergo metamorphosis do not exhibit the puffs specific for metamorphosis.

Actinomycin C and puromycin introduced into the medium on which *Chironomus* larvae are raised affect RNA and protein synthesis and, at the same time, puffs and Balbiani rings disappear (Clever, 1964). These structures reappear when RNA and protein synthesis resume.

However, ecdysone injection 6 hours after the inhibitor treatment does not lead to resumption before a lapse of 15 to 20 hours. Clever has assumed that an inducible gene might act as an intermediate regulator. Puromycin, protein inhibitor, and ecdysone simultaneously injected, delay the puffing for 15 to 20 hours.

It seems that synthesis of new proteins, while not partaking directly in puff formation, might be necessary in the processes which precede puff appearance, and this implies that the genes which change their activity during molt are controlled by a complex system (Clever, 1964).

3. Role of Ionic Balance in the Hormonal Regulation of the Genome

Kroeger (1962) tried experiments involving explantations, isolation of nuclei, and removal of parts of the genome by microsurgery and looked for substances imitating hormone action. Ecdysone action is imitated by injection of $ZnCl_2$, $CaCl_2$, or narcotics which do not induce metamorphosis. The drastic treatments of microsurgery induce rejuvenation of the nuclei which seem to react to juvenile hormone. The control system of the nuclear sap may be simple. It may consist in the inversion of the ratio Na^+/K^+ at the end of development. These Na^+/K^+ concentration inversions occur effectively. According to Kroeger (1964), an alteration of ion concentration permits rejuvenation of the cells. Ecdysone might cause an active ion transport through the nuclear membrane, and this might induce the activation of certain genes. Pelling (1964) and Berendes et al. (1965) observed that while some puffs appear a long time after the modification of the ionic concentration, most of them appear and disappear in an independent way. Induction of the single puff III dl cannot be compared with ecdysone effect on Drosophila hydei (Berendes et al., 1965).

4. Synthesis of Ribosomal RNA, Messenger RNA, and Transfer RNA

The ecdysone effect is more complex than action on a single puff, and the molecular mechanism of gene activity is so complex that little is known of it. Thus, it is too early to propose a simple scheme. Each puff arises from a chromosomal band rich in DNA. The nucleolar organizers and the Balbiani rings belong to this structure (Yankofsky and Spiegelman, 1962a,b; Ritossa and Spiegelman, 1965), and they synthesize ribosomal RNA (Pelling and Scholtissek, 1964).

Messenger RNA may be synthesized on the loci. The puff size may be a measure of the amount of mRNA formed while the level of RNA synthesis in the whole cell does not change. The expansion of a puff indicates an increase in the synthesis of a special type of RNA. Puffing should be understood to be not only a process influencing the production of special types of ribonucleic acids and characteristics of specific tissues or developmental stages, but also as a fundamental mechanism of regulation of RNA synthesis. Moreover, puff size and RNA synthesis seem to be determined by the concentration of specific inducing substances such as ecdysone (Clever, 1964).

Howells *et al.* (1967) studied the activation of labeled amino acids and their incorporation into proteins by incubating the amino acids with an extract of *Lucilia* larvae centrifuged at 105,000 g and containing soluble RNA and amino acid-soluble RNA synthetase; they showed that transfer RNA exists in insects as in bacteria. The simplest concept is that this regulation is the consequence of the activation of a variable number of the thousands of DNA molecules which are present in the bands of the giant chromosomes.

Morphologically, puffing is the unbinding of the DNA previously highly concentrated in chromosomal bands, puffs, Balbiani rings, and the nucleolar organizers seem to contain long, extensible DNA fibers analogous to lampbrush chromosomes. The unraveling of the DNA may be necessary for RNA synthesis because inactive DNA is bound to histones that seem to be inhibitors of genetic activity (Huang and Bonner, 1962).

5. Synchronization of Protein Synthesis with Visible Activity of the Chromosomes

Laufer and Nakase (1964) studied specific proteins, enzymes, and antigens of *Chironomus thumii* salivary glands during development. The study showed that the gland composition reflects variations in secretory and chromosomal activity. Above all, changes in deoxyribonuclease concentration seem to play a role in the consecutive development of the gland. Total protein concentration doubles between the 4th intermolt period and the beginning of the prepupal stage, then decreases at the end of the prepupal stage. Malate dehydrogenase, trehalase, hyaluronidase, esterase, and protease follow this pattern; deoxyribonuclease increases several times before the prepupa while the others decrease.

C. INHIBITION AND DEREPRESSION OF CELLULAR METABOLISM

The discovery of enzymic and antigenic activities in the cytoplasm coinciding with their temporary appearance with certain specific puffs suggests a relationship between chromosomal activity and cellular events. Insect hormones permit the derepression of specific regulator, either directly by gene activation of DNA and RNA synthesis or as allosteric effectors.

I have been able to obtain genetic information transmission, modified by growth hormone absence, by genic activation by pterines. As is known, folic acid and its formyltetrahydrogenate derivatives are necessary cofactors for the synthesis of some metabolites, thymidine in particular, interfering thus in DNA synthesis. By modification of the normal balance of growth cofactors, growth hormones, it has been possible to obtain an abnormal DNA which transmits false information to the genome, and then hereditary and definitive transmission occurs.

To obtain these results, an injection of folic acid into diapausing *Pieris* chrysalids which do not have any hormones in sufficient. The DNA synthesized in the *Pieris* nymph and reinjected into *Drosophila* is *transmitted by the cytoplasm* (L'Hélias, 1957b, 1964). This DNA is evidenced:

1. By the mortality of transparent larvae which seem like the mutant *ltr*, or by the presence of melanoma.

2. By the sex-ratio decrease. The surviving *Drosophila* give rise to a progeny with low and constant sex ratio (0.7). Purification attempts led to the identification of a very low molecular weight DNA (sedimentation constant between 4 and 8 S) somewhat analogous to soluble RNA (L'Hélias, 1966). Radioautographic studies have shown the migration of tritiated thymidine from the nuclei of the nutritive and follicular cells and the penetration through the peripheral membrane of the oocytes (L'Hélias and Houlou, 1970).

It seems that the absence of hormones in the chrysalid is responsible for the derepression of certain genes and the synthesis of small DNA molecules (a hundred nucleotides according to the sedimentation coefficient). Tritiated thymidine incorporation in the gonads of chrysalids treated with folic acid is higher than in controls which retain a certain synthetic activity. The DNA is not specific perhaps because it could not polymerize in the absence of ecdysone, and, once injected into *Drosophila*, it remained in storage or penetrated into the cytoplasm of the gonia.

3. By genetic information transmission of *Drosophila melanogaster* mutants by simultaneous incubation with folic derivatives in diapausing chrysalids.

When folic derivatives and extracts of *sepia* and *Muller* mutants are simultaneously injected in diapausing chrysalids and an extract of these chrysalids is reinjected in *Drosophila melanogaster*, surviving wild-type *Drosophila* females (controlled for many years) give, in their progeny, the mutants *sepia* and *Muller* 5 accompanied by the mutant *ebony*. In second generation, there are 8% to 10% *sepia* and *ebony*, and 1%-*Muller* 5 mutants. Following the injection, many larvae die or abort at the beginning of pupation and exhibit at the same time cessation of larval tissue lysis and partial development of the imaginal discs; imaginal red pigments—hallochrome or ommochrome—develop in the existing larval fat body. Metamorphosis can proceed as far as partial nymphosis. There is real competition between larval and nymphal information. The larvae and pupae are lemon colored due to the presence of sepia pterine in the blood and the tissues. The mechanism of inhibition of the normal pheno-type is still unknown but it is striking to see that folic derivatives injected into the chrysalid induce anomalies of the enzymic metabolism of pterines as well as preferential definitive mutations of ommochrome or melanic type (L'Hélias, unpublished).

V. Conclusion

Important results have been collected and have led to the conclusion that insect metabolism is as complex as and not much different from mammalian metabolism. One substance, trehalose, is as important to insects as glycogen is to mammals. During the different stages of development, sugar catabolism can be effected through the classic Embden-Meyerhof glycolysis pathway or the pentose phosphate pathway.

The fat body, from a metabolic point of view, plays the same synthetic role as the liver of mammals. In this tissue, proteins and trehalose are formed, carbohydrates coming from the diet are transformed into lipids, proteins, and purines, and pterines are synthesized.

The study of hormone action by more sophisticated techniques support earlier results. Under neurocerebral hormone control, growth hormones lead to the normal development of tissues, thus safeguarding specific characters of species. Juvenile hormone influences energy metabolism and activates the synthesis of structural elements. Ecdysone seems to act first in nucleic acid synthesis and controls the information for the elaboration of specific structures and mitoses.

But the scheme of hormone activity is complicated. In different species localization of secretory elements is different. Sometimes one organ, sometimes another, has the same metabolic action or interferes with the action of another gland and produces a feedback effect. These apparent contradictions result from evolution, ecology, and behavior; geographic climates have provoked the selection of species, which present more or less perfect endocrine complexes.

The study of the mechanisms of control of growth and development promises to be most fruitful in the future. The facts that have been established these last few years show that growth hormones are effective in derepressing certain genes specific for different development stages and that low molecular weight substances may modify these mechanisms regulating the gene activity which controls development. But this derepression is probably not a direct action on genes. Maybe these hypotheses can be postulated: Is there a slow modification of ionic concentration of nuclear gel which denudes DNA and permits it to communicate its information? Can weak molecular weight substances (hormones or cofactors) modify development by activation as allosteric effectors?

REFERENCES

Agrell, I. (1948). *Acta Physiol. Scand.* **16,** 9–19.
Agrell, I., and Lindh, N. O. (1966). *Comp. Biochem. Physiol.* **19,** 691–698.
Akino, M., and Matsubara, M. (1963). *Nature* **199,** 908–909.
Albert, A. (1957). *Ciba Found. Symp. Chem. Biol. Purines* p. 97–107.
Alfert, M. (1954). *Intern. Rev. Cytol.* **3,** 131–176.
Allais, J. P., Bergerard, J., Etienne, J., and Polonovski, J. (1964). *J. Insect Physiol.* **10,** 753–772.
Altmann, G. (1956). *Insectes Sociaux* **3,** 33–40.
Asahina, E., and Tanno, K. (1964). *Biochem. J.* **97,** 715–722.
Bade, M. L., and Wyatt, G. R. (1962). *Biochem. J.* **83,** 470–478.
Balbiani, E. (1881). *Zool. Anz.* **4,** 637–641.
Becker, H. G. (1959). *Chromosoma* **10,** 654–678.
Beermann, W. (1963). *Am. Zoologist* **3,** 23–32.
Bell, W. J. (1969). *J. Insect Physiol.* **15,** 1279–1290.
Berendes, H. D. (1967). *Chromosoma* **22,** 274–293.
Berendes, H. D., Van Breugel, F. M. A., and Holtz, T. K. H. (1965). *Chromosoma* **16,** 35–46.
Bergmann, E., and Levinson, Z. (1966). *J. Insect Physiol.* **12,** 77–81.
Berreur, P. (1965). *Arch. Zool. Exptl. Gen.* **106,** 531–692.
Berridge, M. J. (1966). *J. Insect Physiol.* **12,** 1523–1539.
Berry, S. J., Krishnakumara, N., Oberlander, H., and Schneiderman, H. A. (1967). *J. Insect Physiol.* **13,** 1511 and 1537.
Blaustein, M. P., and Schneiderman, H. A. (1960). *J. Insect Physiol.* **5,** 143–159.
Bodenstein, D. (1943). *Biol. Bull.* **84,** 13–33.
Bodnaryk, R. P., and Morrison, P. T. (1966). *J. Insect Physiol* **12,** 963–976.
Bowers, B., and Williams, C. (1964). *Biol. Bull.* **16,** 205–219.
Boyd, J., and Mitchell, H. (1966). *Arch. Biochem. Biophys.* **117,** 310–319.
Breuer, M. E., and Pavan, C. (1955). *Chromosoma* **7,** 371–386.
Brookes, V., and Williams, C. (1965). *Proc. Natl. Acad. Sci. U.S.* **53,** 770–777.
Buckmann, D. (1965). *J. Insect Physiol.* **11,** 1427–1462.
Candy, D. J., and Kilby, B. A. (1961). *Biochem. J.* **78,** 531–536.
Carey, F. G., and Wyatt, G. R. (1963). *J. Insect Physiol.* **9,** 317–335.
Chefurka, W. (1954). *Enzymologia* **17,** 73–89.
Chefurka, W. (1958). *J. Biochem. Physiol.* **36,** 83–102.
Chen, P. S. (1959). *J. Insect Physiol.* **2,** 38–51.
Chen, P. S. (1962). *Proc. 11th Intern. Congr. Entomol., Vienna, 1960* Vol. 3, pp. 201–207.
Chen, P. S. (1966). *Advan. Insect Physiol.* **3,** 53–132.
Chen, P. S., and Backman-Diem, P. (1965). *J. Insect Physiol.* **10,** 819–829.
Chen, P. S., and Baumann, L. Cited by Chen in *Adv. Insect Physiol.* **3,** 53–132.

Chen, P. S., and Briegel, H. (1965). *Comp. Biochem. Physiol.* 14, 463–473.

Chen, P. S., and Hadorn, E. (1965). *Rev. Suisse Zool.* 62, 338–347.

Chen, P. S., and Hanimann, F. (1965). *Z. Naturforsch.* 20b, 307–312.

Chen. P. S., and Kühn, A. (1956). *Z. Naturforsch.* 11b, 305–314.

Chen, P. S., and Levenbook, L. (1966a). *J. Insect Physiol.* 12, 1595–1609.

Chen, P. S., and Levenbook, L. (1966b). *J. Insect Physiol.* 12, 1611–1627.

Chippendale, G. M., and Beck, S. (1966). *J. Insect Physiol.* 12, 1544–1566.

Chippendale, G. M., and Kilby, B. A. (1969). *J. Insect Physiol.* 15, 905–926.

Claret, J. (1970). *Arch. Zool. Exptl. Gen.* (in press).

Clark, A., and Bloch, K. (1959). *J. Biol. Chem.* 234, 2589–2594.

Clark, K., and Gillott, C. (1967a). *J. Exptl. Biol.* 46, 13–25.

Clark, K., and Gillott, C. (1967b). *J. Exptl. Biol.* 46, 29–35.

Clegg, J. S., and Evans, D. R. (1961). *J. Exptl. Biol.* 38, 771–792.

Clement, G., and Frisch, A. M. (1946). *Compt. Rend. Soc. Biol.* 140, 472–473.

Clements, A. N. (1967). *J. Insect Physiol.* 13, 1024–1050.

Clever, U. (1962). *J. Insect Physiol.* 8, 357–376.

Clever, U. (1964). *Science* 146, 794–795.

Clever, U., and Beermann, W. (1965a). *Proc. 16th Intern. Congr. Zool., Washington, D.C., 1963* Vol. 4, pp. 210–215. Nat. Hist. Press, Garden City, New York.

Clever, U., and Beermann, W. (1965b). *Proc. 16th Intern. Congr. Zool., Washington, D.C., 1963* Vol. 4, pp. 256–263. Nat. Hist. Press, Garden City, New York.

Clever, U., and Karlson, P. (1960). *Exptl. Cell Res.* 20, 623–626.

Cromartie, R. I. T. (1959). *Ann. Rev. Entomol* 4, 59–76.

Crone, M. D. (1967). *J. Insect Physiol.* 13, 81–90.

Crone-Gloor, V. (1959). *J. Insect Physiol.* 3, 50–56.

Davis, R. P., and Schneiderman, H. A. (1960). *Anat. Rec.,* 132, 348.

Delbrück, A., Zebe, E., and Bucher, T. (1959). *Biochem. Z.* 331, 273–296.

DeLoof, A. (1970). *Gen. Comp. Endocrinol.*

Demyanovsky, S. Ya., and Zubova, V. A. (1959). *Biokhimiya* 21, 698–704.

Dennell, R. (1947). *Proc. Roy. Soc.* B134, 79–110.

Dennell, R. (1958). *Biol. Rev.* 33, 178–196.

Desai, R. M., and Kilby, B. A. (1958). *Arch. Intern. Physiol. Biochim.* 66, 248–259.

DeWilde, M., and Stegwee, D. (1958). *Arch. Neerl. Zool.* 13, Suppl. 1, 277–283.

Dinamarca, M. L., and Levenbook, L. (1966). *Arch. Biochem. Biophys.* 117, 110–119.

Drilhon, A., and Busnel, R. G. (1950). *Compt. Rend.* 230, 1114–1116.

Duchâteau, G., and Florkin, M. (1959). *Arch. Intern. Physiol. Biochim.* 67, 306–314.

Duke, E., and Pantelouris, E. (1963). *Comp. Biochem. Physiol.* 10, 351–355.

Edström, J. E., and Beermann, W. (1962). *J. Cell Biol.* 14, 371–379.

Engelmann, F. (1968). *Ann. Rev. Entomol.* 13, 126.

Evans, J. J. T. (1968). *J. Insect Physiol.* 14, 107–119.

Faulkner, P. (1955). *Biochem. J.* 60, 590–596.

Faulkner, P. (1956). *Biochem. J.* 64, 430–436.

Faulkner, P. (1958). *Biochem. J.* 68, 374–380.

Florkin, M. (1937). *Mem. Acad. Roy. Med. Belg.* 16, 1–96.

Florkin, M. (1959). *Proc. 4th Intern. Congr. Biochem., Vienna, 1958* Vol. 12, pp. 63–73. Pergamon Press, Oxford.

Fogal, W., and Fraenkel, G. (1969). *J. Insect Physiol.* 15, 1437–1448.

Forrest, H. S., Stephen, M., and Morton, L. (1967). *J. Insect Physiol.* 13, 359–367.

Fourche, J. (1968). *J. Insect Physiol.* **13,** 1267–1277.

Fraenkel, G. (1935). *Proc. Roy. Soc.* **B118,** 1–12.

Fraenkel, G. (1963). *Science* **141,** 1057–1058.

Fraenkel, G., and Hsiao, C. (1962). *Science* **138,** 27–29.

Fraenkel, G., and Rudall, K. M. (1940). *Proc. Roy. Soc.* **B129,** 1.

Gelperin, A. (1966). *J. Insect Physiol.* **12,** 331–345.

Gersch, M., Unger, H., and Kapitza, W. (1964). *Zool. Jahrb., Abt. Allgem. Zool. Physiol. Tiere* **70,** 455–458.

Geyer-Duszynska, I. (1966). *In* "Chromosomes Today" (C. C. Darlington and K. R. Lewis, eds.), Vol. I. pp. 174–179. Oliver & Boyd, Edinburgh and London.

Gilbert, L. (1964). *In* "The Physiology of Insecta" (M. Rockstein, ed.), Vol. 1, pp. 149–225. Academic Press, New York.

Gilbert, L. (1966). *Advan. Insect Physiol.* **4,** 70–210.

Gilbert, L., and Goldberg, E. (1966). *J. Insect Physiol.* **12,** 53–65.

Gilbert, L., and Schneiderman, H. A. (1959). *Anat. Record* 131–569.

Gilbert, L., and Schneiderman, H. A. (1961). *Am. Zoologist* **1,** 11–51.

Gilmour, D. (1960). "The Biochemistry of Insects." Academic Press, New York.

Girardie, A., and Cazal, M. (1965). *Compt. Rend.* **261,** 4525–4527.

Glassman, E., and Mitchell, H. K. (1959). *Genetics* **44,** 153–162.

Gloor, H. (1949). *Rev. Suisse Zool.* **56,** 281–285.

Goodfellow, R. D., and Gilbert, L. I. (1964). Cited in Gilbert and Schneiderman (1964).

Gros, F. (1965). *In* "Molecular Biophysics" (B. Pullman and M. Weissbluth, eds.), pp. 1–13. Academic Press, New York.

Grzelakowska-Stabert, B., and Zielinska, Z. (1967). *J. Insect Physiol.* **13,** 1207–1221.

Hackman, R. H. (1953). *Biochem J.* **54,** 371–377.

Hadorn, E. (1961). "Developmental Genetics and Lethal Factors." Methuen, London.

Hadorn, E., and Mitchell, H. K. (1951). *Proc. Natl. Acad. Sci.* **37,** *U.S.* 650–665.

Hadorn, E., and Schwinck, I. (1956). *Nature* **177,** 940–941.

Hadorn, E., and Stumzollinger, E. (1953). *Rev. Suisse Zool.* **60,** 506–516.

Harmsen, R. (1966a). *J. Insect Physiol.* **12,** 9–22.

Harmsen, R. (1966b). *J. Insect Physiol.* **12,** 23–30.

Harvey, W. R. (1962). *Ann. Rev. Entomol.* **7,** 57–80.

Harvey, W. R., and Haskell, J. A. (1966). *Advan. Insect Physiol.* **3,** 133–205.

Harvey, W. R., Haskell, J. A., and Nedergaard, S. (1968). *J. Exptl. Biol.* **48,** 1–12.

Harwood, R. F., and Halfill, E. (1964). *Am. Eut. Soc. Am.* **57,** 596–600.

Heller, G. (1936). *Compt. Rend. Soc. Biol.* pp. 121–414.

Hidaka, T., and Ohtaki, T. (1963). *Compt. Rend. Soc. Biol.* **157,** 928–930.

Highnam, K. C. (1964). *Symp. Roy. Ent. Soc. London,* **2,** 26–42.

Highnam. K. C., Hill, L., and Ginzell, D. J. (1965). *J. Zool.* **147,** 201–215.

Hill, L. (1962). *J. Insect Physiol.* **8,** 609–619.

Hines, R. H. (1953). *Biochem. J.* **54,** 370–377.

Hines, W. J. W. (1953). *Biochem. J.* **54,** 362–367.

Hines, W. J. W., and Smith, M. J. H. (1963). *J. Insect Physiol.* **9,** 463–468.

Hirano, C., and Gilbert, L. (1967). *J. Insect Physiol.* **13,** 163–175.

Horie, Y. (1967). *J. Insect Physiol.* **13,** 1163–1175.

Horie, Y., Nakasone, S., and Ito, T. (1968). *J. Insect Physiol.* **14,** 971–981.

Horowitz, N. H., and Fling, M. (1955). *In* "Amino Acid Metabolism" (W. D. McElroy, ed.), pp. 207–218. Johns Hopkins Press, Baltimore, Maryland.

House, H. L. (1962). *Ann. Rev. Biochem.* **31**, 653–672.

Howells, A. J., and Birt, L. M. (1964). *Comp. Biochem. Physiol.* **11**, 61–83.

Howells, A. J., Birt, L. M., and Finch, L. R. (1967). *J. Insect Physiol.* **13**, 1221–1236.

Huang, R. C., and Bonner, J. (1962). *Proc. Natl. Acad. Sci. U.S.* **48**, 1216–1222.

Idris, B. E. M. (1960). *Z. Morphol. Oekol. Tiere* **49**, 387–429.

Irrevere, F., and Levenbook, L. (1960). *Biochim. Biophys. Acta* **38**, 358–360.

Ito, T., and Horie, Y. (1959). *Arch. Biochem. Biophys.* **80**, 174–186.

Joly, L. (1960). Thesis, Strasbourg.

Karlson, P., and Bode, C. (1969). *J. Insect Physiol.* **15**, 111–118.

Karlson, P., and Schweiger, A. (1961). *Z. Physiol. Chem.* **323**, 199–210.

Karlson, P., and Sekeris, C. E. (1962). *Biochim. Biophys. Acta* **63**, 489–495.

Kaufman, S. (1964). *Proc. 3rd Symp. Intern. Organ. Chem. 1962, Stuttgart.* pp. 307–326. Pergamon, Oxford.

Keeley, L., and Friedman, S. (1967). *Gen. Comp. Endocrinol.* **8**, 129–134.

Keeley, L., and Friedman, S. (1969). *J. Insect Physiol.* **15**, 509–518.

Kilby, B. A. (1963). *Advan. Insect Physiol.* **1**, 111–174.

Kilby, B. A., and Neville, E. (1957). *J. Exptl. Biol.* **34**, 276–289.

King, D. S. (1969). *Gen. Comp. Endocrinol.* **13** (No. 3), 512.

Kinsella, J. E. (1966). *J. Insect Physiol.* **12**, 435–438.

Kobayashi, M., and Kirimura, S. (1967). *J. Insect Physiol.* **13**, 545–552.

Krishnakumaran, S. J., and Schneiderman, H. A. (1965). *J. Insect Physiol.* **11**, 1517–1532.

Krishnakumaran, S. J., Berry, H., Oberlander, H., and Schneiderman, H. A. (1967). *J. Insect Physiol.* **13**, 1–57.

Kroeger, H. (1962). *J. Cellular Comp. Physiol.* Suppl., 45–59.

Kroeger, H. (1964). *Chromosoma* **15**, 36–70.

Kurland, C. G., and Schneiderman, H. A. (1959). *Biol. Bull.* **116**, 136–161.

Laidman, D. L., and Morton, R. A. (1962). *Biochem. J.* **84**, 386–389.

Lambremont, E. N., Bumgarner, J. E., and Bennett, A. F. (1966). *Comp. Biochem. Physiol.* **19**, 417–429.

Lamy, M. (1967). *Compt. Rend.* **265**, 990–993.

Lang, C. A. (1959). *Exptl. Cell Res.* **17**, 516–518.

Lang, C. A. (1961). *Federation Proc.* **20**, 471.

Lang, C. A., and Meins, F. (1966). *Proc. Natl. Acad. Sci. U.S.* **55**, 1525–1533.

Larsen, J., and Bodenstein, D. (1959). *J. Exptl. Zool.* **140**, 343–382.

Laufer, H. (1961). *Ann. N.Y. Acad. Sci.* **94**, 825–839.

Laufer, H., and Nakase, Y. (1964). *J. Cell Biol.* **23**, 524.

Leuthardt, F. (1963). "Lehrbuch der physiologischen Chemie." de Gruyter, Berlin.

Levenbook, L., Dinamarca, M. L., and Lucas, F. (1965). *Federation Proc.* **24**, 471.

Levinson, Z. H., and Silverman, P. H. (1954). *Biochem. J.* **58**, 294–297.

L'Hélias, C. (1953a). *Compt. Rend.* **236**, 2164–2165.

L'Hélias, C. (1953b). *Compt. Rend.* **236**, 2489–2491.

L'Hélias, C. (1954a). *Compt. Rend.* **238**, 2352–2354.

L'Hélias, C. (1954b). *Compt. Rend.* **238**, 2558–2559.

L'Hélias, C. (1954c). *Compt. Rend.* **239**, 778–780.

L'Hélias, C. (1957a). *Bull. Biol. France Belg.* Suppl. 44.

L'Hélias, C. (1957b). *Compt. Rend.* **244**, 1678–1679.

L'Hélias, C. (1957c). *Bull. Biol. France Belg.* **91**, 241–263.

L'Hélias, C. (1964). *Bull. Biol. France Belg.* **98**, 511–537.

L'Hélias, C. (1966). *Ann. Endocrinol.* **27**, 342–352.

L'Hélias, C., and Houlou, N. (1970). *Archiv. Zool. Exp.* (in press).

Lipke, H., and Fraenkel, G. (1956). *Ann. Rev. Entomol.* **1**, 17–44.

Lipke, H., Graves, B., and Leto, S. (1965). *J. Biol. Chem.* **240**, 601–608.

Locke, M., and Collins, J. V. (1968). *J. Cell Biol.* **36**, 453–483.

Ludwig, D. (1954). *Physiol. Zool.* **27**, 325–334.

McCarthy, R., and Ralph, C. L. (1962). *Am. Zoologist* **2**, 429–430.

Madhavan, K., and Schneiderman, H. A. (1968). *J. Insect Physiol.* **14**, 777–781.

Mansingh, A., and Smallman, B. N. (1967). *J. Insect Physiol.* **13**, 447–469.

Mattingly, E., and Parker, C. (1968). *Chromosoma* **23**, 255–270.

Meyer, A., Schneiderman, H. A., Hanzmann, E., and Ko, J. (1968). *Proc. Natl. Acad. Sci. U.S.* **60**, No. 3, 853–860.

Mills, R. R., and Nielsen, D. J. (1967). *J. Insect Physiol.* **13**, 273–280.

Mitchell, H. K. (1966). *J. Insect Physiol.* **12**, 755–865.

Mitchell, H. K., and Simmons, J. R. (1962). "Aminoacids and Derivatives (Aminoacid Pools)," pp. 136–146. Elsevier, Amsterdam.

Mitchell, H. K., and Weber, U. M. (1965). *Science* **148**, 964–965.

Mitchell, H. K., Chen, P. S., and Hadorn, E. (1960). *Experientia* **16**, 410.

Mitlin, N., Lusk, G., and Weygal, G. (1967). *Ann. Entomol. Soc. Am.* **60**, 1155–1158

Mitlin, N., Gleen, W., and Gordon, L. (1968). *J. Insect Physiol.* **14**, 1277–1285.

Mochnacka, I., and Petryszyn, C. (1959). *J. Prakt. Chem.* [3] **73**, 65–70.

Monroe, R. E., Hopkins, T. L., Valder, Sue, A. (1967). *J. Insect. Physiol.* **13**, 219–235.

Munn, E., Price, G. M., and Greville, G. D. (1969). *J. Insect Physiol.* **15**, 1601–1607.

Murphy, T. A., and Wyatt, G. R. (1965). *J. Biol. Chem.* **240**, 1500–1508.

Nair, K. S., and George, J. G. (1964). *J. Insect Physiol.* **10**, 509–517.

Nakasone, S., and Ito, S. (1967). *J. Insect Physiol.* **13**, 1237–1246.

Neugebauer, W. (1961). *Arch. Entwicklungsmech. Organ.* **153**, 314–352.

Niemierko, S. (1959). *Proc. 4th Intern. Congr. Biochem., Vienna, 1958* Vol. 12, pp. 185–197. Pergamon Press, Oxford.

Niemierko, S., Wlodawer, P., and Wojtezak, A. F. (1956). *Acta Biol. Exp. Polish Acad Sci.* **17**, 255.

Nuñez, J. A. (1956). *Z. Versleich. Physiol.* **38**, 341–354.

Oberlander, H., and Schneiderman, H. A. (1965). *J. Insect Physiol.* **12**, 37–41.

Oberlander, H., Berry, S. J., Krishnakumaran, A., and Schneiderman, H. A. (1965). *J. Exptl. Zool.* **159**, 15–32.

Oelhafen, F. (1961). *Arch. Entwicklungsmech. Organ.* **153**, 120–157.

Pearincott, J. V. (1960). *J. Cellular Comp. Physiol.* **55**, 167–174.

Pelling, C. (1959). *Nature* **184**, 655–656.

Pelling, C. (1964). *Chromosoma* **15**, 71–122.

Pelling, C. (1968). *Arch. Anat. Microscop. Morphol. Exptl.* **54**, 645–647.

Pelling, C., and Scholtissek, C. (1964). *Angew. Chem.* **76**, 881–888.

Pflugfelder, O. (1940). *Z. Wiss. Zool.* **153**, 108–133.

Pflugfelder, O. (1958). "Entwicklungs Physiologie der Insekten." Akad. Verlagsges., Leipzig.

Price, G. M., and Bosman, T. (1966). *J. Insect Physiol.* **12**, 741–745.

Raabe. M. (1959). *Bull. Soc. Zool. France* **84**, No. 4, 278–316.

Raabe, M. (1966). *Compt. Rend.* **262**, 303–306.

Ribbert, D. (1967). *Chromosoma* **21**, 296–344.

Ritossa, F. M., and Spiegelman, S. (1965). *Proc. Natl. Acad. Sci. U.S.* **53**, 737–795.

Rizki, T. M. (1961). *J. Biophys. Biochem. Cytol.* **9**, 567–571.

Rodriguez, J. G., and Hampton, R. E. (1966). *J. Insect Physiol.* **12**, 1209–1216.

Röller, H., Dahm, H., Weeley, C. C., and Trost, B. M. (1967). *Angew. Chem. Intern. Ed. Engl.* **6**, 129.

Röller, H., Bjerke, J. S., Holthaus, L., Norgard, ᒧ., and McShan, W. (1969). *J. Insect Physiol.* **15**, 379–391.

Rothstein, F. (1952). *Physiol. Zool.* **25**, 171–173.

Rudkin, G. T., and Corlette, S. L. (1957). *Proc. Natl. Acad. Sci. U.S.* **43**, 964–968.

Rudkin, G. T., and Woods, P. S. (1959). *Proc. Natl. Acad. Sci. U.S.* **45**, 997–1003.

Russo-Caia, S. (1960). *Ric.-Sci. suppl.* **30**, No. 12.

Scharrer. B. (1964). *Z. Zellforsch. Mikroskop. Anat.* **62**, 125–148.

Scheurer, R. (1969). *J. Insect Physiol.* **15**, 1411–1421.

Schmidt, G. (1966). *J. Insect Physiol.* **12**, 227–237.

Schnal, F., and Slama, K. (1966). *J. Insect Physiol.* **12**, 1333–1342.

Schneiderman, H. A., and Gilbert, L. I. (1964). *Science* **143**, 325–333.

Schoonhoven, L. M. (1963). *Science* **141**, 173–174.

Schweiger, A., and Karlson, P. (1961). *Z. Physiol. Chem.* **523**, 199–210.

Selwinck, I., and Hadorn, E. (1956). *Nature* **177**, 940–941.

Sekeri, K., Sekeris, C. E., and Karlson, P. (1968). *J. Insect Physiol.* **14**, 425–431.

Sekeris, C. E. (1964). *Arch. Anat. Microscop. Morphol. Exptl.* **54**, 651–653.

Sekeris, C. E., and Karlson, P. (1961). *Biochim. Biophys. Acta* **62**, 103–113.

Sekeris, C. E., and Lang, N. (1964). *Life Sci.* **3**, 625.

Seligman, M., Fraenkel, G., and Friedman, S. (1969). *J. Insect Physiol.* **15**, 1085–1102.

Shappirio, D. G. (1960). *Ann. N.Y. Acad. Sci.* **89**, 537–538.

Shappirio, D. G., and Harvey, W. R. (1965). *J. Insect Physiol.* **11**, 303–307.

Shappirio, D. G., and Williams, C. (1957a). *Proc. Roy. Soc.* **B147**, 218–232.

Shappirio, D. G., and Williams, C. (1957b). *Proc. Roy. Soc.* **B147**, 233–246.

Shappirio, D. G., Eichenbaum, D., and Locke, B. (1967). *Biol. Bull.* **132**, 108–127.

Shigematsu, H. (1956a). *J. Ser. Sci. Japan* **25**, 49–53.

Shigematsu, H. (1956b). *J. Ser. Sci. Japan* **25**, 115–121.

Shigematsu, H. (1960). *Bull. Ser. Exptl. Sta. (Tokyo)* **16**, 141–170.

Simmons, J. R., and Mitchell, H. K. (1962). "Metabolism of Peptides in Drosophila," pp. 147–155. Elsevier, Amsterdam.

Simon, H., Wacker, M., and Walter, J. (1964). *Proc. 3rd Symp. Intern. Organ. Chem., 1961* Stuttgart pp. 327–339. Pergamon Press, Oxford.

Sirlin, J. E. (1960). *Exptl. Cell Res.* **19**, 177–180.

Sissakian, N. M. (1959). *Proc. IVth Int. Cong. Biochem.* **12**, 73–76.

Slama, K. (1965). *J. Insect Physiol.* **10**, 282–303.

Slama, K. (1965). *J. Insect Physiol.* **11**, 1121–1129.

Slama, K., and Hrubesova, H. (1963). *Zool. Jahrb., Abt. Allgem. Zool. Physiol. Tiere* **70**, 291–300.

Slama, K., and Hrdy, M. (1967). *Biol. Bull.* **134**, 154–159.

Slama, K., and Janda, V. (1965). *Zool. Jahrb., Abt. Allgem. Zool. Physiol. Tiere* **71**, 345–358.

Smith, K. D., Ursprung, H., and Wright, T. R. (1963). *Science* **146**, 226–227.

Sridhara, S., and Bhat, J. V. (1963). *J. Insect Physiol.* **9**, 693–701.

Sridhara, S., and Bhat, J. V. (1965). *J. Insect Physiol.* **11**, 449–462.

Stanley, F. (1967). *J. Insect Physiol.* **13**, 397–407.

Steele, J. E. (1961). *Nature* **192**, 680–681.

Steele, J. E. (1963). *Gen. Comp. Endocrinol.* **3**, 46–52.

Steele, J. E. (1965). *Proc. 13th Intern. Congr. Entomol., London 1964* p. 211.
Steele, J. E. (1969). *J. Insect Physiol.* **15**, 421–424.
Steinhauer, A. L., and Stephen, W. P. (1959). *Ann. Entomol. Soc. Am.* **52**, 733–738.
Stevenson, E., and Wyatt, G. R. (1962). *Archiv. Biochem. Biophys.* **99**, 65–71.
Stevenson, E., and Wyatt, G. R. (1964). *Arch. Biochem. Biophys.* **108**, 420–429.
Strong, F., and Sakamoto, S. (1963). *J. Insect Physiol.* **9**, 875–879.
Stutinsky, F. (1953). *Bull. Soc. Zool. France* **78**, 202–204.
Takahashi, S. (1966). *J. Insect Physiol.* **12**, 789–801.
Takata, N., and Harwood, R. F. (1964). *Ann. Entomol. Soc. Am.* **57**, 6749–6753.
Takata, N., and Harwood, R. F. (1965). *J. Insect Physiol.* **11**, 711–716.
Tanno, K. (1962). *Low Temp. Sci.* **B20**, 25–34.
Tanno, K. (1964). *Low Temp. Sci.* **B22**, 51–57.
Tawfik, M. F. S. (1957). *J. Insect Physiol.* **1**, 286–291.
Telfer, W. H. (1954). *J. Gen. Physiol.* **37**, 539–558.
Telfer, W. H. (1960). *Biol. Bull.* **118**, 338–351.
Telfer, W. H. (1965). *Ann. Rev. Entomol.* **10**, 161–184.
Telfer, W. H., and Williams, C. M. (1953). *J Gen. Physiol.* **36**, 389–413.
Telfer, W. H., and Williams, C. M. (1960). *J. Insect Physiol.* **5**, 61–72.
Terando, L., and Feir, D. (1967a). *Comp. Biochem. Physiol.* **20**, 431–436.
Terando, L., and Feir, D. (1967b). *Comp. Biochem. Physiol.* **21**, 31–38.
Tetsuya, O., and Ohnishi, E. (1967). *J. Insect Physiol.* **13**, 1569–1574.
Thomas, K. K., and Nation, F. L. (1966). *Biol. Bull. Wood, Hole,* **130**, 254–264.
Thomas, K., and Gilbert, L. I. (1967). *J. Insect Physiol.* **13**, 963–980.
Thomsen, E. (1949). *J. Exptl. Biol.* **26**, 137–149.
Thomsen, E. (1952). *J. Exptl. Biol.* **29**, 137–172.
Thomsen, E., and Hamburger, K., (1955). *J. Exp. Biol.* **32**, 692–699.
Tobe, S. S., and Loughton, B. G. (1969). *J. Insect Physiol.* **15**, 1331–1347.
Tsujita, M. (1961). *Jap. J. Gen.* **36**, 235–243.
Tsujita, M., and Sakurai, S. (1963a). *Japan J. Genet.* **38**, 97–105.
Tsujita, M., and Sakurai, S. (1963b). *Proc. Japan Acad.* **39**, 247–252.
Tyschtchenko, V. P., and Mandelstam, J. E. (1965). *J. Insect Physiol.* **11**, 1233–1239.
Umebachi, Y., and Katayama, M. (1966). *J. Insect Physiol.* **12**, 1539–1547.
Urich, K. (1961). *Ergeb. Biol.* **24**, 155–190.
Ursprung, H., and Hadorn, E. (1961). *Experientia* **17**, 230–231.
Van der Geest, L. P., and Borgsteede, F. A. (1969). *J. Insect Physiol.* **15**, 1687–1693.
Van der Kloot, W. G. (1955). *Biol. Bull.* **109**, 276–294.
Van Handel, E., and Lea, A. O. (1965). *Science* **149**, 898–300.
Villeneuve, J. L. (1962). *J. Insect Physiol.* **8**, 585–588.
Vroman, H. E., Kaplanis, J. N., and Robbins, W. E. (1965). *J. Insect Physiol.* **11**, 897–904.
Wang, S., and Dixon, S. E. (1960). *Can. J. Zool.* **38**, 275–283.
Weed-Pfeiffer, I. (1939). *J. Exptl. Zool.* **82**, 439–461.
Weed-Pfeiffer, I. (1942). *Anat. Record* **81**, Suppl. 1, 57.
Weed-Pfeiffer, I. (1945). *Anat. Record* **84**, 486.
Weygand, L., and Waldschmidt, M. (1955). *Angew. Chem.* **67**, 328–330.
Wiens, A. W., and Gilbert, L. I. (1967a). *J. Insect Physiol.* **13**, 779–795.
Wiens, A. W., and Gilbert, L. I. (1967b). *J. Insect Physiol.* **13**, 587–594.
Wiens, W., and Gilbert, L. (1968). *Comp. Biochem. Physiol.* **67**, 145–159.
Wigglesworth, V. B. (1957). *Symp. Soc. Exptl. Biol.* **11**, 204–227.
Wigglesworth, V. B. (1963). *J. Exptl. Biol.* **40**, 231–245.

Wigglesworth, V. B. (1964). *Advan. Insect Physiol.* **2**, 247–336.

Williams, C. (1959). *Biol. Bull.* **116**, 323–338.

Williams, C. (1968). *Biol. Bull.* **134**, No. 2, 344–355.

Williams, C., Law, J. H., and Ynan, C. (1966). *Proc. Natl. Acad. Sci. U.S.* **55**, 576–578.

Wimer, L. T. (1962). Ph.D. Thesis, University of Virginia.

Wimer, L. T., and Lamb, R. H. (1967). *J. Insect Physiol.* **13**, 889–898.

Wlodawer, P. (1956). *Acta Biol. Exp. Vars.* **17**, 221–230.

Wlodawer, P., and Baranska, J. (1965). *Acta Biochim. Polon.* **12**, 23–37.

Woods, P. S., Gay, H., and Sengiin, A. (1961). *Proc. Nation. Acad. Sci. U.S.A.* **47**, 1486–1493.

Wren, J. J., and Mitchell, H. K. (1959). *J. Biol. Chem.* **234**, 2823–2828.

Wyatt, G. R. (1959). *Proc. 4th Intern. Congr. Biochem., Vienna, 1958* Vol. 12, pp. 161–178. Pergamon Press, Oxford.

Wyatt, G. R. (1961). *Ann. Rev. Entomol.* **6**, 75.

Wyatt, G. R. (1963). *In* "Biochemistry of Diapause Development and Injury Insect Physiology" (V. J. Brookes, ed.), pp. 23–41. Oregon State Univ. Press, Corvallis, Oregon.

Wyatt, G. R. (1967). *Advan. Insect Physiol.* **4**, 287–375.

Wyatt, G. R., and Raghupathi Rami Reddy, S. (1967). *J. Insect Physiol.* **13**, 981–994.

Yamashita, O. (1965). *J. Serie Sci. Tokyo*, **32**, 1–8.

Yamashita, O., and Hasegawa, K. (1964). *J. Ser. Sci. Japan* **33**, 407–416.

Yankofsky, S. A., and Spiegelman, S. (1962a). *Proc. Natl. Acad. Sci. U.S.* **48**, 1069–1078.

Yankofsky, S. A., and Spiegelman, S. (1962a). *Proc. Natl. Acad. Sci. U.S.* **48**, 1466–1472.

Yao, T. (1950). *Quart. J. Microscop. Sci.* **91**, 89–105.

Ziegler, I. (1961). *Advan. Genet.* **10**, 349–403.

Ziegler, I. (1963). *Biochim. Biophys. Acta* **78**, 219–220.

Ziegler, I., and Nathan, H. (1961). *Z. Naturforsch.* **16b**, 262–264.

Author Index

Numbers in italics refer to the pages on which the complete references are listed.

A

Abramowitz, A. A., 332, *338*
Abramowitz, R. K., 332, *338*
Ackman, R. G., 233, *251*
Acree, F., 48, *87*
Adams, J. B., 131, 132, *142, 144*
Adelung, D., 333, *338*
Adiyodi, R. G., 151, *164*, 328, *338*
Adomako, T. Y., 328, *341*
Agosin, M., 181, 183, 184, 190, 191, 192, *194*
Agrawal, V. P., 101, 102, 104, 105, 106, 110, 111, *113, 114*
Agrell, I., 205, *223*, 328, *338*, 363, 369, *393*
Akino, M., 377, *393*
Akov, S., 52, 63, 66, *87*
Albert, A., 376, 377, *393*
Alfert, M., 343, *393*
Alikhan, M. A., 59, *87*
Allais, J. P., 69, *87*, 231, 232, *251*, 356, *393*
Allen, K., 269, *282*
Altevogt, R., 100, 101, *114*
Altman, P. L., 39, 54, 55, 60, 68, *87*
Altmann, G., 378, *393*
Alvarado, F., 181, *197*
Amos, T. G., 292, *316*
Anders, F., 132, *142*
Anderson, B. S., 234, *252*
Anderson, D. T., 23, 27, 29, *33*
Anderson, J. F., 288, *316*
Andrews, P., 149, *164*
Applebaum, S. W., 61, *87*, 124, 128, 134, 136, *142*
Arai, N., 51, 56, 57, 62, *87, 91*
Aravena, L., 192, *194*
Arese, P., 186, *196*
Arthur, D. R., 79, *87*
Asano, Y., 177, *197*
Asahina, E., 346, *393*

B

Ashrafi, S., 121, 129, *144*
Astell, C. R., 331, *338*
Attwood, M. M., 169, *194*
Auclair, J. L., 40, 77, *87*, 123, 126, 131, 132, *142, 145*
Avi-Dor, Y., 48, *90*, 189, *195*
Ayre, G. L., 131, *142*

Bachmann-Diem, C., 217, *224*
Backman-Diem, P., 361, *393*
Bade, M. L., 72, *87*, 175, 193, *194*, 346, *393*
Bahadur, J., 298, 299, *316*
Bailey, E., 182, 184, *194, 197*
Baker, C. M. A., 328, *340*
Baker, H., 36, *91*
Balashov, Y. S., 306, 308, *316*
Balbiani, E., 386, *393*
Baldwin, E., 218, *223*
Banks, W. M., 125, *142*
Baranska, J., 352, *400*
Barbier, M., 69, *87*
Barker, R. J., 74, *88, 90*
Barlow, J. S., 37, 53, 61, 72, 73, 76, 78, *87, 91*, 233, 234, *251*
Barnes, F. J., 241, *251*
Barnes, H., 150, 151, 157, *164*, 334, 335, 336, *338, 339*
Barnes, R. S. K., 256, *282*
Barrington, E. J. W., 122, *142*, 163, *164*
Barton Browne, L., 40, 41, 43, 47, *87, 89*, 291, 292, 315, *316*
Bartsch, G. E., 191, *196*
Bar-Zeev, M., 48, *90*
Bauchau, A. G., 163, *164*, 332, *338*
Bauer, A. C., 183, *194*
Baumann, L., 361, *393*
Baumberger, J. P., 331, 332, *339*
Bayer, J., 163, *165*
Bayer, S., 250, *253*

401

Subject Index

A

Acarus sior, water uptake, humidity and 312

Acetate,
amino acid synthesis from, 207–209, 212–213
fatty acid synthesis from, 234, 238
incorporation, molt cycle and, 324
labeled, nutritional requirements and, 72, 81, 84, 356
tricarboxylic acid cycle and, 215

Acetylcholine, saliva secretion and, 139

Acetylcoenzyme A kinase, insect, 189

Acetyl coenzyme A,
amino acid synthesis and, 206
chitin synthesis and, 172
condensing enzyme and, 188
sclerotization and, 328, 373

N-Acetyl dopamine, sclerotization and, 327, 328, 369–370, 373, 375

N-Acetyl-D-glucosamine,
chitin and, 156, 240
metabolism of, 177

N-Acetylglucosamine 6-phosphate, chitin synthesis and, 172, 173

β-Acetylglucosaminidase, occurrence in insects, 127

3-Acetylpyridine, insect nutrition and, 66

N-Acetyltyramine, sclerotization and, 373, 375

Acheta, see also Cricket
mineral requirements, 75
tocopherol requirement, 74

Acheta domesticus, blood sugar, 148

Aconitase, insect, 189

Actias selene, glyceraldehydephosphate dehydrogenase of, 183

Actinomycin C, chromosome puffs and, 388–389

Acylsarcosyltaurine, crustacean gastric juice, 107, 112

Acyrthosiphon, mineral requirements, 76

Adenase, arthropod, 219

Adenine, requirement for, 64

Adenosine deaminase, crustacean, 98, 219

Adenosine diphosphate,
glycerol kinase and, 188
pyruvate kinase and, 185

Adenosine monophosphate,
cyclic,
function of, 161
phosphofructokinase and, 182
phosphorylase and, 177
saliva secretion and, 139
glycerol kinase and, 188
phosphofructokinase and, 182
phosphorylase and, 161, 177, 346

Adenosine phosphate(s),
enzyme secretion and, 135
feeding and, 48–49, 80

Adenosine triphosphate,
condensing enzyme and, 188–189
diapause and, 348
glutamate synthesis and, 281–282
phosphofructokinase and, 182
phosphorylase and, 161, 177
pyruvate kinase and, 185

Adipose tissue,
glycerides, two-compartment theory and, 249

Aedes, see also Mosquito
amino acid requirement, 56
anal papillae, osmoregulation and, 266
antimetabolites and, 66
carnitine and, 63
carotenoids and, 74
cobalamine and, 64
glutathione and, 63
malate dehydrogenase of, 189
metamorphosis, enzymes and, 369
nutrition, ribonucleic acid and, 64
proteinase secretion by, 137
sucrase secretion by, 135
sugar requirement, 52

Aedes aegypti,
amylase of, 180
feeding of, 48

Juvenile hormone,
  allatectomy and, 357
  ecdysone and, 388
  functions of, 379, 383
  isolation of, 358
  lipid mobilization and, 352
  phosphatases and, 347, 365
  respiration and, 349–350
  ribonucleic acid and, 367, 382–383
  vitellogenesis and, 365–366

K

Keratin, digestion by insects, 121–122,
    129
Ketoacylthiolase, crustacean, 251
α-Ketoglutarate,
  amination of, 278, 281
  formation in crustacea, 210
α-Ketoglutarate dehydrogenase, insect,
    189
Kinase(s), insect development and, 347
Krebs cycle, see Tricarboxylic acid cycle
Kynurenine,
  accumulation of, 372, 373
  formation of, 60

L

Laccotrephis maculatus, proteases of, 128
Lactase, crustacean, 102, 103, 104, 111,
    112
L-Lactate,
  feeding and, 48
  production of, 239
Lactate dehydrogenase,
  larval, 368
  localization in insects, 185, 188
  sodium chloride and, 276, 277, 279
Lactose, hydrolysis by insects, 125, 130
Laelaps echidnina, water exchange, half-
    life, 313
Larvae, food passage time, 120
Lasioderma,
  sterol requirement, 67
  vitamin requirements, 60
Leafhoppers, see also Cicandella
  salivary enzymes, 131
Leander serratus,
  amino acid pattern of, 201
  osmoregulation, 256

amino acids and, 269, 271
Leander squilla,
  amino acid pattern of, 201
  osmoregulation, amino acids and, 269,
    271
Leander xiphias, molt cycle of, 323
Lecithin,
  embryogenesis and, 335
  feeding response and, 45
  insect enzymes and, 130
Lepidoptera, see also Butterfly, Moth
  adults,
    digestive enzymes, 122
    nutrition of, 54
  amino acids in, 203
  amylases of, 124
  developmental stages, nutrition and,
    77–78
  excretory system of, 300
  fatty acid requirement, 71
  larvae,
    amylase and, 123
    midgut pH, 121
  proteases of, 128
  sexual dimorphism, lipid and, 351
  sterol requirement, 67
Leptinotarsa, see also Potato beetle
  yitellogenic protein, hormones and,
    366
Leptinotarsa decemlineata,
  amino acid pattern of, 204
  response to known chemicals, 45
Leptophragmata, 300
  solute uptake and, 301
Leucine,
  feeding and, 49, 80
  incorporation,
    insect larvae and, 361
    molt cycle and, 324–325, 329
Leucine p-nitranilide, insect enzymes
    and, 128
Leucophaea,
  endocrine glands of, 358
  juvenile hormone and, 366
  larval enzymes, 368
  proteinase secretion by, 136, 137, 138
  reproductive cycle, glycogen and, 345
Leucophaea maderae,
  development, lipid and, 231–232
  phospholipid release and transport in,
    247

lipid release and transport in, 244, 250
nutrition, 40
osmoregulation in, 290
phosphofructokinase of, 182
phosphoglucomutase of, 181
3-phosphoglycerate-1-kinase in, 184
phosphoglycerate phosphomutase in,
    184
pyruvate kinase in, 184
pyruvate oxidation by, 186–187
scylloinositol in, 180
triosephosphate isomerase of, 183
vitamin A in, 74
water loss by, 294
yolk deposition, hormones and, 366
Locusta,
β-carotene requirement, 73
coloration, 375
enzyme secretion by, 137
invertase secretion by, 134
phospholipid in, 232
pyruvate dehydrogenase in, 188
sterol requirement, 69
water loss by, 294, 296
Locusta migratoria,
amino acid pattern of, 204
carbohydrate requirement, 53
development,
    lipid and, 231
    sterols and, 356
hexokinase of, 181
neurosecretion in, 367
phosphoglucose isomerase of, 181
proteases of, 128
trehalose 6-phosphatase of, 175
Lophocereine, immunity to, 71
Lophocereus schottii, sterol requirements
    and, 70–71
Losaustrin, insect feeding and, 44
Lucilia, see also Blowfly, Flesh fly
glucosidases, specificity of, 125
Lucilia cuprina,
amino acid activation in, 386, 390
chitin of, 168
development,
    amino acid activation and, 362
    carbohydrate metabolism and,
        175–176
thirst in, 43, 315
Lung books, water loss and, 295
Lygaeids, salivary enzymes, 131

Lygus, macerating enzyme of, 131
Lymantria dispar, protein turnover in,
    364
Lysine, feeding and, 48

M

Macrobrachium equidens, osmoregulation
    in, 256
Macrocheira, 1
Macrosiphum pisi,
    glucose 6-phosphate dehydrogenase in,
        190
    phosphoglucomutase of, 181
Macrura, mouth parts, 98
Magnesium,
    amino acid incorporation and, 361
    α-ketoglutarate dehydrogenase and,
        189
    phosphatidate phosphohydrolase and,
        238
    requirement for, 75, 76
    trehalose 6-phosphatase and, 175
Maia, see Maja
Maja,
    molt cycle,
        blood protein and, 328, 329
        stages of, 322
    proteases, 110
        activation of, 111
    sodium flux in gills, 264–265
Maja squinado,
    amino acid pattern of, 201
    deoxyribonucleic acid of, 330
    digestive juice of, 101, 109
    tissue growth, molt cycle and, 332
Malacostraca,
    food resorption in, 99
    gastric juice of, 100
    stomach of, 97
Malate dehydrogenase,
    crustacean, 206
    development and, 390
    insect, 189–190
    larval, 368
    metamorphosis and, 368
    sodium chloride and, 277, 279–280
Malate hydro-lyase, sodium chloride and,
    280
Malic enzyme, insect, 193
Mallophaga, feather digestion by, 122

Oogenesis, supernumerary deoxyribonu-
cleic acid and, 384
Ophiactis arenosa, osmoregulation in, 269
Orchestia gammarella,
    carbohydrases of, 102, 104, 110
    digestive juice of, 101, 109
    lipase of, 106
    protease of, 105
Orconectes, 222
    digestive juice, extrusion of, 107
    fatty acid oxidation by, 251
Orconectes limosus,
    blood sugar, 149
    hyperglycemia in, 163
Orconectes virilis,
    blood sugars of, 149
    glycogenolysis in, 151
    glycolysis in, 153, 239
    molt cycle,
        integument and, 325–327
        lipid and, 324
        muscle and, 329–330
    lipid,
        synthesis, 238, 239, 241
        transport, 243–244
    pentose phosphate cycle in, 154
    proteases of, 105, 106, 110
Organophosphates, esterases and, 368
Ornithine, occurrence of, 360, 362
Ornithine transcarbamylase, occurrence
    of, 218
Ornithodorus moubata,
    water elimination by, 306–307
    water uptake, humidity and, 312
Ornithodorus tholozani, feeding of, 79–80
Orthoptera,
    developmental stages, nutrition and,
        77–78
    digestive enzymes of, 123–124
    excretory product, 220
    fatty acid requirement, 71
Orya, burrowing by, 18
Oryzaephilus,
    carnitine and, 63
    nucleic acid requirement, 65
    nutrient balance for, 77, 78–79
    polyamine requirement, 65, 83
Osmoregulation,
    arthropod, 16
        terrestrial, 288–290

crustacean, amino acids and, 202,
    215–216
insect, 378–379
    amino acids and, 203–204, 266–267
    quaternary ammonium compounds
        and, 222–223
    reduction of water loss and, 290–303
Osmotic pressure, water uptake and, 314
Ostrea edulis osmoregulation in, 269
Oulema, fatty acid synthesis in, 72
Oulema melanopus, sterol requirement,
    67
Ovary,
    glycogen, hormones and, 344–345
    lipid in, 231–232
Oxalacetate,
    condensing enzyme and, 188
    malate dehydrogenase and, 189
Oxalacetate decarboxylase,
    crustacean, 206
    insect, 193
    sodium chloride and, 277, 279–280
2-Oxo-3-dioxyarabonate, 210
2-Oxoglutarate, *see* α-Ketoglutarate
Oxydesmus, humidity and, 291
Oxygen, consumption, osmoregulation
    and, 280, 282

P

Pachygrapsus,
    blood sodium of, 303
    cellulase in, 103, 104
    molt cycle of, 323
Pachygrapsus crassipes, osmoregulation
    in, 256
Pacifastacus leniusculus,
    blood sugar, 149
    glucuronic acid circuit in, 155, 159
    glycolysis in, 153
    pentose phosphate cycle in, 154
Palaemonetes, metamorphosis, 338
Palaemonetes varians, osmoregulation in,
    255, 256
Palaemonetes vulgaris,
    osmoregulation, respiration and, 280
    ribonuclease, molt cycle and, 333
Paleoptera, excretory product, 220
Palinurus japonicus,
    carbohydrases of, 103, 104

Wounding, nucleic acid synthesis and, 381–382

X

Xanthine oxidase,
  occurrence of, 219
  pterins and, 377
Xanthommatin,
  ommochrome synthesis and, 371–372
  pigment changes and, 373
Xanthopterin, synthesis of, 377
Xenopsylla brasiliensis, water uptake, humidity and, 312
Xenopsylla cheopis,
  amino acid requirement, balance and, 58
  water uptake, humidity and, 312, 313
Xenylla welchi, excretion bv, 220

Xiphosura, relationships of, 27
X-organ, molting and, 331, 332, 333
Xylose,
  crustacean metabolism and, 154
  storage compounds and, 171
α-Xylosidase, crustacean, 103, 112

Y

Yeast(s),
  fruit fly diets and, 77
  insect nutrition and, 59, 64
  symbiotic, 67
Y-organ, molting and, 331, 333

Z

Zinc, requirement for 75, 76